100 YEAR STARSHIP®

canopus   310 LY

100 YEAR STARSHIP®

2013 Conference Proceedings

Pathway to the Stars, **Footprints on Earth**

Published by 100 Year Starship®
www.100yss.org

ISBN-13: 978-0-9903840-0-7
ISBN-10: 0990384004

100 YEAR STARSHIP ®
canopus 310 LY

The 100 Year Starship® exists to make the capability of human travel beyond our solar system a
reality within the next 100 years. We unreservedly dedicate ourselves to identifying and pushing the radical leaps in knowledge and technology needed to achieve interstellar flight, while
pioneering and transforming breakthrough applications that enhance the quality of life for all
on Earth. We actively seek to include the broadest swath of people and human experience in
understanding, shaping and implementing this global aspiration.

For more information, visit www.100yss.org

Edited by Mae Jemison, M.D., Jason D. Batt, and Alires J. Almon
Design and Layout by Jason D. Batt

Cover Logo Credit:
the barbarian group

PRINTED IN THE UNITED STATES OF AMERICA

100 YEAR STARSHIP®
Table of Contents

Interstellar Enhances Life on Earth

Becoming an Interstellar Civilization: Culture, Governance, and Ethics

Key Factors in Time and Distance

Interstellar Aspiration—Commercial Perspiration: The Next 30 Years of Space Start-ups and Commercialization

Life Sciences in Interstellar

Destinations: Hidden Objects

Student Track: The Next Generation

Design: Space

100 YEAR STARSHIP®

2013 Public Symposium

Pathway to the Stars, Footprints on Earth

Across the globe, calls are being made for bolder human expansion into space beyond earth orbit. It is against this backdrop that the 100 Year Starship 2013 Symposium is held.

Achieving the interstellar human journey in many ways, must necessarily build upon, promote and establish fundamental research, technology development, societal systems and capacities that facilitate ready access to our inner solar system. And to truly have the best opportunity for the aspiration to be long-lived enough to actually be accomplished, organizations and individuals involved must work to ensure it leaves a positive, indelible mark upon life right here on Earth.

100 Year Starship (100YSS) is working to create new avenues that foster innovative, robust collaborative, transdisciplinary research, project design and technological development. The 100YSS 2013 Public Symposium—*Pathway to the Stars, Footprints on Earth*—seeks to highlight both the small incremental steps and radical leaps required to make significant progress on the way to interstellar space.

"Meeting the challenge of 100YSS® stands to be even more transformative to our world than Sputnik..."

- Dr. Mae Jemison

11

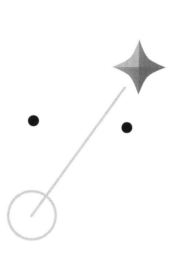

canopus 310 LY

Symposium Overview

100 YEAR STARSHIP'S 2013 PUBLIC SYMPOSIUM HIGHLIGHTS INTERCONNECTIVITY OF INNOVATION, THE ECONOMY, DEEP SPACE EXPLORATION AND PUBLIC ENGAGEMENT

*The 100 Year Starship® (100YSS®) 2013 Public Symposium held September 19-22, 2013 in Houston, Texas, brought together over 200 scientists, engineers, officials, thought leaders, musicians, artists and enthusiasts from across the United States, as well as from England, South Africa, Turkey, Finland, Dubai, Russia, Argentina, New Zealand, Belgium, Italy, Ireland and China. This year's theme, "**Pathway to the Stars, Footprints on Earth,**" focused attendees on international aspirations, transdisciplinary thinking and how audacious goals for the future are the building blocks for transformation to a better society today.*

(continued on next page)

In Friday's opening session, **Dr. Mae Jemison***, the Principal of 100YSS, pointed out how addressing the very difficult challenge of a human interstellar journey fosters explosive innovation, technical achievement and societal advances in economics, governance, behavior and education, not just in the hard sciences.* "No one organization can do it all," *said Dr. Jemison.* "It is an audacious, bold venture that won't be led by naysayers or the overly cautious." *She further added that that such a bold vision* "won't happen without engaging the full spectrum of human experience—including people across ethnicity, gender, disciplines and geography." *The guest speaker for the Opening Plenary,* **co-creator of Yuri's Night Loretta Hidalgo Whitesides***, challenged attendees to ensure that as they strive to make interstellar travel a reality, that they commit to it working to improve life on earth.*

Friday's luncheon on International Space and Science brought together both researchers and thought leaders from across the globe to discuss innovation, vision and collaboration in science and deep space exploration. Speakers included **Adrian Tiplady, PhD**, project scientist for the Square Kilometer Array (SKA) who spoke of the exciting advances and challenges faced by the groundbreaking international project being built in South Africa and neighboring countries. The SKA when completed will be 50 times more powerful than any existing radio telescope and generating as much data daily as the internet does today. **Mr. Mmboneni Muofhe**, Deputy Director-General for International Cooperation and Resources at South Africa's Department of Science and Technology, spoke of the critical importance of bold projects in science and how all people must be a part of pushing the boundaries of human knowledge and experience. *"You must never deny people the opportunity to dream. If you don't dream you can't hope. When we dream we begin to walk on the path that dream wants to take us."* Muofhe responded to the inquiry of why a developing country like South Africa and its African partners would invest in the SKA which may not 'directly feed people'. Mmbonene said that everyone has dreamed of the stars and want to accomplish great things. He said that dreams fuel hope. *"Even a person sleeping on a mud floor without a blanket has dreams!"*

Also speaking at the luncheon were **Amy Millman** of Springboard Enterprises; **Jennie Yeung**, Founder, UN Education Science Cultural Health Advancement Foundation, who discussed her work with philanthropy and science in China, and **Lou Friedman, PhD** Co-Founder of The Planetary Institute, who discussed the precursors to interstellar flight and the people of tomorrow (or their avatars) who will carry out that mission. The luncheon was moderated by **Dan Hanson** of Technology Innovation Group.

Saturday's plenary sessions informed attendees of progress and advances across the spectrum of astronomy and physics, biotechnology, finance and human systems. During "The State of the Universe," led by **Jill Tarter, PhD**, co-founder and Bernard Oliver Chair of the SETI Institute, presenters revealed that we are on the verge of finding Earth 2.0. Attendees heard from **David Black, PhD** of the Lunar and Planetary Institute and **Ariel Anbar, PhD,** Arizona State, about the startling number of exoplanets found, and that they seem to come in planetary systems. **Jeff Kuhn, PhD,** of the Institute for Astronomy, Maui, described a new project, the Colossus Telescope, which will help researchers search for advanced life in other solar systems by identifying for atmospheric markers of power consumption and produce energy. **Hakeem Oluseyi, PhD,** of the Florida Institute of Technology spoke about new developments in 2013, what he called "a banner year in cosmology." Oluseyi posited that life adapts wherever it is in the universe, noting that "every life form on every planet is in a space race" and that "our environment--the universe-- selects life forms that will go out and populate the universe".

In the second morning plenary session "Trending Now," attendees heard from Rutgers biomedical engineering professor **Ronke Olabisi, PhD** on laboratory production of food; economist **Armand Papazian, PhD** delivered a powerful address on the need for new finance models that promote investment in research and far reaching exploration rather than inherently risk adverse, low innovation projects. **Roy Marcus, PhD** founder of the DaVinci Institute commented on the need for new ways to approach human problems and how the wide diversity of the participants at 100YSS provides a window into that new paradigm.

Saturday's luncheon with keynote speaker **Casey Hudson**, Executive Producer of the blockbuster video game Mass Effect, highlighted a dominant theme of the 2013 Symposium: the interplay between creativity and science. Answering a question from the audience on how games are often criticized for being violent, Hudson noted that the Mass Effect games actually offer players the choice resolve conflicts without violence and explore building relationships. He also emphasized the value that role-playing has to society and may have to research into how humans might adapt beyond the Earth. Hudson explained how Mass Effect evolved such that the video characters show appropriate emotion, facial expressions and responses to the game players' decisions. He then related a letter he received from a man who said his autistic son had been helped in learning to interact with real people socially by playing Mass Effect -- in the context of a game, which is a safe, private environment. *"Reality is not a limitation; it is a challenge to your creativity,"* said Hudson.

Friday and Saturday afternoons were devoted to Technical Track sessions where attendees formally presented ideas on a range of topics and discussed and debated them others with participants in an open forum. **Pamela Contag, PhD** of CygnetBio; the Technical Track Chairs oversaw the coordination of the technical tracks and the work of the Track Chairs who selected papers to be presented. The Symposium Technical Tracks and Chairs were: Design: Space led by **Karl O. Aspelund, PhD** of Rhode Island University; Enhancing Life on Earth led by **Dan Hanson**, The Innovation Group, Inc.; Becoming an Interstellar Civilization: Culture, Ethics and Governance was led by **John Carter McKnight, PhD** of Arizona State University; Life sciences in Interstellar by **Ronke Olabisi, PhD;** Interstellar Inspiration, Commercial Perspiration by **Amy Millman** of Springboard Enterprises; Time-Distance Solutions by **Eric W. Davis, PhD** of the Institute for Advanced Studies, Austin; Destinations, Hidden Objects by **Joe Ritter, PhD,** University of Hawaii; and College Track was led by **David Alexander, PhD,** of Rice Space Institute.

Attendees had the opportunity to participate in topical classes including **Hakeem Oluseyi, PhD, Frank Brunner** educator; and **Charles Lindsay, PhD,** artist in residence at the SETI Institute, aerospace engineer **Marc Millis,** Tau Zero Foundation and astronomer **Bobby Felice-Rubio.**

Of the 120 papers were presented and topics ranged from life sciences to exotic space propulsion systems to understanding how civilizations make rapid shifts to design. Discussions were held on the impact of microgravity on the human body and how deep space

might affect the "microbiome" of the body, altering how microorganisms such as bacteria may become more or less pathogenic in space, e.g., some proliferate at a faster rate than on Earth. Technical Track participants also considered the development of new telescopes that can examine distant planets, the problem of human generated space debris, modified gravity and dark matter. **Jeffrey Nosanov** (Jet Propulsion Laboratories) presented details of his recently accepted proposal to NASA's Innovative Advanced Concepts (NIAC) on "solar sails," a near-term project he proposes to follow up the work of Voyager with multiple solar-powered spacecraft sent out in different directions at the same time. Discussions focused on advanced fusion-fission hybrid rocket engines, nuclear fission fragments using black holes to power starships, **Harold White, PhD** updated his research on warp field studies; papers were delivered on prosthetics, robots, communication systems, food textures and flavors, how public education can support deep space exploration, and the commercial innovations and economic systems that could propel and support an interstellar civilization

David Alexander, PhD from Rice University led the student track, attended by college and high school students, where the dominant theme was sociological readiness, and building the means and message to make it happen. *"Going into space is not just building a big shiny thing, it's a human endeavor"* concluded Dr. Alexander in his closing remarks to 100YSS attendees.

Evening programs at the 2013 Symposium centered on provoking discussions and thoughts outside of strictly technological boundaries. During Friday's Sci Fi Stories Night award-winning writers in the genre along with **LeVar Burton** and Dr. Jemison came together for a panel centered on science and views of the future. Author **Mary Doria Russell, PhD** a biological anthropologist, started the evening with insight into her award winning novel *The Sparrow* about humanity's interstellar journey and contact with intelligent civilization; a story driven by the science of evolutionary biology, cultural norms, religion and miscues instead of plasma engines. Authors **Jack McDevitt, Karin Lowachee,** and **Ken Scholes** and addressed these issues of envisioning the future, other worlds and other ways of technology design and social development. The evening was concluded with a special showing of the recently released movie *Europa Report* and popcorn!

"Hard science needs creativity and storytelling," observed Burton. *"A starship will need more than engineers."*

Saturday evening's "Accelerating Creativity" celebration brought to the stage Kenji Williams' unique, beautiful multimedia presentation Bella Gaia, which uses live music, video, and facts to illuminate our "Beautiful Earth" providing a phenomenal display of data on human impact on Earth from the perspective of an artist and musician.

Creating a path for the inclusion, and development of the ideas and talent from among 100YSS members and attendees, Dr. Jemison closed the Symposium on Sunday by announcing starter funding for up to five projects initiated by 100YSS Special Interest Groups (SIGs) that had been formed during the Symposium. SIGs started at the symposium centered on the areas of new technology, gaming, education, public engagement, and the 2014 Symposium.

Summing up the feelings of many people at the gathering, aerospace engineer and 100YSS member Robyn Ringuette said the challenge of making innovation happen today by tackling the difficult problem of interstellar travel in the next century is what both unites and excites 100YSS participants. *"I want to take the next illogical step – a challenge so great that what is between the 'here 'and 'there' seems easy."*

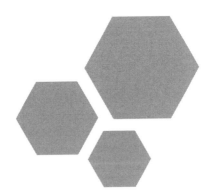

symposium activities

There were several presentation tracks, each being led by a distinguished and knowledgeable track chair.

PLENARY SESSIONS

Opening Plenary Session
Dr. Mae Jemison, Principal 100 Year Starship
Loretta Whitesides, The Overview Institute

Technical Track Show and Tell
Facilitated by Pamela Contag, PhD, Overall Technical Track Chair

State of the Universe Panel
Facilitated by Jill Tarter, PhD

Trending Now Panel
Facilitated by Hakeem Oluseyi, PhD

2013 SYMPOSIUM CLASSES

From Sci-Fi to the Scientific Method
Led by Marc Millis, Tau Zero Foundation

Astrophysics 101
Led by Hakeem Oluseyi, PhD, Florida Institute of Technology

Art and Space
Led by Charles Lindsay, Artist-in-Residence, SETI Institute

Life Sciences in Interstellar
Led by Ariel Anbar, PhD, Arizona State University and Ronke Olabisi, PhD Rutgers University

Earthlings Guide to Our Neighborhood
Led by Bobby Farlice-Rubio, Fairbanks Museum and Planetarium

SPECIAL EVENTS

International Space Luncheon
Hosted and Facilitated by Dan Hanson, Technical Innovation Group

Sci-Fi Stories & Europa Report
Hosted by LeVar Burton and Jason Batt

Interactive Storytelling and Gaming
Led by Casey Hudson, Executive Producer and Creative Director "Mass Effect"

Accelerating Creativity with Bella Gaia
Led by Kenji Williams

TECHNICAL TRACKS

Factors in Time Distance Solutons
Chaired by Eric Davis, PhD

Life Sciences in Interstellar
Chaired by Ronke Olabisi, PhD

Becoming an Interstellar Civilization: Culture, Governance and Ethics
Chaired by John McKnight, PhD

Destinations: Hidden Obstacles
Chaired by Joe Ritter, PhD

Student Track: The Next Generation
Chaired by David Alexander, PhD

Design: Space
Chaired by Karl Aspelund, PhD

Interstellar Aspiration–Commercial Perspiration: The Next 30 Years of Space Start-ups and Commercialization
Chaired by Amy Millman

Interstellar Enhances Life on Earth
Chaired by Dan Hanson

distinguished speakers & guests

MAE JEMISON, MD
Principal, 100 Year Starship
Texas, United States

DAVID ALEXANDER, PhD
Rice Space Institute, Rice University
Texas, United States

ARIEL ANBAR, PhD
Arizona State University
Arizona, United States

KARL ASPELUND, PhD
University of Rhode Island
Rhode Island, United States

DAVID BLACK, PhD
President Emeritus, Universities Space Research Assoc.
Texas, United States

LEVAR BURTON
Writer, Director, Actor, Education Activist
California, United States

PAMELA CONTAG, PhD
CEO, Cygnet Biofuels
California, United States

ERIC DAVIS, PhD
Austin Institute for Advanced Studies
Texas, United States

PAUL GILSTER
Writer and Curator of "Centauri Dreams"
United States

DAN HANSON
Technology Innovation Group
Texas, United States

CASEY HUDSON
VP EA/BioWare, Executive Producer/Creative Director of "Mass Effect"
Alberta, Canada

JEFF KUHN, PhD
University of Hawaii
Hawaii, United States

LOUIS FRIEDMAN, PhD
Co-founder, The Planetary Society
California, United States

KARIN LOWACHEE
Speculative Fiction Author, "Warchild"
Ontario, Canada

CHARLES LINDSAY
Artist-in-Residence, SETI Institute
New York, United States

ROY MARCUS, PhD
Chairman of The DaVinci Institute
Johannesburg, South Africa

JOHN C. McKNIGHT, PhD
Arizona State University
Arizona, United States

MARC MILLIS
Founder, Tau Zero Foundation
Ohio, United States

MMBONENI MUOFHE
Deputy Director, Science and Technology
Republic of South Africa
Johannesburg, South Africa

JACK McDEVITT
Nebula Award Winning Author, "Omega", " Seeker"
Nevada, United States

AMY MILLMAN
Springboard Enterprises
New York, United States

JEFFREY NOSANOV
NASA Jet Propulsion Laboratory
California, United States

RONKE OLABISI, PhD
Rutgers University
New Jersey, United States

HAKEEM OLUSEYI, PhD
Florida Institute of Technology
Florida, United States

ARMEN PAPAPZIAN, PhD
Keipr, Inc.
England, United Kingdom

JOE RITTER, PhD
University of Hawaii
Hawaii, United States

BOBBY FELICE-RUBIO
Fairbanks Museum and Planetarium
Vermont, United States

MARY DORIA RUSSELL, PhD
Hugo Award Winning Author, "The Sparrow" & "Doc"
Ohio, United States

KEN SCHOLES
Fantasy Author, Psalms of Issak Series
Oregon, United States

FOLA SOARES, PhD
Contek Research
California, United States

START MOTION PICTURES/MAGNOLIA PICTURES
Producers of the Movie "Europa Report"
New York, United States

JILL TARTER, PhD
Bernard M. Oliver Chair, SETI Institute
California, United States

ADRIAN TIPLADY, PhD
Project Scientist, South Africa Square Kilometer Array Telescope
Johannesburg, South Africa

LORETTA WHITESIDES
The Overview Institute, Co-Creator of Yuri's Night
California, United States

RICHARD WAINDERDI, PhD
Former President/CEO Texas Medical Center
Texas, United States

KENJI WILLIAMS
Creator, Bella Gaia
Arizona, United States

JENNIE YEUNG
United Nations Education Science Cultural Health Advancement Foundation
Shanghai, China

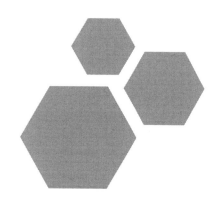

sponsors

Scholastic, Inc.

the barbarian group

The Jemison Group, Inc.

NASA

Greater Houston Convention and Visitor's Bureau

Greater Houston Partnership

Land O'Lakes

Houston Airport System

EA/Bioware

Houston Fine Arts Fair

NASA Johnson Space Center

Milken Foundation

support teams

The Wright Touch, LLC

J&S Audio Visual

Lorelle Media, LLC

Scott Circle Communications

Brazos Bookstore, Houston, TX

Start Motion Pictures

Magnolia Pictures

location

Hyatt Regency Houston
1200 Louisiana Street
Houston, TX 77002

acknowledgments

In many ways, the second time a unique event is held is more difficult than the first. Producing the 100 Year Starship 2013 Public Symposium required including the tasks of generating the energy of 2012, while expanding the interstellar audience and making it even more "100YSS!" Once again, I was fortunate for the team of creative, dedicated, capable and stalwart individuals who applied their considerable talents to the 2013 Symposium. Each year is an opportunity to share the vision of 100YSS to more and more individuals, ensuring we include the broadest swath of people in understanding, shaping and implementing our mission.

I want to thank each of our Track Chairs, who built environments engendering open discussion, curiosity, and pursuit of excellence. The work, commitment, and expertise of David Alexander, PhD; Karl Aspelund, PhD; Eric Davis, PhD; Dan Hanson; John C. McKnight, PhD; Amy Millman, Ronke Olabisi, PhD; and Joe Ritter, PhD are so appreciated—the programs could not be done without them. Exceptional gratitude goes to Pamela Contag, PhD for not only agreeing to take on the challenge of overall Technical Track Chair, but for bringing a level of professionalism, insight, discipline and expanded thought that is needed to generate the radical leaps in capabilities for which 100YSS pushes. Dr. Contag guaranteed that a full range of ideas were considered and provided the platform for healthy, productive participant and author engagement.

100YSS Public Symposiums are more than just the published proceedings, many other sessions and events make the Symposium a singularly unique experience for all attendees. First, I want to thank our sponsors for believing in the mission of 100YSS. And while it is not possible to thank everyone who contributed, thank yous go to Gwen Artis and Rodney Johnson standing in whenever needed. Gratitude goes to Rich Greene and John Miller for capturing the 100YSS Symposium experience on video and in photographs. Jason Batt, newly anointed the 100YSS Creative Editor, led the Sci-fi Night and put together these proceedings. Thanks to The Wright Touch responsible for the wondrous overall Symposium event experience. Juliea Robinson-Nelson and Glorious Watt, foundation staff, as always, had our backs. Big kudos to Lynda Bradford who aptly handled the logistics throughout. And of course, I give my sincerest thanks to Alires Almon—without whom, quite literally—the incredible, memorable 2013 Public Symposium would not have happened.

Mae Jemison, MD
Principal, 100 Year Starship

21

100 YEAR STARSHIP®

Technical Track Papers

I, Too, Look at the Stars

Pamela Reilly Contag, PhD

Overall Technical Track Chair, 2013 100YSS Public Symposium

CEO, Cygnet Biofuels

Although my feet are firmly planted on earth, I, too, look at the stars. In 2012, 100YSS began a journey with the scientific community and I was lucky enough to be invited to the party. Dr. Mae Jemison, the head of 100YSS had asked us a simple question: What do we need to get to the Stars? And, we made the simple assumption that whatever we need to ensure our reaching the goal of interstellar travel, the advances would also improve our life here on Earth. It was with that in mind that a global, cross-disciplinary approach was used to create the beginnings of our 100YSS scientific and technical mission.

There was one caveat. It was not simply advances in fields of engineering, physics and biology that were needed to reach our goal of interstellar travel. We as scientists were compelled to include the advances in the arts and humanities as core components of the 100YSS mission. Dr. Mae eloquently led us to that conclusion and action. The words—eloquently led—are a massive understatement of the actual persuasion required to induce both scientists and artists to jump the perceived chasm between our worlds. I say perceived because once we all made the leap to the other side, we turned to see no chasm at all. Thank you, Dr. Mae.

Early in 100YSS discussions, I believe the community had some areas of discord. First, why combine science, art and humanities? If we don't get the propulsion right, none of us are going anywhere, so let's do that first. We then reasoned that any positive result of our migration to the stars required that we carry the beauty of art within us, and allow the kindness and conciliation that comes with human understanding to be our opening salvo to a new world. This seemed to be the 100YSS paradox. An astute student, attending this 2013 Symposium from the Houston area, made the observation that "Everything begins with a challenge". Our challenge was to find unity of purpose in 100YSS. Ironically, this paradox, the introduction of art into science and science into art, became the basis for our ability to work with each other on opposing theories and yet find our common ground, whether in art or science.

This year, we had eight tracks that brought together a myriad of disciplines.

"Time-Distance Solutions" invited speakers to address the question of "How fast, how far? Ideas varied from gravitational lenses to propulsion mechanisms. From fission/fusion hybrids to compact condensed quark matter, ways to produce enough energy and propulsion mechanisms for faster that the speed of light travel were presented.

"Enhancing Life on Earth", was a session about training the next generation of students in fields relevant to interstellar travel, especially STEAM; Science, Technology, Engineering, Arts and Mathematics. The burgeoning field of Astrobiology was also discussed.

One of our most popular tracks was "Becoming an Interstellar Civilization: Culture, Ethics and Governance." In this track, formation of community, religion, family, conflict resolution and psychosocial issues of life in an isolated community were discussed.

"Destinations: Hidden Objects" addressed the most likely destination, and the obstacles, both physical and scientific, that will stand in our way. Remote sensing and resolution of interstellar imaging and precursor probes to sense the environment and seek living organisms will pave the way understanding our destinations.

"Interstellar Inspiration, Commercial Perspiration" explored the entrepreneurial nature of technical development and the short and long term investment models. Opportunities created by our presence in space, such as mining minerals, have additional challenges in acquisition and distribution.

"Life Sciences in Interstellar" covered the natural diversity and complexity of biology and its use in biotechnology. The topics ranged from the preservation and testing blood in space, effects of microgravity and radiation on the human body, and the microbes that we all carry.

Another popular session was "Design: Space" in which art literally met science. Lifeboats, clothing with enhanced functionality, closed loop environment and novel agricultural systems were covered along with optimization of living environment.

Our student participants wrapped it up with robots, artificial intelligence, entrepreneurship and a rousing discussion of how we create games and other play in the confines of a starship.

I believe that "Game Changing" science begins with an inspirational vision. We need problem solvers with deep domain expertise but not just in technical fields. We need cross-disciplinary thinking. Solutions are a relay race from understanding the gap in knowledge to engineering a visionary solution. At the interface of diverse disciplines lie game changing discoveries waiting to be made.

Overall Track Chair Biography

Pamela Reilly Contag, PhD

Assistant Professor, Biomedical Engineering Department, Rutgers University

Pamela R. Contag, Ph.D., founded and is Managing Partner of the Starting Line Group, LLC a virtual ecosystem for the commercialization of advanced technologies. She is also currently the CEO of Cygnet Inc. Cygnet develops technology platforms for the research and development of advanced materials, biologics and industrial enzymes.

Dr. Contag founded Xenogen Corporation in 1995 and took Xenogen public in 2004. She served as CEO, President and Founder at Xenogen from 1995 to 2006, and concurrently, the CEO of Xenogen Biosciences from 2000-2006 when Xenogen merged with CaliperLS. In 2000, Xenogen Corporation was listed as one of the "Top 25 Young Businesses" by Fortune Small Business and in both 2001 and 2003 received the R&D 100 award for achievements in Physics. In 2004, Xenogen was named in one of the top 100 fastest growing companies by the San Francisco Times and received the Frost and Sullivan Technology Innovations awards. Dr. Contag was named one of the "Top 25 Women in Small Business" by Fortune magazine. She was also awarded the Northstar Award from Springboard Enterprises.

In 2005, Dr. Contag founded Cobalt Technologies, Inc., a venture backed company that produces biobutanol from renewable feedstock. She was the Chairman and CEO of Cobalt Biofuels from 2005-2008. In 2008 Cobalt was named one of the top 20 Cleantech Companies and in 2009 one of the top 100 Cleantech Companies. In 2007, Dr. Contag co-founded ConcentRx, Inc. a biotechnology company developing a unique cancer therapy developed by three Researchers from Stanford University. Dr. Contag founded Cygnet BioFuels in 2009. Cygnet BioFuels, her second biofuels company, is a company focused on the utilization of novel organisms for feedstock and biofuel production. In 2011 Dr. Contag was awarded "Cleantech Innovator of the Year" award for Cygnet technology.

Dr. Contag has held board positions, public, private and not-for-profit sectors. Dr. Contag was a Director of Xenogen Corporation (Nasdaq) (1995-2005) and a Delcath (Nasdaq) Board Member (2008-2011). In the private sector she was CEO and Chairman of Cobalt Technologies (2005-2008), Cygnet Biofuels (2009-present), Director at ConcentRx (2007-present) She also joined in 2009 the DOE Biomass technology Advisory Committee and two nonprofit boards, Springboard Enterprises, an accelerator of women entrepreneurs and the Molecular Sciences Institute as executive chairman and in 2011 merged that entity into MSI/VTT, and remains a Director. Dr. Contag also consults in biotechnology for academics and industry, including consulting Professorship at Stanford School of Medicine in the Department of Pediatrics (1999-present), the Dean's Advisory Board of the Johns Hopkins Bloomberg School of Public Health (1999-2005). In 2010 Dr. Contag joined the Merrick Engineering Consultancy specializing in the energy field and in 2011 Dr. Contag was named to the Start-up America Foundation National Board.

With more than 25 years of microbiology research experience, Dr. Contag is widely published in the field of Microbiology and Optical imaging and has over 35 patents in Biotechnology. Dr. Contag received her Ph.D. in Microbiology at the University of Minnesota Medical School in 1989 studying Microbial Physiology and Genetics (for Alternative Fuels) and completed her Postdoctoral Training at Stanford University School of Medicine in 1993 specializing in "Host/Pathogen Interactions".

technical tracks

There were several presentation tracks, each being led by a distinguished and knowledgeable track chair.

FACTORS IN TIME DISTANCE SOLUTIONS

Chaired by Eric Davis, PhD

In considering potential time-distance solutions, what are the possible paths to leap from current knowledge and capabilities to those needed to meet the interstellar challenge?

LIFE SCIENCES IN INTERSTELLAR

Chaired by Ronke Olabisi, PhD

The life sciences in space exploration today make assumptions about the type of crew members, their tasks and even the requirements for life to be carbon based elsewhere. What strategies, techniques, basic science, uses of space as an experimental platform, and philosophies about life must be addressed to transition to human interstellar space exploration?

BECOMING AN INTERSTELLAR CIVILIZATION: CULTURE, GOVERNANCE AND ETHICS

Chaired by John C. McKnight, PhD

Space Exploration creates excitement and wonder in everyone. However there's a lot of work that is needed to prepare society for the pathway of space travel. Space travel allows us to examine our selves and society through a different lens. The lens that other will view us. It is an opportunity to engage, challenge and perhaps correct our society in many ways. This session invited papers which explore the evolution of culture, governance and ethics that will challenge us as we prepare for an interstellar journey.

DESTINATIONS: HIDDEN OBSTACLES

Chaired by Joe Ritter, PhD

Papers in this track were invited to offer strategies, techniques, processes and solutions will help us continue to explore and understand what is really going on in space.

STUDENT TRACK: THE NEXT GENERATION

Chaired by David Alexander, PhD

College undergraduates were invited to present papers on any of the topics of the Symposium technical tracks during this session. Or, students are asked to imagine how if on earth during their lifetime would be with or without a global interstellar ambition.

DESIGN: SPACE

Chaired by Karl Aspelund, PhD

How might we best design the habitats, clothing and equipment for daily use on board a craft on such a journey? This panel will consider how to sustainably fulfill the basic human needs for creature comforts within the constraints presented by long-range, long-term space travel. What innovations and systemic changes may need to be seen first? How would the resulting design solutions benefit the population of Earth? How might they contribute to the establishment of communities on Mars? The panel addressed these questions by exploring larger questions of design process and theory as well as focused examinations of concepts for specific design areas.

INTERSTELLAR ASPIRATION—COMMERCIAL PERSPIRATION: THE NEXT 30 YEARS OF SPACE START-UPS AND COMMERCIALIZATION

Chaired by Amy Millman

The Internet. Global Positioning Systems (GPS). Autonomous Systems. Cordless Tools. None would exist if it were not for government funding, but it is through the private sector that these technologies reach our everyday life. This session will include current and potential commercial applications for space technology and exploration in the next 30 years. Papers illustrated business and technology innovations spanning several years, strategies for crossing valleys of [funding] death, and creating market with revenues and profits from application in space and on earth.

INTERSTELLAR ENHANCES LIFE ON EARTH

Chaired by Dan Hanson

Session seeks papers on new and novel current or proposed application of interstellar disciplines, research and knowledge to enhancing and understanding life on earth.

100 YEAR STARSHIP™

Interstellar Enhances Life on Earth

Interstellar Enhances Life on Earth

Chaired by Dan Hanson, MILR, MCRP

Technology Innovation Group

Track Description

Session seeks papers on new and novel current or proposed application of interstellar disciplines, research and knowledge to enhancing and understanding life on earth.

Track Summary

"We believe that pursuing an extraordinary tomorrow will build a better world today."

This fundamental principle of the 100 Year Starship describes the "why" behind the mission of the organization. From a broad rubric, most speakers in this track focused on methods for bridging the social, biological and physical sciences.

We were first introduced to the burgeoning subject of astrobiology, a multidisciplinary field that researches the social behavioral patterns of people related to space. This scholarly pursuit tries to address the beliefs and value systems centered on the human dimension when we go to space. More questions than answers dominated the discussion: How do we define the human dimension of space exploration, settlement, and resource exploitation? How do we perform research on these topics while we are grounded here on earth? How do we make policies today for future astronauts and colonies of space travelers? A new publication, *The Journal of Astrobiology*, is launching to examine these and other fundamental questions. The publication's goal is to prepare for real world challenges created when humans interact with space.

We next were treated to a lovely aria that set the tone for the next set of presenters who believe that incorporating the Arts is the way to STEAM power STEM (Science, Technology, Engineering, Math) education. This simple but nuanced act of incorporating creativity in artistic expression in the way we look at the world and how our mind makes new connections translates directly in how we could live today. Discussion first revolved around how to encourage female students to become "STEAM girls" to prepare for careers in science and technology. Girls are equally engaged as boys in STEM classes during primary and middle schools. However, in high school girls' interest in these fields declines, especially in engineering and math. A promising trend is to encompass arts and sciences in core curricula at secondary schools.

There are many benefits to STEAM education:
- Incorporating Arts enhances creativity, imagination and reach.
- Including women doubles the amount of professionals that support a myriad of fields necessary for space exploration.
- There is a shortage or people to fill jobs in traditional STEM careers.
- More women involved makes space exploration richer and more supportive of diverse astronauts.

The topic of STEAM education continued with the observation that where art and science overlap is where magic happens. The presenter then gave a short history of arts and science and described that artistic and technological revolutions often occur simultaneously. While sometimes innovation in the arts and sciences diverge, they mostly interact--and therefore it is very productive for society to encourage that interaction. In schools and efforts to encourage public literacy in STEM education, the arts were first employed to "dress up science." Hence, the term "Edutainment," which was the successful infiltration of science into entertainment.

A newer, more effective way to encourage the interaction of arts and science is represented by STEAM: Art is one of a set of STEM tools to use to solve complicated problems. The Arts are quite effective at changing attitudes and perspectives, so they can lead behavioral changes on board an interstellar spaceship. And the Arts can make science and technology more accessible and actionable to all.

From these discussions on the importance of STEAM education, the next presenter highlighted the fact that starships will be controlled by computer systems, and made a compelling argument that current education programs need to evolve in order to better prepare students for interstellar travel. The concept of learning can be expanded to include inside schools and outside activities. For example, volunteer programmers are the key in outside instruction. Some of these volunteers train teachers as well as students, and perhaps the most effective learning occurs with peer teaching among students. A current event that exemplifies this theme is the International Autonomous Robot Competition (iARoC) that is about young people learning to program autonomous robots that can perform simple skills without any remote control.

We watched a video of robots at a competition that found their way through a set of fixed obstacles, located an infrared home station beacon, and activated a mechanical push-action switch at the home station. A fifth grade student programmed the robot that we watched, which highlighted the ability for students to learn seemingly complex tasks of programming. This skill will be of critical importance for interstellar expeditions. We do not know what challenges and opportunities await these adventurers, but we do know that software will be as important as food and water for successful missions.

Our final presenter brought us back to earth with a discussions of how to manage psycho-social problems associated with space flight preparation and travel. The discussion was very practical and dealt with a variety of issues astronauts and their families have to manage. During the pre-flight stage, NASA has a team of specialists to assist the astronauts with issues such as their absence from home, invited guests problems, pre-flight expense stress, family pressures, pre-launch fears, and the astronauts motivation to refly another mission.

During the flight, the list of issues is even longer:
- Adaptation to no gravity
- Life threatening events
- Confinement and isolation
- Inability to attend children's events
- Being forgotten by the public
- Low morale
- Religious isolation
- Inability to keep up with current events
- Loss of recreational events
- Potential conflicts with crew and ground
- Personal business disconnects
- Home maintenance problems

Complicating these psychological stressors is that the further out the interstellar spacecraft travels, the longer the time it takes for communications to and from earth. Perhaps the psycho-social elements may be the largest obstacle for interstellar travel. Overcoming these obstacles will require unprecedented recruiting, and it will be difficult to get the right people on board. In terms of extending our knowledge, the problems on an interstellar spaceship will tax our understanding of humans and their interactions and emotions.

Yet it is a journey that beckons.

Track Chair Biography

Dan Hanson, MILR, MCRP

Technology Innovation Group

Dan Hanson has over 30 years experience addressing public policy, education, and economic development issues. His professional experience includes public private partnership establishment, investment portfolio management and risk management, capital raising through the bond and securitization markets, and public policy and program development for various government agencies.

Dan has a keen interest in leveraging art, science, and education infrastructure to promote economic development in regional economies. He helps build sustainable engines by forging partnerships among business, government, and nonprofit corporations. These partnerships often are a mix of organizations operating on a local, national, and international level. His efforts are realized through a combination of business and volunteer activities.

Dan is noted for his outstanding analytical and his commitment to promoting regional economic development and achieving equitable outcomes of government policy and program initiatives across communities. He has held volunteer board positions for local and state governments, nonprofit organizations, and foundations in Texas.

Dan is currently a principal with Technology Innovation Group, Inc. (TIG), which he co-founded in 2002. His company's mission is to connect innovation to societal needs. TIG pursues it mission through two primary service offerings: advising entrepreneurs, researchers, academics, technology professionals, and communities wanting to build technology-based economies; and serving as translational consultants with institutions and private companies to commercialize specific technologies, primarily those with public health or economic development benefits. TIG clients include local, regional, and national governments and economic development agencies, large corporations that manage portfolios of intellectual property, young companies that are developing products and services based on complex technologies, and universities and research institutions that desire to move discoveries from the laboratory to businesses.

Dan's academic qualifications include a Bachelor of Science and a Master of Industrial and Labor Relations from the University of the Oregon. He also attended the Kennedy School of Government at Harvard University and graduated with a Master of City and Regional Planning degree.

Getting All Hands On Deck: Using S.T.E.A.M. Education Strategies To Include Girls And Women In Interstellar Space Exploration

Adrienne Provenzano

P.O. Box 40604, Indianapolis, IN 46240

adrienneprovenzano@yahoo.com

Abstract

Space exploration is a challenging human endeavour. Women and men have demonstrated their interests in space travel and their abilities to provide the necessary skills for it. It is important and worthwhile to enable girls and women to play a vital role in exploring within their own solar system and beyond. The 20th and 21st centuries have seen an increase in opportunities for girls and women in the S.T.E.M. (Science, Technology, Engineering, and Mathematics) fields that are the foundation of space exploration. However, there is a significant gap between the number of women and men in many S.T.E.M. fields, especially engineering, computer science, and physics. There are effective programs and materials to encourage girls to study S.T.E.M., and a need to increase both awareness of and access to such enrichment activities and resources. As female students advance from secondary to higher education and into the workforce, their participation in S.T.E.M. areas declines. Recent studies from both the AAUW (American Association of University Women) and Girl Scout Research Institute include suggestions to address these challenges. This paper explores how S.T.E.A.M. (Science, Technology, Engineering, Arts, and Mathematics) strategies can enable girls and women to train for, work in, and advance in S.T.E.M. fields. There is reflection on how interstellar space exploration is currently part of S.T.E.A.M. education, and recommendations for additional ways to incorporate interstellar space exploration into S.T.E.A.M. programs and resources.

Keywords

S.T.E.M., S.T.E.A.M., girls, women, education, arts

1. Introduction

Interstellar human space travel has been imagined and may become a reality in the future. Human space travel has been achieved in low earth orbit, and with trips to the Moon. Human travel to Mars is anticipated to occur in the 21st century, and there are ongoing efforts to make that goal a reality. Already, humans have sent missions to the farthest reaches of our solar system and it appears that Voyager 1 has even exited our solar system and someday may reach another star.

Space travel of any kind is a challenging endeavour. The scientists, technologists, engineers and mathematicians responsible for the accomplishments of the early days of space exploration were mostly men. In the 1950's and 1960's, the space race between the U.S. and U.S.S.R. was the focus of human space exploration. Since then, many more nations have become involved in such efforts.

For purposes of this paper, the focus will be on American space exploration and education. The ideas presented here can have relevance to educational efforts that benefit girls and women around the world. More and more countries are involved in space exploration – most recently India, with a successful launch of a robotic mission to Mars in November, 2013, and in recent years, China, with the establishment of a space station and launches of both male and female taikonauts into space. Women from nine countries have traveled into space, as of November, 2013 and women work on ground teams and in other capacities in aerospace around the world.

Women have studied the stars as astronomers for thousands of years, including EnHeduanna around 2350 B.C.E. in ancient Babylon and Hypatia (370 C.E. - 415 C.E.) in Alexandria, Egypt. As the American Astronomer Helen Sawyer Hogg once said: "The stars belong to everyone." [1] Women were involved at all stages of the American space program and space exploration efforts from the earliest days to the present, such as astronomer Dr. Nancy Grace Roman, astronomer Dr. Carolyn Leach Huntoon, life sciences researcher Francis Miriam "Poppy" Northcutt , and aerospace engineer Marjorie Rhodes Townsend.

As space exploration developed in the latter part of the 20th century, there were increasing roles for women – as astronauts and engineers, among other careers. Since the start of the 21st century, two women, Dr. Peggy Whitson and Sunita Williams, have commanded the International Space Station. Women such as Eileen Collins, Pam Melroy, Stephanie Wilson, and Kalpana Chawla participated in Space Shuttle missions as astronauts and others served on ground teams. Women have also played significant roles in projects such as the Mars Curiosity Rover mission and continue to do so, such as Suzanne Dodd, current Voyager project manager. Women in the 21st century have served in important administrative positions at NASA, such as Lori Garver as former Deputy Administrator and currently, Dr. Ellen Ochoa directs the Johnson Space Center. Women can be found in a variety of roles throughout NASA and elsewhere in the field of aerospace and related fields in industry and academia. Now, in the 21st century, there is the opportunity to strive for and and even achieve equal involvement of women and men in the next chapters of space exploration.

There are many good reasons to provide opportunities for women to be more actively involved in space exploration. However, there are also challenges to be overcome if such equal opportunity is to become a reality. Space exploration requires experts in many fields of work, with a special emphasis on S.T.E.M. (Science, Technology, Engineering, and Mathematics) fields. While there are women working successfully in a variety of S.T.E.M. fields – and in significant numbers in fields such as mathematics and life sciences, there is a significant gap between the number of women and men in some S.T.E.M. fields, particularly those associated with space exploration – such as engineering, computer science, and physics. In addition, while the numbers of women have been consistently going up in most S.T.E.M. fields since the 1960's, they have been going down in computer science since the 1990's. [2]

In order to redress the S.T.E.M. gender gap, there are many possible strategies and initiatives. This paper focuses on how S.T.E.A.M. (Science, Technology, Engineering, Arts, and Mathematics) education strategies can play a critical role in helping girls pursue interests and education in S.T.E.M. fields, thus helping create a larger pool of female talent in the workforce to participate in a variety of S.T.E.M. endeavours, including interstellar human space travel. Because of its complexity and because it seeks to take our species on a unique journey, interstellar travel may best be advanced as a global initiative – an effort by humanity for humanity. This paper focuses primarily on American education and workforce opportunities, with an understanding that there are similar challenges and opportunities throughout the world and with the thought that by exploring one country's challenges and opportunities in this area ideas might be generated to later study across countries and regions. Moreover, while beyond the scope of this paper, it is also recognized that studying and applying effective strategies and initiatives currently in place and planned around the globe, as well as programs with international collaboration, can also enhance and advance opportunities for girls and women in the United States.

2. What is S.T.E.A.M. and How Does It Enhance Learning?

When it comes to connecting the arts with S.T.E.M. studies, there is a recent acronym gaining popularity - S.T.E.A.M. - which stands for Science, Technology, Engineering, Arts, and Mathematics. The initiative of "STEM to STEAM" is spearheaded by John Maeda, President of the Rhode Island School of Design, an academic institution which is actively striving to advance the integration and collaboration of the arts into S.T.E.M. studies and include S.T.E.M. in arts studies as well, and to connect people working in different disciplines in collaborative projects. Maeda has said that "Innovation happens when convergent thinkers, those who march straight ahead toward their goal, combine forces with divergent thinkers, those who professionally wander, who are comfortable being uncomfortable." [3]

The idea of S.T.E.A.M. is to integrate S.T.E.M. and arts fields together, to accentuate learning and innovation. The basic formula to be applied is STEM + Art = STEAM. In different contexts, the term "arts" can be narrowly or widely construed. For purposes of this paper, the term "arts" is considered broadly, to include a wide variety of arts, design, and even humanities fields – as all of these areas can enhance creative and critical thinking and bring new perspectives to S.T.E.M. studies and activities. Thus, the term "arts" can include visual arts such as 2D, 3D and animation; performing arts such as dance, music and theater; literary arts, such as poetry, novels, and plays; humanities, such as history and criticism; and design, such as digital design and architecture.

There are many benefits to integrating the arts in the studies of S.T.E.M. fields - such as emphasis and opportunity for creativity, imagination, self-expression and shared experiences, collaboration and communication, discipline and skills development, experimentation, willingness to take risks and fail, participation in a process, and problem solving. In January, 2010, a report from the National Science Teachers Association included comments from a variety of science educators who valued the ways that S.T.E.M. and arts concepts are related and that there are many ways that using the arts to learn and represent understanding of S.T.E.M. subjects can be beneficial for students and teachers. [4]

In space exploration, the arts have been involved in many ways, from science fiction authors such as Jules Verne imagining trips to the Moon, to astronauts like Chris Hadfield performing music by David Bowie while commanding the International Space Station and Cady Coleman performing flute music while on the International Space Station in concert with musicians on Earth, to scientist-designers such as Dava Newman envisioning new spacesuit designs. From graphic artists creating images to help us "see" Voyager 1 moving out of our solar system to the work of Apollo astronaut Alan Bean including moon dust in his paintings of space travel, connections between the arts and space exploration are numerous and varied. The imaginative efforts of science fiction authors have inspired development of real technologies, such as the cell phone, which was inspired by communications technologies imagined for the television program Star Trek. Moreover, the arts have been an effective tool to foster and facilitate S.T.E.M. studies in a range of areas, including space topics.

3. Women and S.T.E.M. Fields

In the United States, women receive 20% of the engineering, computer science and physics degrees. [5] Women have been earning the majority of bachelors degrees in the U.S. since 1982 [6] and are currently the majority of students in undergraduate programs. [7] There has generally been a rise in women receiving S.T.E.M. degrees, but the growth rates vary among and within fields of study and there has been a decline in women receiving computer science degrees and working in computer science since the 1990's. [8] In most S.T.E.M. fields, there has been an increase in the number of S.T.E.M. doctorates received by women, and here, even in computer science, the numbers have all gone up between 1966 and 2006. [9]

According to a recent U.S. Department of Commerce report on S.T.E.M., women account for 26% of workers in S.T.E.M. [10] Women make up 61% of social scientists, 47% in math, and 41% in life and physical scientists, while they account for 27% in computer science and 13% of engineers. [11] Moreover, while women accounted for 34% of computer scientists in 1990, that number has declined, while in other STEM fields, the numbers have generally increased at varying rates. [12] However, of women who receive S.T.E.M. degrees, only 26% practice in a S.T.E.M. career. [13]

A significant part of the challenge to include more women in space exploration is the rate of growth of women in S.T.E.M. fields. For example, women represented 9.1% of engineers in 1990 and 10.6% in 2011. [14] If this rate of growth continues, it would take several centuries to achieve 50% participation by women. If a goal of 50% is desirable by 2113, the rate of growth would need to be accelerated significantly from 1.5% per decade. What might be a necessary growth rate is beyond the scope of this paper – as well as how realistic a goal that might be. However, setting an ambitious goal does not mean it is impossible to achieve – and to paraphrase President Kennedy's famous comment about sending humans to the Moon and returning them safely to Earth – this goal is not to be pursued because it is easy, but because of the very challenging nature of achieving it and because of the vast benefits to humanity that can be generated through the pursuit as well as the accomplishment of the goal.

In 2010, the American Association of University Women (AAUW) published a report entitled *Why So Few? Women in Science, Technology, Engineering, and Mathematics.* The report determined that socio-cultural and environmental factors such as subtle biases and internalized stereotypes play a role in whether women pursue S.T.E.M.

studies and careers. A variety of suggestions were made in the report as to how to cultivate and support interests and studies in S.T.E.M. by girls at the preK – 12 grade levels, as well as in higher education and in the workforce.

Many girls seem to be interested in S.T.E.M. topics and activities at young ages, but as they transition into middle school and out of high school, the interest wanes, or at least, advanced studies in these areas and pursuit of S.T.E.M. careers are not prioritized or sought actively. [15] Thus, the potential number of female students who might pursue S.T.E.M. in higher education diminishes due to these leaks in the pipeline of potential S.T.E.M. professionals. Once in higher education and the workforce, women do not consistently receive the support and encouragement to stay in S.T.E.M. majors and enter S.T.E.M. fields in the workforce. Plugging up the leaks and narrowing the gaps can be done beginning at preK – 12 levels, as well as in higher education and in the workforce to enable increased participation of girls and women in S.T.E.M. fields, thus enhancing the likelihood of their participation in interstellar space exploration projects in particular.

4. Girls and S.T.E.M. Fields

Girls are interested in space exploration, as active participants in NASA competitions such as the Moon Buggy Race, SPHERES- Zero Robotics competition, and the Student Launch Initiative, as attendees at space camps, as entrants into space-themed art competitions, and as participants in social media events such as Google Hangouts. They are also visitors to websites with S.T.E.M. and space exploration content , such as that run by Astronaut Abby (www.astronautabby.com), a teenager who is determined to be the first astronaut on Mars and who crowd-funded a trip to Baikonaur to watch the launch of Karen Nyberg, Luca Parmitano and Fyodor Yurchikin to the International Space Station in 2013. However, an interest in space exploration at a young age does not necessarily translate into pursuing higher education in S.T.E.M. and working in a S.T.E.M. field.

In 2012, the Girl Scout Research Institute released a report entitled *Generation STEM: What Girls Say About Science, Technology, Engineering, and Math*. It was based on surveys and interviews with girls to determine their interest in S.T.E.M. fields and suggests ways to foster and encourage such interest. The study identified several characteristics of so-called "STEM Girls" - those with an interest in S.T.E.M. fields. S.T.E.M. Girls were found to like creative thinking and problem solving – which is an integral part of S.T.E.M. fields.

What the study showed is that while many of the girls surveyed were interested in S.T.E.M. fields – 75% of those surveyed [16], those more likely to pursue S.T.E.M. studies and S.T.E.M. careers generally had strong adult support systems, exposure to S.T.E.M. fields when young, and interest in S.T.E.M. subjects. STEM Girls are high achievers with high aspirations, hard workers , persistent and confident. There were differences noted for some African-American and Hispanic girls, as having less adult supports and exposure to S.T.E.M. fields and lower academic achievement, but being strong in confidence and aspirations and greater awareness of gender barriers and greater financial motivation. The study noted a gap in girls having an interest in S.T.E.M. and considering such fields as a career choice.

It should be noted that there have been some academic studies suggesting that women may not be pursuing S.T.E.M. careers because they have many options available to them, particularly when they have good communication skills. [17] Also, workplace environments can play a critical role in what careers women pursue, including the attitudes towards women in a particular workplace and work-life balancing policies. The issue of equal opportunity is complex, and considering and addressing it from a variety of perspectives is necessary and worthwhile.

According to the Girl Scouts study, there are a variety of strategies to consider to facilitate more girls pursuing S.T.E.M. studies and careers. At the conclusion of the Girl Scout Research Institute report *Generation STEM*, there is a list of ten recommendations and observations [18] as follows:

- Encourage young girls to ask questions about the world, to problem solve, and to use natural creativity through play, creativity, and experimentation.
- Foster girls' internal assets such as confidence, self-esteem, initiative, and a work ethic.
- Expose girls to people who have careers in STEM, so they can observe firsthand what these careers are, and what they can offer.
- Keep girls interested and engaged in STEM over time and beyond transition points.
- Support and encourage STEM interests.
- Show girls that what they want out of their careers can be achieved through STEM
- Many girls prefer working in groups and collaborating with others to solve problems.
- Steer clear of obvious or subtle stereotypes about girls' and women's abilities in math science. (sic)
- African American and Hispanic girls have just as much interest in STEM as Caucasian girls, yet they have had less exposure to STEM, lower academic achievement, and less adult support.

- Use this research to create awareness an advocate for girls to be engaged in STEM opportunities.
- In the AAUW report *Why So Few?*, there are also recommendations to for "cultivating girls' achievements, interest, and persistence in science and engineering." [19] These are as follows:
- Spread the word about girls' and women's achievements in math and science.
- Expose girls to successful female role models in math and science.
- Teach students about stereotype threat.
- Teach girls that intellectual skills, including math and science skills, grow over time.
- Encourage and help girls to develop their spatial skills.
- Help girls recognize their career-relevant skills.
- Encourage high school girls to take calculus, physics, chemistry, computer science, and engineering classes when available.
- Teachers and professors can reduce reliance on stereotypes by making performance standards and expectations clear. [20]

One way to show female role models in S.T.E.M. and challenge stereotypes is via the media – to equalize the representation of men and women, girls and boys, in television programs and films, for example. Research by the Geena Davis Institute on Gender in Media indicates that female characters are less frequently included in film and television and less likely to have speaking roles. [21] In a recent report on gender roles and occupations, it was found in a study of family films that of 160 characters with STEM careers, 134 of the characters were male and there were no females in leading roles. [22] Girls are less likely to be represented than boys in media as featured characters, in STEM fields or otherwise. Girls are more likely to be stereotyped and sexualized in their portrayals. [23] The exceptions seem to be found primarily in PBS programming. [24]

5. S.T.E.A.M. Strategies for Girls

What girls want, according to the AAUW and Girl Scout studies, can be provided, in part, by including the arts in S.T.E.M. programs. The arts naturally lend themselves to creating meaning, allowing for positive collaborations, and engaging students in critical thinking and creative expression. There is great power in S.T.E.A.M. Already many programs exist which incorporate the arts in direct and indirect ways in connection with a variety of S.T.E.M. areas, and some with space themes or applications. Such programs can also be modified to have a more direct connection with interstellar exploration – as well as new programs and materials being developed.

Organizations play a critical role in providing girls and young women with access to S.T.E.A.M. programs. In 1989 inventor Dean Kamen founded FIRST Robotics. As he has stated, FIRST was intended "to transform our culture by creating a world where science and technology are celebrated and where young people dream of being science and technology leaders". [25] FIRST involves artistic aspects of design and team costuming, as well as hands-on robotics work. FIRST participants are more likely to study S.T.E.M. at higher educational levels [26]. Girls participate in FIRST at all levels, and there are some girl-only teams, many of which are sponsored by Girl Scouts organizations.

In addition to sponsoring FIRST Robotics teams, the Girl Scouts have badges which enable participants to explore a variety of S.T.E.M. fields. They have also launched a new program in 2013 entitled Imagine Your STEM Future, which involves hands-on activities which are fun, engaging and collaborative. Many of the skills involved are similar to those in arts activities and include teamwork.

At space camps – such as those in Huntsville, Alabama and at the Kennedy Space Center, as well as at the Challenger Learning Centers, students regularly act out space missions, thus involving them in role play, dramatic arts, and imaginative play. Boys and Girls Clubs is an organization which impacts millions of children. Some of the S.T.E.M. oriented arts programs they offer include Digital Arts and Clay Tech. Similarly, Black Girls Code is an organization which hosts workshops in metropolitan areas including web design and game design.

Online, the Women@NASA website [http://women.nasa.gov/] is an excellent resource with video interviews with women in a variety of occupations. One possible S.T.E.A.M. extension activity would be to encourage girls and young women to watch the video interviews and then create their own videos by interviewing women in S.T.E.M. fields in their local area or elsewhere, with the use of telecommunications devices such as Skype.

Some of the recommendations of the AAUW study regarding pre-12 education are geared to help girls and young women cope with stereotype threat – the internalization of negative views towards girls' and women's potential in S.T.E.M. activities. Positive media portrayals in books, TV programs, and on websites can help put these suggestions into action.

For example, there are a variety of publications and other media resources that can be used to show positive images of women in S.T.E.M. and also inspire arts activities. Examples include the Magic School Bus books and DVD's, the PBS programs Sci Girls and Design Squad, which have companion websites, books from Sally Ride Science as well as the company's EarthKam and MoonKam projects, and Scholastic, Inc book series such as the 100 Year Starship books and the series entitled Women's Adventures in Science. A new publication in 2013 is *The Amazing Adventures of the Princesses from Planet STEM* by author Erin L. Albert and illustrator Pam Fraizer. This book is about 20 princesses who each represents a different S.T.E.M. area and who work together to save themselves and their planet from ignorance. Another girl-centric publication, *FashionablyMashed: The STEM of Fashion Design* by Heidi Olinger comes from her not-for-profit company Pretty Brainy, which connects fashion design and S.T.E.M. subjects such as 3D printing.

Hands-on arts projects can also be effective tools for learning and motivating further study. In 2010, students from the Art School for Children and Young Adults at the University of Houston-Clear Lake visited the Johnson Space Center in Houston, Texas and created a variety of imaginative artworks, imaginary moon landscapes, and mission patches, in connection with attending art classes and meeting astronaut-artist Alan Bean. [27] More recently, while on the International Space Station, astronaut Karen Nyberg demonstrated how she created a quilt square based on the classic star pattern. She then invited people to create squares to submit for displayed at a quilt show in 2014. At a November, 2013 quilt show - while she was on the International Space Station, working, tweeting, and posting to her Pinterest page regularly, some of Dr. Nyberg's creative work was on display, along with textile work used in the space program.

Another thriving program is the Humans in Space Youth Arts Competition first held in 2010 and again in 2012. Students ages 10–18 created artistic expression in a variety of ways on space oriented themes. The 2010 event included 600 artists from 22 countries on the topic "What is the future of human spaceflight and why is it important? "And the 2012 event included 2600 artists from 52 countries on "How will humans use science and technology to explore space, and what mysteries will we uncover." Selected artwork and music compositions are available via www.lpi.usra.edu/humansinspaceart/. Competitions such as this can ignite the imagination and enable students to imagine the spinoffs from interstellar exploration that can enhance life on earth and better understand how space exploration makes a positive difference and helps others. They allow girls to use the expressive arts to engage with S.T.E.M. topics in meaningful ways.

The examples listed above are merely a subset of the many programs and resources available to help inspire and encourage girls and young women to develop and pursue interests in S.T.E.M. subjects and careers. Moreover, new programs and materials are being developed and can be found through Internet searches and by contacting professional organizations and educational institutions. By checking sites such as the National Girls Collaborative Project at www.ngcproject.org, a variety of programs can be discovered by geographic location.

6. S.T.E.A.M. in Higher Education and the Workforce

In addition to providing suggestions regarding preK – 12 education, the AAUW report *Why So Few?* also provides the following recommendations for creating supportive environments for women in S.T.E.M. majors:

1. Actively recruit women into STEM majors.
2. Send an inclusive message about who makes a good science or engineering student.
3. Emphasize real-life applications in early STEM courses.
4. Teach professors about stereotype threat and the benefits of a growth mindset.
5. Make performance standards and expectations clear in STEM courses.
6. Take proactive steps to support women in STEM majors.
7. Enforce Title IX in science, technology, engineering, and math. [28]

S.T.E.A.M. can be applied in a variety of ways at the higher education level to enhance women's education and opportunities. An in-depth discussion of this aspect of S.T.E.A.M. and women's opportunities is outside of the scope of this paper; however, here are a few ideas to consider.

At the recruitment stage, campaigns such as that recently implemented at Indiana University Bloomington's School of Informatics and Computing "Own Your Awesome" campaign doubled undergraduate women's enrollment in 18 months between 2010 – 2012 and demonstrates how interests in the arts can translate into careers such as web design. [29] Positive language in the recruitment materials included the following: "Want to do something amazing with your life? Studying computing will change the way you think – and expand your opportunities. Discover the connection between technology and your talents in INFO 101: Intro to Informatics." and "We transform hobbies, talents, and interests in awesome careers."

Once enrolled in a degree program, women students can find support and encouragement at some academic campuses through special departments such as the Women in Engineering Program at Purdue University. At Purdue, there are also student organizations such as the Computer Science Women's Network and the Women in Technology club which provide opportunities for mentorships and volunteering in programs for preK – 12 girls. Adding arts activities could add another level of engagement to help women students such as those in Purdue continue in their programs, by adding additional meaning to their studies in working collaboratively to help others and make a difference – some of the items highlighted in the Girl Scout Research Institute's *Generation STEM* report as relevant for making positive connections with S.T.E.M. fields.

Another important area for further development in higher education and in the workforce is to provide opportunities for interdisciplinary study and interdisciplinary collaboration. Such programs occur regularly at some institutions, such as the Rhode Island School of Design (RISD) to connect scientists and artists in unique projects. One recent program at RISD linking arts and sciences was the creation of an exhibit entitled Wander, to help visualize data about marine plankton and help people better understand the role such creatures play in the world's ecosystems. [30]

Both during higher education studies and once in the workforce, it is good to let women know S.T.E.M. fields can provide interesting, enjoyable work in a positive work environment with flexibility and good pay. The arts can connect girls and young women with women working in S.T.E.M. fields to explain the nature and the relevance of their work and to enable younger women to imagine working in such fields.

Another critical area to consider is creating a positive climate for female faculty in S.T.E.M. fields and to help all faculty, female and male, consider their own gender biases and how they might address the impact of such biases on their teaching styles and course content. A better climate can thus be created for all students and faculty, and a more inclusive and diverse academic environment can help prepare students for working with inclusive and diverse teams in the workforce – and appreciating the value of such teams. While beyond the scope of this paper, the arts could play a role in this area as well.

7. Connecting the Dots to Interstellar Exploration

Interstellar space exploration will involve people working in a variety of fields – with S.T.E.M. at the heart of these efforts. Some examples of interstellar careers include nuclear engineering, electrical engineering, aero-astro engineering, robotics, astrobiology, communications, physics, medicine, computer science, life sciences, and informatics. Moreover, there are fields which have yet to be developed which will likely come into being as new technologies and materials are invented and new problems identified to be solved. As well, there will likely be interstellar specializations within existing fields that develop, such as the emerging field of astrosociology.

Less women working in the S.T.E.M. fields at the heart of space exploration adds to the challenge of solving the many problems involved in such endeavours. More women in such S.T.E.M. fields provides a better pool of human resources for interstellar exploration while also reflecting a more accurate and inclusive representation of humanity in these expeditions. Already, women work in a variety of S.T.E.M. fields, and also in other relevant fields, such as medicine and education. By building on the current breadth and depth of women in the workforce and inspiring girls of current and future generations to continue to push the boundaries of what they can study and accomplish, what has been described by Dr. Mae Jemison, Principal for the 100 Year Starship Foundation, as a transformative "inclusive and audacious journey" [31] can be realized with human creativity and effort.

The rate of change at which more women are entering S.T.E.M. degree programs, completing degrees, and entering the workforce in S.T.E.M. fields might be accelerated by creating a sense of urgency and importance about developing and achieving human interstellar travel, in the same way the space race in the 1950's and 1960's led to a growth in S.T.E.M. education and training for people to fill S.T.E.M. jobs. There are decades of research on the benefits of space exploration to solving Earth-based problems and enhancing life on Earth and ever increasing ways to share that information broadly. There is great potential for innovative solutions being achieved by exploration beyond our solar system – and such potential benefit may well spark new enthusiasm in the coming years for S.TE.M. studies. Certainly, the widespread public enthusiasm about the landing of the Curiosity Rover on Mars in August, 2012, suggests there is popular interest in space exploration and such human curiosity can be perhaps be further leveraged into concrete goals and actions – including increased study of S.T.E.M. subjects by girls and women.

Space exploration is challenging and diverse and inclusive groups are better at solving challenging problems and driving innovation. [32] Missing out on women's participation in such projects at all levels and aspects means missing out on the vital contributions those women might have brought through their intelligence, creativity, problem solving, experience, and perspectives. [33] [34]

Moreover, it can be seen as a social justice and human rights issue if half of the world's population is left out of this ambitious undertaking – or if included, at levels much less than their actual representation as part of the human species. Article 3 of the Convention on the Elimination of All Forms of Discrimination Against Women, as adopted by the UN General Assembly in 1979 states that the document was created "to ensure the full development and advancement of women" including in education and employment. [35] Thus, efforts to include women in S.T.E.M., and space exploration in particular, help to meet the goals of this visionary document.

It is also a matter of economic good sense to foster opportunities for girls to become trained in S.T.E.M. fields – with increases in S.T.E.M. jobs projected by the United States Department of Commerce to increase 17% between 2008 – 2018 and not enough men or women to fill them. [36] Moreover, some S.T.E.M. jobs can only be filled by American citizens, due to security regulations and considerations. Also, women who work in "non-traditional," that is, male-dominated, fields, benefit from the higher wages in S.T.E.M. fields. [37]

Individuals and organizations have an opportunity to seek out local S.T.E.A.M. programs that include girls and to encourage additional outreach by expanding current programs and by starting new programs on local, regional, national, and international levels. In addition, there is a need to continue and develop both girls-only and co-ed programs, as there are benefits of both types of structures and because learners and workers vary in terms of which environments foster their abilities to flourish.

There are many ways to assist in closing the gender gap in S.T.E.M., such as providing S.T.E.A.M. resources like books and art supplies, being a mentor or advocate, and supporting professional organizations making a difference as well. Through groups such as the IEEE's Women in Engineering section, the American Association of University Women, the Girl Scouts, the Boys and Girls Clubs of America, and the Society of Women Engineers, effective outreach is being accomplished – and there is still room for many more partnerships and programs. It would also be useful to study and assess the short term and long term impact of such programs, as has been done with FIRST Robotics, for example.

There are many potential benefits of interstellar space travel, similar to the technology spinoffs from NASA missions. Better understanding of our solar system, including our Earth, can also come from interstellar exploration. Moreover, the idea of such travel can be an inspiration for people of all ages to pursue a variety of studies, and thus be an engaging topic for creative and critical thinking.

In science fiction, humans have traveled throughout the universe. Human boots have only stepped on the Moon. However, new science fiction can engage people of all ages – and young people can be encouraged to be creators of such materials as well as consumers. [38] It can also be noted that while humans have only traveled in person to the Moon, as well as around Earth in various low-earth orbit craft, they have traveled virtually to Mars, Saturn, and even beyond our solar system through a variety of missions. Moreover, projects like the Kepler mission have helped humans envision life on exo-planets and the Hubble space telescope has forever transformed how we perceive our universe and our place in it.

Still, much of the educational materials and hands-on programs that exist are are focused on our solar system, especially the Moon and Mars. Humans are intrigued by what is beyond our solar system, as indicated by the excitement surrounding Voyager 1's recent exit from the solar system, and the ongoing work at the Center for SETI Research which has been seeking evidence of extraterrestrial intelligence in the Milky Way Galaxy for almost 20 years. Moreover, humans have been looking up and wondering about the universe for eons, and by building telescopes and observatories – those on Earth as well as in space – have provided windows to many worlds, insights and inspiration.

There is also room for inclusion of information on how the technologies and innovations that have helped achieve human exploration of low earth orbit and visits to the Moon are, in fact, stepping stones to travels to Mars and elsewhere in our solar system and galaxy. Adding such materials to programs geared towards girls and young women can help foster and develop their enthusiasm for interstellar travels and inspire their efforts to participate actively in this grand adventure. With creativity and initiative, interstellar exploration components can be added to existing programs and resources. By taking into consideration the reports from the AAUW and Girl Scout Research Institute, along with research into the value of S.T.E.A.M. education, current and future resources and materials can include girls and women in S.T.E.M. studies and work in relevant and engaging ways.

8. Conclusion

Interstellar space exploration is a topic which can spark enthusiasm and active engagement in S.T.E.A.M. studies for girls and women, in the same way that sports can be used to connect a student with studies of statistics, physics, and other S.T.E.M. concepts. There is a universe of possibilities in how to connect S.T.E.M. and the arts for exciting educational programming at all age and education levels for girls and boys, women and men. With an emphasis on lifelong learning through S.T.E.A.M. and a diversity of ways to inspire and connect learners of all age with space exploration topics, efforts towards achieving interstellar human exploration can benefit current and future generations for centuries to come. Increased opportunities for girls and women in S.T.E.M. fields will help to gather all hands on deck for this next chapter of human adventure.

Acknowledgments

Thank you to Laurie Goldman for her encouragement and constructive suggestions on this paper. Thank you to Kevin Erdman for his insights, particularly on the concept of rate of growth.

Thank you to 100 Year Starship for the opportunity to be a presenter at the 2013 Public Symposium.

References

1. Armstrong, M. (2008). *Women Astronomers: Reaching for the Stars.* Marcola, Oregon: Stone Pine Press.

2. U.S. Census Bureau, 1960, 1970, 1980, 1990 & 2000, Census of the population (Washington, DC)

3. Maeda, J. (2013). "STEAM: Adding Art and Design to STEM." Arcade 31 (2). arcadenw.or/article/stem

4. Shapiro, D. (2010) "Reaching Students Through STEM and the Arts." NSTA WebNews Digest.

5. 1/7/2010 http://www.nsta.org/publications/news/story.aspx?id=56924

6. Modi, K., Schoenber, J. & Salmond, K. (2012) *Generation STEM: What Girls Say about Science, Technology, Engineering, and Math.* http://www.girlscouts.org/research/publications/stem/generation_stem_what_girls_say.asp

7. Snyder, T.D., Dillow, S.A. & Hoffman, C.M. (2009) Digest of Education Statistics 2008 (NCES 2009-020). National Center for Education Statistics, Institute of Education Sciences, U.S. Department of Education. Washington, D.C.

8. Modi, K., Schoenber, J. & Salmond, K. (2012) *Generation STEM: What Girls Say about Science, Technology, Engineering, and Math.* http://www.girlscouts.org/research/publications/stem/generation_stem_what_girls_say.asp

9. National Science Foundation, Division of Science Resources Statistics, 2008, Science and enginering degrees: 1966 – 2006 (Detailed Statistical Tables) (NSF 08-321) (Arlington, VA), Table 25, Author's analysis of Tables 34, 35, 38 & 39.

10. Ibid.

11. U.S. Census Bureau, 1970, 1980, 1990, and 2000 decennial censuses and 2011 American Community Survey.

12. Ibid.

13. Ibid.

14. Modi, K., Schoenber, J. & Salmond, K. (2012) *Generation STEM: What Girls Say about Science, Technology, Engineering, and Math.* http://www.girlscouts.org/research/publications/stem/generation_stem_what_girls_say.asp

15. U.S. Census Bureau, 1960, 1970, 1980, 1990 & 2000, Census of the population (Washington, DC).

16. Hill, C., Corbett, C. & St. Rose, A. (2010) *Why So Few? Women in Science, Technology, Engineering, and Mathematics.* Washington, DC: American Association of University Women and Modi, K., Schoenber, J. & Salmond, K. (2012) *Generation STEM: What Girls Say about Science, Technology, Engineering, and Math.*

17. http://www.girlscouts.org/research/publications/stem/generation_stem_what_girls_say.asp

18. Modi, K., Schoenber, J. & Salmond, K. (2012) *Generation STEM: What Girls Say about Science, Technology, Engineering, and Math.*

19. http://www.girlscouts.org/research/publications/stem/generation_stem_what_girls_say.asp

20. Brooks, C. (2013, March 21) Women's STEM Careers A Matter of Choice, Not Ability, Study Suggests 3/21/2013, BusinessNewsDaily, Huffington Post.com, http://www.huffingtonpost.com/2013/03/21/women-stem-math-science-skills-career_n_2923388.html

21. Modi, K., Schoenber, J. & Salmond, K. (2012) *Generation STEM: What Girls Say about Science, Technology, Engineering, and Math.*

22. http://www.girlscouts.org/research/publications/stem/generation_stem_what_girls_say.asp

23. Hill, C., Corbett, C. & St. Rose, A. (2010) *Why So Few? Women in Science, Technology, Engineering, and Mathematics.* Washington, DC: American Association of University Women

24. Ibid.

25. Geena Davis Institute on Gender in Media, http://www.seejane.org/research/index.php

26. Smith, S., Choueiti, M., Prescott, A. & Pieper, K. (2012) *Gender Roles & Occupations: A Look at Character Attributes and Job-Related Aspirations in Film and Television*

27. Geena Davis Institute on Gender in Media, http://www.seejane.org/research/index.php

28. Ibid.

29. FIRST Robotics, Vision & Mission, http://www.usfirst.org/aboutus/vision

30. FIRST Robotics, Impact, http://www.usfirst.org/aboutus/impact

31. Waltz, A. (2010) The Art of Space. JSC Features. www.jsc.nasa.gov/jscfeatures/articles/000000927.html

32. Hill, C., Corbett, C. & St. Rose, A. (2010) *Why So Few? Women in Science, Technology, Engineering, and Mathematics.* Washington, DC: American Association of University Women

33. IU Communications, School of Informatics and Computing Women's Recruitment Campaign http://communications.iu.edu/work/case-studies/soic-awesome.shtml

34. SURFing Underwater, (2013, August 22) http://www.risd.edu/about/news/2013/surfing-underwater/?dept=4294968230

35. Jemison, M. and Rau, D. M. (2013) . The 100 Year Starship, New York: Scholastic, Inc.

36. Ohr, R. (2012, March 27), "Innovation and Diversity." Game-Changer. http://www.game-changer.net/2012/03/27/innovation-and-diversity/#.Uo2VIX-u408

37. Iguchi, V. (2013, September 29("Adapt, change or die, says the famous business motto." Center for Talent and Innovation Report. http://www.glaxdiversitycouncil.com/2013/09/29/center-for-talent-and-innovation-report/

38. "LBS Study Shows Addition of Women to Teams Improves Performance" 20-First. http://www.20-first.com/968-0-lbs-study-shows-addition-of-women-to-teams-improves-performance.html

39. UN General Assembly. (1979). Convention on the Elimination of All Forms of Discrimination Against Women. http://www.un.org/womenwatch/daw/cedaw/

40. Economics & Statistics Administration. United States Department of Commerce. (2011, July 14). "STEM: Good Jobs Now and For The Future." http://www.esa.doc.gov/Reports/stem-good-jobs-now-and-future

41. Ibid.

42. Toerpe, K. (2012). From the Moon to the Stars: Tapping into Shared Culture to Create Public Momentum for Interstellar Travel. In Jemison, M. & Almon, A. (Eds.)100 Year Starship: 2012 Symposium Conference Proceedings (pp. 393 - 399) . Lexington, KY.: 100 Year Starship.

Grappling with 100YSS Psychosocial Problems

Frank E. Hughes

Chief of NASA Space Flight Training (Ret.)

VP, Tietronix Software, Inc.

1. Introduction

All humans traveling in space carry with them a variety of problems that have plagued humans throughout the history of spaceflight - their own humanity. Humans create their own set of problems far apart from the simple needs of a robot. Unlike a robot, a human being is continuously interconnected with other humans, places, and things on a daily basis. Severing these connections create problems that must be addressed in order to produce a successful spaceflight. Taking these concerns into consideration, we will attempt to further examine the impact of getting a crew ready for interstellar flight.

Psychosocial problems occur on short or medium length spaceflights today. The US and Russia keep a cadre of specialists that support crews on social and psychosocial issues. This support not only includes the flight crew but for their families as well. The NASA support crew handles preflight, in flight and post flight problems. For the International Space Station, this care is currently provided on a semi-formal basis through the activities of the astronaut organization, other astronauts and their families. For flights lasting 12 to 36 months and perhaps years, these semi-formal methods will not be adequate.

2. Preflight

What problems occur on flights today? The following list shows what happens today and what would change on the preparations for an interstellar flight. Problems in italics will not be a considered a problem for an interstellar flight.

1. Absence from home because of preflight travel
2. Invited guest list problems
3. *Preflight expense stress*
4. Family pressures
5. Pre-launch fears or concerns among family members
6. *Motivation to refly another mission*

2.1 Potential Solutions

All individuals assigned to a space flight basically face the same problems. Counseling is provided to the astronauts and their families during the flight preparation phase. This phase guides the astronaut through the process of getting ready for flight and, hopefully, avoids the pitfalls of other individuals who flew before them. It also provides valuable information to their families.

Much of this preflight training is to keep the crewmember interested in reflying whenever possible. The huge training investment when someone is readied for space flight is amortized if the person flies more than once. Much of this training for families is very different since the whole family may be on the crew. Stress relief activities during the training would be great but there will be no second flight.

3. Inflight

Today, there are three main areas of interest where crew problems occur:
- the crewmember as an individual,
- the relationships with others on the flight, and
- the relationships the crewmembers will have with persons back on Earth.

These relationships occur routinely during our normal lives but can be severely interrupted during a flight like the one we are discussing.

For an interstellar flight, we need to determine how to teach the crew members to successfully co-operate and to master the tools needed to resolve conflict. Steps should be taken to ensure that a crewmember does not feel cut off from society, even if that society now is only the crew on the starship.

As we all know, training must be provided to assist each crewmember to withstand the rigors of interstellar flight and its environment. Problem areas anticipated can include but not limited to: (Problems in italics will not be a problem on an interstellar flight.)

1. Physiological adaptation to zero gravity or reduced gravity
2. Life threatening events on flight
3. Confinement and isolation, absence from special events
4. Inability to attend or support children's activities
5. Feelings of being forgotten by public
6. Low morale, boredom, or fatigue
7. Religious preference or isolation
8. Inability to keep up with current and local events
9. Loss of recreational and extracurricular activities
10. Conflicts and anger over intentional or unintentional slights
11. Jealousy and hostility toward other crew members
12. Frustration with the work regimen on the vehicle
13. Frustration with the computer systems
14. Competition between crew members
15. *Hostility toward ground or toward new arrivals*
16. *Disagreements with ground personnel over technical issues*
17. Disagreements over chain of command, decision making
18. Disagreements with other scientists or investigators about technique and processes
19. *Estrangement from mate, money problems at home*
20. Serious illness in the family, death in the family
21. School or behavioral problems with children
22. Personal business relationships
23. *Home or auto maintenance problems*
24. *Absentee balloting, income tax preparation and filing, expiring driver's licenses and other similar items*

3.1 Potential Solutions

Preflight orchestrated discussions and training sessions are scheduled on these interpersonal subjects. Each crewmember and their family should be able to access counseling on these topics and should be allowed to create a list of preferences that reflect what they wish to happen during their flight. For example, during one space flight, his mother died unexpectedly. However, the ground controllers did not tell him about that. He only received that news when he landed back on Earth. That is an intolerable shock.

Family support services may be available on call for a period of time during the flight. For this flight the counselor will be part of the crew. And the family is either with the astronaut on the interstellar flight or there is little that can be done about the family on Earth after communications dwindle to nothing with the flight entering deep space.

This system could follow the model of the US military activities where the dependants are supported while the active soldier, etc. is deployed overseas. The crewmember would be much more at ease if a system were in place to support their family who remained back home for the rest of their lives. Counteractions during the flight could include:

1. Access to a private personal space and a personal computer (in living quarters) allows each person to have electronic mail access, private diary, and communications with family, friends, and colleagues for as long as possible (Done on ISS today)
2. Physical exercise: ergometer, rowing machine, exercise machines, jogging must be available not only for physical health but also for psychological benefit
3. Physical games (individual and group) can be useful diversions
4. Mental games such as video games, puzzles, academic classes, and video enhanced exercise equipment
5. Accessibility to news, athletics, or special events broadcasts as well as access to local (home) news, could be accomplished over the web for as long as possible.
6. *A voting system that was used on the Mir and the ISS by astronauts and cosmonauts for local and national elections*
7. Diet improvements, variety, and personal preferences would all help the time to pass more pleasantly
8. Blooming plants or similar living organisms (bromeliads, orchids, etc.) should be kept on board
9. *Integrated training would be utilized to develop a sense of unity and team cooperation within the crew*
10. *In-flight testing of psychological responses (voice stress analysis, other tests) may be considered to allow real time analysis of the crew*

4. Post-flight Problems

Today, significant issues surrounding a crew member's reintegration into society, into his family, and into their professional life may occur. Long flights exacerbate this problem since the absence are longer. However, for a flight that will not have a return date, these problems disappear. They are absorbed with the other problems addressed above.

5. Flight Length

When Leif Ericson, Chris Columbus or James Cook were recruiting crews, those people all planned for a long and dangerous trip but they also planned to get home. The flight length we face for flights to other planets will be more extreme. Planning for a interstellar trip involves no return to Earth. It is unprecedented and the recruiting will be interesting to say the least. We have seen people volunteer this year for a one-way trip to Mars. However, I am not sure that those people would be selected to take part in an interstellar trip in terms of stability, teamwork, or other psychological measurements.

6. Exceeding our Current Knowledge

The problems on a 100YSS flight will tax our understanding of humans and their complex emotions as well as their psychosocial wellbeing. Research today will lead to reasonable responses to the problems of long-duration flights. But the first interstellar flights will be research experiments in themselves. No one can research a 100 year fight without actually doing that flight. In testing hardware or personnel, we have no really good way to test a stability or longevity for a specimen without allowing time to actually elapse on that subject.

For example, the leading edges of the Shuttle Columbia wings were made of the toughest material available when they were built. However 30 years later, the reinforced carbon carbon panels were not tough enough to withstand an impact of a piece of external tank foam. Once tough bulletproof vests have to be replaced every five years. We did not know that until people were getting hurt from bullets penetrating their old vests.

We will not know how people or their equipment will withstand interstellar flight until we actually do it.

7. Instant Communications

The near instant communications that humans expect to stay in touch with friends, family and colleagues will gradually dwindle until there is no possibility for immediate conversation. The communications with Earth will be reduced to email and text communication and then to even less as the light speed induced transmission delays mount. Contact with Earth will gradually cease. News of Earth can keep on arriving each day but the news will be stale since the time it was sent will be further in the past. There will be effectively no two-way communications back to Earth that is not stilted and business-like.

In Mars testing at NASA facilities, it is difficult to have a conversation with a family member even with a 20 minute delay inserted. Humans are so used to talking to a person right by them or over the phone and getting instant response, that delay is intolerable. The participants talked over each other, when the delays were just seconds. Once the delays got to be minutes, they resorted to asking a list of questions and then waiting for the answer to be sent back in another answering list. There was no chance of a regular dialog conversation.

8. Speed and Propulsion

The reason for this delay in communication change? The speeds that we may attain during an interstellar mission are unknown but they must be extreme by today's standards. However, what if we reach only 1% of the speed of light or about 1860 miles per second (6,696,000 miles an hour). This shows that the delay in communications with Earth will increase by 36 seconds every hour. In other words, every 24 hour period at those speeds, the delay in communications will lengthen by 14.4 minutes. In a little more than four days, the delay will accumulate more than an hour.

Meanwhile, 1% C is a paltry value in astronomical terms. In Star Trek, many times the Captain asked for speeds exceeding their normal cruise speeds of about 7 or 8 C (or 7 or 8 times the speed of light). Sometimes, Scotty would complain to the Captain that if they get nearer to 9.0 C, the ship may break up or explode or whatever. If our ship ever reaches nine times the speed of light, a journey to Canopus which used to be 89 light years away, it would take 9 years. Somehow, in the TV show it seemed like it took just a few minutes to get there. Travelling at 90 C would still take our crews a long time to get anywhere interesting.

How to get these speeds is a problem for someone else to address. However, getting up to these speeds could be difficult. The most efficient propulsion systems today (such as the VASIMIR drive by Franklin Chang Diaz company) would allow a constant thrust for long times rather than a high acceleration for a short time. Humans have never gone that fast so we don't know how they will behave. In the 1890's, traveling at 25 mph in a train was terrifying to some people. The fastest humans so far are the Apollo 10 crew who travelled at 24,790 mph (6.87 miles/sec.) during reentry from the Moon in May 1969. That would be 3.7×10^{-5} C, not very fast.

The vessel we envision will be mammoth considering all the people it will carry. Today, the vehicles we build are 1- 2% mass consists of the passengers and their life support systems and the rest is fuel and propulsion equipment. If we can create a system that will produce an acceleration of 1 foot/second continuously, it will take one hour to achieve 3600 feet/second speed or about 0.67 miles/second. In 100 hours, the ship would accumulate to 67 miles/sec. If we keep that thrust going for about 2800 hours, the ship would exceed the velocity of 1% C or 1860 miles/sec.. So in less than 120 days, given that you have enough fuel mass, you can accelerate to a useful velocity that humans can understand and tolerate. We just have to conserve enough fuel to turn around and slow down when we get to wherever we are going.

9. Time

Over time, all the people you have left behind on Earth will have died. All of the original passengers on the space ship will also die during the journey. The methods of keeping the ship operating must include the education and training of new people to allow replacement of the crew in route. We have to either bring infants and young children on the trip as well as producing a lot of new people during the flight. How many people are needed on this flight? There is no answer yet.

10. Knowledge

It will be critical for the crew on this interstellar cruise that they carry with them the accumulated knowledge of the entire world - technical, social, cultural, etc. We have to create in detail the kind of library that Carl Sagan and Ann Druyan extracted to place on the Voyager probes launched in 1978. They only included examples of who we are here on Earth. On an interstellar flight, there would have to be extensive data banks on everything human plus the capability to add new data. The amount of data needed would be enormous. It would, more than likely, be in an electronic format to allow efficient storage on the ship. As many of you know, carrying this treasure of knowledge would be one of the most important reasons to set off on this journey. Spreading the human DNA across the universe would protect us from getting wiped out by a super volcano or a wayward rock from space. A serious problem is that electron storage is not perfect and it is not permanent. All electronic storage methods have serious shortcomings in long-term storage. Our data will be vulnerable. How should this material be stored remains an open question but the material must travel safely with these voyagers like the golden records did on the Voyagers.

11. Questions

Once this spaceship leaves Earth and the direct communications gradually decrease, what will happen? These Earth people will live on in their closed environment, developing new thoughts and new perspectives on life and their purpose on this trip. Some science fiction stories show that Earth has forgotten some of these preliminary expeditions. But it is possible that the explorers may gradually forget about Earth too. As many as four or five generations of people will be born on the ship in its 100 year journey. The group that arrives after 100 years may not have the same culture and mindset as the original group who set out. Who will they be? How will they get along together and with any new beings they may encounter?

12. Summary

The methods that humanity uses to construct and staff this ship will shed more light on how humans should be educated and trained, how crews are selected and prepared, and how humans and humanity as a whole behaves as it begins to spread out into deep space. This will be the most interesting and complicated undertaking that mankind will ever do. Exporting themselves into the universe will be the ultimate evolutionary step.

Space Education and Exploration: Astrosociology in the Classroom

Jim Pass

Chief Executive Officer – Astrosociology Research Institute, Huntington Beach, CA

714-317-6169, jpass@astrosociology.org

Kathleen D. Toerpe

Deputy Chief Executive Officer for Public Outreach & Education,

Astrosociology Research Institute Baileys Harbor, WI

920-421-3963, ktoerpe@astrosociology.org

Abstract

Education is a key component to preparing humanity for a spacefaring and starfaring future. Current educational efforts focus on the STEM disciplines of "hard" science, technology, engineering and mathematics. Missing from these educational mandates is instruction in the human dimension of exploration. The ultimate success or failure of current and future space initiatives hinges on humanity's ability to create sustainable social structures in precarious space environments. The very process of imagining, creating, and refining these social structures affect human societies right now. Further, all future space efforts depend upon the consent of space-literate constituencies who value and support research, exploration, and eventual settlement beyond our solar system. Thus, education is a key social dimension related to space exploration.

To fill this gap, we present Introduction to Astrosociology, a competency-based, college course offering a multidisciplinary and evidentiary approach to instruction covering this astrosocial dimension of space exploration. Developed as part of the Astrosociology Research Institute's Astrosociology in the Classroom initiative, this course draws upon research in the social and behavioral sciences, the humanities, and the arts to facilitate student understanding of the reciprocal relationship between outer space and human societies.

Course themes include analysis of:
- Humanity's deep desire to explore Earth and now space
- Impact of space research and exploration on core institutions in human societies
- Privatization and commercialization of space exploration
- Reciprocal technology transfers between astrosocial and non-astrosocial applications
- Search for extraterrestrial life - microbial and intelligent - and social, cultural, and institutional reactions to such discoveries
- Applied astrosociology and social problems

- Planetary defense, space law and policy, medical astrosociology, space tourism and settlement, space societies, spacefaring societies and other subfields

In short, Introduction to Astrosociology prepares students to adopt an astrosociological perspective as humans evolve from a global society to a potentially galactic one.

Keywords
astrosociology, space education, space research, space outreach, spacefaring, space culture

1. Introduction
The multidisciplinary field of astrosociology was organized in 2003 to research the human social, cultural, and behavioral patterns related to space. Known as astrosocial phenomenon, these patterns inform and impact STEM-based space research and warrant detailed academic inquiry. The non-profit Astrosociology Research Institute (ARI) was established in 2008 to research, educate, and present outreach programming on this important human dimension of space exploration. With collaboration from the social and behavioral sciences, the arts, and the humanities, ARI's current initiatives include a quarterly newsletter, an upcoming peer-reviewed journal, original academic research, a readings-based textbook, and educational coursework targeted to K-12, college and professional audiences. This presentation details the foundational curricular component of ARI's classroom programs: a college/professional level course entitled Introduction to Astrosociology.

2. History of Astrosociology
The founding of astrosociology in its current form originated when co-author Jim Pass found an article on the Internet in December 2002 called "Positive Consequences of SETI before Detection" by Allen Tough. In passing, Dr. Tough mentioned that SETI research would benefit from creating an organized field such as "social astronomy" or astrosociology. [1] That passage inspired Dr. Pass, who as a sociologist, had begun to entertain the idea of pursuing outer space issues from a true social science orientation. Pass selected the "astrosociology" term and, with colleagues, Dr. Marilyn Dudley-Flores and Mr. Thomas Gangale, formally co-founded the field of astrosociology following the 2004 meeting of the American Sociological Association.

The formal introduction to the field took the form of a two-part introductory essay called "The Definition and Relevance of Astrosociology in the Twenty-First Century." "Part One: Definition, Theory and Scope," provides an initial working definition of astrosociology:

Astrosociology is defined as the sociological study of the two-way relationship between astrosocial phenomena and other aspects of society (i.e., non-astrosocial phenomena or other social phenomena) at the various levels of social reality and organization (i.e., the micro, middle, and macro levels of analysis). The concept of astrosocial phenomena (have I coined a new concept?!) pertains to all social conditions, social forces, organized activities, objectives and goals, and social behaviors directly or indirectly related to (1) spaceflight and exploration or (2) any of the space sciences (e.g., astronomy, cosmology, astrobiology, astrophysics). [2]

"Part one" also introduces a general model of astrosociology related to the definition above that portrays an interaction between the astrosocial sector (including astrosocial phenomena) and the non-astrosocial sector (including non-astrosocial phenomena) that contributes to social and cultural change in a given society. (See Figure 1). This area of research is currently relatively ignored, but it deserves future attention.

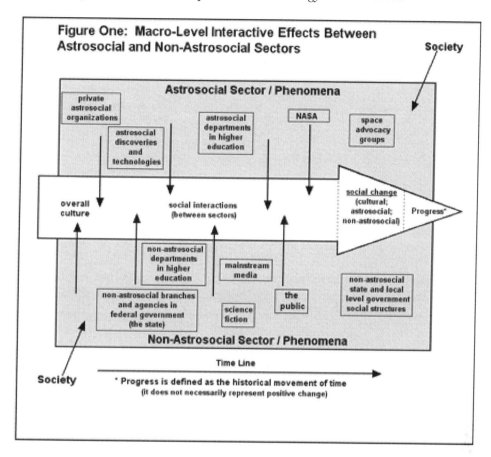

Figure 1. Macro-Level Interactive Effects Between Astrosocial and Non-Astrosocial Sectors, Source: J. Pass

The Inaugural Essay's second half, "Part Two: Relevance of Astrosociology as a Sociological Subfield," continues the earlier emphasis on alerting the sociological discipline to the importance of space issues to societal concerns, while focusing on the development of astrosociology as a new sociology subfield. Still, important areas of theory and research are emphasized here including: (1) astrosocial phenomena and culture, (2) contrasting between spacefaring and space-capable societies, (3) the social impact of the space sciences, and (4) space policy and space law, among several others. [3]

In 2009, Pass further refined the definition of astrosocial phenomena as "the social, cultural, and behavioral patterns related to outer space."[4] Though slightly refined, the emphasis remained on the two-way relationship between space and human society.

While the Inaugural Essay attracted initial criticism – mostly by sociologists who either did not think this new subfield was needed or favored addressing space issues from within existing disciplines and fields - the idea eventually attracted a broad range of advocates. Originally slated as a subfield of sociology, hence the selection of the name, astrosociology quickly became a multidisciplinary field quite based on the input of social and behavioral scientists, humanities scholars, and artists – as well as some members of the traditional space community who recognized the importance of the human dimension of their work. It soon became clear that the complexity of space and society issues required collaboration between the two major branches of sciences commonly referred to as the "soft" and "hard" sciences.

While Pass, Dudley-Flores, and Gangale continued to introduce astrosociology to colleagues at conferences such as the Pacific Sociological Association and American Sociological Association; significant opportunities were arising from within the space community. In 2007, Pass presented the idea of astrosociology to the Space Architects Subcommittee at the American Institute of Aeronautics and Astronautics (AIAA) Space Conference. The presentation was received with enthusiasm and the field of astrosociology found a home in the AIAA within the Society and Aerospace Technology Technical Committee. Efforts that started out with the Astrosociology Working Group later advanced to the status of the Astrosociology Subcommittee. Ongoing astrosociology sessions continue today.

From 2009-2011, the Space, Propulsion, and Energy Sciences International Forum (SPESIF) conference sponsored a separate Astrosociology Symposium. Future ARI officers Christopher Hearsey and Simone Caroti took part in the first symposium. The initial symposium in 2009 included a session focusing on the "Astrosociology in the Classroom" concept, which has been fully fleshed out in the following course documentation.

3. Astrosociology Research Institute

The course presented here, Introduction to Astrosociology, was created under the auspices of the Astrosociology Research Institute. In 2008, the Astrosociology Research Institute (ARI) was established by the original founders of the field of astrosociology. Jim Pass, Marilyn Dudley-Flores, and Thomas Gangale believed that the establishment of a nonprofit organization could implement the projects and programs needed to promote astrosociology in a structured and professional manner. Additionally, the existence of ARI would make it possible to attract competent professionals to help carry the mission forward. The Institute is successfully accomplishing these goals.

ARI has made great strides. The website, www.astrosociology.org, currently hosts a Virtual Library providing access to astrosociological research and is a resource for students, space professionals and the general public. Based on its past success, ARI has been able to attract well-regarded officers and advisors to assist in carrying out its mission to develop astrosociology as an academic field and thereby help "settle" the astrosociological frontier (see www.astrosociology.org/aboutari.html for a complete current listing). Upon the departure of Dr. Dudley-Flores and Mr. Gangale, Christopher Hearsey and Simone Caroti took their positions. As the second highest officer in the organization, along with co-author Pass who serves as the Chief Executive Officer, Mr. Christopher Hearsey strongly contributed to a steady and progressive leadership that resulted in a number of successes in carrying out its mission.

- *The Journal of Astrosociology* (See the ARI's Journal page at www.astrosociology.org/joa.html). This is ARI's flagship publication of contemporary astrosociology education and research. A diverse group of well-respected professionals from diverse backgrounds serve on the journal's Editorial Board. The journal will allow for longer and more comprehensive articles than possible in the newsletter (see below).
- ARI's *Astrosociological Insights* newsletter (See the newsletter section on ARI's Virtual Library page: http://www.astrosociology.org/vlibrary.html#VL_Newsletter). The newsletter allows ARI to publish more timely contributions by authors on contemporary topics that is not possible in the journal. Together, they offer a comprehensive and informative overview of current astrosociological research.
- The *Astropolitics* Astrosociology Special Issue. (See details on the ARI's Virtual Library page: http://www.astrosociology.org/vlibrary.html#VL_SpecialIssue)
- Japanese Space Symposium called "Constructing the Future Society in Japan" that included recorded astrosociology presentations by co-author Pass and Christopher Hearsey at Meiji University in Japan on March 31, 2013. This effort helps to make astrosociology a globally recognized and accepted field of study and practice. (See the second newsletter: http://www.astrosociology.org/Library/PDF/Newsletters/ARI-Newsletter_Vol-2_Iss-1_02-2013.pdf; and the third newsletter: http://www.astrosociology.org/Library/PDF/Newsletters/ARI-Newsletter_Vol-2_Iss-2_05-2013.pdf)
- *Launching Astrosociology* textbook reader – due out in the first quarter of 2014. This upcoming book will include guest chapters by professionals from the social and physical sciences. It is intended to serve as the main reader for the *Introduction to Astrosociology* course.

Each of these accomplishments and ongoing projects continue to further ARI's mission of developing the field of astrosociology and training others to help in the sustainable effort to present astrosociological education and research to all those interested in space exploration and related issues. It will allow for individuals and organizations to participate in ongoing outreach, education, and research efforts and to stay informed about important astrosociological issues. Social media, including Facebook and especially Twitter allow for updates and timely news that strongly bolsters its inspired agenda. It is within this context that Dr. Kathleen Toerpe, ARI's Deputy CEO for Public Outreach and Education, created the formal course documentation for ARI's flagship educational offering, Introduction to Astrosociology.

4. Introduction to Astrosociology

This introductory course provides a comprehensive and flexible learning experience to students in the social and physical sciences, to instructors who wish to incorporate the human dimension of space into their existing curriculum, and to space professionals who seek to understand the relationship between humans and space within the larger scope of their research, experiments, and engineering efforts.

This curriculum has been greatly enriched by earlier introductory courses on astrosociology taught by co-author Jim Pass at the Kepler Space Institute, by Renato Rusca-Rivera at Meiji University and by one developed and envisioned by ARI Advisor, Ken Duffy. Their understanding of the pedagogical significance and relevance of astrosociological themes has laid a firm foundation for the current and future incarnations of this course.

4.1 Course Documentation

This documentation links competencies, learning objectives, learner outcomes, and core abilities to achieve a comprehensive and integrated curricular platform for this course. Competencies stress the qualitative characteristics of astrosociology, its relevance to space research and exploration, as well as its multidisciplinary connections to the physical/chemical/biological sciences, the humanities, and the arts. The learning objectives for each Learning Module are directly derived from these competencies. Learner outcomes and core abilities reflect a basic alignment with multiple intelligence and whole brain theories. Taken together, the linked components are mutually reinforcing and form the cohesive structure of the course.

4.1.1 Description

The course units are structured in a learner-centered, inquiry-based approach using guiding questions at the beginning of each learning module to frame the topics. Real-life case studies and newly emerging research, combined with a customized readings anthology (currently being edited by ARI), comprise the main textual material for the course. Assignments will be completed both individually and in teams, promoting collaborative teamwork while stressing individual competency. Pedagogical methods will reinforce critical and creative reasoning skills to encourage students to draw broader and deeper connections among the course themes. Course content can be customized, adapted to fit client semester or session lengths, and can be offered in online, in-person or blended formats.

4.1.2 Course Overview

Unit 1: Understanding Humanity and Outer Space Through Astrosociology
    Module #1 - Introduction to Astrosociology
    Module #2 - Human Exploration of Earth and Space
    Module #3 - Imagining Space Knows No Frontier

Unit 2: Social Dimensions of Outer Space
    Module #4 - Impact of Space Research, Exploration and Settlement on Earth
    Module #5 - Exporting Terrestrial Societies to Outer Space
    Module #6 - Creating New Cosmic Societies

Unit 3: Enterprise, Governance and Risk in Space Exploration
    Module #7 - Privatization and Commercialization of Space Exploration
    Module #8 - Law and Order in Outer Space
    Module #9 - Health and Well-being on Earth and in Space

Unit 4: Present Challenges Lead to Future Possibilities
    Module #10 - Extraterrestrial Discovery and Contact
    Module #11 - Planetary Defense in a Precarious Cosmos
    Module #12 - Astrosociology in a Space-faring Future

4.1.3 Course Competencies

Mastery of applied knowledge, skills and abilities measured by the successful attainment of corresponding Learning Objectives and signifying successful completion of course of study

- Utilize an astrosocial perspective to evaluate and address social issues and problems on Earth related to outer space.
- Apply an astrosocial perspective to evaluate and address challenges in space research, policy, exploration and possible future extraterrestrial settlement.

- Evaluate impact of astrosocial phenomena, activities and forces on individuals and on core institutions in human societies (family, religion, education, governance, law, medicine, etc.)
- Demonstrate an understanding of astrosociology as a vibrant, multidisciplinary field for both theoretical research and applied practices in the human dimension of space activities.
- Expand collaborative circle of stakeholders in space research, exploration, education and other activities to include scholars, practitioners and students of the social sciences, humanities and the arts.
- Appreciate the cognitive, inventive and affective impact of outer space on the human imagination and its varied manifestations in the applied sciences, engineering as well as the literary, dramatic and visual arts.

4.1.4 Learning Objectives

Measurable and defined outcomes that demonstrate a student's successful completion of specific learning module content (12 Modules X 3 Objectives/each).

Learning Module #1 – Introduction to Astrosociology
- Define astrosocial phenomena and distinguish it from non-astrosocial phenomena.
- Describe the multidisciplinary nature (social and behavioral sciences, humanities and the arts) of astrosociology.
- Explain contributions that astrosociology makes to the study of human activities in space and the impact of space on humans and Earth.
-

Learning Module #2 – Human Exploration of Earth and Space
- Compare and contrast human space exploration activities over time and across diverse societies, including "push-pull" factors.
- Evaluate the impact of the "Overview Effect" as a catalyzing force for space exploration.
- Identify and distinguish the range of individuals, organizations, institutions and societies that pursue outer space research and exploration.

Learning Module #3 – Imagining Space Knows No Frontier
- Identify and summarize range of genre (science fiction, gaming, performing and visual arts, etc.) that has fueled humanity's collective space imagination.
- Evaluate the reciprocal relationship between science fiction and technology/engineering as creating a blueprint for human innovation in the 20th and 21st centuries.
- Propose ways that space imagination and the media forms that express it can be used to further scientific space research and exploration.

Learning Module #4 – Impact of Space Research, Exploration and Settlement on Earth
- Analyze types and impacts of space-related technology transfers and "spin-offs" on different human societies across the Earth today.
- Predict how enhanced computing capabilities in robotics and AI will affect space research and exploration.
- Compare and contrast the STEM and STEMA models of contemporary education. Is one more conducive than the other to producing the literacies needed for the 21st century and beyond?

Learning Module #5 – Exporting Terrestrial Societies to Outer Space
- Identify and analyze the stakeholders (social, cultural, political, economic, religious, etc.) in creating extraterrestrial space settlements and societies.
- Construct a process to determine what elements of terrestrial human societies should be exported to future space settlements and societies.
- Describe ways that human societies on Earth and in space can interact with one another.

Learning Module #6 – Creating New Cosmic Societies
- Construct various social/cultural models of what a future space society might be like in terms of institutions, norms, roles, etc.
- Weigh the relative benefits and disadvantages of robotic vs. manned space settlements.

- Identify and evaluate criteria currently used to select astronauts. Will the criteria used to select future space explorers and settlers need to change? Why?

Learning Module #7 - Privatization and Commercialization of Space Exploration
- Evaluate the impact of private entrepreneurial and commercial initiatives on overall space research and exploration.
- Analyze how governments spearhead space research and exploration through policy, legislation and funding (NASA, JAXA, ESA, etc.).
- Explain the role of the mass media and crowd-sourced funding and research in influencing the direction and content of space research.

Learning Module #8 - Law and Order in Outer Space
- Compare and contrast present-day space policy in regulating space research, exploration and creation of future settlements.
- Construct a hypothetical, yet realistic governing structure for a future space settlement or society.
- Describe how political and legal rights in future space societies may differ from those currently in force on Earth.

Learning Module #9 - Health and Well-being on Earth and in Space
- Analyze known human health risks from long-term space exposure and summarize basic treatment protocols.
- Evaluate benefits of space-based medical research for treating terrestrial diseases.
- Identify areas of medical concern for future long-term space missions and settlement.

Learning Module #10 - Extraterrestrial Discovery and Contact
- Analyze the apparent social, psychological and cultural need for humans to answer the question "Are we alone?"
- Compare and contrast different possible contact scenarios arising from the discovery of both microbial and intelligent extraterrestrial life forms.
- Hypothesize on the social, cultural, philosophical and theological effects of never knowing for sure if we are alone in the universe.

Learning Module #11 - Planetary Defense in a Precarious Cosmos
- Analyze how governments and scientists are reacting to acknowledged threats from space (asteroids, solar flares, space debris, etc.)
- Assess the social and cultural expressions of humanity's concern for Earth's safety.
- Evaluate the effects of class, race, nationality, etc. on how governments and private enterprises prioritize planetary defense.

Learning Module #12 - Astrosociology in a Space-faring Future
- Anticipate and address future ethical dilemmas in law, medicine, social relations that may arise from long-term space exploration and settlement.
- Debate the inevitability of long-term human exploration and settlement of outer space.
- Recommend concrete steps for continued collaboration between the STEM disciplines and astrosociology.

4.1.5 Learner Outcomes
Knowledge, skills and behaviors that directly reflect the individual student's learning process rather than mastery of specific content
- Demonstrate oral, written and non-verbal communication skills in an organized and coherent manner.
- Accomplish tasks successfully as an individual or as part of a team.
- Show respect to diverse points of view.
- Analyze and use empirical evidence to test hypotheses.
- Apply ethical reasoning to controversial, multifaceted issues.
- Apply critical and creative thinking skills to a variety of sociological issues.

- Appreciate the diverse origins and expressions of human knowledge and activities.
- Appreciate the dynamic influence of technology in contemporary, industrialized societies.
- Cultivate a personal response to space-related issues and astrosocial phenomena.

4.1.6 Core Abilities
Basic individual and social skill sets which are transferable to any setting, occupation or field of study
- Communicate effectively
- Think critically and creatively
- Solve problems effectively
- Work cooperatively and professionally
- Value individual differences and abilities
- Demonstrate personal accountability
- Demonstrate community and global accountability [5]

5. Course Implementation

The Astrosociology Research Institute (ARI) is currently exploring formats to launch the pilot session of *Introduction to Astrosociology*. Leading implementation strategies include:
- Accelerated, in-person or online workshops geared to space sector industries as corporate training modules
- Asynchronous online course sponsored by a host institution such as the Kepler Space Institute
- Independently self-produced course offered through a gateway provider such as YouTube or Moodle, and available by subscription
- Traditional quarter/semester "special topics" undergraduate or graduate course sponsored by a college or university

Multiple, concurrent venues will be explored as ARI's commitment is to provide broad and deep educational support to individuals, institutions and industries interested in applying a sociological perspective to their space-related endeavors. To that end, our goal is to offer flexibility in the course's delivery, length and content and to customize syllabi to suit student, professional and institutional needs.

6. Conclusion

The emerging field of astrosociology contributes to our understanding of the reciprocal relationship between humans and space, and the behavioral patterns among humans as they engage in space-related activities. These astrosocial phenomena mark the human dimension of outer space and have a profound impact on the outcomes of space research, exploration, and possible future settlement. To that end, it is imperative that we include an astrosociological perspective both in preparatory space studies curricula and in general programs offered to undergraduate and graduate students. These students - and their descendants – may very well be living in a spacefaring future, so we must prepare ourselves by starting to study astrosocial phenomena as soon as possible.

Astrosociology, with its multidisciplinary spirit, offers a rigorous and inclusive lens through which to understand both our present efforts and our future aspirations. The Astrosociology Research Institute is committed to facilitating research and education in this important, and often underserved, area of study. Thus, the "Astrosociology in the Classroom" program serves to provide a solution for students pursuing the social sciences, humanities, and arts who also happen to have a strong interest in outer space – and thus, astrosocial phenomena – yet can find very few schools to offer such a combination of interests on the still unsettled astrosociological frontier. Such a lack of academic programs and departments arguably slows the potential growth of human spaceflight, space resource exploitation, and settlement. Our program addresses this void in space education and research.

Additionally, ARI's program encourages interdisciplinary/multidisciplinary cooperation and formal collaboration between the "hard" sciences popularly characterized as STEM education, which focuses on the physical and natural sciences, technology, engineering, and mathematics.. While this focus is necessary, it represents only half of what is required to understand space exploration fully. The human dimension, the relationship between space and society, are also vitally important. The "soft" sciences provide the other largely neglected lens through which the relationship between humankind and space can be fully understood. Here, ARI has made some modest inroads, and we need to formalize this progress by adding a significant level of acknowledgement of astrosocial phenomena and how they relate to the issues taught in STEM-based courses.

This initial course, Introduction to Astrosociology, is the place to begin. The course can be utilized intact or Learning Modules can be interwoven as appropriate into specific STEM offerings or professional workshops. Your assistance is most welcomed. We invite you to contact us with questions, provide comments and suggestions, and inquire about hosting this course for your staff or students.

References

1. Tough, Allen. (1995) "Positive Consequences of SETI before Detection," 6. Accessed on 10/25:13: http://www.astrosociology.org/Library/PDF/Positive%20Consequences%20of%20SETI%20Before%20Detection.pdf.

2. Pass, Jim (2004a). "The Definition and Relevance of Astrosociology in the Twenty-First Century (Part One: Definition, Theory and Scope)," 7. Accessed on 10/25/2013: http://www.astrosociology.org/Library/Iessay/iessay_p1.pdf

3. Pass, Jim (2004b). "The Definition and Relevance of Astrosociology in the Twenty-First Century (Part Two: Relevance of Astrosociology as a New Subfield of Sociology)." Accessed on 10/25/2013: http://www.astrosociology.org/Library/Iessay/iessay_p2.pdf

4. Pass, Jim (2009). "Pioneers on the Astrosociological Frontier: Introduction to the First Symposium on Astrosociology." Accessed on 10/28/2013: http://www.astrosociology.org/Library/PDF/Pass2009_Frontier_SPESIF2009.pdf

5. Core abilities from Northeast Wisconsin Technical College, Green Bay, WI. Although the specific choice and wording of core abilities vary among institutions, the ones listed here are representative of current instructional design.

100YSS Education in Space: Are We Ready?

Paul D. Webber

Star Flight Academy

11076 Corte Playa Merida, San Diego, CA, 92124

Captain.Webber@gmail.com

Abstract

There are several organizations trying to "fill the gap" in educating teens and preteens, and sometimes adults, in all areas of education. The immediate objective of this research is to identify organizations which are focused on Computer Science and proposing why this is important to the 100 Year Starship program. I will be presenting a comparative analysis on the techniques these organizations are using to fill a specific gap of Computer Science in education.

There is a grassroots uprising in enabling our children to learn in a more proactive way. I belong to one such organization, Wintriss Technical Schools, which has a unique way of teaching teens and preteens how to program using the Java programming language. Through this we created an autonomous robotics competition based loosely upon DARPA's Grand Challenge, for students in K-12 as well as adults. Other organizations are also trying to fill this gap in education such as Code.org, Codecademy.com, KhanAcademy.org, and many others. Each organization has its novel approach in trying to "fill the gap" but as with any evolutionary process, time will tell which methodology will survive.

This paper will present a synopsis of current nonprofit educational organizations focused on "filling the gap" of Computer Science. It will identify areas, within the scope of Computer Science, that are needed from a 100 Year Starship perspective. This paper will propose some delivery concepts which should interest the "next generation" in the areas needed for a 100 YSS project and postulate on what the ongoing education on a starship could be like.

Keywords

programming, robotics, education, computer science

1. Introduction

There is a large amount of material being made available on the internet which is geared toward education [1, 2]. There is also a lot of information dealing with our current education system in the United States and throughout the world [3, 4, 5, 6]. We are at the point in time where organizations, both for profit and nonprofit, are promoting a new form of education in order to find a more optimal way in educating the youth, and adults, of today in our ever changing global society. These issues are large in scope, essentially effecting how the world teaches the next generation and how this next generation will learn. The scope and focus of this paper will be on the one particular area of education, that of Computer Science (CS). The relevance of CS to the 100 Year Starship endeavor is apparent because software is used everywhere. All disciplines needed to meet the mission of the 100 YSS will have a software component!

At the present time, our education system appears to leave a gap in the area of CS [7, 8]. Many organizations have been formed to fill this gap by working within the current system of education or entirely outside the accredited system. Various techniques are being used by these organizations to supplement the learning process. A new term has been coined for the organizations with an online teaching presence, MOOC (pronounced moōk) for Massive Open Online Course [9, 10, 11, 12, 13]. Other techniques, such as mentoring or workshops, are also being used. Section 2 will describe a few of these organizations and the techniques they are using. It is not known which organizations will survive or if their methodology will persist, even as this paper was written, new organizations came into being. The change in our education system is inevitable; the organizations outside the current system are helping with that change. In Section 3 a close up of one organization, Wintriss Technical Schools, and its techniques for instruction will be highlighted. Finally, in Section 4, a look into the future on how we might educate the next generation in a small self-contained society while on starship in transit.

2. Organizations and How They Are Teaching

A survey of organizations which have an online presence was made to ascertain if CS was being taught and how. The organizations were separated into two groups, those that have online courseware and those that instruct in a group setting, such as a classroom or a workshop. The sample set obtained from the internet does include both for profit and nonprofit organizations. A discriminator was added to indicate if there was a cost associated with taking the course.

Table 1.1 lists the organizations surveyed which are offering online courses and sites were selected from various online lists [14, 15, 16]. Data was collected by going to each website and obtaining information about the organization and the classes offered. An attempt was made to actually take a course and identify common attributes across the organizations. Online courseware can be updated at any time and the number of courses can change as well as the cost.

Table 1.1: Organizations offering online courses

Name	URL	CS	Nonprofit	Cost
edX	https://www.edx.org	15 Classes	Yes	Free
Coursera	https://www.coursera.org	70 Classes	No	Free
Udacity	https://www.udacity.com	18 Classes	No	Free
Open 2 Study	https://www.open2study.com	1 Class	No	Free
Khan Academy	https://www.khanacademy.org	1 Class	Yes	Free
Codecademy	http://www.codecademy.com	5 Classes	No	Free
Future Learn	http://futurelearn.com	0 Classes	No	Unknown
The Open University	http://www.open.ac.uk	27 Classes	No	Cost
iversity	https://www.iversity.org	0 Classes	No	Free
openlearning	https://www.openlearning.com	8 Classes	No	Free/Cost
Academic Earth	http://academicearth.org	87 Classes	No	Free
P2PU	https://p2pu.org	1 Class	Yes	Free
Udemy	https://www.udemy.com	>100 Classes	No	Free/Cost
University of the People	http://www.uopeople.org	21 Classes	Yes	Cost
Saylor	http://www.saylor.org	21 Classes	Yes	Free

Table 1.2 lists a summary by numbers of the sites visited in Table 1.1.

Table 1.2: Summary of Table 1.1

Sites Surveyed	15	100%
CS Courseware	13	87%
Free (No Cost)	10	67%
Nonprofit	5	33%
For Profit, CS and Free	5	33%

Table 1.3 list the organizations surveyed which are nonprofit organizations that reach out to students by conducting sessions within the current school system's classrooms or outside via workshops or completely independent facilities. These sites were selected from previous awareness or from various online lists [17]. Data was collected by going to each website and obtaining information about the organization and the teaching techniques used. Once again the information about the sites can be updated at any time as well as the cost.

Table 1.3: Organizations instructing in a classroom

Name	URL	Nonprofit	Cost
Wintriss Technical Schools	http://wintrisstech.org	Yes	Cost
Teaching Kids Programming	http://teachingkidsprogramming.org	Yes	Free
Girl Develop It	http://girldevelopit.com	Yes	Cost
Girls Who Code	http://www.girlswhocode.com	Yes	Unknown
Black Girls Code	http://www.blackgirlscode.com	Yes	Unknown
CFY	http://cfy.org	Yes	Cost
Code to Learn	http://codetolearn.org	Yes	Unknown
Scratch	http://scratch.mit.edu/	No	Free

The organizations surveyed in Table 1.3 seem to fall into two groups. One group being those who help within the school system and those helping outside the school system but all are capable of helping within the school system. Some of the cost information was not found online and was marked as unknown.

2.1 Techniques Used To Fill The Gap

For general subject matter courses most online sites are using video of a classroom lecture usually one person, the instructor, talking and projecting information. Other means of communicating the information are being used, such as hand and pen writing in the video frame or just the writing. Instruction time frames vary from a few minutes to over 60 minutes. Basic quizzes can also be given during the lecture period on some of the more sophisticated sites. Khan's Academy has done an outstanding job in the mathematical arenas using audio and video along with quizzes, badges and challenges to make the online experience very effective and appealing.

Narrow the focus down to online CS courses and the attributes become very small. Some sites, Codecademy and Scratch, even forego the audio/video and use an interactive workbook style where you read the instructions and write the code or manipulate code blocks to see results. This is where the organizations with classroom type instruction step up to the challenge. And other organizations are pulling instructors from the professional community. "Our historically sold-out classes are taught by volunteer professionals in the community and sponsored by awesome local companies!" as seen on KidsCodeCamp [18].

2.2 Summary

Most online courses use audio and video as the primary means of instruction. For programming there is also a coding scratch pad, where you can write and execute code to get immediate feedback on your understanding.

There are some with automated quizzes and some with homework. A few are using rewards other than test scores to keep interest levels up. And most use an online community for peer to peer discussions. Not all online courses are available on demand but must be scheduled and taken over time just like traditional schooling. Some of these courses are made available online after the course ends.

The organizations that use classroom instruction of some type depend on CS professionals to instruct students or teachers. Instructing teachers with a toolset of programming courseware helps in extending the reach of teaching basic CS to students but these teachers still have to account for other courseware instruction in the school. The mentoring nature of the organizations teaching outside the classroom allows for a more focused instruction session and leads to a better understanding by the students overall.

3. Close Up of Wintriss Technical Schools
3.1 Brief History
Wintriss Technical Schools was founded in 2006 by Vic Wintriss.

Vic is a successful technical businessman with 3 companies under his belt and a 20 year career in the Navy. Inspiration hit Vic for his fourth company when he decided it was time to give back to the community and in an area where the school systems were lacking, that of computer programming. In order to accomplish this he went back to school taking UCSD Extension courses, which is where I met Vic as his instructor for a Java programming course. I was intrigued by having a student of his age in my class as normally the classes are with young professionals already in the workforce and sometimes high school students. Vic and I developed a rapport and he told me about his vision about "changing kids' lives with Java programming". Vic continued with his extension program and created Wintriss Technical Schools as a nonprofit company teaching kids how to program in Java. A year later I joined Wintriss as a volunteer teacher and now reside on the board of directors.

3.2 What They Do
WTS uses volunteer professionals from the community to instruct students in grades 4 through 12 and has even taken on children with autism. Over the years the organization has evolved but still adheres to the guidelines set forth by Vic: get the students engaged at the first class. As a software engineer myself I can attest to the statement from Vic that "writing computer programs can be a very satisfying personal experience and lead to a rewarding high-tech career." The very first course has the students writing the simple program for the High-Low guessing game. At this point the students may not know the "how" but they are able to tie their actions of typing to the output when running the program. Once the students are "hooked" on their ability to control the "game" they continue through the courses because they want to, not because they have to. The ratio of four students to one teacher has been found to be a very good ratio in allowing students to learn and not overwhelming the volunteer instructor. Currently there is a waiting list of about 50 students and this is due to the number of teachers on hand for the various time slots. WTS is open 7 days a week and due to the generosity of Vic, transportation is even provided to students who cannot otherwise get to the classroom.

WTS has grown since 2006 and now has one full time paid position of a lead instructor. This position was filled by one of the volunteers, a successful software development professional, who was "bitten" by the rewards of teaching. This is important in the sustainability of WTS since the operational costs of WTS are kept at a minimal allowing for nominal fee per student of $35 per hour of instruction. But WTS has also not refused to take on any student due to financial hardship. In fact they reach out to low income areas because school systems are not equal in all areas [19].

You can divide the operation of WTS into three areas of concern: Instructors, Students and Curricula.

Instructors are located through professional networks and organizations. Since WTS has adopted Java as the general purpose programing language, they have reached out through the San Diego Java User's Group, the Agile User Group, and various other organizations. Instructors must have a desire to teach, and do so on their own time while maintaining their current paying job. Under the mentorship and evaluation of the lead instructor a new teacher will observe a class and then start teaching that class. This usually takes a couple of sessions and within 12 sessions the new teacher is able to handle a class on their own. There are many factors which contribute to a good professional, volunteer instructor. A desire to teach and the reward that teaching brings is a discovery process for the teacher. If the self-gratification is not there then the volunteer ceases to come back. Another factor is the ability to teach and at various levels of maturity. Some volunteers have the desire to teach but lack a "sense" to teach. They are very good as software developers in their own right but being able to take their knowledge and teach how to solve a programming problem is challenging. Instructors who fall into this category do not take on a class by themselves. One solution is to pair a Java professional with a volunteer who is professional instructor but also has the desire to learn how to program.

An additional aspect of teaching is the peer teacher, using a student from a higher level to teach students at the lower levels. WTS has found this extremely beneficial for both the students being taught and the student teacher as teaching reinforces the knowledge learned earlier. There is a basis for peer teaching emerging online and elsewhere in the world [20, 21].

Rewards are an important part of learning and WTS, along with other organizations, are cognizant of this. At WTS a colored "belt" system has been developed not unlike the colored belts of Karate, except at WTS the colors are related to the color codes of the resistor used on some circuit boards. Not only do students get feedback from the computer programs they write but are recognized as they complete various levels of instruction.

Student participation and volunteer professionals as instructors along with parental understanding contribute to the right combinations for allowing student to learn programming in a very effective manner. WTS is operating on many different levels in attempting to fill the gap in computer science that the education systems are lacking. They do so by engaging the student through the use of software professional from the community. The students are initially encouraged by the parent, but the positive feedback from programming seems to make this less of a concern as the student continues learning.

Students come from many different backgrounds and for many different reasons. Initially the students came by the professional network Vic had already established. Community events such as the San Diego Science Festival are also used to promote interest in the school. Today students are coming from a variety of areas and backgrounds due to the success WTS has in inspiring kids to program at such an early age and some of the accolades that the students have achieved. One student, while in the 6th grade, was able to take the Apple Certified Support Professional exam and pass. Others have taken and passed the Advanced Placement test at their schools.

The curriculum was initially developed by Vic and subsequently modified by the volunteers that have come to teach at WTS. By using trial and error, the basic form of what to teach and when to teach has developed. The student's capability is also assessed and given the small class size of 4 it is not unreasonable to arrange students based upon common rates of learning as assessed by the instructor. The students learn by doing and by what they want to do. Depending on the interests of the students and the instructor, focused curriculum tracks are also provided. Some tracks include the preparation for the Advanced Placement, called AP Exams, given in high school and other tracks for taking the professional exams given by Oracle for various Java certifications. One special track open to all is pertaining to autonomous robotics.

3.3 International Autonomous Robot Competition (iARoC)

In 2008 WTS organized a friendly robotic competition which was to promote the school and possibly raise funds to help the school along. WTS has completed its 6th annual International Autonomous Robot Competition at the Reuben H. Fleet Science Center in June of 2013. It has been invaluable as a promotional tool and subsequently challenging other public schools to focus their Robotics Clubs on a challenge different from others like First [22] and Botball [23]. The basis of iARoC was derived from the Defense Advanced Research Projects Agency (DARPA) Grand Challenge. The organizers from WTS wanted something that was non-destructive but still fun and challenging. The driving factor of the competition is fully autonomous operations of the robot. The current theme used in iARoC is celebrating Curiosity on Mars and the challenges were given a Martian flavor. The competition extends over two days and is open to any group but is mainly attended to by K-12 students along with WTS students. Prior to the competition is a one week long RoboCamp where all are invited to attend and perfect their robots for the challenges that await them. Various professional mentors are on hand during the RoboCamp to assist the students when needed.

The challenges of the competition have varied over the years but have settled into 5 distinct areas:

1. Mars Mission Briefing: the technical presentation where the team has 15 minutes to explain their robot and the algorithms it uses to compete in the other challenges.
2. Earth to Mars Speed Challenge: A double elimination drag race.
3. CAPCOM: Akin to the old National Aeronautics and Space Administration's Capsule Communicator the team must reach out to the public explaining their robot and the competition for 30 minutes.
4. Mars Navigation Challenge: This is the main challenge where the robot must navigate and learn a maze within 20 minutes. Only one team has ever completed this challenge of having the robot learn the maze.
5. Mars Beacon Run: This challenge puts all the robots into the same playing field trying to locate one of three infrared beacons. The winners are determined by the robots which tap one of beacons.

The iARoC has led to some interesting tactics by students over the years but has also focused the instruction at WTS during the months preceding the competition which is very exciting to the students. The iARoC has the additional benefit of teaching students how software and the "real" world interact and unlike a videogame not always in a precise pattern.

4. Education For Space
4.1 How Students Might Be Taught Before Transit To Another Star System

Education has been thought of as preparing for the future or as being needed to get a good paying job. There is growing movement that our current education system can be improved in radical ways. Technology, Entertainment, Design (TED) talks from Sir Ken Robinson [4, 5, 6] and Sugata Mitra [20] and their research have given compelling reasons for a change. Is the next generation being prepared for what may be the adventure of a lifetime, going to another star system? Computer Science will be an important aspect and is one that our current education system is not prepared for. "It is clear there are major gaps in education policy needed to support quality computer science instruction for all K–12 students." as stated in the 2010 study by The Association for Computing Machinery and The Computer Science Teachers Association [8].

It is envisioned that most if not all systems on board a starship will be controlled by a computer program of some sort. The ability to correct or update these programs on board will be essential. The challenge is ensuring that the students of today have an understanding of creating and writing programs, as opposed to just using programs. The changes in the education system being observed today will need to produce specialists in the areas needed for creating and building a starship. I also believe it will take a concerted effort in all disciplines to foster an environment where success is inevitable. In a small way WTS, Khan's Academy, Teaching Kids Programming, and all the rest, are starting to fill the gap. I would like to believe humanity might be prepared for an interstellar endeavor within a generation.

4.1 How Students Might Be Taught While In Transit To Another Star System

Education in space will be dependent on many factors and it is assumed that these factors would be defined before the launch thereby customizing the education environment. But no matter how the starship is conceived, with travel to another star system and an inhabitable planet, education will have to continue. It could be a small community which grows into a larger one, either on board the starship or at its destination but the optimization of having groups taught by others will occur. Self-driven learning can begin at a young age [20] and the environment must be set up to nurture and promote this attribute. On a starship specific areas will need to be utilized for education much like any small isolated community with limited facilities. The educators will also be from the community and all disciplines would be involved at some point. A large question as to what will be taught is just as important as how it will be taught. What will be taught would be directly related to the mission profile of the starship.

A simple thought exercise, given a set of initial conditions for a thriving community of 500, awake and living, during a long duration trip of 100 years. There would be a need for education on starship maintenance and operations as well as general education topics. Even though not everyone is born with a desire for maintenance and operations understanding these topics would be required for the survival of the community. The social aspect of the community must also be accounted for in the education system. Even though topics relating to the Arts may not directly relate to keeping the air at acceptable levels of breathability they are just as important to keep the community thriving while on the journey. There might also be a need to keep certain skills in practice even though there may be no need on the starship but a real need after landing. Will a 4th generation starship occupant be able to colonize a planet?

Some other questions should be thought about. Can all the knowledge of the current world be taken on the starship? Presently not all books and publications are in electronic form but providing a "backup" on a starship is an appealing idea. Can all the knowledge taken on a starship be in a form that promotes learning? Advances today in the how teaching is conveyed is currently happening, it is conceivable that advanced artificial intelligence might be able to organize the information into way which promotes learning.

5. Education In Space, Are We Ready?

Though all areas of learning could be equally important, the context within which a community lives will most likely dictate the focus of subjects to be taught, but it is really the student who ultimately decides which course of study to pursue. We, as leaders and educators, need to develop our ability to determine and guide the students with the aptitude and desire for particular areas of study.

I can envision the need for an educational system on a starship that will have to be available for all ages of students but, in particular, the young students who will have the opportunity to grow up in space. The current system for teaching, of having a dedicated instructor teaching all subjects, may not be viable due to the size of the population. It could be that everyone on board a starship will take turns at educating as part of the duty cycle.

Learning is a lifelong experience that we can take advantage of now more than ever. In our earlier years mentorship seems to provide a way to motivate students to learn and, then later on, we develop self-learning behaviors. Part of the self-motivation is a curiosity to know something or to obtain rewards while we learn. Is what we learn useful? It will be interesting to observe what subjects make it at the end of a 100 year long journey through space. Which subjects stay in the computer until the appropriate population density allows for activities not directly related to survival.

It is apparent that the education system on Earth is changing and needs to change if we want to travel to the stars. 100YSS identifies areas that could be incorporated in this change. Indeed, the education system on board a starship is an area that will need to be thought out and is very dependent upon the community within the starship. The vision of Star Flight Academy is to provide an area where these changes can be considered. Establishing a curriculum for the programs needed on board a starship and using advanced computer techniques to facilitate learning. The course to the stars has been set. The techniques on how we get there can be inspirational to the generations that come and the one generation that will travel to the stars!

Acknowledgements

I would like to thank Vic Wintriss and the members of Wintriss Technical Schools for inspiring me to change kids' lives through programming. I also want to thank the 100YSS committee for selecting my paper to present at the 2013 conference. And finally a special thanks to my editor and my wife Sofia Webber. Live Long and Prosper!

References

1. "Education - Wikipedia, the free encyclopedia." 2003. 7 Sep. 2013 <http://en.wikipedia.org/wiki/Education>

2. "E-learning - Wikipedia, the free encyclopedia." 2003. 7 Sep. 2013 <http://en.wikipedia.org/wiki/E-learning>

3. "National Science Foundation Slowly Turning STEM to STEAM." 2011. 7 Sep. 2013 <http://www.huffingtonpost.com/john-m-eger/national-science-foundati_b_868449.html>

4. "Sir Ken Robinson: Bring on the learning revolution! | Video on TED …" 2010. 7 Sep. 2013 <http://www.ted.com/talks/sir_ken_robinson_bring_on_the_revolution.html>

5. "RSA Animate - Changing Education Paradigms - YouTube." 2010. 7 Sep. 2013 <http://www.youtube.com/watch?v=zDZFcDGpL4U>

6. "Sir Ken Robinson: How to escape education's death valley | Video on …" 2013. 7 Sep. 2013 <http://www.ted.com/talks/ken_robinson_how_to_escape_education_s_death_valley.html>

7. "Computer Science: Filling the Education Pipeline Gap | blog …" 2012. 7 Sep. 2013 <http://cacm.acm.org/blogs/blog-cacm/158113-computer-science-filling-the-education-pipeline-gap/fulltext>

8. "Running on Empty: The Failure to Teach K-12 Computer Science in …" 2010. 7 Sep. 2013 <http://www.acm.org/runningonempty/>

9. "Massive open online course - Wikipedia, the free encyclopedia." 2011. 7 Sep. 2013 <http://en.wikipedia.org/wiki/Massive_open_online_course>

10. "Major Players in the MOOC Universe - The Digital Campus 2013 ..." 2013. 7 Sep. 2013 <http://chronicle.com/article/Major-Players-in-the-MOOC/138817/>

11. "Instruction for Masses Knocks Down Campus Walls," Tamar Lewin Published: March 4, 2012 http://nyti.ms/11j6E1D

12. "Stanford Engineering Everywhere: Stanford School of Engineering." 2008. 7 Sep. 2013 <http://see.stanford.edu/>

13. "Are MOOCs the Answer? Preserving the Value of Higher Education." 2013. 24 Aug. 2013 <http://www.quickanded.com/2013/08/are-moocs-the-answer-preserving-the-value-of-higher-education.html>

14. "A Comprehensive List of MOOC (Massive Open Online Courses ...)" 2013. 8 Sep. 2013 <http://www.technoduet.com/a-comprehensive-list-of-mooc-massive-open-online-courses-providers/>

15. "MOOCs: Top 10 Sites for Free Education With Elite Universities." 2013. 8 Sep. 2013 <http://www.bd-pa-detroit.org/portal/index.php?Itemid=20&catid=29:education&id=57:moocs-top-10-sites-for-free-education-with-elite-universities&option=com_content&view=article>

16. "MOOCs Directory." 2012. 9 Sep. 2013 <http://www.moocs.co/>

17. "AzureDev - Nonprofits." 2013. 8 Sep. 2013 <http://www.azuredevs.com/Programs>

18. "KidsCodeCamp - Teaching The Kids of Planet Earth To Code." 2012. 24 Aug. 2013 <http://kidscodecamp.com/

19. Baker, BD. "Is School Funding Fair? A National Report Card (PDF)." 2010. <http://www.schoolfundingfairness.org/National_Report_Card.pdf>

20. "Sugata Mitra: Build a School in the Cloud | Video on TED.com." 2013. 25 Aug. 2013 <http://www.ted.com/talks/sugata_mitra_build_a_school_in_the_cloud.html>

21. "Salman Khan: Let's use video to reinvent education | Video on TED ..." 2011. 25 Aug. 2013 <http://www.ted.com/talks/salman_khan_let_s_use_video_to_reinvent_education.html>

22. "First." 25 Aug. 2013 <http://www.usfirst.org/>

23. "Botball® Educational Robotics Program | Smart Robots. Smarter ..." 2002. 25 Aug. 2013 <http://www.botball.org/>

100 YEAR STARSHIP™

Becoming an Interstellar Civilization: Culture, Governance, and Ethics

Becoming an Interstellar Civilization

Chaired by John Carter McKnight, JD, PhD

Research Associate, Department of Sociology, Lancaster University

Track Description

Space Exploration creates excitement and wonder in everyone. However there's a lot of work that is needed to prepare society for the pathway of space travel. Space travel allows us to examine our selves and society through a different lens. The lens that other will view us. It is an opportunity to engage, challenge and perhaps correct our society in many ways. This session invites papers which explore the evolution of culture, governance and ethics that will challenge us as we prepare for an interstellar journey.

Track Summary

The *Becoming a Interstellar Civilization: Governance, Culture, and Ethics* track included 22 accepted presentations across three tracks. Civ A focused on religion, ethics and social relationships; Civ B on politics, economics, and other analyses grounded in social science methods; and Civ C's presentations addressed communications and outreach.

Rather than a format in which individual authors present their work and then take questions, we followed blocks of three or four presenters with a substantial open discussion amongst everyone attending, presenters and audience alike. This format allowed for an outpouring of creative expression and the emergence of themes, teasing out commonalities among the various presentations in a serendipitous way.

Civ A saw a discussion focusing on biophilia and the role of nature in a long-duration starship, in ways ranging from the design of public spaces to childrearing. One commenter noted that such a starship could be seen as a multi-species, not just multi-cultural, undertaking, in which our relations with other species might be as important to success as our relations with each other.

In Civ B, the discussion focused on marketing and message, as we struggled to understand why space advocates have done such a poor job in preaching beyond the choir. We agreed that our storytellers will play a crucial role in the hundred-year effort to develop starflight.

Civ C's discussion followed a similar thread, with participants stressing the importance of the personal narrative in outreach and networking, and examining narratives and lessons from non-dominant cultures for means to shape a multi-generational endeavor.

The range of topics, styles and approaches among our presenters, while different from the more tightly-focused tracks, turned out to be a great strength: we had something for everybody, an exciting creative ferment, and the foundation for conversations and collaborations which may carry on well past the Symposium's end.

Track Chair Biography

John Carter McKnight, JD, PhD

Research Associate, Department of Sociology, Lancaster University

John Carter McKnight is a former corporate finance lawyer with a PhD in Human & Social Dimensions of Science and Technology from Arizona State University. His research focuses on emergent community governance, ethics and social norm enforcement in technologically-mediated spaces from internet gaming communities to spacecraft. His current work examines the role of social media platforms in changing the practice and communication of planetary science. He has developed and taught a range of graduate and undergraduate courses in games and culture, and the governance of emerging technologies. He has practiced corporate finance law with global law firms in New York and San Francisco, and served as officer and director of organizations involved in space exploration, science education and public policy.

The Dangers of Religious and Ideological Extremism and the Mission of Interstellar Exploration

Jason D. Batt

Sacramento, California

www.letsgotothestars.com, @Letsgo2thestars, @jdanielbatt

Abstract

100YSS has promoted itself as "everyone's starship." Individuals from a variety of ideological and religious beliefs have contributed to space exploration throughout its history. Does the challenge of inclusion apply to variables of ideological extremism? From the destruction of the World Trade Center towers to Westboro Baptist Church, the dangers of religious and ideological extremism are obvious and present. This paper will present the dangers of extremism pre-ship launch and post-ship and the environments that create religious and ideological extremism. It will also review these questions: Is terrorism always religious in nature? Can there be strategies made to preventing extremism in interstellar efforts? Interstellar efforts will need to be prepared to face the topic of religious extremism and develop strategies pre- and post-launch to challenge it.

Keywords

extremism, terrorism, religion, ideologies

1. Introduction

At the 2012 100 Year Starship Symposium, I presented two different papers on the topic of religion and interstellar travel: "Engaging the Church as Champion" and "The Off-Planet Church." During these talks, I provided these conclusions:

- Where humans go, they carry their religion. Where humans go, they take their beliefs and practices. They will take their religion off-planet. Just as exercise of religion is a freedom valued here in democratic nations, it is expected that same freedom will accompany humans in their off-planet explorations.
- The practice of religion in space has a long history. The concept of religious expression off-planet is not just a consideration for the future; it has happened and continues to happen. Where humans go, they take their beliefs with them. They take their religion with them. James Hartfield, spokesman for the Johnson Space Center, said: "Although NASA does not provide spiritual resources, religious objects—crosses, Bibles, icons, prayer cards—are among the most common personal items taken into space." [1] Buzz Aldrin, an Apollo 11 astronaut and a believer, performed communion on the moon. [2] On Christmas Eve in 1968, while aboard Apollo 8 in orbit around the moon, Frank Borman read from the first ten verses from the book of Genesis. [3]

- Three potential relationships between organized religion and the 100YSS: neutral and uninvolved observant, as hostile opponent, or as active proponent (a champion).
- There are parallels in the mission between the 100YSS and organized religion, specifically Christianity.
- The 100 Year Starship's mission is a challenge to engage as many aspects of humanity as possible to achieve this great goal. The elements of Christianity, the world's largest religion based on number of adherents, can not be overlooked. There is the potential of a negative relationship between elements of Christianity and the mission of space exploration. However, there is great possibility in a positive relationship between the two. The Church can be an active champion of interstellar exploration. To engage the Church, it is recommended and encouraged that a focused and professional effort occur early on in the mission of the 100 Year Starship.
- In a vacuum of religions, religions will be formed.

It it this last point which serves as the key starting point for a look at the challenges of religious extremism and interstellar travel. At the 2012 Symposium, Stephen Taylor presented pieces of his musical *Paradises Lost* by Ursula K. Le Guin about a religion that formed on a generational ship. There have been suggestions that an interstellar effort should be done without any religious expression at all. The history of space travel already includes numerous episodes of religious expression. Repeating Hartfield, the most common personal items taken into space are of a religious nature.

Eli Berman and Laurence R. Iannaccone in their book *Religious Extremism: The Good, the Bad , and the Deadly* argue that the imminent death of religion has been oft-cited but has yet to materialize. Berman and Iannaccone state: "For centuries, scholars have confidently, and incorrectly, predicted the immanent demise of religion. With powerful prose, but no real proof, Hume, Comte, Marx, Freud, the Huxleys, and other influential intellectuals, pronounced religion a dying vestige our primitive, pre-scientific past ... Throughout the world – in Latin America, India, Africa, Europe, the Middle East, formerly communist countries, and the United States – religion continues to flourish, especially its more fundamentalist variants. In short, the demand for supernaturalism is as basic and irrepressible as the wants it seeks to satisfy." [4]

Religion, whether beneficial or damaging, continues to be sought by humanity. It is shortsighted to assume that even in our ascent to the stars that religion will not find its way there. The great predictions of science fiction writers actual proposes the opposite. Dune shows an evolution of the Catholic church as it follows a multi-star society. Orson Scott Card's Ender's Game series find Catholic missionaries accompanying colony ships to the stars to encounter newly-discovered sentient races.

There was an alternative point of view proposed by Rev. Alvin Carpenter that no religion should be allowed. His abstract claims, "If there are two words that sum up earth religion it is 'divisive' and 'intolerance' and these two things, with the fury of religion behind them, would introduce a pathology to the space pilgrims they could never overcome." [5] In his paper, he makes an interesting point on the natural rise of religion within the interstellar ship: "Religion in space must be must be able to rise unhindered by earth priests, earth religions, and earth's holy books. If religion is necessary for the human mind to function, then it must rise from where that mind resides, its unique interstellar environment." So while he argues overall that earth-based religions are destructive to humanity's future, he does provide that religion, even in a potential vacuum, will still arise as we seek to explore the stars.

2. The Inclusive Nature of the 100 Year Starship

The 2012 Symposium held a workshop titled "Is It Everybody's Space Mission?" In the workshop, Dr. Henry Williams challenged the workshop group: "How do we solve the limitations to diversity for the 100yss?" In the workshop summary session at the end of the Symposium, the workshop team reported: "People aren't asking if we should have diversity. We are asking how to overcome the barriers to it." Making diversity a goal seems to be a priority for the 100 Year Starship team.

Second, the goal of the 100 Year Starship is to travel to another star. This means quite a far distance, and at current propulsion technology, quite a long time. Proxima Centauri is about 4.25 light years from Sol. A light year is equal to just under 10 trillion kilometers. NASA had launched the Voyager 1 traveling at more than 17 kilometers per second. At that speed, the Voyager 1 would take 74,485 years to reach Proxima Centauri. Even if propulsion technology is significantly expanded, the trip will definitely take years to achieve. Even if a ship could approach speeds of a tenth of light speed, a trip to Proxima Centauri (over 25.6 trillion miles away) would take nearly 70 years. This leads to discussions about the possibility of a generation ship or multi-generation ship— a ship where the individuals, and their offspring for a few generations, live their entire lives on board.

At the minimum, the crew of an interstellar ship, assuming no super-relativistic speed discoveries, will be larger than any space mission so far. It will be composed of a widely diverse group of individuals. The crew will be working and living together for a very long time in a locked, unescapable environment.

3. The Dangers of Extremism on a Starship

Where there are people, there is religion. However, not all religious expression is positive. In the last decade, the destructive effects of religious expression have been center point in our global dialogue. The horrific tragedy of 9/11 was spawned from religious extremism. The protests of the Kansas-based Westboro Baptist church have invaded funerals and other social functions with the declarations of "God Hates America" and "God Hates the World." Extrapolate this behavior to a starship and the potential results are frightening to consider. The dangers of religious extremism are only compounded when brought aboard a tightly confined space, with precariously precise working parts all subject vulnerable and all possibly mission-killing if disrupted.

The environment of the starship will be:

- closed
- communal
- homogenous

The closed, communal yet homogenous environment of the starship can produce extremism. We must avoid the rigorous/high-demand elements which foster extremist thought.

The dangers of religious extremism must be addressed and prepared-for from two perspectives: pre-launch and post-launch. The ability to confront extremism pre-launch which actually be quite easy. While the building and dreaming of ship is inclusive, we can be very critical in selection of the actual crew for the ship. We can screen for dangerous belief patterns. However, just the statement of "dangerous belief patterns" brings up its own questions: who will be defining dangerous beliefs? How do we maintain religious freedom and yet screen for this type of belief? These questions will be addressed in this paper. It should be noted here that this paper is not proposing a limitation of religious thought or simply accepting only a narrow spectrum of religious expression. We argue that it will actually be an openness to a "wide variety" of religious thought that may prevent the rise of extremism later on the actual mission.

What about after the ship in en route? If this is a generational ship of six to ten generations, with hundreds to thousands of individuals, the potential for extremism can arise from within a seemingly docile group. What strategies can be developed to manage and mitigate potential for extremism?

4. Defining and Identifying Religious Extremism

What is extremism and what is religious extremism? This exercise in definition is critical to 100YSS as we interact with future possible candidate pools. We need to be aware of potential elements which could develop into religious extremism and thus mission-threatening behaviors and beliefs.

The title of religious extremist has been applied to everyone from former President George W. Bush to the Taliban. Neil J. Kressel, in his book *Bad Faith: The Danger of Religious Extremism*, addresses the definition of religious extremism: "To cut through the confusion in defining and identifying religious extremists, one might turn to William James, who-in an invocation of New Testament scripture-asserted that religions should be judged not by their roots, but by their fruits. But which fruits are best to cultivate, and how we are to evaluate religions that produce both sweet and bitter fruits?" [6]

Religious extremism, especially in Western cultures, is often viewed as synonymous with Islamic extremism. Kressel states: "The Islamic religious tradition provides the extremist with abundant source material. But most major religious traditions contain messages that may, without much creativity, be interpreted hatefully. And theologians in every tradition, including Islam, have found ways to modify, reinterpret, counterbalance, or otherwise incapacitate such verses." [7] It is not just Islam which produces extremism. It is not a certain type of religious text that produces it.

Kressel digs into the elements that create extremism in religion: "One way we might identify pathological religion is similar to the way the doctor identifies psychiatric abnormality in the patient. In that context, no single dimension separates the normal from the pathological, and the difference between health and illness is a matter of degree." [8] And it is Kressel that provides us our most concrete definition for religious extremism: "Religious extremists can be defined as those persons who-for reasons they themselves deem religious-commit, promote, or support purposely hurtful, violent, or destructive acts toward those who don't practice their faith." [9] There is still quite a broad area of interpretation within this definition, however, it gives us a base to work from. Extremism is defined when it turns destructive.

5. The Spectrum of Religious Expression

Even within common belief systems, there exists a wide denominational continuum from lenient "churches" to extreme "sects." "[W]hile one group is singing Kum Ba Yah, the underdeveloped one is convinced of conspiracy, planning to wipe whole nations off the earth, and rationalizing their actions via beliefs about the afterlife and rewards they will receive in Heaven." [10] There is from all of these groups, there can arise a spectrum of negative religious expression from dysfunction to extremist: "When the fruits of a religion frequently include attacks on the life, liberty, and happiness of nonbelievers or those who don't practice the faith, the religion can be reliably classified as extremist. When a set of religious beliefs is incidentally hurtful to some individual or group, the classification is trickier. Moreover, when the fruits of a religion include impediments to the health, happiness, and development of believers who are allowed to leave freely if they so choose, the religious system should be dubbed dysfunctional but not labeled as religious extremism. Faith that leads one to harm only oneself is also dysfunctional, but it belongs in a separate category and poses a different type of challenge." [11]

Berman and Iannaccone contribute to the definition of the spectrum:

"Toward one end of the continuum, we expect to find "extremist" groups that demand very high levels of sacrifice. Toward the other end, we expect to find "lenient" groups that demand very little of their members. If the theory is correct, then groups that demand similar levels of sacrifice will display similar social characteristics despite their differences in organization, history, and theology. Thus, the high-cost groups of any religious tradition will tend to be exclusive, strict, small (at the local level), suspicious of other groups, and critical of secular society. Members will learn to fully embrace the group's distinctive lifestyle, devoting their resources to the group's activities and goals, or else face penalties, up to and including expulsion. As a result, these high-cost groups will also maintain tighter social ties, as shown for extreme Christian sects in the U.S. by Iannaccone (1992). In contrast, low-cost groups will tend to be inclusive, lenient, tolerant of secular values, and open to loosely affiliated members, while providing less cooperatively provided services." [12]

To pinpoint the the religious climate which spawns religious extremism, we reference a two axis system. The Y axis focuses on the belief system ranging from rigorous to relaxed. The X axis focuses on the social management and environment: communal social focus to individual social focus. Extremism occurs in the top-right quadrant. Religious extremists groups most often have a very rigorous belief system. They also have a very strong communal social focus. While these two qualities alone don't necessitate extremism, extremist groups do possess both of these qualities.

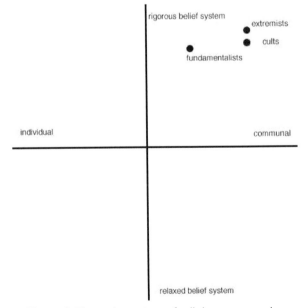

Figure 1. Two axis system of religious expression

Berman and Iannaccone reaffirm this conclusion: "Within the religious marketplace there naturally arise different niches, not all of which provide equally intense experiences. Some religious traditions, notably Judaism, Christianity, and Islam, have a much stronger communal orientation than others, such as Buddhism and Hinduism. Within each religious tradition, moreover, some firms maintain rigorous systems of shared beliefs and morality, whereas other firms demand very little. It is the former that we label 'extremists' (or 'sects,' 'cults,' and 'fundamentalists'); the latter are more known as 'moderates,' 'liberals,' or 'mainstream churches.'" [13]

In regards to screening for dangerous belief patterns, we must be aware of our own individual perspectives on religion. Every other religious belief can also be found on this spectrum:

The Individual

ACCEPTED   FAMILIAR   TOLERABLE   ANNOYING/DISAGREEABLE   DISRUPTIVE   DANGEROUS

Figure 2: Spectrum of Other Religious Belief

Every belief that an individual encounters will either be accepted, familiar, tolerable, annoying/disagreeable, disruptive, or dangerous. We should be careful to not exclude a religious belief simply because it is annoying or disagreeable from our own perspective. However, beliefs that are disruptive and/or dangerous should be the ones we begin to screen for.

6. Fundamentalism Versus Extremism

Pursuing this line of thought further, we must be cautious in not confusing fundamentalism with extremism. "Moreover, one must avoid confusing the religious extremist with someone who is just extremely religious. There are many ways in which manifestations of religiosity can be intense without necessarily having dangerous ramifications." [14]

What is fundamentalism? "One team of psychological researchers-Ralph W. Hood Jr., Peter C. Hill, W. Paul Williamson-explained that "[w]hat distinguishes fundamentalism from other religious profiles is its particular approach toward understanding religion, which elevates the role of the sacred text to a position of supreme authority and subordinates all other potential sources of knowledge and meaning" Along with many writers, they note that such positions have typically been adopted as part of a defensive reaction to modernism. They also note that some have attempted to draw a line between fundamentalism and evangelicalism on the grounds that adherents to the former have far greater hostility toward mainstream society." [15] Without diverting too far off topic, it is important to note that fundamentalism carries with it, from some perspectives, a derogatory connotation. Kressel pursues this: "In an article titled "Fundamentalism Isn't the Problem," Kenneth Minogue objects that "'fundamentalism' is an all-purpose expression denigrating the peoples of the Book (as the Muslims call them). Anyone who takes the Bible (either Testament) or the Koran seriously falls under the terminological lash of terrorism-inducing fundamentalism. How is it that millions of harmless American Christians, or orthodox Jews, living pretty blameless lives, come to be incorporated under such a denigratory slogan?" He then offers an answer, claiming that especially for American liberals, "it is an irresistible rhetorical triumph to be able to package all the people of whom you disapprove in one nauseous bundle." [16] Fundamentalists are not by this definition religious extremists and violent militants. However, in certain environments and under specific conditions, fundamentalists can become extremists.

7. Myths and Facts of Extremism

What are these conditions? What are the causes of extremism? We've already reviewed that religious extremists have two consistent qualities: rigorous religious belief and strong communal social focus. Beyond this, what creates extremism?

Reza Aslan, in his book *How to Win a Cosmic War*, argues that we should not confuse extremism with irrational behavior. It is not. "It is tempting, even comforting, to consider such abominable acts of terror to be the result of irrational or pathological behavior. But the truth is that terrorism is almost always a calculated choice. Terror is purposefully chosen, because it is often seen as the most effective, most expedient, and most economical method of pursuing a group's aims." [17] Kressel reaffirms that "religious thoughts, feelings, and experiences propel most violent antiabortion activists, and sometimes provide their central inspiration. Far from being impulsive or insane, these extremists contemplate and calculate their terror as a means of achieving what they consider to be a religiously certified objective." [18]

Often extremism is argued to arise from poverty situations. In their paper "Education, Poverty and Terrorism: Is there a Casual Connection," Krueger and Maleckova argue that poverty does not necessarily lead to extremism. "Perhaps surprisingly, our review of the evidence provides little reason for optimism that a reduction in poverty or an increase in educational attainment would meaningfully reduce international terrorism. Any connection between poverty, education and terrorism is indirect, complicated and probably quite weak. Instead of viewing terrorism as a direct response to low market oppor- tunities or ignorance, we suggest it is more accurately viewed as a response to political conditions and long-standing feelings of indignity and frustration that have little to do with economics." [19] Simply reducing poverty does not provide an easy solution for eliminating extremism.

Although the focus of this paper is on religious extremism, we should be careful to note that not all extremism is religious in nature. Extremism can arise from groups that are entirely not religious. "If theology is so important, why are most terrorist organizations not religious? And if afterlife rewards are key, why has a nonreligious group – the LTTE "Tamil Tigers" – been responsible for more suicide attacks than another other organization? Why is suicide bombing associated with all sorts of theologies but just one style of religious organization (best described as "sectarian")? And why do most militant sects devote much of their energy to benign and noble activities, such as running schools, health clinics, and social services agencies?" [20]

As well, not all violent acts by believers are caused by the religion and its belief structure. "Not all-or even most-evil acts perpetrated by Christians throughout two millennia can be reasonably described as religiously motivated or Christian, much less as instances of religious extremism. Many people who do dastardly deeds of one sort or another may be Christians in name alone, only pretending or perhaps not even pretending to be believers." [21] While the banner of religion is waved, often there are underlying motivations or goals that extend far past religion. 9/11, while perpetrated by religious extremists, also has a strong cultural motivation. In fact, often the religious belief system becomes manipulated to encourage their violent goals. Berman and Iannaccone state: "This is typical of religious extremists. Their militancy varies dramatically over time, even as their underlying sectarian traits remain fairly stable. Moreover, they prove remarkably adept at reworking their theology, and even reinterpreting their most sacred texts, so as to justify their changing orientations." [22] So, we should be careful to not simply reject religious beliefs because those beliefs have been used to justify violent acts.

We must also confront the belief that Islam itself is a more fruitful breeding ground for extremist thought. Extremist beliefs do tend to rise more readily within Islamic worlds, although are by no way limited or unique to those religious systems. Kressel concludes that it is a lack of social evolution and reformation that has led to a climate where religious extremism can develop. "The Islamic world has not experienced the unique confluence of historical events that ultimately produced in the West a tradition of tolerance and a check on religiously inspired hatred. There was no Renaissance, no Reformation, no Peace of Westphalia, no Enlightenment, no theory of the separation of church and state, and no Vatican Council II. In the West, religious messages nowadays enter public debate primarily through the tempering prism of modern culture and constitutionally based values. In the world of Islam, the dictates of the faith can have a more direct and deleterious impact on social and political affairs." [23] It is not actually the religious belief system alone that creates extremism but the cultural environment that the religion is found in. However, there is grounds for argument that that culture is created by the religious system of Islam. However, within the discussion of extremism, it is to be noted that the religion alone doesn't provide the environment for extremism alone.

Interpretation of sacred texts is key to understanding defense of violent behavior by members of those groups. It is not just the beliefs that matter but how those beliefs are interpreted. There are major texts in the majority of religions. However, two groups can interpret key scriptures in those texts in completely different way. Kressel expands this: "As we have already seen, the question of how individuals and religious groups interpret their sacred scriptures-the Jewish Bible, the Catholic Bible, the Protestant Bible, and the Koran-is critical. No matter what believers may say, none is truly a literalist. Everyone picks and chooses, at least a little. Everyone interprets. When there are additional religious traditions and additional sacred books, the importance of interpretation extends beyond scripture to these sources as well. The same texts in each faith can be used to support diametrically opposed political, social, psychological, and theological stances. Hence, understanding how religionists make decisions concerning the interpretation of their religious texts and traditions is the key to deciphering when and how religion becomes a force for evil in the world." [24] To future prevent the dangers of religious extremism, it is needed to have an understanding of these texts and to analyze how those text are interpreted. The various religious texts often have a violent aspect to them, however, the question is whether this element is interpreted as a literal directive or simply a historical fact. If the group considers the violent aspects as a literal directive, the group then steps into the disruptive and dangerous end of the spectrum. Kressel argues that if individuals adhere closely to their religion's moral and ethical elements then extremism is less likely to arise: "To avoid extremism, people would have to attend more closely to the moral, social, and political consequences of their religions. Unfortunately, many believers see little reason to do this if a religion feels like it is working, especially with regard to matters of ultimate concern. Religious militancy is frequently a consequence of individuals choosing to pursue their personal 'immortality projects' and 'quests for meaning' by traveling down the wrong paths-wrong in the sense that they are socially and morally destructive." [25]

So, why not jettison the whole mess? Wouldn't it do well if we simply removed religion altogether? This paper has addressed the fact that within a vacuum of religious beliefs, religious belief will arise. Kressel addresses this at length: "One might point out that without scripture, the belief in god, or religious traditions, the potentially dangerous syndrome they have identified could not exist. For this reason, some atheists and skeptics ask a very controversial question about holy books, faith traditions, and religious law. Why not jettison the whole necrotic mess and start from scratch? They argue that too much killing, hatred, and distress has resulted from books purporting to speak the word of God. Perhaps a better way of life might be grounded in science, humanism, or something else. Religion, they argue, serves no useful purpose, or least none worth the price that has been paid. Repair and reform are too difficult, maybe impossible. There is, they suggest, no reliable way to separate peaceful fundamentalists from potentially deadly extremists, and no method to ensure that more liberal believers will not fall prey to dangerous impulses sooner or later. This critique is impractical. Religion speaks poignantly to the needs and desires of billions of people. A more attainable goal, in my opinion, is to focus our efforts on identifying and understanding the appeal of extremist religious visions and the circumstances under which they are most likely to thrive." [26]

One proposed concept that attempts to eliminate religious extremism, developed along the lines of "jettisoning the entire mess," is that in a purely atheistic environment the thought processes that lead to religious extremism won't develop. A launching atheistic society does not ensure future religious development. Within a vacuum of religious thought, humans tend to religious belief. Religious belief then can lead to religious extremism. "The children of atheists are more likely to abandon their parents' beliefs than are the children of any (other) religion." [27] Berman and Iannaccone state: "The resilience of religiosity is nowhere more evident than in Russia, where despite sixty years of state-sponsored atheism, bloody church purges, widespread religious persecution, and pervasive secular indoctrination, only eight percent of the people remained atheistic by 1990 and religious belief was especially widespread among the young ." [28] There seems to be a cyclical effect within modern society shifting from belief to atheism, often along generational lines. We cannot expect that this will not continue to occur on the starship. An atheistic society at launch could still spawn religious thought that could lead to religious extremism years later.

8. Potential Dangerous Beliefs to Screen For

Neil Kressel has created a list (although not exhaustive) of potential beliefs that could reveal extremist leanings: [29]

- The faith, or the rule of the faithful, should be spread by violent means.
- Nonbelievers must obey the rules of the faith, even though there is no convincing nonreligious justification for such obedience.
- People cannot freely convert out of the faith.
- Certain geographical locations must be controlled by believers, even though there is no convincing nonreligious basis for this control.
- God requires earthly punishment of, or discrimination against, those who make certain sexual or lifestyle choices, even though there is no convincing nonreligious foundation for such a judgment.
- Certain individuals have been anointed to carry out God's punishments on earth.
- All means are acceptable when one is doing God's work.
- Blasphemers must be punished in the here and now.

He also provides a following of beliefs that while may not directly lead to extremism could be the beginnings of extremist thought:

- All or some nonbelievers are hated by God or destined to be punished by God after they die.
- God prefers some races, ethnic groups, or nationalities to others.

- The government and laws ought to favor believers, though there should be some protection for nonbelievers too.
- God prefers to see women in a subjugated role.
- God disapproves of certain sexual and lifestyle choices, even though there is no convincing nonreligious basis for this disapproval.
- No one may blaspheme against God or the faithful, lest they be punished by God in the afterlife.
- Certain leaders have access to God's wishes via a channel that is not subject to accuracy checks by others, and these leaders are endowed by God with the power to make life decisions for other believers.

9. The Creation of an Extremist

As we have stated earlier, it is not belief alone which creates extremism. Screening for beliefs is a great method for detecting potential extremism but these beliefs alone don't necessarily give rise to the extremist. We must look at the extremist as an individual. What motivates an individual to become an extremist? Kressel states:

"[I]f we are serious about addressing these underlying sources, we must think also about the political, social, and psychological underpinnings of religious militancy in its various manifestations. The psychology is complex. Most likely, individuals drawn to carry out extremist behaviors in the name of religion experience threats to some central components of their identities and, hence, to their self-esteem. They are often preoccupied with questions of pride and may feel humiliated in some aspect of their personal lives. Or they may feel that their national, religious, or local group has somehow been humiliated. Along similar lines, they may be deeply frustrated people, consumed by thoughts that their lives have been spoiled or wasted. They may be racked by guilt for real or imagined wrongdoings. They may be especially likely to come from families lacking in normal love and support. And they are most at risk of turning to extremism in late adolescence and early adulthood. Such extremism-prone individuals may be found in any culture and any religion. However, they are much more likely to come from times and places where events are unpredictable, unstable, confusing, and potentially dangerous. Modernization and globalization have unleashed destabilizing forces in many parts of the world, and the consequences have been most intense for latecomers to modernity. Failed societies are most at risk, where political and social systems deny basic gratifications to large segments of the population." [30]

Charles Liebman, in "Extremism as a Religious Norm" summarizes this in three elements that lead to religious extremism for both a society and an individual· [31]

- Expansion of Religious Law
- Social Isolation
- Cultural Rejection

Within the starship environment, the issue of religious extremism now becomes a social strategy one. And this is one that we can engage. Social isolation and cultural rejection can happen just as easily in space as it does on earth. So, part of the elimination of religious extremism requires efforts to elimination isolation and rejection.

10. The Economic Model of Religion as a Path to Understanding the Development of Extremism

Berman and Iannaccone present a solid model that predicts the conditions that give rise to religious extremism. This model can be used in both pre-launch and post-launch infrastructure and strategy development to prevent the dangers of religious extremism. Specifically, post-launch, their economic model of religion can be used as a guide to eliminating extremism on the starship. "The approach thus views people as rational religious consumers. . . . The combined actions of religious consumers and religious producers form a religious market, and as in other markets the consumers' freedom to choose constrains the producers of religion." [32] Religious involvement, according to this model, follows standard consumption and production behavior of other economic models. The demand for supernatural, while from the outside seeming as unreasonable and irrational, "can be viewed as a reasonable response to inescapable scarcity, insatiable wants, and irrepressible hope." The institutions of religion become the providers. Not only do they become the providers, but they expand to become entrepreneurs in a manner "selling" a specific type of religious experience. Denominations, sects, religions all provide different variations of the same product much as different cell phone providers offer different variations of the same product. "Groups of religious entrepreneurs establish firms and franchises, offering distinctive services, terms of trade, apprenticeship programs, rites of initiation, and rules of membership. The organizational features we associate with religion in contemporary Western countries, including congregations, denominations, and clergy, are strictly analogous to those of secular industries." [33]

There is also a cost and demand element which provides for the rise of extremism. The costs of production and/or purchase are not standard (although in some institutions, there is a monetary exchange). The costs demand sacrifice. The higher costs, assumingly paid for higher-quality goods, actually "invite stigma" including destruction of material goods, specific clothing guidelines, sexual and diet guidelines. "Such costs are present to some degree in all religions, but they are especially pronounced in the groups we label 'extremist.'" [34]

Extremist groups demand higher levels of sacrifice ("cost"). Berman and Iannaccone expand on this (and this quote is repeated from before): "Toward one end of the continuum, we expect to find "extremist" groups that demand very high levels of sacrifice. Toward the other end, we expect to find "lenient" groups that demand very little of their members. If the theory is correct, then groups that demand similar levels of sacrifice will display similar social characteristics despite their differences in organization, history, and theology. Thus, the high-cost groups of any religious tradition will tend to be exclusive, strict, small (at the local level), suspicious of other groups, and critical of secular society. Members will learn to fully embrace the group's distinctive lifestyle, devoting their resources to the group's activities and goals, or else face penalties, up to and including expulsion. As a result, these high-cost groups will also maintain tighter social ties." [35] The economic model of religious behavior fits well within the two axis system of religious belief.

So, why would someone join a religious group, and in particular, why would one join a religious extremist group? There is an initial social support for those members within the religious community.

"Case studies and survey data provide strong support for all these claims. Sectarian denominations are more supportive of community members, as evidenced by the high proportion of income members of U.S. Christian sects donate to their own communities (Iannaccone, 1992). This mutual support has many concrete benefits. In America, for example, adolescents raised in sectarian denominations manifest lower levels of most "deviant" behaviors including drug use, smoking, drinking, and criminal activity (Bock, et al. 1987; Stark and Bainbridge 1998). Sect members who marry within their religion have substantially lower divorce rates than couples from different, or less sectarian, religious backgrounds (Lehrer and Chiswick 1993). Moreover, a large body of empirical research, published in numerous medical and psychological journals, links high levels of religious faith and participation to improved mental and physical health. Religiosity in general and sect membership in particular, seems to increase life satisfaction, promote healthy behaviors, and insulate people against emotional and physical stress (Ellison 1991 and; 1993)." [36]

These very same benefits extend to those within an extremist group. Often, the higher cost of group entry will provide higher level of social support within that community.

Does the economic model actually translate beyond the Islamic world? The Westboro Baptist Church in Kansas is a supporting case study of the economic model. Jason Harper, one of only four outside individuals provided access to the internal production rooms of the Westboro Baptist Church and a key individual in a former member's flight from the cult, stated: "Extremism developed in Westboro as an attempt to differentiate themselves from an environment with very low religious diversity. Because everything was the same (the Bible-belt), Westboro had to ratchet up what brought them attention." [37] The Bible-belt provided very low religious diversity. From an economic perspective, the goods offered by the various distributors were nearly identical. To differentiate themselves amongst a potential customer base, Westboro pursued extremism.

11. Starship Planning Strategies to Eliminate the Dangers of Extremism

In review of the research and discussion on religious extremism, several strategies and approaches can be extrapolated for use both pre-launch and post-launch on an interstellar starship. It could be argued initially that engaging this topic begins to infringe on limitation of religious freedom. That is specifically not a suggestion at all in this paper. Kressel's own suggestions for societal responses to extremism are also applicable here: "Finally, religious beliefs-whether mainstream or otherwise, whether agreeable or distasteful-deserve protection. Society need not respect dysfunctional and destructive beliefs, but it must tolerate them. Religious conduct, on the other hand, may sometimes require limitation. As some legal scholars argue, 'Religious entities have the capacity for great good and great evil, and society is not duty bound by any constitutional right to let them avoid duly enacted laws, especially where their actions can harm other.' When religion becomes evil, it must be treated as such." [38] The strategies suggested below are not for religion by itself. However, they are provided in order to confront dangerous behavior that is religious in nature.

11.1 What Doesn't Work

It's easy to assume that democracy as a political situation will prevent the rise of extremism. Extremism can form within democratic societies (as it often has).

As well, the next tendency is to support a certain type (or brand) of religion as an example of what is considered legitimate religion. Berman and Iannaccone state: "To support 'good' religion while repressing 'bad' religion is to invite violence." The economic model of religion predicts that state (or ship) sponsored religion actually facilitates the rise of religious extremism. When one religion is given access to opportunities or goods that others can't gain, extremism rises as an alternative way to gain those benefits (or goods).

We must be careful to assume that religious extremism is just a fringe problem that will not arise. Religious extremism, as evidenced in the last decade, is a consistent threat to societies. Due to the nature of the starship environment, the dangers of religious extremism cannot be exaggerated in the planning and strategy stages.

Once more, it is important to remember that elimination of religious expression will also eliminate religious extremism. It will not. The vacuum of religious belief is only one point of the cyclical nature of a society's expression of religion. It is reasonable to assume the cyclical nature will continue on the starship.

11.2 Strategies to Integrate and Consider

• Developing a "national identity" that umbrellas all beliefs and actively encouraging this identity. "In the United Kingdom, the government has begun placing far greater emphasis on addressing the socioeconomic obstacles, not to mention the religious and racial discrimination, that have kept a great many Muslim immigrants from feeling like equal members of British society. Nationality laws have been revamped so as to develop a more universal, more easily accessible conception of British national identity. Immigrants seeking citizenship in the United Kingdom must now demonstrate sufficient language skills, as well as become adept in British history, culture, and national customs.   All of this is an attempt to construct a collective identity based not on ethnic or cultural homogeneity but on a common national narrative, one in which every member of society can share." [39]
• Resist the environments that create extremism:
  • Expansion of Religious Law
  • Social Isolation
  • Cultural Rejection
• Create a series of "leadership checks and balances." "What is needed is not the abandonment of religion, but rather a social, psychological, theological and political system of checks and balances, a way to shout 'whoa!' when faith starts galloping down the wrong path." [40]
• Improved social services. "Religious radicals are less likely to flourish and less likely to embrace violence when there is strong competition in their non-core markets: including education, health care, poverty programs, and political representation." [41] On a starship, the potential for rations and lack on a wide-scale exists. Scarcity of essential services could quickly occur if design errors are made.
• Encourage policies that:
  • Raise the direct costs of violence [42]
  • Foster religious competition
  • Improve social services
  • Encourage private enterprise
  "Religious militancy is most effectively controlled through a combination of policies that raise the direct costs of violence, foster religious competition, improve social services, and encourage private enterprise."
• Ensure severe separation between political decisions and religious influence
• Promote a vibrant, unregulated religious market with numerous sects.

Of all of the suggestions for strategy, this is the one this paper most encourages. The economic model of religion proposed by Berman and Iannaccone predicts that a vibrant religious marketplace actually reduces the potential of extremism. Capitalism benefits from more capitalists, not less. "And, yes, religious laissez-faire will stimulate the clergy's self-interested "industry and zeal," leading them to "use every art which can animate the devotion of the common people" and encouraging numerous sects to enter the religious market and vigorously compete for members. But in the end, it is this vibrant, unregulated religious market that most benefits the state, the general populace, and religion itself. . . . America was the world's first laissez faire religious economy, and as Tocqueville and many other 19th century European traveler noted, the result was exceptional levels of religious participation, an abundance of religious sects, and very little religious conflict." [43] At the 2012 100 Year Starship Symposium, during a discussion in the "Becoming an Interstellar Civilization" track, it was suggested that there should be singular religions ships (a Mormon ship, a Buddhist ship, a Muslim ship). This is a concept which science fiction has played with. However, the economic model of religion predicts that this might be the precise environment that would spawn religious extremism.

12. Conclusion

Religion will exist on the starship. If it is not carried there, it will form there as history as shown. Religion can be beneficial and provide benefits for the "religious consumer." However, the danger for extremist views to develop exists, especially within a closed environment, with a limited population, and with always-potential scarcity issues. The encouragement of a "vibrant religious market" that is not state-supported along with a reinforcement of a strong "cultural identity," and strong checks and balances can deter the flourishing of religious/ideological extremism.

References

1. Shellnutt, Kate, "Exploring the Heavens, Christian Astronauts Reflect on Their Creator," Houston Chronicle, July 8, 2011.

2. "Communion in Space," Guideposts, 1970.

3. Haney, Paul, "Further Reflections on a Golden Space Era," http://www.collectspace.com/news/news-081009a.html, 2009.

4. Berman, Eli and Iannaccone, Laurence R. "Religious Extremism: The Good, The Bad, and the Deadly", September 2005, page 8.

5. Carpenter, Alvin L., Rev. "The Non-Promise of Earth Bound Religions into Space", published in the 2012 100 Year Starship Symposium Proceedings.

6. Kressel, Neil J. *Bad Faith: The Danger of Religious Extremism* (Kindle Locations 352-356). Kindle Edition.

7. Kressel, Neil J. *Bad Faith: The Danger of Religious Extremism* (Kindle Locations 430-432). Kindle Edition.

8. Kressel, Neil J. *Bad Faith: The Danger of Religious Extremism* (Kindle Locations 436-441). Kindle Edition.

9. Kressel, Neil J. *Bad Faith: The Danger of Religious Extremism* (Kindle Locations 485-486). Kindle Edition.

10. Baum, Steven K. "Book Review: Bad Faith: The Danger of Religious Extremism," page 134.

11. Kressel, Neil J. *Bad Faith: The Danger of Religious Extremism* (Kindle Locations 490-494). Kindle Edition.

12. Berman, Eli and Iannaccone, Laurence R. "Religious Extremism: The Good, The Bad, and the Deadly", September 2005, page 13.

13. Berman, Eli and Iannaccone, Laurence R. "Religious Extremism: The Good, The Bad, and the Deadly", September 2005, page 10.

14. Kressel, Neil J. *Bad Faith: The Danger of Religious Extremism* (Kindle Locations 456-457). Kindle Edition.

15. Kressel, Neil J. *Bad Faith: The Danger of Religious Extremism* (Kindle Locations 467-470). Kindle Edition.

16. Kressel, Neil J. *Bad Faith: The Danger of Religious Extremism* (Kindle Locations 475-479). Kindle Edition.

17. Aslan, Reza. *How to Win A Cosmic War*. Page 101.

18. Kressel, Neil J. *Bad Faith: The Danger of Religious Extremism* (Kindle Locations 1027-1028). Kindle Edition.

19. Krueger, Alan B., and Maleckova, Jitka. "Education, Poverty and Terrorism: Is there a Casual Connection?" Journal of Economic Perspectives, Volume 17, Number 14, Fall 2003, Page 119.

20. Berman, Eli and Iannaccone, Laurence R. "Religious Extremism: The Good, The Bad, and the Deadly", September 2005, page 2.

21. Kressel, Neil J. Bad Faith: The Danger of Religious Extremism (Kindle Locations 1150-1156). Kindle Edition.

22. Berman, Eli and Iannaccone, Laurence R. "Religious Extremism: The Good, The Bad, and the Deadly", September 2005, page 18.

23. Kressel, Neil J. *Bad Faith: The Danger of Religious Extremism* (Kindle Locations 2121-2127). Kindle Edition.

24. Kressel, Neil J. *Bad Faith: The Danger of Religious Extremism* (Kindle Locations 1539-1544). Kindle Edition.

25. Kressel, Neil J. *Bad Faith: The Danger of Religious Extremism* (Kindle Locations 2639-2642). Kindle Edition.

26. Kressel, Neil J. *Bad Faith: The Danger of Religious Extremism* (Kindle Locations 2168-2174). Kindle Edition.

27. Berman, Eli and Iannaccone, Laurence R. "Religious Extremism: The Good, The Bad, and the Deadly", September 2005, page 7.

28. Berman, Eli and Iannaccone, Laurence R. "Religious Extremism: The Good, The Bad, and the Deadly", September 2005, page 7.

29. Kressel, Neil J. *Bad Faith: The Danger of Religious Extremism* (Kindle Locations 2663-2673). Kindle Edition.

30. Kressel, Neil J. *Bad Faith: The Danger of Religious Extremism* (Kindle Locations 2721-2730). Kindle Edition.

31. Liebman, Charles S. "Extremism as a Religious Norm." The Journal for the Scientific Study of Religion, page 76-78, 2001

32. Berman, Eli and Iannaccone, Laurence R. "Religious Extremism: The Good, The Bad, and the Deadly", September 2005, page 4.

33. Berman, Eli and Iannaccone, Laurence R. "Religious Extremism: The Good, The Bad, and the Deadly", September 2005, page 8.

34. Berman, Eli and Iannaccone, Laurence R. "Religious Extremism: The Good, The Bad, and the Deadly", September 2005, page 12.

35. Berman, Eli and Iannaccone, Laurence R. "Religious Extremism: The Good, The Bad, and the Deadly", September 2005, page 13.

36. Berman, Eli and Iannaccone, Laurence R. "Religious Extremism: The Good, The Bad, and the Deadly", September 2005, page 15.

37. Harper, Jason. Private interview conducted on September 16, 2013, Sacramento, California.

38. Kressel, Neil J. *Bad Faith: The Danger of Religious Extremism* (Kindle Locations 2898-2901). Kindle Edition.

39. Aslan, Reza. *Beyond Fundamentalism: Confronting Religious Extremism in the Age of Globalization* (Kindle Locations 2549-2554). Random House Publishing Group. Kindle Edition.

40. Kressel, Neil J. *Bad Faith: The Danger of Religious Extremism* . page 29.

41. Berman, Eli and Iannaccone, Laurence R. "Religious Extremism: The Good, The Bad, and the Deadly", September 2005, page 19

42. Berman, Eli and Iannaccone, Laurence R. "Religious Extremism: The Good, The Bad, and the Deadly", September 2005, page 19.

43. Berman, Eli and Iannaccone, Laurence R. "Religious Extremism: The Good, The Bad, and the Deadly", September 2005, page 20.

Families in Space:
A Review of Family Structure and Conflict in the Starship Environment

Jason D. Batt

Sacramento, California

www.letsgotothestars.com, @Letsgo2thestars, @jdanielbatt

Karen S. Batt

M.S. Marriage, Family and Child Counseling

Clinician, Marriage and Family Therapist Intern

karbatt@gmail.com

Abstract

The 100 YSS website states: "If a journey to another star takes longer than one human lifespan, generations may be born and die in space, leaving their descendants to complete the mission." Family units will likely be a component of future interstellar exploration. Human relationships are a great variable in potential future space exploration. Family structure determines family conflict. Several questions are proposed and reviewed: How will children be raised and educated on a starship? How will children adjust to a closed environment? How will family conflict be handled? How will divorce be handled? Does isolation due to the starship environment effect the family environment? What strategies need to be explored to create the environments for healthy family relationships? These questions will be reviewed in light of modern family therapy theory and research.

Keywords

family, family conflict, children, parenting, divorce

1. Introduction: By the Numbers

The 100 Year Starship states that the trip will possibly require "Multigenerational Spacefarers:" "If a journey to another star takes longer than one human lifespan, generations may be born and die in space, leaving their descendants to complete the mission." [1] The goal of the 100 Year Starship is to travel to another star. This means quite a far distance, and at current propulsion technology, quite a long time. Proxima Centauri is about 4.25 light years from Sol. A light year is equal to just under 10 trillion kilometers. NASA had launched the Voyager 1 traveling at more than 17 kilometers per second. At that speed, the Voyager 1 would take 74,485 years to reach Proxima Centauri. Even if propulsion technology is significantly expanded, the trip will definitely take years to achieve. Even if a ship could approach speeds of a tenth of light speed, a trip to Proxima Centauri (over 25.6 trillion miles away) would take nearly 70 years. This leads to discussions about the possibility of a generation ship or multi-generation ship— a ship where the individuals, and their offspring for a few generations, live their entire lives on board. At the minimum, the crew of the 100 Year Starship will be larger than any space mission so far. It will be composed of a widely diverse group of individuals. The crew will be working and living together for a very long time in a locked, unescapable environment. All of these are to be considered with strategizing the social dynamics of the crew for this mission.

The concept of multi-generational space travelers is not new. The Generation Ship idea was first proposed in 1928 by Konstantin E. Tsiolkovsky, father of the astronautic theory. He described in his essay "The Future of Earth and Mankind" (1928) a space colony equipped with engines which travels thousands of years, which he called "Noah's Ark".

2. The Potential Problems

This paper could be considered part two of last year's "A Search for Successful Social Strategies." Suggestions were provided during the discussion period following the presentation which has led to this topic. Family relations are going to be the center-point of successful social strategies for interstellar travel. "Imagine taking a trip cross-country with your family," says Mark Shepanek, a psychologist and NASA's manager of aerospace medicine. "Now imagine that it lasts for months on end. And that you can't open the windows. You can't even get out of the car. The bathroom and the meals are in the car with you. Think there might be a problem getting along?" [2] On the first night of the 100 Year Starship Symposium 2012, Dr. Mae Jemison raised the question, "What happens when you get two light years away and someone says 'I'm not going to listen to you?'" Dr. O'Brien, when interviewing Nichelle Nichols, asked about the family problem of a generation ship, "Will the kids get along?" Nichols answered, "Of course! They're born into it." However, this seems to be an understatement in regards to social dynamics. In reflection of his own time in space, Russian cosmonaut Valery Ryumin said, "All the conditions necessary for murder are met if you shut two men in a cabin and leave them together for two months." [3]

Mars One is attempting to avoid this altogether: "In the first years, the Mars settlement is not a suitable place for children to live. The medical facilities will be limited and the group is too small. Furthermore, the human ability to conceive in reduced gravity is not known, neither is there enough research on whether a fetus can grow normally under these circumstances. Mars One will therefore strongly advise the settlement habitants not to attempt to have children. However, they conclude by stating: "In order to establish a true settlement on Mars, having children is very important. This will be an important point of research on Mars." [4] Space.com's reporter, who has covered 100YSS the past several years, Clara Moskowitz writes: "Eventually, humans will likely have to experiment with pregnancy on Mars. And if that's not hard enough, just wait 'til they try raising teenagers on Mars." [5]

It is of note that modern interstellar literature overlook the issues of families. Neither *The Starflight Handbook: A Pioneer's Guide to Interstellar Travel* nor *Centauri Dreams: Imagining and Planning Interstellar Travel* mention families or social connections whatsoever.

3. The Goals of Interstellar Travel: Exploration and Colonization

One of the potential goals of interstellar travel is colonization. If the efforts are crewed, then colonization becomes a priority goal. Foregoing superluminal travel breakthroughs, interstellar travel will require multi generations with low likelihood of return. So planning for colonization becomes a center point of the effort.

Anthropologist John Moore, University of Florida-Gainesville, in 2003, made a presentation on the potential of organizing the ship and colonization efforts along family lines. He provides these figures of potential ship population:

> *"Assuming a 200 years' travel which is to say from eight to ten generations, the minimum number of individuals able to autosupport a colony is, according to Moore, between 150 e 180. This number would grant ten potential partners per person, in a monogamic system, and could lower down to 80 or 90 by social engineering techniques. . . . [Ask] the crew to postpone reproduction creating long intervals between one generation and the other. According to Harrison (2002), the minimum number should be 500, even though they shouldn't necessarily travel together, but separated, when needed in groups of 25 which would gather just in order to select each others' partners."* [6]

His population overview suggests a very detailed structural organization all developed around family lines. Moore argues that organizing in families would actual assist to counter the psychosocial difficulties that could possible arise: ""We are much less likely to go crazy in space and much more likely to accomplish our interstellar missions if we send crews into space that are organized along family lines.'" [7] Not only would we have to deal with family issues on an interstellar travel as a byproduct of colonization, its possible that the overall success of the mission would be determined by organizing the entire effort along family lines. Moore believes interstellar travel need not be an awful ordeal. He argues that family-based crew can have a rich and varied life. "Space travel can be organized so it is pleasant and full of adventure," he said. Moreover, the families "can have the privilege of designing a new culture." [8]

Past exploration and colonization efforts have also organized around family lines. Moore states: "Whenver colonization is done on Earth, it's always by people looking for a better life. All of the colonizations I know about as an anthropologist have been done by families, especially young couples." [9]

The role of families in interstellar colonization have been tackled in science fiction over the years. Rob Grant's Colony tells the story of a generation ship "in which breeding is strictly controlled and a crew member's offspring automatically inherit their parent's role on the ship. Several generations on, the Captain is struggling with puberty, the Chief Science Officer is a fundamentalist Christian, the security officer's have become so inbred as to be barely functional and the ship's chaplain is a pervert who spies on other crewmembers quarters. The colonists have forgotten how to read and the ship is falling apart because nobody knows how to repair anything." [10] This rendition warns us against the dangers of aligning too tightly along family lines in mission planning.

4. The Circle of Influence: the Importance of Family on Development

Family relationships are key to the overall development of the individual. In Understanding Social Exclusion, John Hills, Julian Le Grand, and David Piachaud state: "The individual is influenced by immediate family, by community, by national forces, and ultimately by global context. The community is not influenced by only broader levels—national and global influences—but also by the families and individuals who constitute it. This may seem obvious, but it contrasts with much existing analysis which treats personal, family, and community influences as essentially separate factions with the independent effects." [11] The overall development of individuals and their role on the ship will be heavily influenced by the families that are on the ship.

As well, the environment the family exists in influences the family dynamics. The environment under consideration is the starship. Does this environment change family dynamics? We need to consider the following elements of family and child life within the environment of the ship:
- Family Dynamics
- Child Development in regards to the environments: physical and communal
- Social Isolation

5. The Goal is Healthy Children

"Basically, space habitats are artificial ecosystems, conceived to be self-sufficient and to ensure the astronauts' survival. For what mentioned above, it is therefore necessary to consider human needs before technological necessities." [12] The United Nations Convention on the Rights of the Child states in Article 3.1: "In all actions concerning children, whether undertaken by public or private social welfare institutions, courts of law, administrative authorities or legislative bodies, the best interests of the child shall be a primary consideration." [13] This directive should serve as the basis to family management on the starship. If colonization is the ultimate goal, it is wise to ensure that healthy children arrive at the destination planet.

6. Children in Closed Environments

The starship will be a closed environment. "A permanent colony must be considered as an enclosed system, in which immigration and emigration are not possible. More it must be composed of a number of individuals higher enough to avoid crossbreed, but low enough to be able to travel in space." [14] A closed environment is one in which there is no emigration or immigration of either people and ideas.

When we began to research "best environments to raise children," we came across an article which listed five key items:
1. Mountains/Hills
2. Agricultural fields
3. Green valleys
4. Open space
5. Natural sounds.

We will have none of these (except in a virtual format) on a starship. The starship is truly a closed environment, not only intellectually, but also naturally. We still fully don't understand the developmental needs of children in regards to nature and open spaces. While adults can function fine in space, we are not sure children can. "Humans have an innate affinity for the natural world, probably a biologically based need integral to our development as individuals . . . That is supported by a decade of research that reveals how strongly and positively people respond to open grassy landscapes, scattered stands of trees, meadows, water, winding trails, and elevated view." [15] If humans respond so well to natural environments, what possible detriments will children suffer when they are raised in an environment without any natural elements? From the basic perspective, natural environments provide a much better environment to raise physical healthy children. "Play in natural settings seems to offer special benefits. For one, children are more physically active when they are outside — a boon at a time of sedentary lifestyles and epidemic overweight." [16] Natural environments simply provide a great mental boost to people, let alone children in development. Children specifically have been shown to develop better when raised near and/or in natural elements. "Swedish researchers compared children within two day-care settings: at one, the quiet play area was surrounded by tall buildings, with low plants and a brick path; at the other, the play area, based on an 'outdoors in all weather' theme, was set in an orchard surrounded by pasture and woods and was adjacent to an overgrown garden with tall trees and rocks. The study revealed that the children in the 'green' day care, who played outside every day, regardless of weather, had better motor coordination and more ability to concentrate." [17]

To achieve the goal of healthy children first begins in designing the actual environment of the ship. The ship design should consider that children need natural environments to develop effectively. In regards to incorporating unique physical structures: "The aim is to build an artificial ecosystem able to grant variability and variation, the two characteristics of the environments in which the human species has evolved. Which is to say, to provide all the stimuluses able to grant the life quality in space. To this purpose, the Japanese artist Ayako Ono (2010) suggested a solution about a possible permanent base on [sic] Moon. It is a zen garden karesansui (literally "dry garden"), on the lunar suface. Actually the garden would be part of the colony, enveloping themodule buildings, if not taking them into its structure." [18] This could be extrapolated to providing a garden element into the ship.

7. How Will Children Be Raised: A Focus on Enrichment Environment

Again, a starship is a "closed" environment with no emigration and no immigration. A healthy environment is one which is an enrichment environment. While there can be no immigration and no emigration of outside ideas, the ship must be sure to have an environment of creativity which spawn new ideas and new though. A solution comes from Article 17.b of The Rights of the Child: "Encourage international co-operation in the production, exchange and dissemination of such information and material from a diversity of cultural, national and international sources;" [19]

What is an enrichment environment? Enrichment environments are those that are intellectually stimulating. These environments have been shown to help in the development of children.

The enrichment environment of the starship should be sure to focus on these aspects intellectual stimulation and growth:

- Verbal/Linguistic: Books and writing supplies
- Logical/Mathematical: Math instruments, tools, and computers
- Visual/Spatial: Arts and craft supplies
- Musical/Rhthmic: Instruments
- Bodily/Kinesthetic: Sporting equipment
- Naturalist: Gardens, play areas, and possibly pets
- Interpersonal: Areas which encourage social play and engagement
- Intrapersonal: Quiet areas

In regards to these environments, it is key that "the most important element in raising a smarter child is altering his or her experiences within his or her environment, not merely altering the environment itself. It's what your kids do and what you do with them, not what they have." [20] One key element of enrichment environments are ensuring that we foster a love of learning within children. The father of unschooling, John Holt states: "Since we can't know what knowledge will be most needed in the future, it is senseless to try to teach it in advance. Instead, we should try to turn out people who love learning so much and learn so well that they will be able to learn whatever must be learned." [21]

8. Parent-child Relationships

The most important aspect of childhood development is the relationship with the parents raising them. The dangers of poor parent-child relationships would be significant in the closed environment. "When a parent's life is unpredictable, the parent's behavior toward the child is also unpredictable with regard to support, neglect, or anger. This unpredictability impedes the child's ability to develop a sense of safety or consistency in his or her view of the parent and the environment. When the parent is unpredictable or the parent dissociates (is psychologically absent while physically present), the child's ability to perceive whether there is danger or safety is impaired and the child becomes hypervigilant, or super organized around assessing the state of the parent." [22] Starship design should consider how the roles of adults effect their involvement with their family. An unpredictable parental life will dramatically affect the child.

Another key aspect to consider in parent-child relationships is fostering attachment between them. "Attachment [is] a "lasting psychological connectedness between human beings . . . a fundamental building block for human development . . . children who have secure attachments are 'inoculated' from adverse outcomes throughout development. Lack of healthy attachment, then, is truly a very traumatic beginning for any child. Early problems with attachment can have long term negative impacts, including "skew[ing] the developmental trajectory of the right brain over the rest of the life span." [23] Children who develop strong attachment in infancy tend to respond better to unique environments. It is not the environment which causes stress. It is the lack of attachment to a parent and the stabilizing element that relationship provides.

What creates unhealthy children? "We know that children who grow up in homes characterized by lack of warmth and support, whose parents lack behvaior management skills, and whose lives are characterized by conflict or maltreatment will more likely be delinquent, whereas a supportive family can protect children even in a very hostile and damaging external environment. Parental monitoring or supervision is the aspect of family management that is most consistently related to delinquency." [24]

David Farrington, in Family Influences on Delinquency, listed these aspects as predictors of violent offending at age 15-25 years:

- "antisocial parents"
- "poor parent-child relations (poor supervision, discipline, low parental involvement, low parental warmth)"
- "parental discord"
- "large family size is a relatively strong and highly replicable predictor of delinquency. Having four or more siblings by his tenth birthday . . . doubled his risk of being convicted as a juvenile."
- "poor parental supervision is usually the strongest and most replicable predictor of offending"
- "Parental discipline . . . predicts a child's delinquency. Physical punishment at ages 7 and 11 years predicted later convictions; 40 percent of offenders had been smacked or beaten at age 11 years, compared with 14 percent of non-offenders."
- "parental warmth could act as a protective factor against the effects of physical punishment." [25]

9. Specific Family Conditions to Consider

9.1 Adolescence

Space.com's Clara Moskowitz asked: "Eventually, humans will likely have to experiment with pregnancy on Mars. And if that's not hard enough, just wait 'til they try raising teenagers on Mars." [26] Stephen Baxter's The Ice Wheel postulates a future where the children of the original explorers are seen as burdens in the way of the mission of the space station. Adolescence is a unique developmental period. It is a time characterized by a strong desire for independence combined with an increased need for social support from friends. This is an age that the breakdown in family relationships reveals itself in anti-social behavior. Again, creating a nurturing environment will be a key to providing for healthy adolescent development. In *Hurt*, Chap Clark writes: "Across our nation, in villages, towns, and even cities, adults and children celebrated life together. They ate together, danced together, and played together . . . Everyone mattered, and that included teenagers, even though they were still a few years removed from full adult status. The benefits of this tribal connection are obvious . . . Adults knew their responsibility to nurture and protect the young, and therefore they held fast, realizing that the young were their most precious resource. They even started activities and programs intended to organize communal nurture of the young." [27] Youth need "a stable and secure loving presence, to experience authentic, intimate relationships with adults." [28] Ship development will need to ensure time and situation to foster this. "Family connectedness refers to a sense of closeness and caring from family members. It is one of the most important contributors to positive outcomes and psychological health of adolescents. Adolescents from families with high levels of family connectedness report later initiation of sexual activity, decreased pregnancy rates, lower levels of substance abuse, and fewer suicide attempts than those with lower levels of family connectedness." [29]

9.2 The Elderly

The value of the elderly in creating stable family relationships is high. However, older people are particularly vulnerable to social isolation or loneliness owing to loss of friends and family, mobility or income. Social isolation and loneliness impact upon individuals' quality of life and wellbeing, adversely affecting health and increasing their use of health and social care services. The interventions to tackle social isolation or loneliness include: befriending, mentoring, Community Navigators, social group schemes. [30] People who use befriending or Community Navigator services reported that they were less lonely and socially isolated following the intervention. [31]

9.3 Divorce

Divorce breaks down stable family relationships. However, divorce will happen on the starship. "The simple fact is that children find unresolved marital conflict deeply disturbing. Kids cover their ears, stand motionless with clenched fists, cry, scowl, ask to leave, beg parents to stop. Study after study has shown that children -- some as young as six months -- react to adult arguments physiologically, such as with a faster heart rate and higher blood pressure. Children in these circumstances are on emotional overload because of the chronic stress which distracts them from their schoolwork, and their ability to achieve suffers." [32] Navigating divorce will be a difficult issue in the tight and social intimate confines of the starship. As will be discussed later in this paper, key outside individuals (counselors and mediators) will be essential to ensure the damages to the family environment are lessened as much as possible.

10. Potential Overall Strategies for Family Development on the Starship

- Time with parents is crucial. Mission planners and managers will need to implement this in the plan. Remember the "mutiny" of Skylab 4 - the workers were overworked. This poor mission planning doesn't just caused tired workers. It can begin to great detachment in children which then plays to a whole host of problems as the child grows.
- Provide children access to three key influences: peers, toys, and each other
- Create enrichment environments
- Integrate natural elements into the starship.
- Create predictability in parental life and create environment and events which foster psychologically physical parents.
- Recruit and choose crew members who have the psychological resilience to parent well along with having the necessary "right stuff" for the mission, and plan to provide "in flight" services to assist the families when issues arise, which they will.
- Anticipate emotional needs of the children. They will need family time and one-on-one parent time with both parents.
- Space and time away to socialize for teens.
- Having experts and care providers for all ages of the human experience.
- Integrate Protective Factors: [33]
  - Family connectedness
  - Nurturing and attachment
  - Parental Resilience
  - Social Connections
  - Concrete support for parents
- Mandatory counseling: individual, couple, family, group. We must move beyond thinking as counselors in regards to relationship and think as social strategists. Counselors are critical for social health.
- Including mediation services
  - Pre-marital counseling. There is a reported 31% lower divorce rate in individuals using pre-marital counseling. [34] "Premarital education is associated with higher levels of marital satisfaction, lower levels of destructive conflicts and higher levels of interpersonal commitment to spouses."
  - Create mandatory "in-marital" counseling (tune-ups).
  - Connect adolescents to nurturing adults. [35]

- Create refocused and nurturing organizations and programs
  - Mentorships
  - Apprenticeships
  - Advocates
- Parenting Training "Parenting style are more important that parenting practices." [36]
- Roles to Establish (beyond Parents and Educators). Moore stated: "For a space crew that is going to colonize for many generations, a midwife is just as important as a propulsion expert." [37]
  - Counselors
  - Social Strategists / Group Life Experts
  - Child / Teen Advocates
  - Wayfinders / Community Navigators. "Wayfinders or Community Navigators are usually volunteers who provide 'hard-to-reach' or vulnerable people with emotional, practical and social support, acting as an interface between the community and public services and helping individuals to find appropriate interventions. The structure and processes of this type of service vary across localities and are dependent on population need. For example, those Community Navigators working with frail older individuals may carry out a series of home-based face-to-face visits to discuss concerns and plan, alongside the older person, what service or community provision may be beneficial." [38]
  - Mentors

11. Case Studies

What will social and family life actually be like on the starship? There are two positive analogs to consider: the McMurdo Station and the Chen family. Both were social environments in physically isolated conditions.

11.1 McMurdo Station

McMurdon Station is in Antarctica. "Connection to the outside world, friends and families back home and global issues is scarce in McMurdo and smaller stations on Antarctica. However, tight knit bonds are prevalent within the community and everyone knows everyone and intimate friendships are made." [39] It is distinctly a more intimate environment than normal life. One member of the station stated:

"It's an experiment in what happens when you put a thousand independent-minded people in one of the most peo-ple-intensive environments imaginable. We live in dorms with shared bathrooms, we eat in a cafeteria, and we regress into cliques with cool-kid hierarchies that can make figuring out which table to sit at for lunch stressful. On top of that are the disorienting realities of twenty-four hours of daylight, no kids, no pets, no cell phones, and usually no family or friends from home . . . A summer at McMurdo is disorienting and transformative; we quickly become detached from our lives back home and concentrate on what's happening around us. But unlike the flight, it's also a bi-zarre retreat, both Bacchanalian and spiritual. We're an obsessively, often indulgently, introspective group, addicted to talking about ourselves and our larger role in the world. Crammed together with others, with no private space or time alone, we confront demons and emotions that wouldn't otherwise surface. Wild mood swings are the norm; we learn to cry in public . . . People also assume that it's a lonely existence, but I never once got lonely. I wish I'd gotten lonely. I would have paid to be lonely. Because that would have required being alone. And that doesn't happen at McMurdo . . . One can be alone while surrounded by strangers, but, of course, there are no strangers at McMurdo. Many nights I'd fall asleep calculating the minutes I'd spent in a room alone that day, including trips to the bathroom. The total often hovered in the high single digits . . . The large amount of time being mashed together does weird things, not all of them bad. Getting together with friends, even in one of the world's last cell phone–free refuges, is easy. And you make friends at lightning speed, with intense, probing conversations often occurring only hours after meeting someone new. A spontaneous night of laughter and silliness can be the best night ever, leaving you giddy for days, unable to imagine life away from these people. But a bad conversation or perceived snub can be devastating, which brings its own set of problems. There's nowhere to be sad. . . . Many tears are brought on by the awful intensity of dating. Imagine going out with someone for the first time and then, regardless of how great or disastrous the encounter was, continuing to see that person three times a day at meals. Imagine that person walking into your favorite bar or restaurant or your gym, perhaps with someone else. It's not normal." [40]

11.2 The Chen Family

Winston Chen chose to move his family from their home in urban Boston to an island north of the Arctic Circle. "Botnen, who'd been staying home as a mom, took a job as a schoolteacher in a place desperate to have one — a place about 3,500 miles from Boston, east and way north, past Greenland, beyond Iceland. The family headed to Rødøy, a small granite island jutting from the Norwegian Sea north of the Arctic Circle." [41]

They had two children, Marcus and Nora, that accompanied them in the move. So how did they manage to keep their family healthy in the isolation of the Arctic Circle?

"To keep their souls stable, Chen mapped out an hourly schedule in a spreadsheet, color-coded for personal and professional times, chores and family time. He dedicated an afternoon to each child. Tuesdays were for Marcus, who was 6 years old; Wednesdays for Nora, who was 4. For the first time, Chen said, it seemed like he had the time to do what he wanted. 'During my first week on the island, I instituted Daddy Days for Marcus and Nora, who are 6 and 4 respectively. On Tuesdays, I pick up Marcus early from school and spend the afternoon with him alone. And I do the same for Nora on Wednesdays. The rules are simple: [42]

* *Only I and the child. Nobody else.*
* *We do one or two things that both of us want to do.*
* *I'm 100% present and engaged.'*

"How would putting your children in a totally different environment for a year affect them? How would they cope going there, and coming back? It's very hard to get good data about this sort of thing from people who've done it before, precisely because nobody would admit they wrecked their children's lives. Really, is there a more painful, more devastating admission?" . . . *"The kids have been here for exactly one month, and they seem to be doing fine. We don't detect any big differences in their behavior. We won't know how they turn out until we're pretty old. And we'll never know for certain if this year in Rødøy will have affected them positively, or negatively. But, one way or another, as I said, we're now a lot more accountable then we were before."* [43]

The extreme isolation actually enabled him to make strides in tech development. He produced an app called Voice Dream in his down-town in the Arctic. His family's entire income is now generated by sales of the app. [44]

12. Conclusion

If the starship is multigenerational, there will be families. Family dynamics are difficult to master here on earth. Poor family relationships effect everything from jobs to child development. In the family dynamic, the raising of children is also critical. The environment of the ship will be a unique one and it will require great strategy efforts to ensure the goal of healthy children and ultimately healthy colonists. Anthropologist John Moore provides a great prediction: "We change jobs, we move to Chicago, we emigrate to a foreign country. The decision made by parents to join a space crew is not different in kind from decisions made by parents on Earth, only different in degree. If educated properly, I think kids in space might one day say, 'Gosh, I'm sure glad I'm on this spaceship and not back on old yucky, dirty Earth." [45]

References

1. 100 Year Starship. http://www.100yss.org

2. Weed, William Speed. "Can We Go to Mars Without Going Crazy?" Discover Magazine. http://discovermagazine.com/2001/may/cover. 2001.

3. Weed, William Speed. "Can We Go to Mars Without Going Crazy?" Discover Magazine. http://discovermagazine.com/2001/may/cover. 2001.

4. "Mars One: No Children." http://www.space.com/21267-private-mars-colony-children.html

5. Moskowitz, Clara. "Could, and Should, Astronauts Have Babies on Mars?" http://www.space.com/20771-mars-one-colony-pregnancy.html

6. Tiziani, Moreno. "The Colonization of Space: An Anthropological Outlook." Online Journal of Anthropology, 2013, Volume 9. Page 232.

7. Bowman, Lee. "Interstellar Travel: A Family Affair." http://news.nationalgeographic.com/news/2002/02/0220_0220_wirelifeinspace.html

8. "The 'Brady Bunch' — a Model for Future Interstellar Travel?" http://www.csmonitor.com/2002/0221/p16s01-stss.html/(page)/2

9. "Distant Space Travel Better Conducted as a Family Affair." UF Researcher. http://news.ufl.edu/2002/02/14/spacefamily/

10. https://en.wikipedia.org/wiki/Colony_(Rob_Grant_novel)

11. Hills, John; Le Grand, Julian; and Piachaud, David. "Understanding Social Exclusion"

12. http://books.google.com/books?id=pZd9NWNbEWIC&pg=PA8&lpg=PA8&vq=family&dq=preventing+social+isolation&lr=&output=html_text, Page 7.

13. Tiziani, Moreno. "The Colonization of Space: An Anthropological Outlook." Online Journal of Anthropology, 2013, Volume 9. Page 227

14. *Convention on the Rights of the Child*. United Nations. http://www.ohchr.org/EN/ProfessionalInterest/Pages/CRC.aspx

15. Tiziani, Moreno. "The Colonization of Space: An Anthropological Outlook." Online Journal of Anthropology, 2013, Volume 9. Page 232.

16. Louv, Richard. Last Child in the Woods: Saving Our Children from Nature-Deficit Distoder. 2008. Page 43.

17. Louv, Richard. Last Child in the Woods: Saving Our Children from Nature-Deficit Distoder. 2008. Page 48.

18. Louv, Richard. Last Child in the Woods: Saving Our Children from Nature-Deficit Distoder. 2008. Page 105.

19. Tiziani, Moreno. "The Colonization of Space: An Anthropological Outlook." Online Journal of Anthropology, 2013, Volume 9. Page 230/

20. *Convention on the Rights of the Child*. United Nations. http://www.ohchr.org/EN/ProfessionalInterest/Pages/CRC.aspx

21. Kagan, Dr. Spencer and Kagan, Miguel. "Enrichment and Brain Development" http://www.kaganonline.com/free_articles/dr_spencer_kagan/raise_smarter_children_2.php

22. Holt, John. "Child-led Schooling." http://web.archive.org/web/20110708144314/http://childledhomeschool.com/2010/08/14/planning-for-child-led-learning/)

23. Furnari, Leona, L.C.S.W. "Born or Raised in High-Demand Groups: Developmental Considerations"

24. Furnari, Leona, L.C.S.W. "Born or Raised in High-Demand Groups: Developmental Considerations"

25. Farrington, David P. "Family Influences on Delinquency." http://samples.jbpub.com/9780763760564/60564_CH10_Springer.pdf. Page 203.

26. Farrington, David P. "Family Influences on Delinquency." http://samples.jbpub.com/9780763760564/60564_CH10_Springer.pdf. Page 207-208.

27. Moskowitz, Clara. "Could, and Should, Astronauts Have Babies on Mars?" http://www.space.com/20771-mars-one-colony-pregnancy.html

28. Clark, Chap. "Hurt: Inside the World of Today's Teenagers (Youth, Family, and Culture)." Baker Book House. 2004.

29. Clark, Chap. "Hurt: Inside the World of Today's Teenagers (Youth, Family, and Culture)." Baker Book House. 2004.

30. Hall-Lande, Jennifer A.; Eisenberg, Marla E.; Christensen, Sandra L.; and Neumark-Sztainer, Dianne. "Adolescence and Family Connections: Social Isolation, Psychological Healthy, and Protective Factors in Adolescence." Publication info: Adolescence 42.166 (Summer 2007): 265-86.

31. Windle, Karen; Francis, Jennifer; and Chamber, Caroline. "Preventing Loneliness and Social Isolation: Interventions and Outcomes." http://socialwelfare.bl.uk/subject-areas/services-client-groups/older-adults/scie/131316briefing39.pdf. Social Care Institute for Excellence.

32. Windle, Karen; Francis, Jennifer; and Chamber, Caroline. "Preventing Loneliness and Social Isolation: Interventions and Outcomes." http://socialwelfare.bl.uk/subject-areas/services-client-groups/older-adults/scie/131316briefing39.pdf. Social Care Institute for Excellence.

33. Barnes, Claire N., M.D. "Family Conflict and Children." http://www.huffingtonpost.com/claire-n-barnes-ma/family-conflict-and-child_b_1370482.html

34. "Promoting Healthy Families in Your Community." http://www.projectabc-la.org/dl/healthy_families.pdf

35. "Premarital Counseling Reduces Divorce Risk." http://phys.org/news70250831.html. June 23, 2006.

36. Clark, Chap. "Hurt: Inside the World of Today's Teenagers (Youth, Family, and Culture)." Baker Book House. 2004.

37. Farrington, David P. "Family Influences on Delinquency." http://samples.jbpub.com/9780763760564/60564_CH10_Springer.pdf.

38. "Distant Space Travel Better Conducted as a Family Affair." UF Researcher. http://news.ufl.edu/2002/02/14/spacefamily/

39. Windle, Karen; Francis, Jennifer; and Chamber, Caroline. "Preventing Loneliness and Social Isolation: Interventions and Outcomes." http://socialwelfare.bl.uk/subject-areas/services-client-groups/older-adults/scie/131316briefing39.pdf. Social Care Institute for Excellence. Page 5.

40. "McMurdo Station: Living In Antartica's Isolated Confined Environment." http://www.environmentalgraffiti.com/news-living-ice-isolated-confined-environment-antarcticans#OfwygQSvBjq3bCPJ.99

41. http://www.environmentalgraffiti.com/news-living-ice-isolated-confined-environment-antarcticans.

42. Stone, Emily. "Antarctica: Cold Comfort." http://theamericanscholar.org/letter-from-antarctica/#.UjTBBGRAS6Q.

43. Nickish, Curt. "Boston Family Finds Riches In Arctic Adventure." http://www.wbur.org/2013/03/11/arctic-app-adventure.

44. Chen, Winston. http://arcticdream.me/2011/09/29/daddy-day/#more-425

45. Chen, Winston. http://arcticdream.me/2011/09/29/daddy-day/#more-425

46. Nickish, Curt. "Boston Family Finds Riches In Arctic Adventure." http://www.wbur.org/2013/03/11/arctic-app-adventure.

47. "Distant Space Travel Better Conducted as a Family Affair." UF Researcher. http://news.ufl.edu/2002/02/14/spacefamily/

Suicide or Adoration: Religion in Interstellar Civilization

Chase Bednarz

Independent researcher, 3812 Shoal Creek Ct, Martinez, GA, 30907

chase.bednarz@gmail.com

Abstract

Interstellar travel has the potential to affect religious practice and communities greatly in their respective roles as functions of civilization. Predicated on the human experience, religion must adapt as interstellar environments offer humanity a new array of exotic experiences. Inversely, religion has the potential to impact the course of interstellar travel as it tempers the dynamics of spacefaring societies.

For example, the closed communities necessitated by space travel carry with them sociological consequences where religious practice can play a major role. While these communities' isolation can maximize their vulnerability to psychological issues, religious practice can also minimize the psychologically detrimental effects of social isolation on individuals of such communities. In my paper, I will examine how certain religious practices could minimize the pathological effects of a spacefaring community's isolation.

As the social impact of these practices will have their ultimate source in the individual, I will study religious practice on a fundamentally individual level following a cursory overview of group dynamics.

As the scientist and Jesuit priest Pierre Teilhard de Chardin said, "The day is not far distant when humanity will realize that biologically it is faced with a choice between suicide and adoration." Phenomenological practice offers a means of approaching the isolation of deep space travel as an opportunity for religious and cultural adoration, rather than as a personal suicide of those culturally dependent elements of religious practice.

Keywords

religion, community, phenomenology, isolation, psychology, philosophy

Deep space travel offers unprecedented environments for human experience. In this endeavor, people are likely to experience isolation in multiple forms, the most fundamental being the physical isolation from one's culture such travel necessitates. As cultural contexts frequently and necessarily mediate religious practice on Earth, the removal of spacefaring people from their native cultural contexts could present radical challenges to their religious practice. On the group level, religious rituals could provide an invaluable sense of regularity in such radical circumstances, also acting as a means of retaining the group's connection to their civilization and culture(s) of origin. According to NASA's Human Requirements for Extended Spaceflight, "spacecrews are likely to have internalized many of the values, goals, and norms of [Earth's social] systems"[1]. Due to the immanence of cultural factors in religious practice and doctrine, these internalized values can be considered intrinsically linked with the religious factors of a crew's psychology. Furthermore, these values can arise in their external practice as mediating factors of group interaction. Such practice, when manifested in the form of a religious community on board a ship, could provide a context for richly meaningful interpersonal contact between crew members. If consonant, these internal and external group religious factors offer stability to a crew environment.

These religious factors could also confer tremendous benefits on crew members on an individual level. Religious practice could combat the negative effects of extended physical and social isolation by acting as a means for participants to reach beyond their individual physical and social conditions. However, this 'reaching beyond' cannot occur independently of the context in which these individuals find themselves. The problem of their isolation could mediate their religious experiences substantially.

Herbert Guenther's phenomenological approach to religious tradition lends insight into how religion is mediated through a culture. Guenther describes tradition as "that which preserves and transmits essential insights", where essential is interpreted to mean "that which is relevant to the actuality of man's existential predicament"[2]. While certain insights to be found within religious traditions may contain universal relevance to the "existential predicament" of all people, the existential context of astronauts will differ substantially from that of most people for whom these insights have been relevant [2]. The transmission of these insights, or encoding in language, may also differ in terms of comprehensibility to spacefarers. Guenther describes comprehensibility as the notion that "the language used to explicate such putatively essential insights must be culturally consonant" with the person trying to understand them [2]. The cultural consonance of the language used to express these insights is a factor fixed temporally and relevant only to a specific set of cultural conditions, however putatively universally relevant these insights are to humankind. As such, the cultural relevance of a religious text to an astronaut is risked as he or she is deprived of the existential and cultural context in which the text was composed. This lack of understanding could consequently impede an astronaut's religious practice. In Guenther's terms, the implementability, or experiential accessibility, of the practices offered by religious texts may be impeded.

Such practices' lack of accessibility could exert remarkable stress on individuals engaged in the already high-pressure pursuit of deep space travel. Individuals situated in cultures on Earth can rely on the perspective of their culture's meaning system to find meaning in their lives, a system which, when internalized, provides a pre-conceptual framework through which an individual may categorize and interpret the world, assigning value to phenomena as they appear (and as the individual recognizes their appearance). When this system has lost its relevance to the existential condition of an individual, the system's decay can place an inordinate pressure on them to exercise their subjectivity in an effort to interpret the world in a new framework – one which necessitates the formation of new categories of reasoning. By virtue of their subjective consciousness, the individual may reform their patterns of thought from a terrestrial, cultural framework to one better suited to their new isolated environment; however, the subjectivity of his or her consciousness also constitutes an unavoidable existential condition. As Teilhard de Chardin asserts, the individual is "obliged to carry with [them] everywhere the centre of the landscape [they are] crossing" [3]. Subjectivity could prove beneficial to isolated individuals as an intrinsically adaptive ability.

Phenomenological practice may further benefit the adaptive exercise of one's subjectivity. Husserl developed his phenomenological method of epoché as a means of exploring the phenomena of one's consciousness in full light of his or her mental framework as it is projected, or in Husserlian terminology, intended, toward such phenomena. This method functions on the principle that "subjective consciousness cannot reflect things as they are in themselves, but only as they appear when schematized according to subjective categories" [4] – the central message of Kant's transcendental idealism. While Husserl primarily concerned his method with the apparently material phenomena of consciousness, epoché could serve to illuminate one's framework of internalized cultural and religious values. If the individual's conceptions of their physical environment may be examined through epoché, their metaphysical conceptions may be as well. With a lucid understanding of which elements of one's mental framework now lack relevance to their existential condition, the individual may prevent the further misapprehension of their environment in terms which no longer make adequate sense of it. The conscious adaptation of one's personal epistemic framework to their new environment through phenomenological inquiry provides an alternative to the inevitable, unconscious decay of such a framework's culturally situated form when it is subjected indefinitely to a culturally abstracted existential state. As a conscious method of adaptation, the phenomenological method gives control to its practitioner, offering a more deliberate, controlled alternative to the spontaneous unconscious breakdown of their internalized values. The locus of control becomes internal rather than externally situated in the circumstances of the individual's environment. Specifically, Domenico A. Conci's radical phenomenology could provide a means of asserting this control.

Conci's radicalization of phenomenology aims to transcend the categorical thinking of Western culture – "the concealed objectivation of phenomenological data" which identifies "the origins of sense with ... a transcendental ego". In its critical and distanced approach to a system of culturally grounded thinking – what Conci refers to in Western culture as "categorical structure" – radical phenomenology naturally lends itself as a means of understanding and transcending culturally-based reasoning [5]. Stefano Gonnella explains the radical element of this method as follows:

"With 'Radical Phenomenology' one intends a kind of analysis dealing with phenomenological residues singled out by radical epoché: this epoché, unlike the Husserlian one, does not only bracket the natural attitude, but also suspends the wider and more complex sphere of objectivation" [5].

In its suspension of objectivation, or the tendency to conflate objects and concepts, radical phenomenological practice aims to transcend a dualism inherent to Husserlian phenomenology (and its culture of origin). This suspension may allow for a mode of reflection in which the nondualistic elements of many religious texts may be more readily apprehended.

The isolation of deep space travel could provide a ripe environment for such radical reflection. Abstracted from the social environment in which the values in question were internalized, the practitioner is no longer subject to its psychosocial pressures; from this distance, they may more easily apprehend the system of thinking instilled by the cultural environment. The practitioner, although largely outside such a system, may remotely analyze its effects through its lasting internalized components as they remain in the practitioner's patterns of thought.

The Kyoto School of philosophy, with its transcultural scope and phenomenological components, parallels radical phenomenology in its potential benefits to the dimension of religious practice in isolation. The Kyoto philosophers approached two millennia of Western thought from the perspective of a Japan just emerging out of two centuries of isolation. Philosophers of the Kyoto School demonstrate particularly well the application of a critically advanced phenomenological method to the exegesis of religious texts. Kitaro Nishida, widely considered the informal founder of the Kyoto School, "[considered] phenomenology to be valuable, but ... maintained a critical distance from it." [6]. His student Nishitani exercised a distinctly subjective style toward the confrontation of contemporary issues with Buddhist insights; Nishitani's method parallels Paul Tillich's method of correlation, which addresses modern issues with Christian symbols. Tillich states, "the method of correlation explains the contents of the Christian Faith through existential questions and theological answers in mutual interdependence" [7]. Radical phenomenological inquiry may facilitate the process of addressing existential questions with theological answers, the interdependence of which lends these questions and answers meaning in and relevance to an existential context. Tillich elaborates that, "Symbols and myths must be criticized on the basis of their power to express what they are supposed to express", a criticism perhaps well-suited for such a method of inquiry [8].

Phenomenological practice eludes the scope of descriptive speech, necessitating its evaluation through the experiential application of injunctive directions; in the case of Zen Buddhist meditation as a form of phenomenological practice, these injunctive directions usually come from a teacher. There is no replacement for this guidance. Ultimately, an evaluation of the effectiveness of phenomenological approaches to religious texts and practices in the context of deep space travel must take place under those existential conditions. These practices may offer a means of approaching the challenges of deep space travel as opportunities for religious and cultural adoration, rather than allowing these challenges to result in the personal suicide of those culturally dependent elements of religious practice. However, the value of these practices may lay as much in their potential to transcend former notions and practices as in their potential to preserve them.

References

1. Connors, M. M., Harrison, A. A., Akins, F. R., "Living Aloft: Human Requirements for Extended Space-flight," Scientific and Technical Information Branch, NASA, Washington D.C., 1985.

2. Guenther, H. V., "Matrix of Mystery: Scientific and Humanistic Aspects of rDzogs-chen Thought," Shambhala Publications, Boulder CO, 1984.

3. De Chardin, P. T., "The phenomenon of man," Harper & Row, 1965.

4. Davis, B. W., "The Kyoto School," Stanford Encyclopedia of Philosophy, Metaphysics Research Lab, CSLI, Stanford University, 2010.

5. Gonnella, S., "Radical Phenomenology," On the Future of Husserlian Phenomenology, The New School for Social Research, 2005.

6. Ogawa, T., "The Kyoto School of Philosophy and Phenomenology," Springer Netherlands, 1978.

7. Tillich, P., "Systematic Theology, Volume 1," University of Chicago Press, Chicago IL, 1951.

8. Tillich, P., "Systematic Theology, Volume 2," University of Chicago Press, Chicago IL, 1957.

The Final Frontier Extends Its Hand
. . . but We Have Clenched Fists

Kirk Frenger, B.B.A.

University of Houston, Downtown

www.urdnotkirk@yahoo.com

Abstract

In the course of human affairs, it is difficult to imagine a more awe-inspiring or more worthy endeavor than space exploration. I believe that we as a species will ultimately develop new technologies to enable us to reach (in person) stars and worlds previously only viewed through telescopes. If we are to become part of a larger galactic community, what exactly do we have to offer other intelligent creatures from a cultural perspective?

Humans still have sharp disagreements about abstract ideas such as philosophy and religion. Charlatans, con artists, and sociopaths have and continue to warp and twist the fears of John and Jane Q. Everyman/ Everywoman into weapons that are aimed at the hearts and minds of the masses, and use people's fear to devastating effect. If I were to cite existing science fiction, I might point out that in the Star Trek universe, humans are at peace by the late 24th century, and coexist with dozens, if not hundreds, of other diverse species within their United Federation of Planets. There is no war, no poverty, and no hunger on Earth, or on any other planet within the UFP.

But how would humans get to that point from where we are today?

Contemporary humans have a very long way to go before they can even begin to approach the utopian vision of the future created by 'Trek creator Gene Roddenberry. I will address areas of human endeavors that must be remedied before any serious attempt can be made to conduct interstellar travel with the possibility of encountering other sapient life. I'll use existing science fiction to illustrate the direction that others have taken this line of thinking, and add my own interpretation to focus on crucial issues such as intolerance, freedom of religion, freedom of speech, fundamental human/sapient species rights, interstellar commerce, and interstellar security.

I. Introduction

The concept of space travel has been a captivating topic for many individuals, and great minds have poured much time and energy into making the dream a reality. The journey is full of pitfalls, and dangers lurk around every corner; great effort has gone into solving problems that based on empirical evidence will arise during a space-faring endeavor. The author would like to leave the scientific problems of propulsion, radiation shielding, hydroponic food growth, and the current necessity for generational voyages to better minds than his own. Instead, other problems in the areas of politics, sociology, and group behavior dynamics will be addressed. As no such voyages have been attempted to date, a non-fiction basis to serve as a frame of reference is impossible. Instead, existing science fiction works will be used for reference to showcase various scenarios of how humans might potentially evolve as a spacefaring species. Successful as well as maladaptive models will be explored.

2. Illustrative Examples
2.1 Successful: *Star Trek*
There is perhaps no greater popular culture science fiction franchise to use as a model for successful human integration into the interstellar community as Star Trek. Starting in the 1960's, Trek has altered lives, taught valuable lessons much in the same way Biblical parables might, and has been instrumental in developing the theory of "If it can be imagined, it can be done." Mr. Roddenberry's vision of the future of humanity is optimistic, and the thought that humans have overcome many of their shortcomings is refreshing, to say the least. In the Trek universe, humanity has become a vital part of a much larger whole. Humans serve as one of the leaders of the United Federation of Planets (UFP), a vast interstellar organization akin to a United Nations that is fully democratic and mindful of the needs, desires, and sensitivities of all of its members.

In this universe, humans have overcome their desire (or need?) for the accumulation of material possessions or wealth. Instead, humans seek to use their talents, intellect, and desires to improve the species as a whole by furthering the enterprises of science, medicine, architecture, literature, music, and other esoteric areas of human development. Within the Federation itself, there is little mention of political and/or economic problems, much less unrest. Rather, these problems manifest external to the Federation in the form of conflict with other Milky Way organizations that might hold views and values that are at times antithetical to the UFP's values. For example, for much of the UFP's history, the Klingon Empire has been a steadfast rival, and at times, a violent aggressor to be engaged in open warfare. Recently, however, the UFP and the Klingons have found great strengths in one another as allies against other, even more belligerent groups, a concept that furthers Star Trek's vision of cooperation as a means to achieve mutual goals.

"There is no reason why our two races can't become allies."
-Jonathan Archer, *Star Trek: Enterprise*, Season Four

2.2 Maladaptive: *Elysium*
Imagine a future Earth where the contemporary problems of the 21st century are not addressed. The problems are effectively ignored, shelved, and left to simmer on a back burner. Over the course of the next 150 years, the problems of overpopulation, pollution, rampant violence, political machinations and corruption, and gross inequitable distribution of resources to meet basic needs continue to multiply and grow increasingly complex. The situation eventually comes to a head, and the few remaining wealthy individuals and families, rather than continue to live among a hugely overpopulated, polluted planet Earth, instead opt to leave the surface and build a space station in orbit on which they can live their lives. This station has every luxury the wealthy could ever afford, and such luxury naturally attracts the best and brightest talent. Over the next decades, scientific and medical research produce breakthroughs at astonishing rates, offering services such as special medical devices that can literally rebuild a human body from the molecular level, greatly increasing life expectancy and offering the ability to cure diseases such as cancer. Life on the station is more or less completely utopian, with no citizen wanting for anything. The name of the station is Elysium, which exists in stark ironic contrast to the Hades that is planet Earth, a mired cesspool of over 20 billion inhabitants that have little or no education, access to healthcare, jobs, or other amenities.

The film vision of writer/director Neill Blomkamp could not be further from the utopian vision of Gene Roddenberry. Due to a mix of factors, the goal of Earth is in dire straits indeed. Rather than risk what gains they have accumulated through surreptitious and underhanded tactics and attempt to effect any truly useful solutions to social and economic problems faced by the majority, the politicians of Elysium fled the problems entirely by building their eponymous space station, thus ensuring their continued comfort while also ensuring that they would never have to face the victims of their own greed (in fact, many were still in positions to freely exploit them, as they owned the large companies of Earth that still had jobs available to the masses).

2.3 Synthetic (Combination Successful/Maladaptive): *Mass Effect*

Finally, a third alternative is addressed: a more realistic approach that combines the relentless can-do attitude and ingenuity of humans with their numerous faults and shortcomings on a galactic scale. The video game trilogy Mass Effect does exactly this and much more, simultaneously allowing humanity to find its place in a much larger galactic community (like Star Trek), but in this universe, while many of humanity's problems have been solved, many still exist, and many more have arisen as a result of human interaction with dozens of other sapient species, all of whom have their own unique culture, agenda, and motives that often conflict with humankind's own.

The races of Mass Effect at some point all discovered the remains of ancient technology within their home solar systems (easily accessible even by primitive sub-light propulsion) that allowed them to develop faster-than-light travel (FTL) and reach beyond the limits of their own systems. Once they had such technology at their disposal, they were able to discover an even greater secret: massive intra-galactic catapults that are able to convey vessels instantaneously from one point in the galaxy to another. These catapults, called Mass Relays, would become the backbone of interstellar travel. Each species would then eventually use the point-to-point network of relays to make their way to a massive space station which served as the hub of the entire network, the Citadel. As more species found the Citadel and began to interact with one another, a burgeoning interstellar government and system of economics would emerge, allowing these disparate yet similar races to intermingle, for the most part peacefully but at times hostile. Humanity itself found the alien technology and the relay network thousands of years after the discovery of the Citadel, and as such, humans were the newcomers to the interstellar scene. The robust pioneering spirit of humanity would give them great power and adaptability, allowing them to colonize areas of the galaxy previously judged to be lawless and dangerous. The choices of the player character over the course of the trilogy largely dictate the fate of the entire galaxy, and it is up to the player how best to proceed given any situation. What is common in each playthrough is the fact that humans are a small part of a much larger whole and while not having solved all of their socioeconomic problems, they have learned the value of cooperation and do work with the other races, as in the majority of circumstances.

"Cooperation furthers mutual goals. We anticipate the exchange of data."
-Legion, *Mass Effect 2*

Also, the galaxy faces a common threat from a force external to it, in the form of an ancient race of sapient artificial intelligence (AI) machines known only as the Reapers. This threat is also present in each playthrough, and the means by which the galaxy responds to it is left largely up to the player. The threat also shows how and why each species has similar technology, as well as why the Reapers are so familiar with not only the technology of 22nd century Milky Way species but also the far more advanced technology found in the Mass Relays and the Citadel. This trilogy is laced with outstanding writing, plot/character development, and mood-setting music throughout, and provides what this author believes is the most realistic vision of humanity's future in the interstellar community.

3. Conclusion

Science fiction must be used as the rubric to grade humanity's future as a spacefaring species, due to the aforementioned fact as of 2013 there have been no successful extra-systemic journeys of any terrestrial origin, save for unmanned space probes. The alien species encountered in both the Star Trek and Mass Effect universes are by necessity colored by human values, beliefs, and systems of thought, and thus have a huge bias when objectively viewed. If and when we as a species encounter extraterrestrial sapient life-forms, we will finally possess the empirical data needed to formulate more accurate judgments about what is needed from us as a species to adapt to interstellar life. In the meantime, sci-fi will do, both by necessity and by quality, and maybe, just maybe,

"If a machine, a Terminator, can learn the value of human life, maybe we can, too."
-Sarah Connor, *Terminator 2: Judgment Day*

Acknowledgments

The author would like to acknowledge and thank the following individuals:
*   Gene Roddenberry, visionary creator of *Star Trek* and its myriad life lessons
*   Neill Blomkamp, writer and director of *Elysium*, a cynical yet sobering film about the folly of humanity

- Writers Drew Karpyshyn, Mac Walters, and designer/ project lead Casey Hudson, without whom the epic space adventures of the *Mass Effect* trilogy would never have been possible
- Writer/director James Cameron for his work on the *Terminator* franchise

Constraints Facing Future Deep Space Missions

Erika Ilves

road:infinity, Jumeirah Islands, Dubai, UAE, 450363

erika@roadinfinity.com

Tyler Emerson

Belong, PO Box 1322, Nixa, MO 65714

temerson@belong.is

Abstract

Voyager 1 has barely left the solar system. Twelve people have walked on the Moon. Twenty-four got to lunar orbit, 530 to Earth orbit. Our Spirit, Opportunity, and Curiosity may be roving on Mars but we are far from being a solar civilization. Worse, seven billion of us on Earth are struggling to coalesce into a single planetary civilization. So is thinking seriously about how to become an interstellar civilization preposterously premature?

We make a case that jumpstarting an interstellar civilization could not be timelier: it is one of our best insurance policies against existential risk and a fast track out of the current sub-planetary civilization quagmire. We then proceed to look at what it would take to initiate an interstellar jump sequence in practice. We offer a qualitative assessment of cultural, technological, and governance transitions we would need to orchestrate, and explore how the interstellar community itself would need to evolve to accelerate these transitions.

Our proposals include launching an Interstellar Art Academy to inject a steady stream of interstellar edutainment into global culture; participating in the world's global public policy and entrepreneurial fora to put interstellar and space development goals on the global agenda; facilitating a roadmapping process among major terrestrial industries to move space commercialization into space industrialization; designing an online game to simulate governance models to underpin interstellar expansion and, finally, turning the interstellar community of thousands into an epic volunteer organization of one million.

Keywords

civilization, interstellar, cultural engineering, prototyping

1. Introduction

Strike up a conversation about starfaring civilization, and a few minutes later you'll inevitably find yourself discussing interstellar propulsion and starship designs. These are the topics that gave rise to the interstellar community and have boggled the minds of a handful of visionary science fiction writers, scientists and engineers since the 1930s. Propulsion that can take humans across light years of space within reasonable time frames is obviously a prerequisite, but it takes more than starflight capability to create an interstellar civilization. Back in 1969 we developed lunar landing capability. Apollo 11 was humanity's first manned mission to land on the Moon. Over the course of the following three years we sent five more missions, putting the total of twelve men on the moon. And then we stopped. Half a century later, the only relationship we have with the Moon's surface is through controlled crashed landings of our satellites. We are not an Earth-Moon civilization, but still very much a terrestrial civilization scrambling to rebuild our lunar landing capability. Six people floating in a can that orbits Earth just 400 km above the ground is as good as it gets.

Like many people in the interstellar community, the authors of this paper believe that we must extend our civilization beyond our solar system. In the end, the choice is simple: settle other star systems or perish with our sun. The stakes are high, the mission is fantastical, and arguably more urgent than most people realize. It is therefore important that from the outset we think about our interstellar expansion in broad civilizational terms, rather than narrow technological terms. Starflight capability is necessary but not sufficient.

The main objective of this paper is to explore the magnitude of the transition from sub-planetary to interstellar civilization and offer initial thoughts on how we might go about jumpstarting this process. First, we'll dive into the very idea of "civilization" and offer a working definition of the term. Grounded in a parametric definition of civilization, we'll look at the desired future trajectory of human civilization and argue that jumpstarting an interstellar civilization now is one of the best strategies for the long-term survival as well as the short-term progress of our species. The bulk of this paper will then focus on looking at the specifics of the how: the qualitative nature of the transitions we will need to initiate and how we might go about making them happen in practice.

2. Civilization

According to an urban legend, a journalist once asked Ghandi during his visit to London: "What do you think of Western civilization?" Ghandi supposedly gave an acerbic response: "I think it would be a good idea." [1] Eighty years later, the notion of civilization has only grown more contentious.

What do we mean by civilization? In a popular online dictionary, civilization is defined as "an advanced state of human society, in which a high level of culture, science, industry and government have been reached." [2] The Oxford English Dictionary echoes the general idea: "civilization is the stage of human social development which is considered most advanced." [3]

For our purposes, these definitions are of course useless. They carry no orienting insight into the nature of civilization other than the assertion that it is "advanced" or "high" relative to other forms of human communities. To make matters worse, these assertions tend to raffle the feathers of many postmodern thinkers who rush in to point out the many ways in which "civilization" cannot possibly be deemed to be an improvement on what came before—large- scale wars, coerced taxation, slavery, epidemics, and subordination of women are among the most frequently-cited charges against civilization. [4]

Interestingly—and perhaps unsurprisingly—not even civilizationists who dedicate their entire academic careers to comparative study of civilizations agree on the definition of the term. [5] And while academics can afford to disagree, interstellar civilization-builders cannot. We must have an idea of what it is exactly we are purporting to construct. The civilization-engineering profession has a much lower level of tolerance for ambiguity.

Since there is no ready-to-use definition of civilization we can pick up off the shelf, we have attempted to piece one together. To create a parametric foundation for our civilization-building efforts, we'll take a quick look at Big History and Big Future. Big History gives us the context in which human civilization emerged and how it evolved. Big Future gives us speculations about plausible future civilizational trajectories, both extraterrestrial and our own. By soaking up insights from the past and speculations about the future, we should be able to get at something fundamental, something we can build.

2.1 Big History

The word civilization itself is derived from the Latin civilis (English civil), related to the Latin civis (English citizen), and civitas (English city or city-state). [6] Early civilizations were social structures that emerged to support the city way of life. [7] First, humans became creative with food production technology (they domesticated animals, made plows, irrigated, and alternated crops, just to name a few agricultural innovations), and started generating a food surplus. That allowed some people to specialize in something other than food production. They became builders and makers of useful things. Several historians have argued that food surpluses had to be protected, leading to specializations like army, priesthood, and centralized governance. [8] Writing and monetary systems had to be developed to keep track of and ease the exchange of value between people who did not know each other personally. With these developments, cities became our first stabs at civilization—social cooperation between strangers leading to concentration of power and extension of human control over nature. It took technology and social organization.

These types of civilizational experiments emerged independently in several places around the planet about the same time, give or take a few centuries. [9] The first known experiments emerged more than 52 centuries ago (3,200 BCE) in Mesopotamia, followed by experiments in Egypt and Nubia about a century later (3,100 BCE), and in the Indus Valley and China 40 centuries ago (2,000 BCE). Depending on how you slice human history, we've gone through 8 to 30 local civilizational experiments.

The word "civilization" only entered our vocabulary during the 18th century Enlightenment. It was first used in a French book L'Ami des hommes (1756) written by Victor de Riqueti, marquis de Mirabeau, and appeared again in Adam Ferguson's 1767 Essay on the History of Civil Society. Both were primarily concerned with the pursuit of personal enlightenment and national progress. To quote Ferguson, "Not only the individual advances from infancy to manhood, but the species itself from rudeness to civilization." [10] Civilization was used as both a description of the process and the condition, and many Enlightenment thinkers were preoccupied with the search for the "true criterion of civilization," "the necessary ingredients of civilization" as contrasted with primitive or barbaric cultures. [11] Until the early 1800s, the word was used only in the singular because it referred to the progress of humanity as a whole. Apparently, this is still the case in French where the communitarian spirit lives on. [12] In English, however, plurality crept in and we've started talking about civilizations.

The question of serious concern to any civilization-builder is why some of our civilizations have fallen in the past. According to the theory of the German historian Oswald Spengler, all cultures have a lifespan of about a thousand years (the final stage of a culture is "civilization") and must pass through a life cycle of birth and death just like living organisms. Ultimately, all civilizations decline—including the Western civilization whose impending demise he predicted in his "The Decline of the West" first published in 1918. Although many aspects of Spenglerian theory have been refuted, the thesis appears to have left a deep and lasting imprint on the psyche of the intelligentsia in the West. One of the most influential cultural and social critics of the 20th century, Northrup Frye, goes as far as to suggest that "The decline, or aging, of the West is as much a part of our mental outlook as the electron or the dinosaur, and in that we are all Spenglerians." [13] That strain of pessimism about the future of the Western civilization and the ongoing human project in general, appears to take up quite a bit of space in our cultural baggage and is something we, as interstellar civilization-builders, have to contend with.

A few years later, an English historian Arnold J. Toynbee offered a more upbeat take on human history. Having analyzed 26 civilizations, he rejected Spengler's deterministic view. For Toynbee, a civilization might or might not continue to thrive, depending on the challenges it faced and its response to them. He concluded in his 12-volume "Study of History" that civilizations rose by responding successfully to challenges under the leadership of creative minorities. The breakdown of civilizations was not caused by loss of control over the physical environment, over the human environment, or by attacks from outside. According to Toynbee, civilizations declined because their creative minorities deteriorated and lost their creative power to respond to the next challenge they face while worshipping their "former selves". Gradually, they morphed into "dominant minorities" that attempted "to hold by force—against all right and reason—a position of inherited privilege which they had ceased to merit." [14] The subsequent loss of social unity in the society as a whole led to the demise of a civilization. [15]

Toynbee's challenge-and-response approach to explaining the history of human civilizations is empowering. If we believe that civilizations fall from suicide or murder rather than inevitable natural causes, then it is within our power to shape the lifespan of our civilization. Civilizations are no longer Spenglerian organisms with predetermined mortality but a network of social relationships whose destiny is determined by the decisions we make. The ethos has been summed up by Toynbee's editor as follows: "Man achieves civilization, not as a result of superior biological endowment or geographical environment, but as a response to a challenge in a situation of special difficulty which rouses him to make a hitherto unprecedented effort." [16] Challenging goals are thus critical for civilizational longevity. The challenge of settling another star system entails an unprecedented effort, but it could catapult us to an unprecedented level of civilization.

So far, we've had a lasting civilization only in the sense of the broadest cultural identity that distinguishes humans from other species. Today, this is hardly the unifying narrative that defines who we are. We do know, however, that historically civilizations with a high degree of internal unity (in language, religion and race) lasted much longer than those without. For example, the Byzantine Empire that included several ethnic groups, but was held together by religion (Christianity) and language (Greek), lasted nearly a thousand years despite internal dissensions and many powerful enemies which included Islam, Persia, Slavic and Germanic invaders, and several Turkish groups. [17] Collective identity is another factor that has played a significant role in civilizational longevity.

At the most fundamental level, we can think of civilization as a cultural infrastructure that has made social cooperation possible at ever-increasing scales, starting with the first cities and evolving to transcontinental empires. Unifying identity, challenging goals, evolving technology, and effective governance mechanisms have all been the building blocks of such an infrastructure.

2.2 Big Future

Our experience with civilizations is limited to our own. We have yet to encounter an exocivilization. But our ongoing search for extraterrestrial civilizations requires us to speculate about them, and by proxy, about our own future. We tend to think about extraterrestrial civilizations in terms of their energy and resource use, cosmographic expansion, and information processing.

Perhaps the most widely cited hypothesis about the possible evolution path of exocivilizations comes from a Russian astrophysicist Nikolai Kardashev. Back in 1964 he proposed to think about "supercivilizations" (that he considered inevitable) in terms of how much power they are able to extract from their environment. The original Kardashev scale consisted of three levels: Type I civilizations would be able to use the entire solar insolation of their home planet ($\sim 10^{16}$ watts for a terrestrial civilization vs. 1.5×10^{13} watts in current usage). Type II civilization would be able to tap into the entire output of its star ($\sim 10^{26}$ watts for our Sun). Type III civilization would be able to tap into the entire energy output of its galaxy ($\sim 10^{36}$ watts for our Milky Way). [18] Later, Kardashev's scale was expanded by others to include Type IV, a civilization capable of tapping the energy of a supercluster of galaxies, extragalactic energy or perhaps even the entire universe ($\sim 10^{45}$ watts), and Type V civilizations capable of toying around with a collection of universes. Many discussions on the subject have centered on informed speculations about the type of advanced technologies that would need to be developed to attain different levels of power usage. No matter how many aeons separate us from Kardashev's supercivilizations, they still must obey the laws of physics.

Speculating at these scales can be helpful. Once we start contemplating the long-term prospects of an exocivilization, it becomes easier to see that we don't live in a universe uniquely designed for our survival. To stick around longer than an average mammalian species, we will need to break a serious sweat and grow our mastery of physics, biology and ourselves. We tend to just assume that the entire universe is the playground for advanced civilizations—thereby expanding the size of our own playground. It's easy to imagine alien intelligence embodying a multitude of biological and non-biological forms, thereby opening the window on our own post-biological future.

2.3 Working Definition

Drawing on Big History and Big Future perspectives, we propose the following working definition for civilization:
> *Civilization is a cultural infrastructure designed for continued survival and evolution of Earth-originating intelligent life in the universe.*

The who is Earth-originating intelligent life, rather than the specific human form we now identify ourselves with. The where is the universe—we have to think in terms of the greatest context we are currently aware of. The why is the continuity of our survival and evolution, which in our universe is anything but assured. Civilization is something we "design" rather than something that happens to us. And the crux of the matter, the what, is cultural infrastructure.

We propose to integrate the material and ethical dimensions and think of cultural infrastructure as consisting of four building blocks: Identity, Goals, Technology and Governance. Identity, or how we see ourselves in the grand scheme of existence, defines our field of vision and our circle of concern. If we see ourselves as Earth-bound terrestrials, then that is precisely what we will remain. Goals give us direction and values. Technology gives us the theoretical means of realizing our goals. Governance—in the broadest meaning of organizing collective action—helps us turn theoretical possibilities into reality.

Together, these building blocks frame the overall scope for civilization building.

3. Trajectory

With a meaningful definition of civilization, we can turn look at the special case of interstellar civilization. How different is it from where we are today and how would we get from here to there?

3.1 Staircase

Interstellar civilization implies that we have traversed light years of space and made a new home in at least one other star system. Our physical path from here to there may be a simple straight line. Our developmental path through spacetime is less obvious. To make sense of the latter, a distinction between intensive and extensive innovation can be helpful. [19] In the case of intensive or vertical innovation, we create a brand new capability that did not previously exist, like inventing a light bulb, an integrated circuit, an airplane or the internet. In case of extensive or horizontal innovation, we find ways to improve and extend the benefits of intensive innovations into new markets and geographies, like making electricity ubiquitous or creating universal access to the internet. Essentially, it means copying things that work. Extensive innovation may take a while but it is reasonably predictable. Intensive innovation is hard and inherently unpredictable.

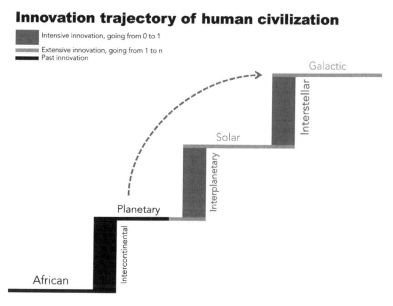

Figure 1. Innovation Trajectory of Human Civilization

If we represent our developmental path to interstellar civilization as an innovation staircase, interstellar is two intensive vertical climbs and one extensive horizontal stretch away. Two vertical climbs is a tall order. It is not entirely dissimilar to fish crawling out of the water 400 million years ago and eventually becoming human—only squared. Not only would we need to crawl out of our home world and adapt to a radically new environment (lower gravity, high radiation, different atmospheric pressures, alien or absent ecosystems), we will also have to traverse unfathomable distances of interstellar space. Given the inherent unpredictability of vertical climbs, it is now hard to imagine who we might become on the other end of this undertaking. Our ancestral fish, had it been temporarily endowed with a foresight capability, would probably not have believed that one day it would have two legs, two arms, a big head, breathe air, drink fermented grapes and work on warp drives.

As a civilization, we are still busy copying our basic transformational inventions like reading, writing, or the internet. We are still a sub-planetary civilization, with conflicting identities, largely terrestrial goals, big resource, environmental and energy challenges and dysfunctional planetary governance. Few of us are bound for the stars. A handful who would entertain the idea, imagine we will just take the stairs one step at a time: first, figure out how to coalesce into a planetary civilization, then do the vertical climb to inter-planetary and take our time to settle our own solar system. And then, hundreds of years from now we can wipe the sweat off our foreheads and start thinking interstellar. No hurry. We have more pressing concerns to attend to.

This is a precarious line of thinking.

3.2 Fast track

111

The ultimate reason to go interstellar is the life cycle of our sun. As our sun ages and expands, it will make all complex life on Earth impossible in less than a billion years. But this still leaves us with hundreds of millions of years to waste.

The aging of our sun is not the only existential risk we face: we must seriously consider anthropogenic technological catastrophes, planetary catastrophes like civilization-killer asteroids or supervolcanoes, supernova explosions, and possible solar-system-level catastrophes that we are not yet aware of. Mitigation of existential risk is a powerful reason to go now. It has been argued that reducing our extinction risk is strictly more important than any other global public good [20]—that is, if we decide to place some value on the existence of future generations, possibly trillions and trillions of descendants, and possibly the future of intelligent life in our galaxy. A multi-planet, multi-star strategy can dramatically reduce our risk of going extinct. It's a good insurance policy. Like with any other insurance policy, we don't know exactly when the trouble will strike or even if it will strike at all, but we still buy the policy.

As long as we remain a one-planet, one-star civilization, we are merely a parochial experiment. Now that we have evolved far enough to understand the existential predicament we find ourselves in, the only rational choice for a civilization that is not ambivalent about its own survival is to fast-forward to interstellar as fast as humanly possible.

Counter-intuitively, mastering the first vertical jump on our way to interstellar would also be a fast track out of our energy, resource and environmental challenges on Earth. When our problem solving space is limited to Earth's atmosphere, our options are unavoidably limited and politically hard. Throughout our history, we've been able to expand the meaning of the word "resources". First, we burned wood, then we discovered coal, then oil and gas. These terrestrial energy sources have finite stocks, we know they will run out. But even before we burn our way through all the stocks, we will cook our biosphere with trillions of tons of CO_2. The wind and solar alternative is clean, but impractical and won't be sufficient to power the continued development of our civilization. Space-based solar and fusion power, on the other hand, would be much better contenders. It may be easier to start beaming power from our solar satellites than getting the world's nations to agree to dramatically curb their CO_2 emissions. It may be more prudent to develop Helium 3-Deuterium (found on the Moon and outer planets) fusion power than invest time and energy into scrubbing CO_2 out of the atmosphere to buy ourselves more time to burn even more fossil fuels. To re-green Earth without reverting to a preindustrial way of life and downsizing our population, we must develop space. [21] With thresholds passed and action windows closing on many of our environmental challenges, now would be a good time to get going.

We should be in a hurry. To continue as a civilization we must initiate an interstellar jump sequence now, rather than hundreds of millions of years from now. It is both, our best insurance policy against existential risk, and a fast track out of environmental, resource and energy challenges that plague us on Earth today.

4. Jump

What would it take to initiate this kind of interstellar jump sequence? A good place to start is to wrap our minds around the order of magnitude of the job at hand.

4.1 Magnitude

One way to do this is to focus on the tangible part of the enterprise—an interstellar mission—and reason by extrapolation from our historical space programs like Apollo. Most estimates for what it would take for human civilization to launch a starship fall in the range of US$1-125 trillion. [22] The bill for the entire Apollo program ran up to US$120 billion (or 1% of the US$12 trillion world GDP back in the 1970s), employed 400,000 people and required support from more than 20,000 industrial firms and universities. [23] If we go with a US$ 125 trillion interstellar mission, we are talking about an increase by a factor of 1,000. If we then assume that our interstellar mission will account for an Apollo-like share of the world economy and bluntly scale the Apollo numbers by that factor, we get an implied dedicated workforce of 400 million (that's the entire population of the EU) and a world economy of US$12.5 quadrillion (that's almost 200 times bigger than our current US$65 trillion economy). Depending on our assumptions about economic growth, we then swiftly arrive at a conclusion that it will take us 100-500 years to get to a place where human civilization can afford the first interstellar mission.

Although intellectually interesting, this back-of-the envelope exercise should be taken lightly. The focus is too narrow (interstellar mission rather than interstellar civilization), and the method too blunt (our mechanical extrapolations are future blind, and many variables can dramatically alter the picture, e.g., breakthroughs and exponential improvements in technology, extent of space industrialization and existing infrastructure within our own solar system).

As we have argued above, launching an interstellar mission is necessary but not sufficient. Our generation's job is to make the transition to interstellar civilization inevitable. The economic cost of this enterprise is at best a secondary consideration. A better way to wrap our minds around the jump sequence is to reason qualitatively, to understand the nature of the transitions we need to initiate and to explore the different ways we can set them in motion. We need to adopt a broad cultural prototyping mindset: we are prototyping a shift in cultural infrastructure, rather than just planning a technological mission.

4.2 The Job

Earlier in this paper, we defined civilization as a cultural infrastructure consisting of four building blocks: Identity, Goals, Technology, and Governance. We'll use these building blocks to structure our inquiry into the qualitative nature of the job ahead of us.

4.2.1 Identity

"No one shows a child the sky." Dr. Mae Jaemison, the principal of the 100 Year Starship, likes to invoke this African proverb when introducing the ambitious endeavor that she is spearheading. Indeed, most of us can probably remember the first time we looked up at the night sky in wonder and pummeled our parents with questions about those sparkling dots of light. But then we grow up, and most of us—with the exception of astrophysicists, astrobiologists and SETI researchers—would probably struggle to recall the last time we looked up at the night sky and felt that the stars had any relevance for our daily life on Earth.

How we see ourselves, our identity, matters. Global Citizens won't build an interstellar civilization. But Cosmic Citizens might. We need to build a critical mass of people who look up at the night sky and see humanity's future homes.

The shift from Global Citizenship to Cosmic Citizenship could be described in terms of a shift in our cognition and in our morality. Cognitively, our civilization still lives in a tiny sliver of spacetime. Judging by the contents of our global public discourse and our global agenda lists, our vision is limited to Earth's biosphere and our time horizon is measured in years. We need to extend our field of vision to encompass the entire cosmos, if we are ambitious, or the Milky Way, if we are conservative. Our time horizons should be limited not by election terms, financial reporting cycles, or even our own lifespans but by the extent of human knowledge. If we can predict a cosmic event that will impact our civilization thousands, millions, or billions of years from now, we need to integrate it into our plans. That's of course emphatically not the way we think today.

Morally, our civilization is an amalgamation of moral tribes with varying circles of concern. Out of the 7.2 billion of us, the vast majority care about a subset of human beings alive today (my family, my tribe, my nation, my region, my continent, my race, my religion). At the leading edge of moral development, the global citizens among us extend their circle of concern to the entire population of our planet. [24] Future generations tend to get the short end of the stick. According to our standard economic models, the value we place on their well-being beyond the next 25 years is zero. Cosmic Citizenship requires a giant leap of moral imagination: at the very least we need to include all future generations in our circle of concern. For a Cosmic Citizen, the far future of human civilization is not an abstract thought. It's a tangible concern than can shape the contents of his or her life today. A Cosmic Citizen could easily decide to spend his or her lifetime working on breakthrough propulsion or starship designs.

If Global Citizens now number in the hundreds of millions, Cosmic Citizens are exotically rare, numbering perhaps in the thousands. Cosmic citizenship is yet to register in the global public awareness as an idea and to the best of our knowledge there have been no serious attempts to define its contents or track the relevant population. Our central task is to dramatically expand this population. Cosmic Citizens are the carriers of drive toward interstellar civilization. Although exceptional individuals can have an outsized impact, as a general tendency, the bigger we grow our Cosmic Citizen community, the more powerful our collective drive can become.

So what can we do practically to grow the number of Cosmic Citizens who care about the long-term future of human civilization? We can keep constructing our moral arguments on the overwhelming importance of shaping the far future [25] or on the need for our civilization to have a billion year plan [26]—but our rational appeals will move but a handful of people. We can flood everybody's newsfeeds with stunning images of distant star systems from our telescopes and wonderful visualizations of exoplanets from our artists—but images alone might not be enough to awaken a burning desire to go and see these exoplanets for ourselves.

We humans are storytelling animals. We tell stories and we are shaped by stories. [27] The most effective strategy would be to introduce a constant stream of future-oriented, well-informed, mind-expanding stories into our global culture. We can think of it as "interstellar edutainment." Three industries in particular give us amazing access to people's minds and hearts: books, movies, and games. We have more than 130,000 cinema screens and more than a billion smart phones on this planet. Science fiction is a marketable genre. It does well at the box office, and in digital book and games sales.

The problem is, for the most part, we have the wrong content. Today, science fiction is mostly what the famed British director Alfred Hitchcock called a MacGuffin, something that moves the story along but is not really its central focus. Take Neill Blomkamp's Elysium (2013) as an example—yes, we have a stunning space-based habitat and body-reconstituting machines, but the plot is really about the present, the implications of global inequality. Although technically a scifi movie, Elysium does not do much to fuel our collective dreams to expand into space.

What do we do? Since we need stories that stretch our identity toward the stars, why don'y we start an Interstellar Art Academy? Imagine creating a graduate program for writers, game designers and film directors where they could come and learn from the masters of the genre (e.g., science fiction writer David Brin, film director David Cameron and game designer Casey Hudson), but also get grounded in a broad-based transdisciplinary understanding of the big picture. We would teach Big History, Existential Risks, Cosmography, Astrobiology, the Scientific Limits of the Possible [28], Propulsion, Starship Designs, and so on. We could get even more deliberate and create a hundred year book-movie-gaming franchise on our future history. Think of it as a prelude to Star Trek that tells the story of how Earthlings reached starflight capability in the first place and what they did with it.

Human civilization won't reach for the stars without the voice of Cosmic Citizens starting to register loud and clear in our collective awareness. To grow their number, we'll need to cultivate dozens of Gene Roddenberry's (the mastermind behind the Star Trek franchise) over the coming decades. Setting up and running an Interstellar Art Academy won't take US$1 trillion in funding and could be developed into a self-funding venture. It will take a small team to get it going and we won't have to wait for 500 years. We can start now.

4.2.2 Goals

What does our civilization want? We may disagree about underlying problem definitions and prefer different courses of action, yet there is a remarkable degree of alignment within our global community around the big four goals: Peace, Sustainability, Prosperity, and Justice. We want to minimize violent conflict and avoid major wars and genocide. We want to live within the limits of our biosphere. We want to relegate poverty to history books and usher in a new era of abundance. We want a more equitable world with a smaller gap between the rich and the poor across and within countries. These goals come in many different right-wing and left-wing flavors but by and large, this is what our civilization is trying to accomplish, with all of our aspirations neatly folded within the Earth's biosphere.

More than 30 years ago, a futurist known as FM-2030 predicted a 90-degree rotation in our political spectrum, from left-wing and right-wing to up-wing and down-wing. The directionality was meant literally: up-wing meant looking toward the heavens or black sky, and down-wing was looking toward the Earth. [29] Back in the 1980s it was perhaps an obvious prediction to make. During the preceding three decades up-wing goals occupied a prominent place on the national agendas of the Cold War rivals and attracted serious levels of funding. The first man-made object in orbit (Sputnik), the first man in space (Yuri Gagarin), the first man on the Moon (Neil Armstrong)—our trajectory was clear, we were bound for space! Yet, a quarter of a century later, up-wing goals are markedly absent from the global agenda.

Sure, we invest billions of dollars in bigger and bigger space telescopes to see what (and who) is out there. We send hundreds of flyby and lander missions to planets, moons and asteroids in our own solar system. We have six people living and administering science experiments in a space station orbiting the Earth. And 100,000 of us sign up for a privately funded volunteer mission to Mars. [30] Yet, few of these activities are seen as central to the future of human civilization. Up-wing goals are not seen as important enough to register on the global agenda.

One thing we can be certain about, we won't wake up to a sunrise in the Alpha Centauri system by accident. How can we expand the current global discourse and put the extension of human civilization beyond the Earth's atmosphere on the global agenda? The simple answer is: show up and make the case. And then, keep showing up and making the case. For a hundred years, if necessary.

Most countries with active space programs have national space-lobbying organizations arguing for more ambitious goals and more funding. That is of course helpful because in the grand scheme of existence it might not really matter whether the next flag on the Moon will be Chinese or the first flag on Mars American (or with a SpaceX logo). Yet, to up-wing our global agenda, we need to think broader. We need to start showing up and speaking up at the world's global public policy and entrepreneurial fora.

So, let's say we are bound for the World Economic Forum meeting in Davos or the Clinton Global Initiative meeting in New York. What should we contribute to the ongoing public discourse? At first sight, the goals we advocate (i.e., jumpstarting an interstellar civilization) are metaphysically as far from the aforementioned big four staples of the global agenda as the physical distance between our sun and Alpha Centauri. But first impressions are deceptive. If you think about it, propulsion aside, the challenge of settling other planets, moons and asteroids within our solar system and beyond are not fundamentally dissimilar to the challenge of figuring out how to live together on planet Earth. It's all about us trying to figure out how to make our home on a celestial body speeding through space: how to build our life support systems, how to allocate our resources, how to get along, how to create good, meaningful lives for ourselves. The Earth just has the first home disadvantage—unavoidably, that's where we make the bulk of our basic mistakes until we can pull together an Operating Manual for Spaceship Earth and Other Celestial Bodies. [31]

Furthermore, introducing an interstellar perspective in the public policy circles can serve as an intriguing thought experiment. Change of context—from the Earth-Now mental box we have locked ourselves in to Some Other Planet-Some Time in the Future—can help see our terrestrial challenges in a new light. Take Sustainability. Imagine you are headed for a planet with no "free" ecosystem services to offer you besides raw materials, either because it's a barren planet or because indigenous biology is incompatible with ours. How would you set up our life support systems? We could go with a planetary-scale terraforming (effectively, the strategy we have been pursuing on planet Earth), or we could build closed loop systems from the outset. We can think about the problem from a terrestrial context and then find a way to implement it on Earth. Making space for "nature" and moving humans onto closed loop life support systems is already a strategy advocated by the Modern Green movement. [32] Or take Peace. What happens when we take the geopolitics of peace into space? According to the Outer Space Treaty of 1967, celestial resources are a common heritage of humanity and weapons of mass destruction are not allowed into outer space. How would we go about advancing human civilization within this overarching framework? Earth is merely another celestial body. So how would the terrestrial geopolitics of peace work if we applied a similar framework on Earth?

Engaging members of the global public policy community around the interstellar thought experiment would allow us to introduce the idea of interstellar into the global public discourse. Even if this idea enters the circulation as a problem-solving prop, it still enters the circulation, paving the way for the more fundamental argument. To quote Carl Sagan, "every surviving civilization is obliged to become spacefaring…for the most practical reason imaginable: staying alive." Existential risk is a problem to which interstellar expansion of our civilization is a good if partial solution. Astro-geographical diversification offers protection from external risks like asteroid impacts, supernova explosions and ultimately the aging of our sun (while human-made existential risks tend to go wherever humans go). To get to a point where expanding human civilization beyond our solar system becomes not just a goal, but a priority, we first need to get to a point where we as a civilization see existential risk as a problem to be solved. That work has only just begun. [33]

Engaging with global public policy stakeholders alone would not be enough. Global agenda are not shaped at the meetings in Davos or New York alone. Another big part of the equation is the goals pursued by the world's entrepreneurs. So let's imagine we are bound for Skoll World Forum, TED, or the Silicon Valley, expecting to encounter thousands of shiny-eyed entrepreneurs. Are they starting the right kind of ventures? Many people bemoan the lack of big-ticket innovation in Silicon Valley and, by extension, many other entrepreneurial hotbeds around the world. [34] It is easy to cite historical precedents ("where are our 21st century Ford's or General Electric's or Intel's?"), but few people are able to offer even an illustrative list of the kind of companies they would like to see started in the next 100 years. With a bit of thinking, we could have something very interesting to share with the world's entrepreneurs. Imagine we have become an interstellar civilization. What are the companies that helped make it happen? What are the goals they pursued? We could paint a very interesting picture, perhaps put forward a list of startups we would need to see in the next 100 years. We could then go around the world and share these ideas in entrepreneurship-focused fora. If we are good at it, they can turn into "ideas worth spreading" and into a new generation of "ventures worth starting".

When it comes to the magnitude of the task, putting the interstellar expansion of our civilization on the global public policy and entrepreneurial agenda would be a marathon task that could be accomplished by a small network of passionate space writers, advocates and enthusiasts. It won't require a ridiculous amount of funding but it may require a ridiculous amount of perseverance.

4.2.3 Technology

Technologically, interstellar civilization is two extremely-hard, intensive-innovation jumps away—we need to pull off interplanetary and interstellar. It's a jump from crude energy, the orbital space station, agriculture and manufacture, global infrastructure, global internet, and human life extension to fusion energy, starships, engineered closed loop habitats, solar system infrastructure, galactic internet, and human body modification. And these are just some of the headlines.

How do we orchestrate or facilitate a technological transition of such massive proportions? This is where it helps to pace ourselves and think through the logical sequence of events. In other words, we need to draw up a high-level plan. Over the past century, several people have given serious thought to how we might sequence our steps. Russian visionary Konstantin Tsiolkovsky put forward his straightforward sixteen-step Plan for Space Exploration back in 1926. [35] In the 1980s, analysts at Rockwell International, a major American manufacturing conglomerate in the latter half of the 20th century, put forward a much more elaborate and sophisticated Integrated Space Plan where they carefully mapped the links and interdependencies among the various steps, all part of their 100-plus-year vision of settling the solar system and beyond. [36] Several nations have produced medium-term visions for their space programs but none of them come even close to the long-range systematic perspective embedded in the plans of Tsiolkovsky or Rockwell. [37]

So we have given our expansion into space serious thought and have been planning it for some time now. Yet our track record at converting plans into action over the last forty years has been modest at best. As long as our ventures into space had been fueled by the needs of the military-industrial complex, to dust off a bit of the Cold War era terminology, we were making fast-paced and serious progress. A lot has changed since then. Government space programs are now primarily about scientific discovery and spinoff innovation. Space agencies like NASA, ESA, the Japan Aerospace Exploration Agency (JAXA), and the Indian Space Research Organisation (ISRO) have all established offices dedicated to promoting the terrestrial use of space technology. The 2012 edition of NASA's annual Spinoff report that sampled fewer than 200 space technologies out of thousands estimated that spinoffs have saved at least 444,000 lives and resulted in the creation of 14,000 jobs, in addition to generating revenue and reducing costs. [38] This type of impact is what is now needed to make a case for increased funding. As government budgets around the world are falling off fiscal cliffs, some government space programs are taking a hit (USA, EU) while others (Russia, Brazil, India, China) make bold plans for increased investment. But on balance, government investment in space programs barely grew in 2012, increasing by slightly more than 1%. [39]

Fortunately, this might matter less and less. Commercialization of space is now an established trend and commercial space now accounts for nearly three-thirds of our global space economy. [40] In addition to the traditional aerospace companies, we are seeing an influx of new blood and new money as several billionaire entrepreneurs are turning their attention to space. Elon Musk (SpaceX) is the most ambitious: he wants to settle Mars and is hard at work building cheap, reusable rockets to get us there while he pays the bills by launching satellites and delivering cargo to the International Space Station. Jeff Bezos (Blue Origin) is also building reusable rockets but is less forthcoming about his long-term plans; his company's motto promises to move Gradatim Ferocita, Latin for 'step by step ferociously'. [41] Paul Allen (Stratolaunch Systems) announced he is building the world's largest aircraft, powered by six 747 engines, to serve as a platform for putting commercial payloads into orbit. [42] Robert Bigelow (Bigelow Aerospace) is working on a private orbital space station to be used for research and space tourism. Richard Branson (Virgin Galactic) is working to offer suborbital flights for space tourists and suborbital launches to science missions, with his eyes set on orbital human spaceflights further down the road. Another four billionaires, Larry Page, Eric Schmidt, Ross Perot, Jr., and Charles Simonyi have recently invested in an asteroid mining venture, Planetary Resources. [43] Their venture is not the only one—the total count of space mining startups now stands at four (Planetary Resources, Shackleton Energy Company, Moon Express, and Deep Space Industries). [44]

Government and commercial activities combined, space is still a modest US$304 billion economy. It is now driven by scientific exploration, Earth-observing and broadcasting satellites, and a nascent commercial interest in space tourism, space transportation and space resources. [45] The good news is that it is growing. The even better news is—now that our motivations and key players have changed—it may be an opportune time to return to the idea of grand planning in the tradition of Tsiolkovsky and Rockwell International. This time however, we should aim for a different kind of plan and, more importantly, a different kind of planning process.

Extending our civilization beyond Earth requires intensive innovation across all major industry sectors. Yet, if you look at the cutting-edge research across most of our terrestrial industries, it is almost without exception blue sky. So how do we get our industrial giants to think black sky? Imagine bringing representatives from all major terrestrial industries together to work on The Interplanetary Technology and Economy Roadmap 2050.

In addition to the usual suspects from space agencies and commercial space industry, we will need people from Mining, Energy, Construction, ICT and Biotech. Here is why they need to be in the room:

Space transport. Today we do fewer than a hundred orbital launches a year and we rely on single-use rockets. Our current space transportation options are nonsensically expensive. [46] Just imagine trying to get the air transportation industry going with single-use airplanes. To be able to expand into space, we will need cheap, reusable rockets and space-based re-fueling infrastructure. Several such rockets and spaceplanes are already in advanced stages of development at SpaceX, Blue Origins, Reaction Engines (UK-based developer of the Skylon spaceplane), NASA, and ESA. In the mean time, the team at Shakleton Energy Company has advanced plans for an in-space network of lunar-sourced propellant depots that will offer refueling services to spacecraft in low Earth orbit—this would allow space vehicles to carry less fuel and take on bigger payloads. This type of space infrastructure could open up the cis-lunar space. [47] Space transport is the backbone of our expansion into space. It will be important for everybody in the room to understand what will be possible by when.

Mining. Whether it's fuel for spacecraft or construction materials for our space-based structures, we will need to get our resources off-Earth because lifting massive payloads out of the Earth's gravity well makes little sense when you can mine them in the neighborhood and move them around without picking a fight with gravity. On Earth, mining is a $650 billion industry with finite stocks of basic materials. Off-Earth, it's an infinite frontier where a single small metallic near Earth asteroid (NEA) can contain more metals than what we have been able to mine on Earth during the entire history of our civilization. Tapping into the population of NEAs would increase our resource base by a factor of about one million. [48] But to tap this potential, our mining companies need to develop new technology for prospecting celestial objects and running remote extraction operations in low gravity and extremely cold environments. The mainstream mining industry has recently been introduced to the idea of space mining when four space mining startups spoke at the Canadian Institute of Mining's annual conference. [49] The mining industry has already been primed for serious black sky roadmapping.

Energy. We will need unprecedented amounts of energy to expand and support our civilization in space but we will also have unprecedented new sources at our disposal. Coal, oil and natural gas may have powered the Industrial Revolution, but it will probably be a mix of space-based solar, nuclear fission and nuclear fusion that will power the Space Revolution. On Earth, Energy is a US$6 trillion sector. Off-Earth, the possibilities are mind-boggling. Take He3-deuterium fusion, for example. Cracking the code on fusion opens up the energy supply that is no longer measured in centuries or even millennia. We have 3 billion years worth of He3 energy on Saturn alone. The three outer planets of our solar system can turn into the Persian Gulf of the Solar System, or remain irrelevant if fusion stays "30 years away" forever. [50] Nuclear players aside, the giants of our Energy sector today are oil and gas companies. Space-based solar, thorium-based nuclear fission and He3-deuterium fusion can dramatically redraw this landscape.

Construction. What would it take to design, build and operate city-scale structures in orbit or develop a city in a volcanic cave on Mars? So far our experience base is limited to launching the grand total of 13 space stations into orbit (ISS and Tiangong 1 are still in orbit, plus the now retired nine Salyut Stations, Mir, and Skylab). Several Tiangong extensions and a couple of private orbital complexes or space hotels are already in the works. [51] All this is invaluable experience in space craft design but it hardly prepares us for the complexity involved in constructing space cities that would not need to rely on spaceship Earth for supplies. At the moment, our US$4.6 trillion terrestrial construction industry is eyeing hundreds of upcoming cities in China. [52] Cities on Mars would raise eyebrows in surprise, but if surprise is where we must start, then that's where we start.

Telecommunications. Here on Earth, we are getting used to information zipping through our fiber-optic cables at the speed of light. But in deep space, our communications infrastructure has not changed much since NASA launched its first probes in the late 1950s. This has recently changed for moon-to-Earth communications when NASA put in place a laser system that has the potential to transmit data at broadband speeds. [53] But by and large, our Deep Space Network relies on radio signals and large radio dishes to catch signals from our rovers on Mars or planetary orbiters. [54] Using light for deep space communications comes with a number of technical challenges: celestial bodies are in constant motion and terrestrial clouds get in the way, just to name a few. Vint Cerf and others contributing to the InterPlanetary Internet project have already developed a basic architecture for interplanetary (and even galactic) internet, [55] but we will need to start building the actual infrastructure. Getting as close to the speed of light in our deep space communications as possible can make a world of difference for both manned and robotic missions far away from Earth. They can also make a difference on Earth: optical systems can enable new satellite networks that will boost our terrestrial internet capacity. [56]

Biotech. There is intensive innovation, and then there is extremely intensive innovation. The technological breakthroughs we have mentioned so far are a matter of physics. Lump them all together and the resulting task would still pale in comparison to what we need to accomplish in biology. Apart from short stays in our space stations, no human has ever lived on another celestial body, outside Earth's atmosphere. We will need to create complete self-sustaining ecosystems, and modify our bodies to be able to survive in radically different gravitational, atmospheric and climatic environments. So far few of our biological experiments in micro-gravity environments are encouraging: bone density drops, conception is most likely impossible, and the human immune system weakens while aggressive bacteria like e. coli thrive and multiply. [57] And we are only starting to scratch the surface when it comes to understanding the complexity behind biological systems.

Introducing black sky thinking across all major industries would not only open up space but also has the potential to shake up every aspect of terrestrial living. We could end resource scarcity (mining NEAs), run our terrestrial civilization on a near-infinite supply of clean energy (space-based solar or He3-deuterium fusion), dramatically shrink terrestrial distances (sub-orbital flights), taste the fruit of the new agricultural revolution (closed loop food production and bioprinted meat), and further extend human healthspan.

But to get there, we must first overcome the chicken-and-egg problem. At a recent planetary drilling summit in Norway, one of the authors had a conversation with executives from a global oil and gas company. They were invited to the summit because their deep sea drilling expertise was considered relevant for asteroid and lunar mining and planetary drilling. Although visibly fascinated by the black sky thinking in the room, they were also understandably perplexed: "Where is the market? Six people on the ISS?" Without space-based resources, it's hard to build anything at large scale in space. Without the funded intent to build something large-scale in space, it's hard to get people to invest in space-based capabilities. So how do we start?

As with any new frontier or any new market, we need pioneers who are willing to take on outsized risks. Getting people from global industries in the same room and thinking black sky would help us to normalize the idea of expanding into space through mutual validation and to take on our chicken-and-egg problem through collective commitment. R&D funding would follow. If we succeed, space commercialization has the potential to turn into space industrialization during our lifetimes. This could take care of the first intensive technological transition to inter-planetary.

But that only gets us half way there. The second intensive technological transition is to interstellar and that's where we are not likely to get much help from the industry. If the commercialization horizon of 10-50 years within our solar system is already a radical stretch for most, a hundred-year time horizon would be swiftly dismissed as laughable. As long as that continues to be the case, we will have to continue doing all the heavy-lifting on breakthrough propulsion and starship designs "in-house", inside the core interstellar community of volunteer scientists, engineers and designers funded by the community of enthusiasts and an odd hyper-visionary billionaire or millionaire.

What is our verdict on this part of the job? It is formidable, bordering on monumental. We will need to do serious legwork to align and re-orient terrestrial commercial interests toward space. And in parallel, we will need to press on with the development of interstellar technologies ourselves. That's a tall order. It's nothing, though, that a committed group of passionate individuals could not accomplish.

4.2.4 Governance

What kind of governance would we need to have in place as a civilization to go interstellar?

We know that transitioning to interstellar civilization would require an unprecedented mobilization of our collective resources, trillions of dollars just for the first human interstellar mission alone. We'll need an economy that is a thousand times bigger, amounts of energy that exceed our entire current production, and resources that exceed our terrestrial stocks. In other words, a purely Earth-based civilization won't be able to afford the mission. This is not a one-generation project.

When we search human history for precedents of long-term or multi-generational missions, interstellar enthusiasts like to cite moving out of Africa and settling the North, the gradual settlement of the Polynesian islands, the conquest of North America, the construction of the Egyptian pyramids and European cathedrals, and, from our more recent history, the Apollo program and the construction of the Hoover Dam. [58] All of these examples may offer some historical comfort in the knowledge that our species is capable of pursuing multi-generational or grand engineering projects. This may be of some psychological value at a time when our civilization's attention span appears to have shriveled down to years and months, and multi-generational projects are rare.

But upon closer inspection, few of these precedents offer good replicable governance models. Our African ancestors advanced into the North gradually and in small tribes. Their initial investment was covering vast distances and crossing inter-continental land bridges on foot, a technology that comes preinstalled as part of the human body plan. The Polynesians built small sailboats, an undertaking a small tribe could afford. The Egyptian pyramids were erected by the pharaohs using slave labor at a time when the pharaonic power was most centralized. The European cathedrals were built by the institutionalized Christian church. The European forays into North America were jumpstarted by kings and queens, the Apollo program by the national government. So we extrapolate from the past and imagine that our foray across the interstellar space will be driven by national governments, religious institutions or the super-wealthy (e.g., trillionaires who make their fortune in the interplanetary resource economy). [59]

Pursue any of these models and we will be exporting our parochial biases across the interstellar space. Unless we will have established some form of an all-inclusive meta-religion, we'll be looking at a dominant religion putting its own believers first. Unless we will have established some form of civilization-wide government, we'll be looking at leading super-powers privileging their own citizens. Unless we will have all become trillionaires, we'll be looking at a wealth-based selection. Some parts of our heritage are best left behind.

But do we really have more palatable alternatives? As a civilization, we face a number of civilization-wide challenges that cannot be addressed by any single existing institution alone, some of them are conceptually comparable in complexity to going interstellar. Take sustainability. We are facing the "perfect storm" of rising food, water and energy needs that are inseparable from our impact on climate, biodiversity and biosphere as a whole. It is hard to imagine how we could weather this storm without mobilizing ourselves at a civilization-wide scale. What are the global governance mechanisms we have in place? The bad news is, our existing global institutions, most of which were conceived more than half a century ago, have proved incapable of making serious progress on the issue of sustainability. The good news is, we have plenty of proposals around for what we could try next: creative coalitions among countries, companies and cities. [60]

It does not take a wild leap of imagination to imagine some form of creative coalition taking the lead role in propelling our civilization to the stars. In real life, we can prototype this coalition at the level of our solar system already today, as part of our push for the industrialization of space (See discussion in 4.2.3 Technology). But we can also experiment with various governance mechanisms through simulations in online game environments.

We will not be the first. A few years back, the then popular online game World of Warcraft captured the imagination of academia. After a "corrupted blood" disease that was initially introduced as a minor hindrance to make combat more challenging turned into a game-wide pandemic and led to pulling the plug on the whole world, microbiologists, mathematicians, psychologists, and epidemiologists woke up to the idea that virtual worlds could be used to model real-world behaviors. Many serious studies have been published in medical journals since. [61]

We already have several interstellar games on the market, with EVE Online being the most prominent. Half a million people play this online game, set in a galaxy of some 7,500 star systems. It is already an established interstellar civilization that comes with warp drives and stargates—a fascinating lab for experiments in interstellar economy and governance but too advanced for exploring the pathways to becoming an interstellar civilization. To create a good experimental lab for the interstellar transition, we will need to create an exciting prequel to EVE Online.

A creative coalition of the willing, aligned around a shared goal is perhaps the most likely path to interstellar civilization. But coalitions don't just form. They are formed. We will need an independent body capable of energizing the interstellar mission and putting coalitions together for hundreds of years to come.

5. Starfleet

Initiating an interstellar jump sequence is formidable but not impossible. The question is, who is going to do it. Throughout this paper, we (the authors) have often used the pronoun "we" to loosely refer to the interstellar community. As it stands today, it might be too small and too inward focused to energize a jump of such magnitude. Below we take stock of where we are today and explore how we might need to evolve to make the transition to interstellar civilization inevitable.

5.1 Thousands

Thousands of people are now actively contributing or rooting for the interstellar cause: we have half a dozen active interstellar organizations, [62] hundreds of people show up at starship conferences and submit papers, and the Centauri Dreams blog attracts almost 50,000 unique visitors a month. The roots of our community go back to the 1933 founding of the British Interplanetary Society (BIS) that from the outset was intended to cover spaceflight to the nearby planets as well as travel across interstellar space. At the time, rockets were seen as a novelty with only limited potential, so it might as well have called itself a Mad Hatter's Society. [63] We've come a long way since then. The National Geographic features interstellar in the New Age of Exploration even if the title is "Crazy Far". [64] Interstellar conferences get coverage in The Economist even if the participants are half-dismissed as "an intrepid band of scientists," "an optimistic bunch," and "iconoclasts and dreamers fitting the activity [starship research] around their 'proper' jobs". [65]

From the outset, BIS had a dual mission: popularize space travel and conduct original research on rocket propulsion and spacecraft design. Most of our interstellar organizations have followed suit and have similar missions revolving around technical starflight capability, albeit the emphasis varies from organization to organization. In the last couple of years, we have started to think broader. Tau Zero was the first organization to explicitly include the relevance of broader civilizational and societal issues to the vision of interstellar flight. 100 Year Starship has been advocating the inclusion of biomedical and social sciences. And the team behind The Starship Century book and events also adopted a broad perspective, exploring what it would take to make this century a starship century. These are very promising signs. Yet, by and large, the vast majority of interstellar members and volunteers are passionate about the nuts and bolts of starflight.

We do need a stronger, bigger starflight-focused core. Without it, we would not be able to justifiably refer to ourselves as an interstellar community. But to initiate the interstellar jump sequence, we should dramatically expand our scope and aim to grow our base by three orders of magnitude, from thousands to one million.

5.2 Million

Imagine one million ensigns around the planet, united by a single purpose: make the transition to interstellar civilization inevitable. An epic purpose calls for an epic organization. Modeled on Star Trek's Starfleet, it is all about action. You don't join Starfleet for its membership benefits, you join for the opportunity to contribute to the single most ambitious endeavor in the history of human civilization. Starfleet is structured into distinct units, each with a clear mandate and well-defined missions for ensigns to carry out, led by an Admiral or a Council. Command is responsible for the overall direction, coordination and funding. Engineering is responsible for propulsion, starship and habitat design. Industrialization runs the interplanetary economy and technology roadmapping process. Culture runs the Interstellar Art Academy and other content-generating initiatives. And so on. Every ensign is assigned to a unit. Every contribution—be it paying an annual membership fee, recruiting new ensigns, submitting a ground-breaking paper, fundraising for a symposium or giving a talk that gets people interested in space start-ups—earns star miles. Rack up enough of them and you move up in rank. Starfleet always gets things done. With a bench a million strong, it can effectively spread the word to hundreds of millions, self-fund its ongoing activities and tap larger networks for funding projects. It is motivated by passion, which, unlike taxes or profits, comes in unlimited supply. [66]

From the viewpoint of a thousand-strong community, one million can look unachievable. Seen through the lens of serious scientific research, Star Trek references can appear unserious. Before we dismiss the idea as unachievable and unserious, let's sanity-check our aspiration—is it practically even possible to accomplish such a feat? Are there that many people who would be available and willing? Do we have any precedents?

With the advent of online tools that allow new forms of collaboration, as a civilization we are now learning how to use more constructively the free time afforded to us since the 1940s for creative acts rather than consumptive ones. The cognitive surplus—the buildup of free time among the world's educated population—is now in the order of magnitude of a trillion hours a year. We are in the middle of a Great Spare-Time Revolution. [67] There is a massive reservoir of volunteer time that we can tap. Availability should not be a problem.

Five decades of behavioural research shows that most enduring motivations are not external but internal—the joy of doing something for its own sake. We do things because they're interesting, because they're engaging, because they're the right things to do, because they contribute to the world. [68] For people looking to contribute to the world, to be part of something bigger, we can create an unprecedented opportunity—contribute to the most ambitious mission in the history of human civilization. But to capture the hearts and minds of a million people, we will need to get creative or drown in the background noise. Star Trek has struck a cord with hundreds of millions around the world. An opportunity to join a terrestrial Starfleet bound for the stars just might be the kind of opportunity many would not want to miss.

There isn't an exact precedent we could copy. But there is plenty we can learn from open-source volunteer projects like Wikipedia. Almost 20 million people are registered as contributors to Wikipedia (even though only a minority of them are regular contributors). All of the articles, edits, and arguments about articles and edits represent around 100 million hours of human labor. For comparison, Americans watch about 200 billion hours of TV every year.

Transforming a loose interstellar community of thousands of people into a disciplined Starfleet of a million ensigns is a formidable task in its own right. It won't happen overnight. But this might be our best shot at initiating an interstellar jump sequence and getting to starflight capability in the next 100 years.

References

1. O'Toole, G., "Mohandas Ghandi? Apocryphal?", Quote Investigator, April 23, 2013, http://quoteinvestigator.com/2013/04/23/good-idea/ (retrieved 6 Aug. 2013).

2. "Civilization", dictionary.com, http://dictionary.reference.com/browse/civilization (7 Aug. 2013).

3. "Definition of civilization in English", Oxford Dictionaries, http://oxforddictionaries.com/definition/english/civilization (6 Aug. 2013).

4. Stokes Brown, C., "What Is a Civilization, Anyway?", World History Connected, October 2009, http://worldhistoryconnected.press.illinois.edu/6.3/brown.html (6 Aug. 2013).

5. Drew, J.,"Civilization: Definitions and Recommendations," International Society for the Comparative Study of Civilizations Spring 2007, http://www.wmich.edu/iscsc/civilization.html (6 Aug. 2013).

6. Sullivan, L.E., "The SAGE Glossary of the Social and Behavioral Sciences", Editions SAGE, 2009, p.73.

7. Bagby, P., 1963 (1958), "Culture and History", University of California Press, 1963 (1958), p. 163.

8. Ibid, 4.

9. Ibid, 4.

10. Benveniste, E., "Civilisation. Contribution à l'histoire du mot" (Civilisation. Contribution to the History of the Word"), 1954, published in "Problèmes de Linguistique Générale", Editions Gallimard, 1966, pp. 336–345 (translated by Mary Elizabeth Meek as "Problems in General Linguistics", 2 vols., 1971).

11. Bowden, B., The Empire of Civilization: The Evolution of an Imperial Idea (Large Print 16pt), pp. 17-19.

12. Velkley, R., "The Tension in the Beautiful: On Culture and Civilization in Rousseau and German Philosophy", in Being After Rousseau: Philosophy and Culture in Question, The University of Chicago Press, 2002, pp. 11-30.

13. Northrup Frye, N., "Northrup Frye on Modern Culture", Volume 11, edited by Jan Gorak, University of Toronto Press, 2003, p. 305.

14. "A Study of History", Wikipedia, http://en.wikipedia.org/wiki/A_Study_of_History, (10 Aug. 2013).

15. "Arnold J. Toynbee", Wikipedia, http://en.wikipedia.org/wiki/Arnold_J._Toynbee, (10 Aug. 2013).

16. Snooks, G., "The Laws of History: Exploding the Myth of Social Evolution", Routledge, 1998, p. 91.

17. Dario Fernandez-Morera in private correspondence to the author, Joseph Drew, "Civilization: Definitions and Recommendations," International Society for the Comparative Study of Civilizations, Spring 2007, http://www.wmich.edu/iscsc/civilization.html (6 Aug. 2013).

18. "Kardashev scale", Wikipedia http://en.wikipedia.org/wiki/Kardashev_scale (12 Aug. 2013).

19. We are borrowing this distinction between intensive/vertical and extensive/horizontal innovation from a venture capitalist Peter Thiel who has recently wrote a book dedicated to the topic: Zero to One: Notes on Startups or How to Build The Future, coming Summer 2014. Notes version of his Stanford course that inspired the book can be found here.

20. Bostrom, N., "Existential Risk Prevention as Global Priority", Global Policy, February 2013, Volume 4, Issue 1, pages 15-31. Also see Nick Beckstead, "On the Overwhelming Importance of Shaping the Far Future", PhD Thesis, Department of Philosophy, Rutgers University, 2013.

21. The case for space development as a path to re-greening Earth is put forward by Matloff, G., C Bangs and Johnson, L. in their book "Paradise Regained", Copernicus, 2010 edition.

22. The cost of "Thrifty Dyson Starship" has been estimated at $1 trillion, "Budget Daedalus" at US$ 20 trillion and "Daedalus Class Starship" at US$100 trillion in Richard Obousy's "Interstellar Flight: Social and Economic Considerations", posted on June 9, 2010, http://www.icarusinterstellar.org/interstellar-space-flight-social-economic-considerations/ (Aug. 14, 2013). Early interstellar mission has been estimated at US$125 trillion in Robert Zubrin's "On the Way to Starflight: The Economics of Interstellar Breakout", in "Starship Century: Toward the Grandest Horizon", edited by James Benford and Gregory Benford, Microwave Sciences 2013, p. 84.

23. "NASA Langley Research Center's Contributions to the Apollo Program". NASA Langley Research Center (14 Aug. 2013).

24. Israel, R. C., "What Does It Mean to Be a Global Citizen?", 13 February 2013, opendemocracy.net (10 Oct. 2013).

25. Beckstead, N., "On the Overwhelming Importance of Shaping the Far Future", PhD Thesis, Department of Philosophy, Rutgers University, 2013.

26. Garretson, P., "What Our Civilization Needs is a Billion Year Plan", September 23, 2012, kurzweilAI.net (7 Oct. 2013).

27. Gottschall, J., "The Storytelling Animal: How Stories Make Us Human", Mariner Books, 2012.

28. A good exploration of the scientific limits of the possible can be found in Clarke, A., "Profiles of the Future", Warner Books, 1985.

29.

30. Fuller, S., "Nighty-degree Revolution", October 24, 2013, Aeon Magazine.

31. Juarez, J., "More than 100,000 want to go to Mars", August 9, 2013, CNNMexico.com.

32. Concept taken from Fuller, B., "Operating Manual for Spaceship Earth", 1968.

33. Pearce, F., "Technology as Our Planet's Last Best Hope", July 15, 2013, theguardian.com.

34. Although we have a few decades of academic discourse on global, catastrophic and existential risks, it is only recently that we have started to introduce the idea of existential risk to the global public policy circles. The most interesting recent example is Nick Bostrom's article February 2013 issue of Global Policy, "Existential Risk Prevention as Global Priority", Global Policy, Volume 4, Issue 1, pp. 15-31.

35. Here is a selection of the more considered complaints about the lack of intensive or big-ticket innovation in technology and in science: "The Danger of Celebretizing Entrepreneurship", "Transformational Entrepreneurship: Where Technology Meets Societal Impact", "Reversing the Decline in Transformational Ideas" — all by Max Marmer on Startup Compass blog; Jerzy Gangi, "Why Silicon Valley Funds Instagrams, Not Hyperloops", August 19, 2013; Sam Altman, "What Happened to Innovation?" June 20, 2013; Neal Steaphenson, "Innovation Starvation", World Policy Journal, Fall 2011; Mark Buchanan, "In Search of Black Swans", April 1, 2009, pysicsworld.com (30 Oct. 2013).

36. The full text of Tsiolkovsky's 1926 "Plan for Space Exploration" can be found in Encelcopedia Astronautica article on "The Foundations of the Space Age", astronautix.com.

37. Rockwell International, "Integrated Space Plan (Preliminary)", version 1.1 February 1989.

38. See "Vision for Space Exploration" announced on January 14, 2004 by US President George W. Bush; "Space policy of the Barack Obama Administration"; International Space Exploration Coordination Group's "The Global Exploration Roadmap", August 2013. European Space Agency's "Cosmic Vision 2015-2025" (30 Oct. 2013).

39. "The Space Report 2013", Space Foundation, spacefoundation.org, p. 5.

40. Ibid., p. 6.

41. Ibid., p. 5.

42. O'Connor, C., "Billionaire Space Race: 2012 Will Be the Year Private Space Transportation Takes Off", December 30, 2011, forbes.com (17 Oct. 2013).

43. Caulfield, B., "Billionaire Paul Allen Building World's Biggest Plane in Effort to Conquer Space", December 13, 2011, forbes.com (17 Oct. 2013).

44. Wall, M., "Asteroid Mining is Just Latest Billionaire Space Club Project", April 25, 2012, space.com (17 Oct. 2013).

45. Lark, E.-J., "Space Mining Entrepreneur Discussion", October 10, 2013, spaceref.biz (17 Oct. 2013).

46. Ibid., 36, p. 5.

47. For a fascinating historical account of how we ended up with nonsensically expensive space rockets and infrastructure, see Zubrin, R., "Entering Space: Creating a Spacefaring Civilization", Jeremy P. Tarcher/Putnam, 1999, Chapter 2, pp. 21-38.

48. Keravala, J., Tietz, D., Stone, B., "Shackleton Energy Company's Propellant Depot and Space Transportation Architecture", volume 1, number 2, 2013, New Space.

49. Lewis, J., "To the Asteroids—and Beyond!", SETI Talks, streamed live on September 10, 2013.

50. Ibid., 42.

51. Zubrin, R., "On the Way to Starflight: The Economics of Interstellar Breakout", in "Starship Century: Toward the Grandest Horizon", edited by James and Gregory Bengford, Microwave Sciences, 2013, p. 94.

52. "Space Station", wikipedia.com (29 Oct. 2013).

53. Davis Langdon, "World Construction 2012", aecom.com.

54. Brumfiel, G., "Netflix on the Moon? Broadband Makes It to Deep Space", October 23, 2013, npr.com (30 Oct. 2013).

55. For an excellent account of our current Deep Space Network and the requirements for interstellar communications and navigation, see Gilster, P., "Centauri Dreams", 2004 Copernicus Books, 2004, pp. 183-210.

56. Cerf, V., "Interplanetary Internet", TEDxMidAtlantic talk, uploaded on December 1, 2011.

57. Talbot, D., "A Successful Moonshot for Laser Communications", October 23, 2013, MIT Technology Review.

58. Research highlights shared by fellow 100YSS Symposium 2013 presenter, Jeanette Hill, during her talk "Microgravity Effects on Human Health and Metabolism" (to be published in Symposium Proceedings in Spring 2014).

59. The Hoover Dam precedent was invoked by Les Johnson at an Eve Online conference in October 2013 in Las Vegas. See O'Neill, I., "Want a Starship? Think Big. Think Really Big", October 28, 2013, news.discovery.com (1 Nov. 2013).

60. For one possible set of future scenarios for who might lead the interstellar expansion of our civilization, see Schwartz, P., "Starships and the Fates of Humankind", in "Starship Century: Toward the Grandest Horizon", edited by James and Gregory Benford, Microwave Sciences, 2013, pp. 27-39.

61. For one such proposal see "Now for the Long Term: The Report of the Oxford Martin Comission for Future Generations", 2013.

62. Christakis, N., Fowler, J., "Connected: The Amazing Power of Social Networks And How They Shape Our Lives", Harper Press, 2010, pp. 252-255.

63. Active interstellar organizations: The British Interplanetary Society, Tau Zero, Icarus Interstellar, the Institute for Interstellar Studies, 100 Year Starship, SpaceGambit. In the neighborhood: The Planetary Society, SETI Institute. An excellent overview of all interstellar organizations and their interstellar activities can be found on Tau Zero website.

64. Watson, N., "Reaching for the Stars", Volume 3, Issue 1 2013, History Today.

65. Folger, T., "Carzy Far", January 2013, ngm.nationalgeographic.com (1 Nov. 2013).

66. "Interstellar Travel: Starship Troupers", October 26th, 2013, The Economist (1 Nov. 2013).

67. You can find a high-level presentation by the authors further detailing the idea behind the 1 million Starfleet at http://www.slideshare.net/erikailves/road-to-k3.

68. Shirky, C., "Cognitive Surplus: Creativity and Generosity in a Connected Age", Penguin Books Limited, 2010.

69. Pink, D., "Drive: The Surprising Truth About What Motivates Us", Canongate Books, 2010.

Indigenous Principles for a Starship Citizen Handbook

Dr. Dawn Marsden

Assistant Professor, First Nations University of Canada,

1 First Nations Way, Regina, Saskatchewan, Canada, S4S 7K2.

dawn.marsden@yahoo.com

Abstract

When planning the culture, ethics and governance of a 100 year starship journey, the best starting place is to consider the best practices from Earth history. To narrow the focus, we should consider similar situations, where the community is a closed system and self-sustaining. The survival of a 100 year starship journey requires principles and practices that sustain not only basic needs for equitable distribution of food, air, water, shelter, and resources but also the philosophical, ethical and social processes for mental health, wellbeing and a meaningful life. We have four major models for mostly closed systems: sea-going vessels, artificial biosphere projects, the International Space Station and Indigenous societies. My knowledge of the first three is limited to recognition of their advancement of systems of propulsion, navigation, logistics, supply, and artificial life support. My knowledge of the latter, as a scholar of Indigenous health education, and woman of Indigenous-Canadian ancestry, has been extensive, with a focus on identity, social structure, environmental sustainability, wholistic theory, health equity, self-determination, spirituality, food systems, evaluation, community-based research, strategic planning, and cultural resilience. This paper will describe 2 concepts and 15 Indigenous principles for enviro-cultural sustainability, and discuss the applicability of these principles to an intergenerational starship journey.

Keywords

Sustainable, Indigenous, environment, culture, systems, citizenship

1. Introduction

This paper represents one person's reflection, examination and summary of the key Indigenous principles for sustaining environmentally limited intergenerational communities, synthesized from stories shared by Indigenous Elders, over the author's lifetime as an Indigenous person. The original motivation for this reflection was to devise some method for communicating the wisdom of Indigenous Elders to youth who are struggling to thrive in this fragmented and environmentally challenged world. The call for papers made to present at the 100 Year Starship Society 2013 Symposium provided the impetus to complete this reflection by focusing on a relevant question: what is needed to design a sustainable intergenerational starship community? The hypothesis is that if Indigenous principles have sustained Indigenous communities for tens of thousands of years, then they should be applicable to an intergenerational starship journey.

2. Elder Stories

The knowledge systems of Indigenous people, have been transmitted orally through thousands of years, and are extremely sophisticated systems, encompassing all facets of reality and daily life. This knowledge is embedded within Indigenous stories, languages, songs, prayers, dances, cultural designs and other teachings, which to the untrained ear or eye can seem like nonsense, but to many Indigenous people, ethno-botanists, archaeologists, historians, social scientists, biologists, builders, counselors and physicists, they hold wisdom on par or exceeding western knowledge systems. As such, Indigenous stories should not be considered fictional as in contemporary western story traditions; the selection of words, images, cadence, characters, tone, settings and story lines must be considered as a complex code. Like Heinrich Schliemann and his discovery of Troy through examination of Homer's Iliad and Virgil's Aeneid, it's time for western scientists to look beyond cultural differences and learn from those who still carry the wisdom of the ancients. According to some Elders, Indigenous people have had a long history of relationships with interstellar societies, and still have encounters and hold Star Nation ceremonies today. Elders have said that there are over 140 different Star Nations that travel by ship or through gateways in space; like humans, they have bilateral symmetry and some are telepathic and some are aggressive. According to Anishinaabek teachings, the people of the Pleiades are our ancestors, documented by Benton-Banai[ ]as the beings that gave us the 7 Grandfather teachings: respect, love, wisdom, courage, humility, bravery, and truth. Most of what follows was shared with me in story form by people I consider my Elders in Indigenous knowledge.

3. What is Indigenous?

In this paper I will use the term Indigenous as both an adjective and as the name many people choose when describing their relationship to a specific territory, in the English language. I tend to define indigenous as an adjective, using environmental terminology, as the multi-millennial co-adaption of species within a specific bioregion, or even shorter, as environmentally embedded. The co-adaptation, or relationship of the human species with other species, within diverse bioregions, has been perfected through trial and error over tens of thousands of years, into wholistic, interacting systems and cycles. Indigenous systems, people, cultures, values, traditions, principles, practices, et cetera, are those that have arisen from this environmentally embedded state of being. In Figure 1, I have represented how this time-tested knowledge arises from the direct experience of individuals, which is translated into beliefs and values, from which principles and practices for daily life are derived. Together these thoughts are called a worldview; when these worldviews are shared, it's called a culture.

Figure 1. Relationship between individual experience of the environment, personal worldview, and shared culture. Credit: D. Marsden (First Nations University of Canada).

While every environmentally embedded Indigenous culture is different from another in the details, there are some commonalities in principle and practice. I speculate that these commonalities (and differences) are directly related to the shared experience of being co-dependent upon specific environments for survival, and the need for social cohesion and cooperation under these conditions. The principles in this paper have been derived by reflection on those commonalities, as necessary principles for survival, social cohesion and environmental sustainability within limited environmental systems, and as such are directly applicable to principles for a starship citizen handbook.

4. Relevance to Starships? Strong Parallels

The following list was derived by consideration of the commonalities between a hypothetical starship and historical Indigenous enviro-cultural systems. For ease of comparison, I will discuss them both in the present tense, as if pre-colonized and starship societies exist in the present.

1. Both Indigenous societies and Starship communities require complete enviro-cultural systems, including all those environmental, biological and social systems necessary for intergenerational survival and fulfillment

2. Starship projects are looking for innovative concepts for enviro-cultural sustainability, while relevant Indigenous knowledge (albeit coded) remains untapped

3. Indigenous societies have lasted for tens of thousands of years, so lasting 100 years on a starship should be relatively easy using the same principles

4. Both Indigenous communities and starship communities are environmentally limited, which defines the boundaries of both environmental and social action.

5. Planning a starship requires consideration and use of reliable systems; Indigenous enviro-cultural systems have been the most reliable on the planet.

6. Given the limitations, both Indigenous and starship societies require a strong ethic towards conservation of resources.

7. Exile from Indigenous communities in history meant death, unless the person learned to value the benefits of communal effort and another community took them in. Exile from a Starship during space travel would mean death, unless there were multiple independent communities on a starship and a location for exiled people.

8. The success of Indigenous communities is dependent upon the diversity of knowledge and skills held by their people, with natural specialization according to gifts or aptitudes, personal interests and community needs. A starship would require the same kind of diversity of knowledge and skills that could be passed on in similar ways, though augmented by knowledge resources.

9. Indigenous cultures were sustainable because they were dynamic, continuously adapting and regaining balance or homeostasis within changing environmental conditions. A starship culture would require the same flexibility, though the changes in environmental conditions would be under the control of personnel, with increasing pressure to address life-threatening resource depletion or environmental damage (which corresponds to current Earth conditions).

10. Indigenous enviro-cultural systems sustained their communities for generations; increases in population were predominately controlled by food supply or lack of it (aka carrying capacity), wear and tear, accidents, and herbal birth control. Population pressures led to the development of new communities linked by familial and trade relationships. A starship would not have the resources or space to create new communities and so would need to limit population through birth control

11. Indigenous enviro-cultural systems were, for the most part, survivable, equitable, healthy and fulfilling. These goals are appropriate for a starship society

12. Indigenous people often refer to the Earth as our mother because we are dependent upon her to provide the food, water, comforts and lessons to survive and live fulfilling lives. Essentially, we are made from, and are as healthy as, the environment around us. A starship could be considered in a similar way, as a surrogate mother, to which we owe our lives and health.

5. Starship Citizenship Vision and Goals

Social cohesion is the capacity of a society to ensure the well-being of all its members, minimizing disparities and avoiding marginalization.

To become a member of a community, or citizen, requires acceptance of the vision and goals of that community. To keep it simple, I propose the adoption of the following vision for starship citizenship:

A community of interdependent people who work together to produce and maintain – not only the means of existence – but also the balance and harmony required for personal and social fulfillment, for generations.

For Indigenous communities, the implicit goal was intergenerational survival and community cohesion. A starship journey would have similar goals:

1. To develop and maintain a socially cohesive and environmentally sustainable community
2. To develop and maintain social cohesion through equitable and fulfilling goals, processes and outcomes
3. To develop and maintain environmental sustainability through healthy and survivable systems.

6. Indigenous Enviro-Cultural Sustainability Model

Indigenous principles and practices for enviro-cultural sustainability are complex and interwoven. The updated model in Figure 2 was designed to represent the interconnected relationships between two unifying concepts (circle symbols and wholistic egalitarianism), three core principles and twelve key principles derived from reflections on Elder teachings. These concepts, principles and applications to starship citizenship, will be the primary focus of this paper.

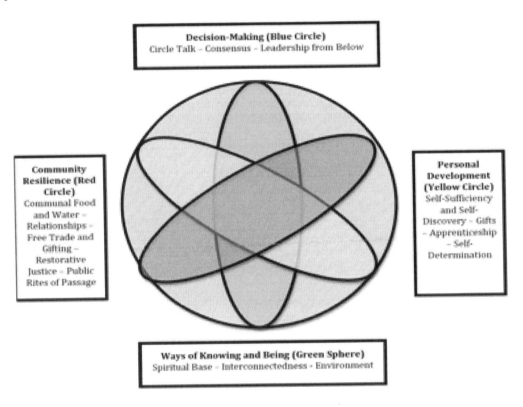

Figure 2. Indigenous Enviro-Cultural Sustainability Model. Credit: D. Marsden (First Nations University of Canada).

The unifying concepts are represented by the totality of the sphere and components. The principles have been artificially separated into four domains of practice, for ease of comprehension and application. In reality, all of these principles are inseparable and work together to create a socially cohesive, environmentally sustainable whole. The rest of the paper will be devoted to discussing the concepts, principles and applications of this model in relation to starship citizenship.

7. Unifying Concepts

7.1 Circle Symbology

The most pervasive symbol you will see in environmentally-embedded Indigenous cultures are circles, because they are unending and encompass everything. As such, they signify Indigenous reality and all the relationships and domains of being within the universe, sometimes called the Circle of Life. As such, circles represent wholism, inclusivity, equality, interdependence, natural laws, and both social and environmental systems and cycles. This inclusivity is sometimes represented by the phrase "all our relations" which means everything and everyone is connected.

The circle also represents the natural process in life of beginnings and endings; rather than a dualistic concept of reality, circular or wholistic concepts of reality theorize that things find their completion when they return to the beginning. An example of this might be a discussion that seems to digress but then returns to the question better informed, or the passing of a life and beginning of another, or a crisis that results in beneficial transformation. The strength of the circle is also a metaphor for the strength of a community and by extension the strength of each individual within that community or circle.

Application to Starship Citizenship: The circle has been embedded in the psyche of all human beings through millennia, is easy to recognize, intuitively understood and easy to use as a visible reminder of starship citizenship according to the principles that follow.

7.2 Wholistic Egalitarianism

By emphasizing an individual's usefulness to society, the Iroquois created a mindset that encouraged their members to contribute even though they received similar benefits no matter how hard they worked.

In Indigenous cultures, where everyone contributes to community survival, there was an understanding that every person and every role was equally important, especially with the high value placed on self-determination. Since contributions were made willingly, people were valued for making those contributions and their status was on par with others who contributed. Contrary to the idea that modern societies require less labour, anthropologists have estimated it only took 12 to 21 hours of labour per person each week to provide the basics for survival. People would then spend the remaining time caring for and guiding their children, strengthening relationships and perfecting the products of their own interests, which they would barter and trade for other specialty goods and services. An egalitarian society is where individuals have equal status and access to goods and services. The sustainability of an egalitarian community is created by the intergenerational diversity of knowledge, skills and experience of that community: a child is valued for their efforts to learn and their future contributions, adults are valued for doing the bulk of the labour, and Elders are valued for sharing their expertise and wisdom with the youth, thereby creating a continuous community of guided, wise practice.

In most Indigenous societies, the concept of inter-personal or social egalitarianism was extended to include the rest of reality. Every season, cycle, rock, tree, plant, animal, insect and bird on the planet contributes something to the balance and harmony of the universe, and when hunted, fished, harvested or grown contributes to the survival, comfort and beauty of the community. Likewise humans were seen as contributing to the natural world in death, and through wise care of the surrounding environment. This symbiotic relationship, this equality of contribution between humans, other species and the natural world can be summarized by the concept of wholistic egalitarianism which places humans on par with each other and the natural world, seen and unseen.

Application to Starship Citizenship: In a starship with limited physical space and freedom, the importance of internal space and freedom becomes amplified. Wholistic egalitarianism would enable a consciousness of personal freedom, while respecting the contributions of other humans, species and systems on the starship.

8. Core Principles: Ways of Knowing and Being

The following core principles form the basis for the remaining key principles. An understanding of a spiritual base to reality leads naturally to a sense of interconnectedness between all things, which include the environments we choose to live in and relationships we develop. These principles are core to sustainable enviro-cultural systems, and provide the spiritual, mental, emotional and physical foundation for all the remaining key principles.

8.1 Spiritual Base

The most fundamental principle to consider, when setting up a society within a limited environment, is the spiritual orientation to that environment. For traditional Indigenous people, the basic substance of the universe is spirit and all matter is made of it and inseparable from it. Matter is merely a transformation of spirit into lower vibration states. Humans, animals, plants, rocks, water, etc, are essentially spirit made manifest, on physical journeys. Everything comes from spirit and returns to spirit, though some things are denser and last longer than others (rocks, mineral, soil cycles). This orientation to reality is informed by direct, ongoing experience and intimate knowledge of the environment and other species, where deepening relationships generate an experience of the unified spiritual essence of all things as sentient, loving, light that is expanding in knowledge with every experience. When considered in its entirety, the spiritual essence of all creation has been called "Gitche Manitou" (Anishnabemowin; meaning literally "big spirit").

This sense of inseparability within creation leads naturally to values of respect for all beings and elements within physical creation as sacred parts within the larger, sacred, whole of reality. On a practical level, considering and caring for the relationships (interpersonal, interspecies, societal, economic, environmental) around us is a form of wholistic self-preservation. Knowing that there is a spiritual reality which we are born from and return to when we die, also lends courage in life, knowing there is a more enduring and joyful reality than the temporary lives we lead. This felt understanding allows people to lead their lives with self-determination and purpose, knowing that no matter the challenges, they will learn and grow in knowledge and wisdom, and ultimately contribute that knowledge to the greater spirit. This direct experience of spirit and interconnectedness was traditionally fostered through processes of questing to test self-sufficiency, for self-discovery (discussed later), and reinforced by daily personal rituals, prayers of gratitude, public ceremony and rites of passage. Within wholistic egalitarianism and exercising of self-determination, it's acknowledged that everyone will have their own experiences of reality and the sacred, and have the right to acknowledge, express and reinforce that personal orientation, as they see fit. The beneficial outcome of this orientation has been the natural development of good relationships and self-discipline in relationship with other people, species and the environment.

Application to Starship Citizenship: Diverse cultures from around the world have different concepts of the substance of being, the presence or nature of souls or spirits, and experience of God, but report similar personal experiences (light, omniscience, joy, belonging, and spiritual beings). Most have teachings about reconnecting with God or heaven, and that we are all one within creation. These commonalities in experience can be acknowledged, fostered and reinforced throughout community practice, to create a citizenry that respects the sacredness and interconnectedness of reality on a deep, personal, and experiential level, regardless of religious orientation.

8.2 Interconnectedness

In Indigenous teachings, the concept of interconnectedness arises naturally from the direct experience of reality as a unified, spiritual whole. If everything is actually connected, despite appearances, then there are unseen forces or relationships between everything we perceive. To teach this concept of separate yet connected reality and interconnecting forces, aspects and domains, many Indigenous cultures have used the metaphor of the spider web, which is a matrix of interconnections within a circle. Within a web of interconnections, our actions - responsible or irresponsible - have reverberations throughout the web or circle of life. You can demonstrate this theory by pulling on a strand of a spider web. In the same way, one person's actions may impact the lives of others in unforeseen ways. One understanding is that the quality and amount of energy you put into the universe will ultimately return and impact you personally. Rather than an equal and opposite force, the return is multiplied and related, like a small wave that becomes a tidal wave or a whole that is greater than the sum of its parts. So if you are aggressive, that aggression will be returned to you in greater force, though it may be in a different form. On the other end of the spectrum, if you give a large portion of your effort to community wellbeing, you will receive much more in return.

Alongside this concept of interconnectedness, Indigenous Elders will teach the concept of balance and harmony. Balance is that awareness of the need to continuously assess, correct and reposition energies within our lives, to create dynamic yet peaceful relationships between diverse aspects of reality. An imbalance is when interconnected aspects of reality are thrown out of healthy positioning perhaps by too much or too little force or energy; for example: if a person concentrates on working and does not exercise, they could be described as living an unbalanced life and destined for ill health. Balance requires an understanding of moderation in all things and between things. A common teaching is that we must learn to create balance between the spiritual, mental, physical and emotional domains within our personal lives, and with the world around us.

Harmony is similar to the concept of balance, and includes balance but on a grander scale, where awareness and self-correction of relationships between diverse aspects of life becomes a natural ebb and flow, according to the situation. For example, a person demonstrates harmony when their cycles become naturally synchronized with those of others and the natural world: sleeping, eating, drinking, resting, working and other cycles. These harmonized cycles provide optimal conditions for health (adequate sleep, food, water, effort, etc). Community harmony is demonstrated when everyone has enough to eat, drink, entertain, challenge and fulfill themselves, in respectful relationships with each other, other species and the environment.

The sense of interconnectedness arising from direct experience, results in the connection of a sense of responsibility with self-benefits. The more you care for others and the environment, the more you will benefit personally. Conversely, by caring for yourself, you are contributing to the wellbeing of the rest of society. It's a win-win philosophy.

Application to Starship Citizenship: Even if the principle of interconnectedness is not grasped initially or through direct experience, it can be taught by exploring the science of matter. Understanding this principle is integral to developing awareness and self-correcting behaviour towards balance and harmony with other people, species and ship systems.

8.3 Environmental Awareness

Closely aligned with the principle of interconnectedness and often used interchangeably, is the concept of inter-dependence. This is best understood by examining the relationships between the food and water we ingest, the air we breathe, the warmth around us and the boundaries of our being. In environmentally embedded societies, the interdependent nature of reality was self-evident. We were what we ate and drank, what we absorbed (sun and heat) and sooner or later we would return those gifts to the world around us through our wastes, breath, decomposition at death, and other natural processes. There was an understanding, through direct relationships with the food system, of the continuous exchange of matter between the self, other species and the environment to the point that – with trained awareness – you cannot determine the point where you stop and the environment begins.

Application to Starship Citizenship: A starship is an isolated, closed system, with finite resources, so the principle of environmental awareness would become the most critical element for enviro-cultural sustainability. By necessity, starship citizens would need to be taught to be extra-sensitive to the conditions of the ship and its systems, and to all the species interacting within those systems. With hypersensitivity, small changes in the environment could be recognized and signal need for attention, before or alongside ship sensors.

9. Key Principles and Practices:

The key principles and practices that follow have arisen naturally from direct experience and the core principles of Indigenous societies, and through generations, have been honed to interconnect and mutually reinforce, the systems within environmentally embedded communities. Collectively, the result of these interactions is a dynamic, self-correcting, self-determining system of wholistic egalitarianism, for intergenerational social cohesion and environmental sustainability.

9.1 Personal Development

Self-identity emerges and grows as we come to grasp our various social statuses and live them out.

Individuals who were born into Indigenous communities (as in any community) spent their formative years exploring themselves, other beings and the natural world, while watching, absorbing and mimicking the lessons of wise (and not-so-wise) practice that surrounded them. In Indigenous communities, where natural law prevailed, principles and practices for wise practice included the guided exploration, identification and acknowledgement of individual learning and value, in relationship to other beings and the natural world, resulting in individuals who were competent, socialized, empowered and ready to take their place as contributors to the community. The following principles laid the foundation for the personal development of empowered and enviro-culturally competent individuals within Indigenous communities.

9.1.1 Self-Sufficiency and Self-Discovery

The Iroquois attempted to eliminate any feelings of dependency during childhood and foster a desire for responsibility. At the same time, the child would have to participate in a communal culture, so children were taught to think as individuals but work for the community.

Rather than the development of silos of knowledge and practice, Indigenous people were expected to become competent in all basic aspects of survival (food, water, shelter, clothing), so they could contribute and assist in all domains of practice, whenever that aid was needed. Individual specialization was developed when personal time allowed and according to abilities and interest. A person who could not survive alone was considered less able to contribute to the community and potentially, created unequal access to community resources; no one wanted to be a burden. This created a strong motivation for children to prove themselves as able as possible in the provision and care of food, water, clothing and shelter, under diverse conditions. Adults were very aware of these motivations as they guided the learning and development of the children, who would converse with other adults in setting up opportunities for the testing of this knowledge.

At the same time as children were learning to become competent in the tasks for basic community survival, they were also learning to interact inter-personally, socially and spiritually in respectful relationships. Over millennia, Indigenous societies came to value competent, fair, critical, caring, collective and intergenerational relationship building and problem-solving, which created affective, daily ritual, intellectual and ceremonial role models for children. Children not only aspired to be competent contributors, they also wanted to be respected for their wise and caring interactions. The community combination of practical and interpersonal role models, created the foundation for personal development as socially and environmentally conscious and competent individuals.

All of this role-model learning took place in the context of a functioning community, within a limited environment. To test a child's independence and self-sufficiency, many Indigenous communities developed a communal "questing" process, whereby children who were considered ready, would be offered protected environments to test their knowledge, wisdom and self-sufficiency, without help. Sometimes this would be done within specific domains of practice, like a young hunter's first kill, or preparation of a first meal, or other first sharing of honed skills. Other times this would be done through separation of a child from the community, to provide for their own survival for a certain period of time, usually with adults stationed nearby to assist if the child was unable to complete the challenge. Sometimes the testing would include a process of initiation, to test the ability, strength, identity and resolve of the child under duress (fasting, isolation, verbal or physical challenges, or reduced comforts, etc), by trusted adults. Under such duress, the process enabled a strong examination and identification of youth with internal strengths, and value of interdependence with community members, other species and the environment. As a child demonstrated full competence in a variety of domains they would gain the right to engage as contributing community members in decision-making in those domains. As a person grew in competence, their accomplishments would be acknowledged and celebrated publicly, in public rites of passage (discussed later).

Application to Starship Citizenship: An intergenerational starship would depend upon the competency and contributions of its members. All members and especially children should be trained and tested in the basics of survival and wise inter-personal relationships, which provides the foundation for community resilience. On a starship this would include a basic competence in the provision of food, clothing, shelter, water, waste, energy, light, temperature and air systems and knowledge of one's strengths and potential contributions within the collective. This competence could be tested within self-sufficient dwelling places without assistance (except in emergency), to enable self-examination of strengths and abilities, and to learn to identify with, and value the wisdom of collaborative effort and respectful inter-personal relationships (by their absence) within limited environments.

9.1.2 Gifts

Many of these hidden potentialities might never be developed if we did not somehow discover and nurture them, for as the great spiritual teachers have taught, all the gifts a person potentially possesses are like the fruits hidden within the tree.

The foundation of personal fulfillment in Indigenous communities was the early identification, nurturing and acknowledgement of an individual's special abilities or interests, also known as "gifts". In Elder's teachings, recognition of these gifts was usually done in the first three years of a child's life, though sometimes people discovered gifts later in life, or through major life events (e.g. serious illness or accident). The early identification was done by those adults closest to the child, often by grandparents, uncles or aunties who were the closest caretakers of the child; other adults would be informed about the gifts, so the gifts could be nurtured by the whole community.

Gifts have the potential to create a personal sense of life long fulfillment, especially if those gifts are held in high community regard. The personal fulfillment of individuals lends to the social cohesion of a society by creating positive energy, excitement, motivation, commitment and satisfaction, during exploration of personal gifts. While others can support or encourage exploration of gifts, the self-determination - whether to develop gifts or not - remains with each individual; coercion was considered disrespectful and potentially harmful. Gifts were known to run in certain families, though not exclusively.

Application to Starship Citizenship: The early identification, recognition and nurturing of gifts on a starship would provide the same lifelong sense of fulfillment and self esteem, social cohesion and early identification of aptitudes and ability for both essential and specialized starship career paths.

9.1.3 Apprenticeship

Traditionally, Native American teaching and learning occurred within very high-contexted social situations. The lesson and the learning of the lesson was intimately interwoven within the situation, the environment of the learner.

The natural exploration of individual gifts in childhood, leads logically to the guidance and training of knowledge and skills in those gifted areas as a child moves into youth and adulthood. As youth explore, they become more adept and gravitate to adults with specialized knowledge and skills in the areas of interest and where relationships are harmonious and respectful. Over time these specialized adults mentor the children by providing them with opportunities to do tasks and learn more knowledge with greater depth, responsibility and comprehension. Every career path requires knowledge and skills in other domains (e.g. math, physics, life sciences, psychology, etc); in Indigenous communities, as these other skills or knowledge sets were needed, youth would be self-motivated or sent to learn them from other adults or Elders and then return to their chosen mentor. Coincident with mentored learning is privileged and appropriate access to resources and areas of increasing sensitivity, relevant to their learning. Over time youth would become competent contributors in their chosen areas, gain privileged access to rare resources and sensitive areas, could remain generalists in certain areas, or delve deeper, as their interests dictated. This process of mentored apprenticeship would encourage and guide youth and adults into areas of personal fulfillment, while providing services for community continuity. Over generations, the wisdom of specialized knowledge holders would be continuously handed down to subsequent generations, through hands-on training and oral instruction. Specializations in expressive arts, innovative thinking, obscure knowledge and spiritual practices were especially revered for their contributions to social cohesion and exploration of relationships with each other and the universe. Individuals with special affiliation to other species, processes or environmental resources would be given caretaking privileges and would then become Elders in their own right in those areas.

Application to Starship Citizenship: Apprenticeships that build on exploration and encouragement of individual gifts and self-selected career paths is directly applicable to intergenerational starship societies where a continuous succession of individuals with specialized aptitudes, knowledge and skills are required for the maintenance of starship systems and fulfillment of starship community members. As needs arise for more personnel in certain fields of specialization, that need can be shared with the community. Individuals can then choose to focus their interests in those areas of need, which adds to both personal fulfillment and social cohesion through sharing and recognition of those commitments and contributions.

9.1.4 Self Determination

Self-determination embodies the right for all peoples to determine their own economic, social and cultural development. Self-determination has thus been defined by the International Court of Justice…as the need to pay regard to the freely expressed will of peoples.

Under the constraints of natural law, where individuals depend upon themselves, extended family and the natural environment for survival, the self-determination of individuals (also known as autonomy or freedom of choice) is fundamental to both individual and group survival. When one person succumbs to illness, infirmity or death, another must take their place, competently. The ability of individuals to be self-determining is dependent upon their self-knowledge, ability to be self-sufficient, and knowledge of their surrounding universe. As discussed previously, the motivation to contribute to the continuity and cohesion of a community is dependent upon the valuing of interdependent contributions, recognition of gifts, and personal choice in deciding where to focus efforts for shared survival and fulfillment.

If this choice regarding if, when, where, why and how to contribute is removed, so are all the benefits of self-determination: mutual valuing of everyone's contribution, fulfillment in chosen exploration of gifts, empowered individuals, diversity in innovation and leadership, resilience under duress, trust of others, and personal self-worth. A lack of self-determining individuals in society, is at the core of social demoralization and environmental destruction; those who are hopeless in the face of inequities can become self-serving, self-destructive and socially sabotaging.

On the other hand, a society where everyone is self-sufficient and self-determining, according to natural law and their own conscience, creates the highest striving, highest performing, and most sustainable of human societies. Most North American citizens are taught to consider such self-determination to be scary and threatening to whichever societal position and comforts they've been able to obtain; if individuals do what they want – it's assumed – there will be lawlessness, murder, slavery and destruction. The opposite has been shown to be true. Indigenous societies have demonstrated sustainable, relatively harmonious, self-determining societies that have lasted for tens of thousands and possibly even millions of years. Murder and lawlessness, alienates the perpetrator from society by their own actions, and is self-limiting in a community of self-determining individuals where status and access to resources is proportional to willingness to contribute in respectful ways. Conversely, large, specialized, sedentary, hierarchical agrarian societies have lasted a maximum of hundreds of years before the free will of individuals is oppressed or sabotaged, resources are exhausted, interpersonal relationships break down, environments are destroyed, inequities are challenged, lawlessness ensues, and is replaced by new hierarchical systems.

The tenet of self-determination in Indigenous societies is that individuals may do whatever they want, except that which is harmful or intends harm to others, to the environment upon which everyone depends, or to the wellbeing of future generations. People may guide or provide advice about your actions, if requested, or if there is family or community concern, but individuals are ultimately responsible for their own choices and behaviour. The judgment of, and restraint of harmful individuals is dependent upon consensus of the community and an ethic of restorative justice, if possible (discussed later). The companion to self-determination is the awareness of natural consequences. The more knowledgeable a person is about the consequences of their actions, the more responsible their choices will be and/or the more accountable they are held for their actions; for example: if you are capable and don't share the expertise and products of your labour, then others will be less likely to share with you, though you may be given the basics for survival out of pity. When individuals become contributing members of the community, they gain the right and obligation to be self-determining in community decision-making (discussed later), as well as personally. This means that they must speak for themselves, and represent the truth as they know it; if they don't exercise their right and obligation to speak or be represented by proxy, then they abdicate their right to the directions, benefits or obligations of the decisions being made.

The principle of self-determination is embedded in the language and culture of Indigenous communities and so children are raised to expect the courtesies and respect that go along with the principle; self-determination is modeled and encouraged, in action and decision-making, by healthy parents, siblings and other adults. Children also learn by the natural and logical consequences of their actions how to be self-determining in respectful ways; if they are being disrespectful or harmful in any way, adults will remind them and limit their privileges to reduce harm and disrespect. As children gain knowledge and awareness they acquire the ability to be self-determining in ways that are beneficial personally, and then communally. Through communal action, self-determination becomes linked with the demonstration of competence and wise action, for the wellbeing of humans and other species, within a consciousness of the limited environment, and becomes an embodiment of the principle of sacred interconnectedness.

Application to Starship Citizenship: From an authoritarian perspective the principle of self-determination might seem inappropriate for an environment where each decision could mean life or death. Under examination, self-determining societies are much more resilient in the face of crises, because the whole society can be mobilized quickly, and are already experienced with organizing to address the issues effectively and synchronously, rather than a depending on the limited knowledge of a few individuals at the top of a hierarchy and communications through a chain of command. As with the principle of self-sufficiency and self-discovery, self-determination develops the ability, right and obligation of every citizen to problem-solve and make decisions in collaboration, which would strengthen the intergenerational resilience of a starship citizenry.

9.2 Key Principles: Community Resilience

The following principles build upon the core principles and upon personal development, by fully integrating and bonding those individuals through the community activities of food and water preparation, interpersonal relationships, free trade and gifting, restorative justice and public rites of passage. This integration and bonding creates community resilience in the face of internal and external challenges. Each of these principles and practices also reinforces the core principles (spirituality, interconnectedness, environment), and supports personal development and decision-making, towards the enviro-cultural sustainability of the community.

9.2.1 Communal Food and Water

Community gardens can provide a source of fresh fruits and vegetables for users, increase physical activity, and provide opportunities for social interaction and cohesion.

If there were one activity that could be chosen to represent Wholistic Egalitarianism in Indigenous societies, it would be the collective care, harvesting, processing and preparation of food and water. Food and water connect us physically, emotionally, mentally and spiritually to our environments, to each other, and to other species. We literally are what we eat. Our relationships with our food and water mirror our relationships with each other, our children, and other species. Indigenous Elders emphasize the importance of being respectful in our relationships with food species and for the contributions they make to our existence and wellbeing. This includes an attitude of gratitude, not taking more than our bodies need, not wasting, not contaminating the habitats of our food, protecting food habitats, returning food wastes to their origins, having a good attitude when preparing food and eating, and respecting those who prepare the food. These considerations are considered integral to maintaining the healthy life cycles of our food species and by extension, ourselves.

In past Indigenous communities, communal food and water activities meant that everyone shared the labour of growing, hunting, fishing, and gathering of food, medicines and water, and their preparation for storage or meals. On a personal level, these activities reminded individuals, through direct experience, about their dependence upon other species and the environment for their survival, and upon the contributions of others for their wellbeing. Everyone was expected to contribute, at an appropriate level, if they expected to eat. Literally eating the fruits of your labour increases warmth and respect for the food and water you are ingesting, gratitude towards the people who helped bring it to the table, and creates a sense of community through communal action. Communal food and water efforts work together to cement the relationships between personal, communal and environmental wellbeing.

Indigenous Elders talk about the importance of communal meals for strengthening social bonds. The collection and preparation of food enables the passing of knowledge through informal sharing of stories and teachings. Historically, eating together builds trust, since it lessens the possibility of interpersonal attack or poisoning, and facilitates relaxed communication. People who refuse to serve you, or eat with you indicate a need to address unhealthy relationships. Communal meals or feasts are also a way of bringing people together to witness or make decisions, or to celebrate accomplishments, where the food and words are digested together.

Application to Starship Citizenship: If only one Indigenous principle is adapted for starship citizenship, communal food and water preparation should be that principle. This principle alone may provide the sustainability required for intergenerational social cohesion and environmental survival. In practice this principle would mean that every starship citizen would contribute their labour to the protection, care, harvesting, and preparation of food and water and recycling of food and water wastes, according to their motivation and ability to complete the tasks throughout the week. The institution of this principle would foster mutual respect and bonding among all citizens, and between all generations.

9.2.2 Respectful Relationships

While the principle of respectful or good relationships is relevant to all relationships within an interconnected reality, I will discuss it here as the foundation of interpersonal cohesion within a community. Relationship, in this sense, includes parent-child relationships, platonic friendships, work relationships, extended family relationships, and intimate relationships. If you remember that these principles arise from a spiritual, interconnected reality, then all beings within that reality are also spiritually based and sacred. As individuals grow, discover themselves, and learn to be self-sufficient, contributing and self-determining in Indigenous communities, they also learn to respect the self-discovery, self-sufficiency, contributions and self-determination of others in that community.

In effect, the bodies and choices of others are considered sacred and not to be touched or controlled without the individual's permission. Everyone is expected to be self-determining in the application of their self-knowledge for the maintenance of healthy boundaries. In some Elder teachings, the best relationships retain this sense of interpersonal sacredness and boundaries, with the added principle of mutual service; good interpersonal relationships are developed over time through the reciprocal gifting of no-strings-attached goods and services (discussed later). On a personal level this may include physical, emotional, mental or spiritual care, affection, problem solving and support. The key, according to some teachings about relationships, is to make offers of service with transparency, with no expectation of return, out of the honest desire to contribute to another's wellbeing; then individuals may accept or refuse with good will as they act upon their own self-determination. Overtime, this mutual service and respect of boundaries creates long-term trusting relationships based on honesty, mutual care and shared experience.

Everyone was expected to be self-determining and to initiate, maintain or terminate close relationships according to their conscience and in consideration of others. This was especially true in the case of intimate relationships where both men and women had the right to enter into relationships of their choosing, with transparency and community acceptance. This usually meant long-term monogamous heterosexual relationships, but occasionally meant short-term, polygamous, polyandrous, or homosexual relationships. Sex was considered a healthy aspect of adult interpersonal relations and personal growth. Competent adults were expected to be honest, responsible and self-disciplined, and to consider the wellbeing and impact of their relationships upon others. In any case, the children of any union were considered gifts to be treasured and nurtured for their wellbeing and the future of the community.

Application to Starship Citizenship: Attempts to reproduce egalitarian communities in Western societies, during the '60s, were not successful, predominately because of the issues around self-determination and inter-personal relationships. "Free love" as a concept was admirable but was not pragmatic in a society where men and women had unequal access to power, wealth, education and ability to contribute equally to the wellbeing of society.

Unequal relationships affect self-determination, self-worth and the ability to provide mutual service. If the other principles in this paper are considered, then respectful relationships arise naturally, and act to reinforce, and are reinforced by, self-determination and the community.

9.2.3 Free Trade and Gifting

Giving away is the traditional norm; accumulating wealth is perceived not
just as antisocial, but as the mark of a dangerous person…

Indigenous communities around the world had free trade and gifting processes. In North America, trade networks intersected the continent, and connected through rivers, lakes, coastlines and mountain passes. While trade enabled the redistribution of goods, knowledge, and services within and between communities, it also enabled the development of trusting and mutually beneficial relationships for further trade, intermarriage and protective alliances. Fair trade meant the mutual acceptance of a bargaining agreement, completed ideally in front of other witnesses. Once trusting trade relationships were developed, gifting and free trade often became synonymous, where individuals would share their goods and services freely, knowing they could depend upon others to assist them if they had a need they could address. In some communities, if an individual indicated they liked something, offering it to them immediately was considered a respectful sign that the relationship was worth more than the object.

The trading of goods and services with interest was considered unethical and unhealthy as it created a destabilization of balanced relationships. Hoarding was similarly considered a sign of an individual's imbalance by having more than needed. Conversely, the giving of gifts or service in appreciation or affection did not create a debt, and expectation of a return was considered unethical or an insult and devalued the gift.

Gifting or gift giving was also done at public events, to acknowledge assistance at important events, and to acknowledge the public contributions of those being gifted. Gifts of goods and services were also given as a form of reparations to people who had been injured. Similar to the ethics around food, trading, giving and receiving of gifts helped to strengthen social cohesion, trust and resilience. Conversely, if a person refused to trade or accept gifts, it indicated an imbalance or distrust in the relationship, and an area in need of attention. In the end, resources - in the form of goods and services - were continuously being circulated within and between communities, as need was identified and community members stepped in to fill those needs.

The goods and services of trade were the product of individual or communal efforts. Individual goods or services were produced after contributions to the community had been taken care of, according to individual interests. As the quality of a person's goods grew, they would be sought after and could be traded for more goods and services. Excess community goods produced by communal activities (hunting, fishing, farming, gathering) could also be traded by consensus. Lands and waters were considered the basis of survival, and as sacred gifts of creation, and therefore could not be traded, only respected for the contributions they made to survival.

Application to Starship Citizenship: While starship resources would be limited, the ability to produce goods through recycling of resources, or trading of services is still a possibility. If additional resources were obtained from asteroids or planets (respectful trade with Indigenous species?) then the possibilities for creation of new goods and services would increase. To create long-term stability and redistribution of resources among citizens, the principles of self-determined direct trade agreements, with no interest, and gifting should be adopted.

9.2.4 Restorative Justice

…individuals need to be encouraged to exercise their own responsibility for con-
flict rather than to entrust the conflict to the care of professional services.

In Indigenous communities where everyone knew each other over a lifetime of familiarity, the culpability and impact of crimes was soon apparent to community members. Considerate, respectful relationships were the norm, so committing harm to people or to the wellbeing of the community indicated the person was unhealthy or unbalanced. A saying that describes such imbalances is "they forget who they are" which indicates their identity has been affected in some way. Respect for self-determination meant that people would be given some space to confront the people who'd harmed them, to work out their difficulties, or offered support to resolve the issues. If children were involved, they might be guided to solve their own issues, with back up. When that didn't work, and especially if crimes or interpersonal issues were harming or affecting the health and safety of others or future generations, then family and community members were obligated to intervene, to keep the peace. In some communities, people would provide peacekeeping services by touring through the community and offering information or assistance to resolve issues, especially if the community was threatened in some way. Individuals might be restrained or protected until a community gathering of affected individuals could be called to resolve the issue, to restore harmony and provide reparations. At these gatherings everyone would have a chance to speak about the crimes, so those committing the offenses would hear about the impacts of their actions, and the wounded could feel heard and empowered. Those committing the crimes, and their allies, would also have an opportunity to speak in defense of, or in remorse for their actions. In the end, everyone would have a more complete understanding of the motivations and impacts, so that resolutions and reparations could be suggested and agreed upon by all. Alternatively, people might be offered the opportunity to "remember who they are" again, and reorient to community by undergoing the same quests for self-discovery and self-sufficiency they had undergone as youth. If a person continued to threaten or attempt harm, despite community intervention, then - as a chronically unbalanced or incompetent person - they might be exiled. On occasion, family members or friends might offer to be responsible for them and to guard the community against their actions. Serious crimes like rape or murder were met with execution or exile to certain death, because of the irreparable imbalances the violations created among the mental, emotional, physical and spiritual wellbeing of the community.

Application to Starship Citizenship: Interpersonal conflicts or damages are inevitable, whether intended or not, and potentially aggravated by the confined spaces and insecurities of starship life. While incarceration may be an option for the short-term, with intergenerational, interrelated and interdependent community members, the limitations and potential damages of incarceration to the whole community would become quickly apparent. Leaving the lives of potentially redeemable individuals to the mercy of a few individuals, and under rules that may not be just under all circumstances would be setting up an imbalance in power dynamics, create subterfuge, and threaten the social cohesion of an otherwise egalitarian community. Restorative justice empowers people to address conflict in ways considered compassionate, acceptable and fair to the whole community and would provide a sustainable process for intergenerational travel.

9.2.5 Public Rites of Passage

Rites of passages often help prepare people for that sense of identi-
ty that needs to run alongside the social status accorded to them.

Personal identification with community wellbeing is a theme that crosses all the Indigenous principles for enviro-cultural sustainability and is an indicator of social cohesion. Public rites of passage strengthen personal and community identities and provide the backbone for intergenerational cohesion. Rites of passage strengthens bonds by bringing community members together to assist individuals to make the transition, or be transformed, from one position or status in the community to another. This process benefits the community as much as the individual, where those who assist or witness the transition adjust and make space - psychologically and logistically – for the new member, among the established roles of the community. The transition process usually includes periods of seclusion and purification, initiations, teachings for the new roles, new names, titles or tools, and finally public revealing and acknowledgement of the new status or role in the community. These public gatherings inevitably include celebratory feasts and giving of gifts. The most commonly celebrated transitions include the transition from the spiritual realm at birth, first contributions to the community, discovery of life's purpose, womanhood and manhood, marriage, adoptions, rebirth from illness or trauma, and release back to the spiritual realm at death.

Public rites of passage also provide secondary social benefits, through communal food preparation, gifting and redistribution of resources, sharing of information, opportunities for self-determination, and reinforcement of community visions and goals. Secondary benefits for the individual undergoing the rite include wholistic healing, increased knowledge, and an increase in self-confidence. In Indigenous communities, the process of transition from one status to another is profound and impacts both the individual and community in a matrix of emotional, mental, physical and spiritual experiences.

Application to Starship Citizenship: Public rites of passage are the ties that bind people together and reinforce the shared goals and principles for living. Contemporary rites have been narrowed down to celebrations of birth, weddings, and graduation, with less community-wide impacts and so, less benefits for social cohesion than Indigenous practices. To ensure high levels of social cohesion among starship citizens, and between the generations, it seems logical to re-expand rites of passage, to include the spiritual, educational, and ceremonial domains, with community involvement.

9.3 Key Principles: Community Decision-Making

In a community that practices wholistic egalitarianism, most day-to-day decisions are made by self-determination or by informal commitments as everyone assesses need and contributes to the functioning of the community; people step up or are invited to combine labour as the situation requires. The need for community decision-making is limited to issues or developments that have community-wide impacts, including restorative justice, environmental stewardship, defense and inter-community relations. The principles that follow summarize processes of inclusive decision-making and have been drawn from stories of Indigenous history, natural law and good relationship. These principles address the process of determining goals, processes and outcomes by providing equitable processes for both individual and community self-determination.

9.3.1 Circle Talk

...the circular and sequential flow of a TC [Talking Circle] respects each perspective as part of the whole, which facilitates long-term integrative understanding and community building.

Circle talk, or talking circles, is a formalized meeting process that enables personal self-determination and wholistic, egalitarian discussions and decision-making. Historically, circles have been used for restorative justice, for healing, for education, for community governance and more recently, for research. Sometimes circles are nested, so that special interest groups can meet before they add their voice to the larger collective; this has included circles for societies (e.g. hunting, ceremonial, healing), clans (role and/or genetically related groups), children, youth, men, women, two-spirited (people with both male and female characteristics) and Elders.

Before a talking circle starts, the area is made comfortable, with blankets or cushions, food, drinks, and a cleansing of the area. For longer circles, community members volunteer to prepare food and drink and care for children. Participants are invited to symbolically wash themselves before beginning the circle, to leave unrelated concerns and interpersonal differences outside the circle. Talking circles are open to anyone, but usually people self-select, depending on the focus. Historically, talking circles began and finished with prayers or ceremony to remind individuals of the sacredness and interconnectedness of all things. The duration of talking circles isn't limited and can last for hours, days or weeks until it is finished. People are allowed to come and go quietly as their physical, parental or work needs required, and children can attend if they don't distract from the discussion, so they can begin learning early.

In talking circles, everyone literally sits in a circle so that there aren't any barriers between individuals, including other individuals. This ensures that everyone can hear, see and display the impact of their words upon each other, which creates a form of visual transparency and accountability, and builds trust and compassion. Usually a facilitator is chosen, to open (begin) the circle, introduce the topic and timelines, desired outcomes, questions and guidelines; summarize the prior points and conclusions at the beginning of each round, and then close (end) the circle once it is finished. In talking circles, everyone has an opportunity to speak, or pass, in the sequence of the circle, without interruption from anyone, including the facilitator. People cannot speak for others unless they've been given permission and specific details about what is to be shared; people must express themselves in the first person from what they know. In wholistic societies, expression and knowledge includes processes of the mind, emotions, body and spirit, which includes: words, stories, prayers, songs, visions, inspirations, and spiritual guidance; as well as evidence from the physical body. A "round" is when everyone has had one chance to speak. Over consecutive rounds, the discussion deepens until all sides of the issue have been examined, goals and objectives are discussed and a plan of action emerges through synchronicity, or by consensus.

The group-specific, sequential and wholistic aspects of circle talk make it a more efficient and comprehensive approach than either the "free-for-all", need-to-know, or Robert's Rules of Order communication processes, which do not usually give everyone an opportunity to speak and (officially) exclude the emotional, physical and spiritual aspects of being.

Application to Starship Citizenship: Circle talk is an effective egalitarian process that fosters social cohesion through inclusivity, respectful process, compassion, synchronicity and wholistic expression. Circle talk would be an effective tool for inviting strong citizen engagement on a starship, and ensure the expertise of the whole community is available for decision-making.

9.3.2 Consensus

The key indicator of whether or not a consensus has been reached is that everyone agrees they can live with the final proposal; that is, after every effort has been made to meet any outstanding interests.

According to Indigenous stories, people used to sit in council and talk about an issue, until everyone agreed about how to address that issue, whether it took hours or weeks; if there were time constraints, individuals could work towards the best goal within that time period. People would use circle talk to ensure everyone had an opportunity to speak about the decision needed. Over multiple rounds the core issues, options for their resolution, needed resources, and best people to implement the resolutions would be discussed and identified. Consensus building is most effective with unhurried decision-making, to ensure that all the wisdom and experience of the community is applied. For consensual decision making to work, everyone potentially affected must be invited to participate. Children, youth and others not fully developed or competent - who may provide unique perspectives – may have their own councils with adult facilitators, and send a representative to speak, but only as the council directed. Historically, people who thought in radically different ways – that might be labeled bipolar or schizophrenic today – were often revered for their uniqueness and proximity to the divine; and their contributions would be taken into consideration. If people disagreed with how the consensus was building, they could – as self-determining people – state their disagreement and remove themselves from the decision, the cost or share of resources, and potential consequences or benefits of the decisions; people may share with them later or they may join in the effort or contribute resources later.

By using circle talk, consensus is built organically, through the implied agreement that follows the end of a circle of contributions on a particular topic: all issues, options and limitations have been discussed, from all perspectives, and the community is in agreement about the decisions that have arisen. Respect for self-determination means that no penalties or social sanctions would be place on people who disagree; this increases the collective motivation to address everyone's ideas or reservations, which only makes decisions stronger and more comprehensive in scope.

Application to Starship Citizenship: The direct democratic process, inclusion of community expertise and cumulative practice of consensus building would ensure the solidarity and quick mobilization of starship citizens, and highest standards of decision-making for starship sustainability.

9.3.3 Leadership from Below

To be a good leader, you have to be a good follower.

In war or competition, the spoils (benefits) and top positions tend to go to the best, strongest, loudest or most dominating competitors; those that attain the top positions develop a sense of entitlement to whatever rewards they are experiencing. This is considered by some to be a form of natural law or survival of the fittest. This creates a social hierarchy, where individuals who want leadership roles must pressure themselves to perform better, stronger, faster, smarter and longer so that they can usurp the role, influence and perks of their competitors or superiors. This is the dominant leadership practice within Canadian society and is known by some as leadership from above, where the will of those in higher positions make decisions about funding, resources and priorities. People in the lower positions are expected to follow, with or without consultation. We see this in local boards, city halls, regional, provincial and national organizations. Hypothetically, the decisions of the higher organizations include the decisions of the smaller organizations, that represent the local people, but this isn't actually what happens, or is done in a limited way through consultations with a few individuals. Recommendations from below may or may not be included, depending on how they fit within established hierarchies of funding and resource distribution, and at the whim of individuals.

In Indigenous (e.g. Anishinaabek) history, leaders (e.g. Pontiacs) would be invited to lead as they were needed, and usually by community consensus that they had the most knowledge, experience and ability to lead. Leaders were often Elders. Leaders were identified to complete specific tasks; for example, they might be a leader for moving the community, for hunting, for facilitating councils, for harvesting, for war, et cetera. This didn't mean that they acted alone, but that they would confer or listen to others and then direct the actions or implement the decisions that had been agreed to by consensus. If that person did not agree with the leadership tasks, they could decline the invitation, which would increase the necessity for consensual decision-making that addressed the concerns of potential leaders. In effect, leaders were chosen for their qualities, but were limited to the specific roles and tasks delegated to them (aka followers); they could not make arbitrary decisions or speak for anyone, except as specifically instructed by the community; this is known by some as leadership from below.

As well as limited, situational leadership by consensus, there were also leadership structures based on the apprenticeship system, where the offer to lead specific tasks would be extended to individuals considered most appropriate, by consensus of Elders in that field. In eagerness to improve and prove themselves, adults, children and youth would often accept the leadership role. This process of developing leadership skills and experience ensured that everyone had equitable opportunities to pursue the roles they desired. To reinforce a sense of self-worth among people of diverse knowledge and skill sets, individuals would be acknowledged in public for their accomplishments and talents, and reminded throughout the community that everyone had strengths and weaknesses, and played a role in the cohesive functioning of society. For example, some people may have physical strength while others might be able to care for people emotionally, inspire caution or be innovative. You could describe this as recognition of lateral or peer leadership. One of the concepts used to describe this, is called "Elders in training", where individuals aspire to become respected Elders and chosen leaders by making their best efforts, in balanced and harmonious ways. The weaving of vertical and lateral leadership structures, ensures a succession of highly trained and experienced leaders in diverse fields of practice. This is essentially a voluntary "command" structure that enables efficient mobilization, consensual solidarity and intergenerational resilience for the whole community.

Application to Starship Citizenship: Leadership from below is an effective structure for sustainable governance, which can address issues dynamically without the destabilizing dissention and lateral violence seen in hierarchical leadership structures. With or without adoption of the other principles, this process can strengthen the community solidarity of a starship by ensuring fulfilling and equitable processes for direct democracy.

10. Discussion

The presented concepts and principles have arisen through generations of Indigenous history, to be synergistic; each principle serves to reinforce the others, by weaving together the mental, emotional, spiritual and physical elements within community roles and practices. While one principle could be adopted within a starship community, I hypothesize that the sustainability of the community would increase proportional to the number of principles adopted. We can see this effect within the "new age" movement where individuals are questing for more wholistic ways of being and interacting; because all the principles have not been adopted, and because they are being applied without community support, the results appear fragmented, disjointed and "flaky" without the effect of sustainability.

The actual adoption of, or resistance to, the principles by the first starship citizens, would be accelerated or alleviated (respectfully) by the built-in processes to address dissention and respect diversity; the principles are mutually reinforcing. In addition, these principles have been presented with Indigenous (English) terminology and practices, the principles could also be adapted to diverse citizen backgrounds, by integrating the equivalent terminology and practices. For example, where some Indigenous people might symbolically cleanse themselves with an aromatic smoke (sage or sweet grass), others may substitute incense, water or washing motions. Through practice, the application of concepts and principles are tested and modified naturally and become second nature or unconscious. The same is true of the concepts and principles presented in this paper. An example of this might be learning to play video games; at first movements are disjointed and death is certain but after time you get the hang of the new rules and your mind, body and emotions adjust, so that your longevity in the game is assured. After a generation of practice, by the first starship citizens, the children being raised would have a more intuitive and fully integrated sense of wholistic egalitarianism and the environmental sustainability and social cohesion would be assured.

11. Conclusions

The unifying concepts and key principles presented in this paper are logically compatible and hypothetically adaptable to an intergenerational starship context, and provide a template for ensuring the social cohesion and environmental sustainability of a starship community for generations.

The greatest limitation to this paper is that while the principles have been tested by thousands of years of Indigenous experience, the application of these principles to diverse contemporary communities has not been tested. The biggest question that arises is whether these principles can be taught to astronauts from diverse cultural and spiritual backgrounds. The best way to answer this would be:

1. Vet the principles and develop a training course with Indigenous Elders; develop indicators of successful adoption of each principle
2. Pilot and test the course with groups of people from diverse cultural and spiritual backgrounds
3. Revise and pilot the course with potential astronauts and
4. Provide a simulated environment to practice and test the principles, with groups of astronauts, perhaps with comparison of groups with different principles removed.

The exciting thing about these principles is that they could provide the needed answers not just for sustaining an intergenerational starship, but also for promoting more environmentally and culturally sustainable societies on Earth.

Quantum Strategy

M.A.Popov

OUSAS , Prime State Quantum Lab Limited

27 Old Gloucester Street London England WC1N 3AX

Abstract

Following the Copenhagen Interpretation (of quantum mechanics), it is wrong to think that the task of human science is to find out how Nature or Cosmos are, because scientists are concerned merely with what humans can say about Nature or Cosmos, actually. In particular, we do not know how life became possible at Earth indeed, but we may know what we can say about it. Thus, deep interstellar colonization of humans (or, may be, cyborg astronauts) cannot be based on an entirely "natural " strategy used by the terrestrial life model. In contrast with relativistically thinking space scientists, we suppose that Copenhagen's asserting Schrodinger's cat is truly both alive and dead is not an absurdity or " a megalomaniac's delusion" of quantum theorists. We try to justify that there are truly mathematical as well as experimental foundations for deep interstellar colonization inspired by Schrodinger's Quantum Absurdity.

1. Introduction

Quantum mechanics (Classical Copenhagen Interpretation) is not a development of Einstein' Relativity. It has different mathematical foundations (Copenhagen's mathematics uses two-dimensional complex numbers and Hilbert's infinite space and time, but Relativity tries to use merely natural whole numbers, the Pythagorean theorem, classical differential equations and modified 3 dimensional pseudo-Euclidean space) and they, correspondingly, suggest different ways for deep interstellar human colonization. Whereas for Relativists any deep interstellar model must be based on Relativity's effects and Einstein's equations, for quantum theorists interstellar travels could be connected with such quantum "megalomaniac's delusions" and typical "absurdities" as Schrodinger's collapse of the wave function ("Schrodinger Cat"), Schrodinger's entanglement and, at least, Kant-like phenomenology of quantum *infinite* complex space and time. The most important and "bizarre" prolegomena for quantum strategy of deep ultra long interstellar human colonization [QS / DISHC], thus, hence, are ideas of Schrodinger's entanglement and complex (expressed by complex numbers) time of Quantum Universe.

2. Entanglement

Quantum randomness is connected with the Schrodinger superposition principle, i.e. the possibility that a system can be in a combination of a variety of different states. For example,the mathematical object may be in a superposition of different places and therefore its position is not definite in time (time is complex number x+yi) If two or more systems are in a superposition of different states, they are called entangled and such "supernatural communication " is usually defined as an entanglement .For instance, one could prepare a pair of two objects, A and B, in a superposition of the entangled state. In such an entangled state, the composite system is completely specified in the sense that the correlations between the objects A,B are well known. In accordance with E. Schrodinger ("The present situation in quantum mechanics", 1935): "Total knowledge of a composite system does not necessarily include maximal knowledge of all its parts, not even when these are fully separated from each other and at the moment are not influencing each other at all."

Recent ESA's quantum experiments suggest an existence of such sort of " super-natural communications " at the distance about 144 km (Ursin, R. et al., 2008), thus, we may await that future experiments could be able to demonstrate ultra-long – distance- entanglement in QS / DISHC context (Popov, 2003)(Krenn, 2013) indeed.

3. Speed and Time Problem. Quantum Solution.

As is known the main challenge facing interstellar travel is the real vast distances between the stars. In order to overcome this kind of limitation both super speed and ultra-time are required. However, entanglement experiments can offer entirely different approach. In 2000 Nicolas Gisin made calculations of the speed of quantum communication in 10 km entanglement experiment in Swiss Alps. Analysis showed a possibility of $10^4 \times c$ (c- Einstein's constant)(!) speed of quantum communication. Actually these figures are very large indeed and some physicists would be tempted to jump to the conclusion that Gisin's experiments demonstrate that there is nothing like a speed of quantum information in real quantum Universe at all. Thus, if entanglement speed is infinite, then quantum information is simultaneously everywhere, in all reference frames." In this case space-time is not really out there, but seems to be part of the quantum state of the Universe " (N. Gisin, Group of Applied Physics, Geneva University, 2005). One would have to explain why there must exist quantum strategy in interstellar communication theory now and why we (observers) would also be part of the Universe Quantum State obeying some sort of "absurd" Schrodinger equation.

Reference

1. Schrodinger, E., Discussion of probability relations between separated systems, Proc.Camb. Phil.Soc.31,553 (1935)

2. Popov, M.A., *In Defence of Quantum Idealism* – Uspekhi Advanced Physics of Russian Academy of Sciences (2003,173: 1382-1384), later it was developed into ESA KANT-mission project (Cosmic Vision 2015-2025).

3. Krenn, M., Huber,M., Fickler, R., Lapkiewic, R.,Ramelow, S.,Zeilinger, A., *Studies of Quantum Entanglement in 100 Dimensions* – ArXiv : 1306.0096 (2013)

4. Ursin, R. et al. Space-QUEST: experiments with quantum entanglement in space – ArXiv : 0806.0945 (2008)

5. Gisin,N. How come the Correlations ? – ArXiv: 0503007 (2005)

Re-imagining Space Outreach: Creating a 100-Year Program Model

Kathleen D. Toerpe

Baileys Harbor, WI 54202, 920-421-3963

stellaroutreach@gmail.com, Twitter: @ktoerpe

Abstract

A comprehensive plan of public outreach is necessary to create robust space-faring societies by 2112. Successful and targeted outreach programs over the next one hundred years will need to inspire upcoming generations to continue groundbreaking innovations and bolster the political and financial support necessary for creating sustained commitments to interstellar exploration. But both short-term and long-range challenges persist. The general public lacks knowledge of basic STEM disciplines and is often impatient with the meticulous nature of scientific research. The profusion of new space initiatives can be confusing for even the most interested of space followers; the number of competing programs makes it challenging to identify target audiences and develop a cohesive message. Content-laden or shortsighted programs that overlook crucial long-range objectives in encouraging critical and creative thinking skills impede nurturing the curiosity that will propel discovery forward.

To maximize successful planning and program delivery, this paper proposes a back-to-basics approach with a reimagined model for future space outreach that

- Emerges from all the interdisciplinary goals of space exploration: physical sciences, social sciences and humanities
- Expands the impact of the message by cross-networking audiences, personalizing delivery modes and providing "takeaway" action steps
- Engages the audience as active problem-solvers, contributors and citizen scientists
- Embraces multiple stakeholder institutes and organizations for a consistent voice and message
- Evolves over time by creating a framework and long-term process for outreach in addition to individual content programs

In short, I suggest a developmental, organic and sustainable outreach model that is simultaneously learner and concept-centered, while flexible enough to "grow up" with us as we progress in our understanding of what it means to be a civilization and a planet capable of interstellar travel.

Keywords

space outreach, space education, interstellar, collaboration, astrosociology, space culture

1. Introduction

We are now in what could be termed a *Goldilocks Zone* of public fascination with space. We are seeing it growing stronger every day:

- The 40th anniversary of the Apollo 11 moon mission in 2009 and the public tributes to Neil Armstrong after his passing in 2012;
- The phenomenally successful landing of the NASA Mars Curiosity mission and the discovery of ancient water beds on Mars;
- The suspense and later, the confirmed passage of NASA Voyager 1 beyond the heliosphere;
- The Twitter sensation of International Space Station Commander Chris Hadfield and his farewell space serenade;
- The reawakening of planetary defense concerns after two Valentine's Day asteroid scares in 2013;
- NASA Kepler Mission's almost daily rising tally of suspected extra-solar planets;
- The successful re-launch of the *Star Trek* franchise and the current runaway success of Gravity;
- The continued celebrity of science spokespersons such as the Smithsonian's Neil de Grasse Tyson and *I Fucking Love Science's* Elise Andrew.

These all point - decidedly and, I would argue, unambiguously - to a renewed captivation by the American public - and much of the world - with the people, the missions and the mystique of outer space. Whether the above examples are the reasons for the renewed captivation or merely the manifestations of them is still unclear - I'll wager they're both. But one thing is clear. Right now is when we, as space educators, should be ramping up our outreach efforts to take advantage of this window of opportunity to educate the lay public about space and space exploration.

Some scientists have disagreed. A poll of biologists and physicists, published in 2012, cited the lack of time, training and institutional support for outreach. Funding streams are drying up and outreach often falls to the bottom of the priority list. More aversive, the poll reveals, are the looming remnants of the so-called "Sagan Effect," the academic a priori disapproval of engaging in popular outreach as somehow demeaning to science, a snickering holdover from Carl Sagan's experiences a generation ago. Thus, for some scientists, the current atmosphere for space outreach offers "a bleak prospect with limited room for improvement." [1]

I cannot disagree more strongly! An abandonment of outreach will not facilitate achieving interstellar travel within the next one hundred years. It will only delay, and perhaps even preclude it. I believe it is only by creating a sustainable long-term outreach program that we will garner the public support necessary for success. But it is clear that the state of outreach is in disarray. Hundreds of national, state and local agencies as well as private organizations and commercial enterprises all sponsor space-related programming. From local libraries to astronomy societies, classroom fieldtrips to church luncheons, space is a popular topic. What is lacking is an underlying theory to draw all the disparate programs together; to evaluate which ones are successful; and to serve as a guide for the development of new outreach efforts. In the same way that proponents of interstellar travel need to re-imagine propulsion, energy and long-term habitability, we need to re-imagine what a space outreach model for the 21st century should look like. How can we create a new theory of outreach that will inform, educate and catalyze the public about outer space? How can we evaluate what we are doing right and where we can improve? Can we nurture space outreach to last one hundred years and more? Where do we begin?

2. What is Outreach?

First, some definitions and disclaimers are in order. I define "outreach" as "delivering a message to a targeted audience to reach a desired result." This translates to space outreach as "delivering a message about space research, exploration, future settlement and the human dimension of all of these to a targeted audience to reach a desired result." That definition is intentionally broad and ambiguous. At this early stage of re-imagining space outreach, we want to throw open the possibilities, not confine them to a narrow definition. Outreach, however, is not the same as teaching, public relations or marketing. Though all these may share similar skills and techniques, the overarching goal of outreach is not curriculum-based instruction, nor is it the purchase of a product or service. It is its own distinct form of public interaction that is defined by 1) a delivery mode; 2) a message; 3) an audience; and 4) a desired result. Let's look at each of these in some detail.

2.1 Delivery

Generally, outreach delivery may be classified as personal or non-personal, individual or group, and local or remote. (See Figure 1)

Personal
- Subjective
- Relationship
- Availability/ Approachable

Individual
- One on One

Local
- Synchronous
- Share Real Time
- Share Real Space

Non-Personal
- Objective
- Professional
- Scheduled

Group
- One to Many
- Many to Many
- Many to One

Remote
- Non-synchronous
- Not Real Time
- Not Shared Space
- Not Real Space
- Virtual Space

Figure 1: Outreach Delivery Modes

Personal delivery relies on a meaningful personal relationship with the audience, while non-personal reflects a more objective, professional or even aloof connection. If you can pick up the phone and pour your heart out, it is a personal relationship. Non-personal may be collegial, but it is not at the level of deep friendship and intimacy. Individual outreach is one-on-one - which may be personal or non-personal - while group programming involves either multiple outreach presenters or multiple people in the audience. Finally, local outreach is synchronous, with presenter and audience sharing real time and real space. I see you and you see me in the real world. Alternately, remote outreach efforts are asynchronous, occurring in online or virtual spaces with no necessary shared sense of time or space. There is no one ideal delivery mode for every outreach program. Personal/individual/local programming - such as mentoring or in-person collaborating can be very effective, but is often of short duration and has a short reach of influence. Non-personal/group/remote outreach, such as NASA-TV, the Science Channel or Commander Hadfield's Twitter postings, can reach millions of space enthusiasts, but the creation and delivery of programs is often bureaucratic, duplicative or advertising-driven, and the impact may be short-lived.

Regardless of initial mode, once delivered, a message takes on a life of its own. The starting point of the outreach may be very different than its final destination. For example, a conversation with a close colleague at a conference (a personal/individual/local event) can morph to form the basis for a new massive, open online course (a non-personal/group/remote event). Similarly, a TED-Talk given by a presenter to a real audience in a public shared space (non-personal/group/local) may find its greatest impact in the months and years ahead in the number of online hits it garners in the privacy of a million homes (non-personal/individual/remote). [2]

These connections are comprehensive, fluid and form a web of expansive and flexible possibilities. Imagine the inward and outward motions of the children's toy known as a Hoberman sphere. One connection leads and expands into another. As the sphere enlarges, the connections become more apparent as the toy forms a cohesive shape. Comprehensive. Connective. Expansive. Flexible. This is what space outreach in the next one hundred years needs to be.

Interpreted as a static two-dimensional image, my outreach theory might look something like this. (See Figure 2)

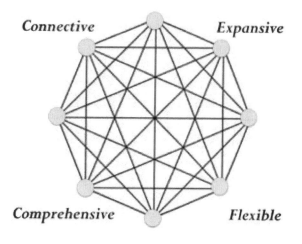

Figure 2: Illustration of an Effective Outreach Model

145

Here we have found the beginning of a new theory of space outreach.

2.2 Message

Effective outreach is specific, content-dynamic and open to change. A message may be tailored in many ways: to inform our audience of new research, persuade them to support our grant proposal, justify our use of their tax dollars, inspire them to become scientists themselves, prepare them for future ETI contact, motivate them to persevere in calculus and physics classes, interpret new inconsistencies in data, or simply to amaze them at the wonders of our universe! A message delivered to a high school class of physics students takes on a different meaning for each one of them; to those students' teacher and parents, a different one still. In designing outreach, we need to be cognizant of how different groups - and various individuals within those groups - will receive and interpret the messages we send. Our message construction needs to be flexible enough to accommodate the different groups who will be hearing what we say.

Comprehensive. Connective. Expansive. Flexible. This is what space outreach in the next one hundred years needs to be.

2.3 Audience

Which leads us to knowing our audience and their embedded perspectives. Effective outreach is learner-centered, but that goes far beyond the people who are sitting in the auditorium or even in their living rooms at home. Most outreach presenters are experienced with conducting effective programming for children and teens; after all, outreach is often seen as a literal reaching out from the academy into the classroom. But for every student reached in a classroom, their teacher, parents, siblings, maybe even grandparents, cousins and neighbors are all in the sphere of outreach influence.

Consider this scenario: Eighth grader Hope participates in a hands-on school assembly presented by a volunteer NASA Solar System Ambassador on the Kepler Mission's discovery of extrasolar planets, or exoplanets. Excited by the possibilities of other Earth-like planets and secretly thinking of hunting planets herself as an astronomer someday, she ventures home and tells her family, siblings and friends about the program. We cannot necessarily control the reaction and response of her audience, yet it is that audience - and not the NASA ambassador - that will ultimately influence her career decisions. As outreach presenters, we need to be aware of how the many varied audiences will engage - for better or for worse - with the material we present. Will Dad bemoan his tax money being spent on exoplanet research? Will Grandma deflate Hope's desire to be a scientist by cautioning her about the many years of study required? Will Hope's friends make fun of her "geeky" fascination with the stars?

In crafting our message, we need to remember all our audiences - apparent and hidden. Children, teens, teachers, parents, siblings, college students, seniors, even our own colleagues and all the future people who may come in contact with our message are our audiences. It is a sincere tribute to the compelling power of both Carl Sagan's message and his delivery, that the original Cosmos series has enjoyed multiple re-broadcasts, a generation after its original debut. Sagan's sincerity and sense of wonder - as crucial to his outreach as the hard physics - has a timeless effect and is a poignant example of how the starting point of a message is not always its final destination.

Comprehensive. Connective. Expansive. Flexible. This is what space outreach in the next one hundred years needs to be.

2.4 Results of Outreach

Outreach should always elicit a response and have a concrete goal or result that it seeks to produce. In practical terms, what is the take-away? Do we want our audience to advocate for increased tax revenues for NASA? Participate in a citizen-science project? Carry the baton forward and engage in their own space outreach efforts? Persevere in their graduate studies? Corroborate our research data? Collaborate on our next grant proposal? Appreciate the dedication of overworked, underpaid civil servants? Wonder if there really is intelligent extraterrestrial life out there? Effective outreach needs to catalyze its audience to do something, not just walk out the door chatting about how great (or not so great!) the program was. But people need to - and, frankly, like to - be asked. As outreach professionals, it is very easy to focus on the mechanics of our presentation - choosing the delivery, honing the message, considering the audience - all good things to be sure, but if we don't pre-plan the goal of the outreach, then we've ultimately failed to accomplish much at all.

Comprehensive. Connective. Expansive. Flexible. This is what space outreach in the next one hundred years needs to be.

3. A 100-Year Space Outreach Model

Now that we have a more specific idea of what good outreach looks like - no matter what the topic or cause - how do we translate that into an effective space outreach model that has long-term staying power? While it is debatable whether any model of space outreach can span the one hundred years projected by 100 Year Starship to achieve interstellar flight, we can stack the deck in our favor by adding these components:

3.1 It Emerges From Our Human Experiences

We are more than our STEM selves. Our outreach needs to be, too. Yes, of course it is imperative that our space outreach target and reflect the physical, biological and chemical sciences; technology, engineering and mathematics. There is no dispute about their necessity and preeminence in space outreach. But the message cannot stop there. To optimize successful outreach - and to honor the integrity of humanity's history and experience of space - we must broaden the message and the goals to include other areas of human knowledge and experience. History, sociology, philosophy, literature, anthropology, economics, political science, law, theater, and so many more disciplines, which have created a rich and robust corpus of studies of the human condition, have something to offer space outreach. We will venture into space as complex social and cultural creatures, connected both to our crewmates as well as to those we leave behind on Earth. We will form fledgling social systems, in part based on those we knew on Earth. We will carry along our myths, beliefs, theologies and philosophies - profound and divergent and, often, seeking a Truth that some argue is ultimately illusory. We will create laws, establish institutions, and formulate policies, which mark us as social beings whose daily experiences are derived from interaction with other social beings and our environment. We need to prepare for that future now with a commitment to multi- and inter-disciplinary outreach, utilizing emerging fields such as astrosociology, astropolitics and space law. These fields analyze the human dimension of outer space research and exploration and need to be an integral part of any space outreach effort.

To hearken back to our comprehensive, connective, expansive and flexible sphere: outreach cannot be successful if connections cannot be made. If we fail to connect our research to large parts of what it means to be a human being, we will leave our very human audience wondering where they fit in and why they should care.

3.2 It Expands Our Understanding

Any outreach is the most effective when it extends our current understanding of a topic, in addition to reaffirming what is already known. Like the synapses in our brains, which develop and are reinforced by repetitive activity, outreach should start out with repeating and reviewing what is known. From there, it can venture into the novel and form new connections, similar to the creation of new neural pathways. This is very easy to do in space outreach today. New announcements seem to spring at us almost daily - Hubble galaxies, Kepler exoplanets, looming asteroids and new cutting-edge - even fantastic - technologies. We can use these media announcements as springboards from which to do a fuller presentation. For example, from announcing the current Kepler tally, we can launch into a deeper discussion on how Kepler works, the problems with its positioning wheels, the type of exoplanets detected, the search for Earth 2.0, exploration as a human quest, and so on. By starting with what is presented in the popular media - what the audience more likely already knows - we can extend the discussion into the deeper science with our audience, examine the human dimension of it, and forge new, connective pathways of understanding.

Outreach also has an organic, cumulative effect, which we can never completely anticipate or access. Think of all the different venues in which you have encountered information about outer space over the course of your lifetime. That might include school, of course, but also space museums, planetariums, science fiction books or television shows, documentaries, summer camps, libraries - or more recently, citizen science projects, video gaming or maker-spaces. Each of these experiences exposed you to space science information and, over the course of your life; the cumulative effect of all these experiences has created your own personal body of knowledge about outer space. Beginning with the first time you saw HAL 9000 or Mr. Spock, or the first alien civilizations you vicariously experienced through Ray Bradbury's or Isaac Asimov's eyes, you have been learning about space. Thus, it is important to remember that any individual program we deliver represents just one space experience - among many - over the course of a person's life. And since every person's experience is different, we can never quite anticipate where our program will fit in the overall scheme of any individual's cumulative space experiences.

3.3 It Engages Us to Take Action

Remember - every program needs a take-away! This is definitely an area where outreach can learn a lesson from marketing. Never let your audience walk away from a program empty-handed. Always produce a handout for your presentation. If you're conducting in-class outreach for students, prepare one handout for students to take home to their families and a separate one for the teacher. On the family one, summarize the program you presented, provide some guiding questions to further delve into the topic and offer some websites where parents can find more information for their children and for themselves. Then, of course, cross your fingers that the handout reaches the parents and doesn't end up lost in the black holes of their backpacks or lockers! On the teacher's handout, provide links to educators' materials and clearly connect your program to the core science competencies required for the grade level they teach. While this requires a little digging into their applicable state standards, it is well worth the effort and makes it more likely that the teacher will reinforce the program's themes in the classroom.

Beyond the handout, before you end your presentation, plug a local citizen science project (Don't know any? Look to NASA's Citizen Science page or pathway site Zooniverse.org); direct them to popular space science websites, Twitter feeds or Facebook pages; or share "read more about it" resources. Click on NASA Kids' Club website and demonstrate a few of the games. Better yet, invite some students to the front and have them demonstrate how to play the games. Involve your audience as active participants. Don't let your audience walk away without something in their hands and at least one, new unanswered question in their minds. This unanswered question will be the hook that will encourage them to attend their next outreach program, click on a website, or choose The Science Channel over MTV. Remember, space outreach is a life-long, cumulative process. Sound familiar? Just as progress in any scientific field is the result of many years of small, painstaking progress by many individual researchers, so too is the progress made in conducting a multi-generational space outreach program. Any individual program is just one hour or one evening in a lifetime of experiences learning about space and engaging with the possibilities. Engage your audience as contributors and problem solvers, rather than passive receptacles, and help lead them to the next learning experience.

3.4 It Embraces Everyone in the Endeavor

A one-hundred-year space outreach model is necessarily collaborative and integrative. No one individual presenter, or perhaps even agency, will be around for the duration of the effort. In prior decades, the traditional collaborative partnership was between leading universities such as the Massachusetts Institute of Technology or the University of California, US agencies, primarily NASA; and leading aeronautic/astronautic sector leaders such as Lockheed or Rockwell. Non-profit space advocacy groups such as the 1970s National Space Institute joined in the effort, and attempted to promote space flight in the waning years of the Apollo program. The web of partnerships today is more diffuse; with entrepreneurial upstarts (e.g. Elon Musk's SpaceX or Richard Branson's Virgin Galactic) vying with or overtaking established industry giants as leaders in a new corporate space race. Advocacy, research and educational profits and non-profits, such as 100 Year Starship, Tau Zero Foundation, The Mars Society, The Planetary Society and Icarus Interstellar (among others) have joined the effort with annual conferences and collaborative programming geared to both professional and lay audiences. Hundreds of blogs, Facebook pages and Twitter feeds spew a daily dose of what is new, fascinating or just weird about outer space.

Everyone is helped by effective outreach. That is, every program that successfully informs, challenges and invites engagement with space science and its human implications benefits every space agency, organization or endeavor. An engaging visit to the local planetarium can help put NASA's Hubble program into perspective, clarify why someone would want to become a space tourist aboard Virgin Galactic, or entice a student into investigating a STEM career. Every stakeholder in space research and exploration is helped by effective outreach. But the inverse is also true. Every stakeholder is hurt by poorly designed, delivered or received outreach. For example, too many technical glitches in a presentation might lead people asking, "If they can't work the projector, how do they expect to get to Mars? It's a waste of money!" Or, "Let's skip the astronomy club viewing tonight. That PBS documentary we saw last week on black holes was really boring!"

As professional space educators, we need to realize that we represent more than the individual organization whose badge we wear or business card we carry. We are the face of space - right then and there - for our audience, whether that is one person seated across from us, hundreds in an auditorium, or millions on YouTube or cable television. For those few moments, we are the link connecting our audience to the stars and the audience may not take heed of which agency, organization or institute we are formally representing. The ultimate success of space outreach - measured in a public more deeply literate about space, in ongoing support for continued research and exploration, and in inspiring future scientists of all physical, social and behavioral stripes to follow in our footsteps - will be a collaborative effort. We must begin that collaboration now.

3.5 It Evolves and Grows with Us

Remember our two-dimensional image above, or our metaphor of the Hoberman sphere? Comprehensive, expansive and flexible connections are not created overnight. Space outreach requires decades of repetition, reinforcement and re-inspiration to solidify the deep connections that equate to space literacy, to sustain public support during economic turndowns or to enthuse both youth and adults to take up space research as a career. Think back to your school days for a moment. How many times did you re-learn that Lincoln freed the slaves? You might have first heard it in kindergarten or first grade in a President's Day skit or song. Then you re-learned it - this time with some basic details - in second or third grade. Then, again in middle school; and yet again, in high school. And every university student learned it in detail in the U.S. History courses that help form the liberal arts core. Each time you learned it, hopefully, you absorbed more complex and sophisticated details, understood more connections, and were able to see farther to the bigger picture. Your understanding evolved and grew with you as you cognitively and emotionally matured, ready to understand the complicated, historical reality of Emancipation. The process of space outreach is similar, but even more messy and uncertain because we don't know what the end lesson is yet. We are still on the historical path to becoming a space-faring civilization and space outreach needs to evolve and grow with us as we travel that path.

In that sense, much of what we do now will build a framework for the future, much like the skeletal toy sphere or diagram that represents this model. New research findings, collaborative partnerships, scientific theories developed and discarded, outreach programming attempted, succeeded and rejected will all flesh out the framework in the decades ahead. This will all succeed to the extent that we can adapt our outreach theories and priorities to the scientific innovation that is surely ahead of us. We will be re-teaching and re-learning the specifics of our space-faring future many, many times in the next century, just as we have re-learned the stories of our past.

4. Conclusion

In this paper, I have introduced a new underlying theory for the next one hundred years of space outreach. It might seem odd that I haven't talked much about faster-than-light travel, quantum computing, the long-term effects of microgravity on the human body, terra-forming planets, the search for Earth 2.0, etc. How to present those topics - and the hundreds of others that will be necessary to achieving interstellar travel and settlement - in a comprehensive, connective, expansive and flexible way to non-scientific audiences remains for another day. Here, my focus has been to look at process, rather than programs, to lay the groundwork - and the ground rules - for a sustainable and developmental model of space outreach that promises to be learner-centered and content-dynamic.

This 100-Year Program Model for Space Outreach capitalizes on the core strengths of effective outreach:

- Utilizes webs of interconnected delivery formats: personal, non-personal, individual, group, local, and remote.
- Stresses active and conscious messaging to inform, persuade, justify, inspire, prepare, motivate, amaze, and interpret space research for our audiences.
- Targets interrelated audience groups: children, teens, parents, seniors, teachers, colleagues, college students, and, most importantly, the future.
- Promotes final take-away activities, leads audiences to future outreach opportunities and invites audiences to advocate, participate, engage, persevere, corroborate, collaborate, appreciate, and wonder.

More precisely, this sustainable, organic, and developmental model emerges from the totality of our human experiences; expands our understanding of space and of ourselves; engages us to take action as conscious participants and collaborators; embraces all of us in the endeavor to reach, explore and settle space; and evolves while it grows with us on the journey. It can serve as a benchmark to measure our progress and to refine our priorities. It can help us make sense of all the disparate programs that is the current state of space outreach by holding them to the light of the process of outreach. We may be surprised by what is illuminated in the effort.

Comprehensive. Connective. Flexible. Expansive. And to that, I would like to add one more . . . Enduring.

References

- Ecklund EH, James SA, Lincoln AE (2012) How Academic Biologists and Physicists

- View Science Outreach. PLoS ONE 7(5): e36240. doi:10.1371/journal.pone.0036240

- My guess here is that most people are engaging with the presenter as individuals surfing the net at home, work or school. Of course, if a classroom is plugging into the presentation, it reverts to its original group classification. Either way, it remains non-personal and remote.

Providing for the Common Good: A Survey of Trends for Creating a Civilized Species Ready for Interstellar Travel

Candy Torres

Technorican, 2267 Broadlawn Drive, Houston, TX 77058

engineertorres@me.com

Abstract

Human life on Earth must be at a highly civilized stage before it can launch into the universe in the next century, which means that the basic needs of all people must be met before such an endeavor is possible. Primary among these needs are peace, food, shelter, education, meaningful work, and civilized behavior. Accomplishing these goals requires institutional involvement, individual spiritual action, and political support. Globally, there are many organizations and methods for addressing the common good, teaching social justice, and empowering the disenfranchised. Women must be a major force in shaping this destiny since they are the producers of humanity and our first connection to others -- the primary socializers. Films and games are being used by mothers to teach their children about social justice. The United Nations established an Entity for Gender Equality and the Empowerment of Women. Organizations such as Amnesty International take an activist role through their Universal Declaration of Human Rights. In addition, businesses are beginning to embrace the concept of social responsibility to protect and benefit society and the environment while developing their products, services, and profits. Educational technology is evolving to provide access to the knowledge base of the planet and global interaction. This paper will provide a useful summary of major activities currently in existence to evaluate their effectiveness and cooperation in protecting the common good. With this information, we can define a spiritual and ethics core curriculum for humanity in creating a stable Earth and a viable interstellar community.

Keywords

women's issues, global social change, diversity, spiritual responsibility

1. Introduction

Exploration, curiosity, creativity, and risk are central elements in the human psyche. We are born with them and enjoy seeing them manifested in children. However, what we cherish in the young often gets extinguished in many ways and for many reasons as they grow. It does not have to be that way and neither does it mean that even under the best of conditions, adults have lost their hold of childlike thinking -- also referred to as "beginner's mind." It is vital to "dream big" early on and be provided the tools for personal growth and contribution to human society.

151

The goal of interstellar travel in 100 years is a tremendous undertaking but the necessary human technology must be at a higher level than physical technology for the dream to become reality.

More than a decade into the 21st century, it is clear that the entire world is struggling with a myriad of problems. Economies are fluctuating leaving bigger gaps between rich and poor. Human capital is wasted with so many unemployed people including the very industry upon which the necessary space technology is required. Wars have not accomplished their goals of improving bad governments nor eliminating the destructors of nations. People need stability and security in access to food, education, shelter, and health. Without a highly civilized planet of human beings, we will fall short of our huge reach into the stars.

Domestically and throughout the world there are efforts made in many ways to change the lives of humanity. The most important place to start in addressing the overwhelming number of destabilizing issues of our times is to focus on women's issues. Despite being the first nurturing environment of human life, the amount of overt hostility and covert exclusion of women is horrifying. This is not one gender against another because women still seem to lack the personal tools they need to step forth in every aspect of human life. It is appalling to this author to see and hear many of the same negative behaviors and attitudes that existed more than half a century ago. Using that as a gauge and seeing how much work that needs to be done in the next century to meet the goal of interstellar travel, there should be concern amongst all participants in the 100 Year Star Ship Symposium. Ultimately, it will take every participant to enlarge the sphere of change for the common good.

2. Global

During the 1960s, the civil rights movement began to make real the dream of equality, jobs, and freedom. It was a great success but it cost many lives and it is not yet fully realized. In fact, it took 50 years for women to be permitted to speak in Washington, D.C. at the commemorative march this year. Yet women had played major roles in organizing and protesting in the original movement. It was more than 50 years after the end of slavery before women were given the right to vote in the United States. It took longer in other countries. It would appear it takes half a century for a significant part of humanity to be allowed to "catch up." This is not acceptable for the dream of interstellar travel. We do not have 100 years to create a civilized human society. It needs to be in place long before then.

Early on the United Nations declared its global support for women: "All human beings are born free and equal in dignity and rights" and that "everyone is entitled to all the rights and freedoms set forth in this Declaration, without distinction of any kind, such as race, color, sex, language, religion, … birth or other status." [1] There have been achievements but in the past year alone, there have been horrific events that underscore the state of affairs in the world regarding violence in a variety of circumstances against all people.

According to a recent United Nations article: "Hardly a day goes by without a news story on some violation of women's rights. In recent months, appalling incidents of violence against women and girls, from Delhi to Johannesburg to Cleveland, have sparked public outrage and demands to tackle these horrific abuses." [2] As a painful reminder and felt experience, the news has shown:

- the horrible rape and death in India of a woman following all safety guidelines in a society hostile to women
- the massacre of school children in Connecticut which has the unexpected result of increased gun sales
- the release of women abused during captivity for over 10 years by a man neighbors thought quiet
- an assassination attempt against a young girl who wanted to go to school
- garment workers who died in a building known to be in deplorable conditions
- refugees fleeing civil war to live in tent camps in other countries with inadequate resources and with their own unstable conditions.

The point is that these are just a handful of the starting conditions that need to be addressed before we travel to the stars. It is implied in the positive vision of the future put forth in Gene Roddenberry's science fiction television series Star Trek so it is part of the 100 Year Star Ship plan.

The same U.N. article recognizes the urgency in developing means in "ending violence against women and girls" because "this violence causes untold physical and psychological harm. It is one of the most pervasive human rights violations, and carries tremendous costs for individuals, families and societies." [2] It calls for "equal access to land and credit, natural resources, education, health services." [2] Women need assistance with child care and financial access to start their businesses so men and women can share the responsibility of raising children in stable homes with education opportunities. Inevitably, problems occur when people are denied basic human rights and freedoms.

The U.N. article stresses the need for the participation of women in household decisions as well as business, educational, government, and judicial sectors of life. The perspectives and experiences of all citizens of the world are valuable. Unfortunately, in news media and online discussions -- even within women's forums -- describe circumstances of being held back. They are intimidated and told not to speak up. The other side of the issue is that women are reluctant to present themselves confidently when provided the opportunity.

3. Gender Gap in Science Views

Representation in Science Technology Engineering Math (STEM) fields needs to increase. Over the years opinion polls and surveys show difference between men and women in support and appreciation of space exploration. According to the Everett Group in 2009: "Most Americans are interested in the space program... Interest is particularly soft among women." [3] Another article examining how the public views U.S. space leadership seems to support that: "More men than women say the program contributes a lot to scientific advances (by 45% to 31%) and encouraging interest in science and technology (44% to 35%)." A National Science Foundation article stated: "Men are much more likely than women to champion the benefits of space exploration." [4] The gap has been narrowing. Pew Research found: "People who have more formal education are more likely than others to say that the benefits of space exploration exceed the costs." [5] The point is women are the first line of defense in education. It is imperative more work needs to be done in supporting women's ability to balance child-rearing, education, and work. Of course, they cannot do this alone. Men are vitally important to the plan.

4. National Memorandum

Earlier this year, President Obama put forth a memorandum to clarify the needs of women and girls throughout the world. The title summarizes goal: "Coordination of Policies and Programs to Promote Gender Equality and Empower Women and Girls Globally." He states their equality and empowerment "around the world remains one of the greatest unmet challenges of our time, and one that is vital to achieving our overall foreign policy objectives. Ensuring that women and girls, including those most marginalized, are able to participate fully in public life, are free from violence, and have equal access to education, economic opportunity, and health care increases broader economic prosperity, as well as political stability and security." [6] The U.S. Secretary State Department's Office of Global Women's Issues is sees women's issues are integral to U.S. foreign policy "to promote stability, peace, and development by empowering women politically, socially, and economically around the world. The memorandum outlines "an interagency working group" which will include "the Departments of State, the Treasury, Defense, Justice, Agriculture, Commerce, Labor, Health and Human Services, Education, and Homeland Security; the Intelligence Community, "the Director of National Intelligence; the United States Agency for International Development; the Millennium Challenge Corporation; the Peace Corps; the U.S. Mission to the United Nations; the Office of the United States Trade Representative; the Office of Management and Budget; the Office of the Vice President; the National Economic Council; and such other agencies and offices as the President may designate." [6]

5. Domestic Initiatives

There are many other organizations such as the Clearinghouse on Women's Issues dedicated to interacting with any agencies, institutions, and organizations "to improve the status of women." [7] The National Organization for Women has a long list of issues it works to address such as women's health and reproductive rights, violence against women, family law, freedom from sexual harassment in the workplace, and many others. It would seem there are a plethora of groups in place to address women's issues domestically and globally. Yet it is clear that funding is limited as well as personnel and the ability to span the globe effectively.

There are additional activities cropping up world-wide to change the hearts and minds of human beings who want a better world. New technologies and gaming concepts are one of those emerging avenues. Games are extremely popular in engaging people in more than entertainment. They are being used for training and education in professional fields. One intriguing game approach teaches children about social and cultural issues. Mothers are taking the lead in "using social games to teach their children about the world and the real issues people face in it." [8] Women know the harsh realities of life and their influence on their children's development. They want to make a positive difference in the world. According to one article, "mothers make up a huge group of social gamers, with 54% of social gamers being female and 64% having children." [8] It discusses a Facebook game called Half the

153

Sky Movement, which uses a young Indian girl as the main character for interaction. The child follows her travels while she encounters and solves women's issues in various countries.

Another cultural game uses a variety of school subjects to teach and encourage players to make a difference in the world. Every time the student provides a correct answer to a question, 10 grains of rice are donated to the World Food Program. A tangible contribution reinforces a connection to other people in the world. Children's behavior are changed when they learn that not everyone has easy access to clean water. One child learned: "Some people don't have water, so it's mean for me to waste it." [8] Another child was exposed to women's rights. He asked: "Why aren't women allowed to drive in some countries? How does a mom take her daughter to the park?" He immediately understood the unfairness of the situation. It is the goal of the mothers to raise children with a sense of responsibility beyond their own community.

6. Spiritual Responsibility

The 100 Year Star Ship goal incorporates the concept of a "common heritage for mankind." [9] The phrase comes from "Lunar Ethics and Space Commercialization" by David M. Livingston who discusses in depth the moral and ethics necessary for living in lunar or space colonies, specifically as commercial endeavors. It centers around sharing the benefits (including profits from a commercial endeavor) derived from off Earth colonies. However, it seems appropriate to switch it around to Earth. That is, developing a society for life beyond Earth should produce a better, civilized humanity. The author Frank White "considers how the permanent presence of humans in space will affect many of our institutions, including those having to do with economics, science, politics, religion, social relations, and psychology." [9] It is Earthlings planning to leave for the stars who must reshape our thinking, behaviors, and modes of living before leaving. We need governments and people of our planet in synchronization to plan and build the spaceships and select the crews for interstellar travel. "The standards that we export to outer space will be with us for many years to come...we need to be addressing these issues now." [9] The steps we need range from the global to the personal.

Organizations, institutions, and groups on the global, domestic, and personal levels are all necessary for improving life on Earth. History has already shown that decades go by before major changes occur. Current events show high levels of instability, which can further hinder the changes required for a civilized humanity ready for interstellar travel. Questions need to be raised as to how the 100 Year Star Ship can influence and push to overcome social and political inertia. Would it have to engage at a level higher than an organization such as the United Nations? Are there more effective ways to achieve the highest level we need for our goal? If we are truly committed to interstellar travel, then at least we can each dedicate our daily personal interactions to being civilized individuals. We must be aware that our every action, word, and behavior can make a difference, a betterment in the world. It would require self-reflection in every moment of our day. It is a spiritual decision: checking quick negative emotions and reactions, thinking ahead, imagining how another person may feel or be impacted. Ultimately, it is the only social activity we can control.

7. Conclusion

Interstellar travel is about the needs of the many being met in order for a few to leave Earth. The many are extremely diverse and complex. History has shown that time does not heal all wounds nor guarantee positive and permanent improvement in the human condition. Many of us in the space industry have heard many times that money would be better spent on social issues before going into space. However, money is always scarce and organizational outcomes are never guaranteed. Political and cultural environments often put up barriers preventing people from receiving what they need. If we wait for social change to improve, we may never get off the ground.

It should be a high priority for the 100 Year Star Ship to actively engage in sociological issues and conditions. Seeking to increase the participation of women and minorities would add new perspectives and ideas. A grass roots movement tied to human rights would increase the viability of our goal. There is too much earth in people's eyes and mouths to see the stars. Many of us grew up believing that future technology would mean a better future for everyone. Many of us still hold onto the vision. Building space colonies and starships would provide jobs and require high educational and vocational levels. People want to meaningful work and to be able to take care of themselves and their families.

Raise the lowest among us to show what can be done, how to dream big. High achievers already know the way. Every day there is an opportunity to make a difference. Planet Earth is full of human potential -- the greatest resource. We must string together the existing entities from the global to the local through the personal. Let us define a core curriculum for humanity through institutional involvement, individual spiritual action, and political support. We must be the force in shaping Earth's destiny and its future in the universe, only then can we succeed in our century plan.

References

1. UN Global Issues -- Women; http://www.un.org/en/globalissues/women

2. OP-ED: A Global Goal on Gender Equality, Women's Rights and Women's Empowerment; Lakshmi Puri (United Nations), May 23, 2013, Inter Press Service; http://www.globalissues.org/news/2013/05/23/16627

3. Public Opinion on Space Exploration Survey; March 16, 2009; http://infinite-frontier.blogspot.com/2009/03/public-opinion-on-space-exploration.html

4. Public Attitudes Toward Space Exploration ; Science and Technology: Public Attitudes and Public Understanding; http://www.nsf.gov/statistics/seind02/c7/c7s2.htm

5. Majority Sees U.S. Leadership in Space as Essential Shuttle Program Viewed as Good Investment; July 5, 2011; http://www.people-press.org/2011/07/05/majority-sees-u-s-leadership-in-space-as-essential/1/

6. Presidential Memorandum -- Coordination of Policies and Programs to Promote Gender Equality and Empower Women and Girls Globally; January 30, 2013; http://www.whitehouse.gov/the-press-office/2013/01/30/presidential-memorandum-coordination-policies-and-programs-promote-gende

7. Clearinghouse on Women's Issues; http://www.womensclearinghouse.org

8. How Mothers Are Using Social Games to Educate Children on Women's Rights; http://www.forbes.com/sites/ericaswallow/2013/05/12/social-gaming-mothers-womens-rights/

9. Lunar Ethics and Space Commercialization; David M Livingston; July 2000; http://www.spacefuture.com/archive/lunar_ethics_and_space_commercialization.shtml

Exovivaria as Simulacra for Generation Starship Societies

Michael Turner

Project Persephone

1-25-33 Takadanobaba Shinjuku-ku Tokyo 169-0075

www.projectpersephone.org

turner@projectpersephone.org

Abstract

Notionally, exovivaria would be unmanned biosatellites hosting ecosystems managed by earthbound online communities, whose "exopolitan" citizens would work and play -- and participate in government -- while telepresent in orbit. As such, exovivaria would pose certain long-term sustainability issues faced not only by those who conceptualize about generation starships but also by those who are more concerned with the long-term viability of the "found generation ship" sometimes called Spaceship Earth. Exovivaria would offer non-experts a way to accomplish things in space, without incurring the exorbitant cost, time and effort per traveler now entailed in true human space travel. These "exopolitan" accomplishments are likely to be relevant to the design of near-term, manned, inner-planet exploration logistics (and, perhaps even sooner, to establishing commercial adventure travel "base camps" in low Earth orbit), but also in the planning of eventual manned interstellar migrations. Whether exovivaria ever fly, explorations of the concept through virtual worlds and terrestrial prototypes might afford ecologists and social scientists opportunities to collaborate on the optimal organization of efforts to establish and maintain global sustainability.

Keywords

interstellar, space, biotech, biology, ecology, economy, polity, sociology, CELSS, logistics, LEO telepresence, sustainability

1. Introduction

This paper takes up the theme of worldship simulacra as learning tools for designing an eventual long-term, self-sufficient human civilization. The concept of the generation starship is viewed here less as a realistic prospect than as a kind of gedanken experiment against which to test proposals. The clarifying value of thinking of a society as situated in a populated ecosystem flying through space should be obvious - we all live in one already. Trying to fly ecosystems in space that host virtual populations - exovivaria - is a way to take the experiments beyond the merely gedanken.

The economy, polity and ecology of generation starships would not only suffer from unintended consequences, such as we see on our own world as human impact intensifies. A starship would also suffer from ever-decreasing

157

access to its one source of external remedies for the more dire of these consequences. Shipment of emergency supplies from the inner solar system to starships begs the question of how to cross interstellar distances quickly enough with relief packages. Information-based solutions would be increasingly bedeviled by speed-of-light delays. In short, the design isn't something that the project planners can afford to get wrong. Running experimental testbeds, including those intended to see what political systems lend themselves to keeping ecosystems balanced, would be a small price to pay.

By the end of the 21st century, the problems of physical design for generation starships might or might not be solved. If the human social problems of interstellar flight aren't satisfactorily assured of solutions, however, the physical design issues might as well be moot - except perhaps for sending unmanned scientific probes to nearby stars. By the same token, toward the the end of the 21st century, absent any "rescue" from our current global predicament by charitable extraterrestrial intelligences, we might be in deep trouble. If humanity doesn't come up with its own solutions in political economy, the physical-artifact engineering for a sustainable human civilization[Fuller1966] will be similarly moot. We will have produced artifacts of possible interest only to extraterrestrial intelligences engaged in archaeology.

Given this conservative assumption that there will be unintended social consequences that must be managed, the main criteria for designing the political economy of generation starships should overridingly concern the State: how to provide the needed resilience - the balance of stability and flexibility - in the face of "unknown unknowns". The political economy should enable citizens to maintain both civic health and the ecosystem that feeds them, even as their society and their ecosystem evolve in unpredicted ways. This paper discusses - and dispenses with - polities other than democracy; brings the problems of democracy to the forefront; then suggests that the analysis used in one proposed solution - Associative Democracy - could be a useful framework for most of the major issues in starship society design. To provide an experimental testbed that admits of ethical experimentation on ecologically insular societies, exovivaria are proposed.[Turner2009] These would be ecosystems in orbit that are tele-operatively managed by online communities on Earth. Exovivaria could be an economical way to begin the test of the cybernetics of starship societies in the Associative Democracy analytic framework. A holistic view comprising not just ecology and economy, but polity, is well within the scope of cybernetics as the term was originally coined and viewed - indeed, an attempt at a science of polity was its origin.[Wiener1954] The lessons learned from the experimental cybernetics of exovivaria may well apply to the problems of how to equitably manage terrestrial resources in a growing global economy, one that is likely to start straining against current resource limits eventually if not sooner.

2. Cybernetics - Again

Ecology is indisputably a science. Economics is becoming one, albeit through political fits and starts. The most important scientific frontiers in the 21st century might well be in political science. None of our scientific understandings are likely to save us unless we understand not only the answers of the sciences, but ourselves. Notwithstanding the various previous systems-theoretic attempts that have come to grief,[Meadows1972] a global cybernetics, one that encompasses ecology and political economy, seems to be what's called for. The inclusion of polity should come as no surprise: the words "government" and "cybernetics" derive from the same Greek root: κυβερνήτης (kubernétés - "steersman, pilot").

Unfortunately, as long as the systems thinking behind a global cybernetics remains opaque to a layman citizenry in a democracy, there is a barrier to acceptance posed by democracy itself: human beings are naturally suspicious of mysterious technical expertise when it's applied to how they are governed. The sales job for the social design - at least in a democracy - will be at best incomplete, and more likely a non-starter. A sufficiently totalitarian order, once established, might make the sale to its subjects through propaganda saturation alone. In so doing, however, the resulting social homogenization would deprive the society's managers of the cognitive diversity that might save it later, through democratic processes, as ever-changing social and ecological conditions pose unforeseen challenges (in one telling metaphor, a "maze") that must be collectively negotiated.[Landemore2012]

Although the term "ship" has a nuance of top-down control, the sense of naval hierarchy is considerably softened when we think of "worldship." A generation starship would be a worldship that travels between stars. We should know what the design constraints must be, including the political constraints.

3. Generation Starships - the Problem Statement

A generation starship can be characterized by a number of parameters. Being a world unto itself, one should expect no less. The most important of these might be the following:

- energy source: internal (thermo)nuclear

- population scale: urban
- population density: high to very high
- technology: very advanced
- ecosystem: significantly managed
- time scale: decades if not millennia
- genetic diversity: medium
- cultural diversity: medium
- cybernetics....

Cybernetics is the big question here: what could adequately control all this? Ecosystem balance on such small scales is precarious - it will require management. But if so, who manages the managers, and how?

4. Generation Starships - Possible Precedents

That generation starships will be very insular falls out of the problem statement: how to get a lot of people across a very wide interstellar vacuum gap. We're not utterly at a loss here for models of self-sufficiency. Among those seen already in history, and even now:

- Still-insular primitive terrestrial
- Insular planetary: Earth itself
- Insular modern terrestrial
- Space stations: Mir & ISS

Let's take these one at a time.

4.1. Still-insular Primitive Terrestrial

It seems that every decade or so, intrepid wanderers stumble upon some hunter-gatherer society that had escaped notice. The very existence of such societies bespeaks significant potential for self-sufficiency and insularity, even as "wild human" biomes shrink. These societies have the following features in our adopted parameter set:

- energy source: external, thermonuclear (Sol)
- population: dozens to hundreds
- population density: low
- technology: neolithic
- ecosystem: humans almost a wild species
- time scale: centuries to tens of millennia
- ecosystem genetic diversity: high
- cultural diversity: very low
- cybernetics: hunter-gather tribal/Malthusian homeostatic…

Can a back-to-the-prehistoric-future polity work as a starship society model? The idea of a neolithic culture in interstellar flight enjoys perennial appeal in science fiction, but its practicality is very doubtful. The weakness of this model is in assuming what amounts to an open system with fairly large per-person natural resource requirements. The challenges of ecosystem instability in a much smaller world might leave cultures of such limited cultural diversity at a loss - potentially, at a fatal loss.

4.1. Insular Planetary: Earth Itself

The Spaceship Earth metaphor has been with us since the days of Henry George, if not earlier.[George1879] This American social reformer premised an entire program on the brute fact of limited resources, and the inequities stemming from their unfair allocation. In terms of our parameters, Spaceship Earth has these features:

- energy source: Sol (external fusion), etc.
- population scale: billions
- population density: can still Stand on Zanzibar
- technology: the future is still "not well distributed"[Gibson1999]
- ecosystem: still mostly wild
- time scale: hundreds of millennia, until … ?
- ecosystem genetic diversity: very high
- cultural diversity: very high
- cybernetics…

The most nettlesome problem with the Spaceship Earth metaphor is that we're not really sure we have a sustainable polity in place now, as a useful guide. Certainly, as I write this, there's evidence from Syria that WMD bans aren't exactly universally accepted or effective. Russia is a petro-economy reverting to statism. With current fossil fuel use trends in the U.S., China, and Europe, we cannot be quite sure we have ecological or resource sustainability. The more modern sense of the Spaceship metaphor originates with Buckminster Fuller. Whatever his genius for physical design, his politics, we'll see later, were (to be charitable) simplistic.

As Adlai Stevenson put the problem, shortly before his death[Stevenson1965]:

We travel together, passengers on a little space ship, dependent on its vulnerable reserves of air and soil; all committed for our safety to its security and peace; preserved from annihilation only by the care, the work, and, I will say, the love we give our fragile craft. We cannot maintain it half fortunate, half miserable; half confident, half despairing; half slave to the ancient enemies of man, half free in a liberation of resources undreamed of until this day. No craft, no crew can travel safely with such vast contradictions. On their resolution depends the survival of us all.

Since Stevenson spoke those lines, there has been some progress, chiefly in the alleviation of poverty and the spread of democracy, even if these do not always proceed hand-in-hand. Nonrenewable resource "liberation", species loss, and atmospheric despoliation continue apace, however. If the root of "cybernetics" is "steersman", Earth appears significantly rudderless. It would be nice if starships could be governed on the principle that all you need is love, but "love for the fragile craft" might be only a necessary, not a sufficient, condition. If polity proves to be the weakest link in the fragile chains binding a closed system together, nostrums about filial piety for the craft, and about "biophilia"[Wilson1984] for its natural order, may not offer much reinforcement. After all, there will be much less to love aboard an artificial starship, compared to the one we are already on.

4.1 Insular Modern Terrestrial

If the situation with the planet is brightening on some fronts while dimming on others, the fate of insular modern societies is an unpleasant reminder of both the worst of the past and the worst prognostications for human civilization. At least one insular modern terrestrial society profiles as follows:

- energy source: Sol, oil, coal, some nuclear.
- population: a few tens of millions
- population density: low to medium
- technology: medium to high
- ecosystem: NE Asian Continental
- time scale: decades to ???
- ecosystem genetic diversity: medium
- cultural diversity: very low
- cybernetics: you had to ask?

If nothing else, North Korea demonstrates that a degree of insularity can be achieved in a modern society even when the society is battered by a series of dynastic succession crises and famines. Juche assumes an external political environment that's characterized (for propaganda purposes) as implacably hostile, and only occasionally as a source of useful resources (framed by its criminal elite as "tribute.") A generation starship assumes an external physical environment that's definitely implacably hostile, but which might have a few resources to be exploited along the way (e.g., the heat sink of the cosmic background, interstellar hydrogen to scoop up for reaction mass). The useful resemblances seem to end there, however.

4.2 Space stations: Mir & ISS

The international space station projects seen thus far should encourage us in the belief that life in a free-flying spacecraft is possible at all. In both cases, intervals of months between resupply were achieved, and operations proceeded despite the umbilicus of radio communications being intermittent from hour to hour. Even with the health challenges in view (posed mainly by microgravity, perhaps secondarily by elevated background radiation), we have at least learned it's possible to spend a year or so in space. Whole lifetimes might be possible even now. Better yet, the known health issues are probably moot for a generation starship: An urban-scale craft could spin for artificial gravity, and it could amortize the mass cost of its radiation shielding over a large human habitat, in which some of the more robust parts of the ecosystem might serve as additional shielding.

In terms of our chosen parameters, space stations seem to shape up as follows:

- energy source: Sol, imports (fuel, food)
- population: peak so far is 13
- population density: high to very high
- technology: some lagging, mostly exotic
- ecosystem: negligible
- time scale: decades
- genetic diversity: very low
- cultural diversity: medium
- cybernetics....

The governance of space stations doesn't provide much of a polity model, unfortunately. ISS governance was recently summarized (drily, but also poignantly) by Canadian astronaut Chris Hadfield's cover of the David Bowie classic, "Ground Control to Major Tom", performed in weightlessness. Indeed, much of the comic relief value of stories from orbit derives from the brief but tempestuous rebellions of cosmonauts and astronauts, as they bridled against their harrowingly tight schedules and the conflicting demands issued from the ground. And if the cybernetics of space stations sometimes resembles that of top-heavy, too-many-chiefs corporate divisions, their lifespans are not much longer.

4.3 Possible Precedents Compared

The following table should be helpful in seeing how far the suggested precedents depart from what's needed for a generation starship.

	Papuans	Earth itself	Juche	ISS & Mir	Worldship
Energy Source	Sol	Sol+fuels	Sol+petro	Sol+fuels	Fusion
Population	~1K	~5B	~20M	v. low	~10K?
Pop Density	low			urban	urban
Technology	lithic	uneven	mix tech	V. hi-tech	U. hi-tech
Ecosystem	wild				
Time Scale					
Gen. Diversity					
Cult. Diversity					
Cybernetics					?????????

Table 1. Precedents compared

Let's allow that thermonuclear power doesn't even meaningfully exist yet, except from Sol, but simply assume we can solve that technical problem. Let's also allow that we might as well not try to predict any other technology a century out, and that, for now, it's fair to crudely extrapolate, within reason, from what we have. We can see that a mix-and-match approach with each precedent could form some kind of model for a generation starship, except for one problem: how do the pieces fit together? We still have no idea of the most appropriate overall cybernetics. Unless perhaps it's Earth's socio-ecological control systems? Let's take a look at what has been proposed for global governance of a Spaceship Earth, by returning to the main question motivating this paper.

5. Why Are We Here Today?

To revisit the assumptions of this paper:

- Starship design can have "spin off" value for Earth civilization
- "It's the cybernetics, stupid": seeking sustainability in economy, polity, and ecology
- Polity is very hard - there's no true science of it yet.

161

It's not as if nobody has ever thought in similar terms before. Buckminster Fuller brought the Spaceship Earth metaphor into the language of everyday discourse. There's even a Spaceship Earth installation at a Disney theme park, largely at Ray Bradbury's instigation. However, for the original progenitors - urban designers ("Ekistics") and social reformers - the ship metaphor was very much a matter of suggesting a command structure for creating eventual economic equity, under the assumption of global resource limits. Longer-term ecological catastrophe had not yet loomed quite as large.

Unfortunately, the metaphor's origin (leaving Henry George aside) imbues most of the thinking on Spaceship Earth with a bias toward substituting one hierarchical control system for another. Indeed, Fuller shows up now, politically, as an embarrassing conspiracy theorist: the world was controlled by the Great Pirates, he claimed, who had shrunk from view by his time, but who still marshalled resources every bit as much as when they'd roamed the seas.[Fuller1966] The political task (to the extent that he concerned himself at all with politics) was to wrest control away from them. What then? Unclear. Whatever the ideology of those promoting the Spaceship Earth metaphor, none seemed to be theorists of democratic polity. One of them, Barbara Ward[Ward1966], a British aristocrat, was even briefly sympathetic to Nazism, attracted to its revitalizing force, before recoiling in horror at (and, to her credit, ferociously opposing) its anti-semitism. We may feel we now know better than to be taken in by the pageantry (not to speak of the banality) of evil. However, our guard may only be up because such excesses are still within living memory, with shrines to the dead never more than an airliner flight away. Passing time and growing distance will gnaw at those connections, on a generation starship.

The following sections draw very much from the work of Joshua Cohen and Joel Rogers, in their book Associations and Democracy, one of series under the imprint, The Real Utopias Project. My goal here is not prescriptive. Cohen & Rogers' concept of Associative Democracy might be fatally flawed; in fact, much of the book is devoted to the piercing comments of invited critics. Rather, the point is to work within a framework of trade-offs developed by real political scientists - people who think about democracy and its discontents (and, more to the point here, its instabilities) for a living.

6. Democracy - the "Least-worst" System

Churchill famously quipped that democracy "is the worst form of government except all the others that have been tried." At that point, the world had had the benefit of some experience with democracy. Critiques of democracy in action long predated its establishment as a permanent tradition within the nation-state complex and yet democracy as a whole has - so far - survived and spread. Its serious flaws have proved tragic only in the most dramatic circumstances. In a small ecosystem, however, the margin for error is greatly reduced. We are speaking of ecosystems that require social choice to balance, and a collective effort that, moreover, must emerge from an insular society with an ever-more tenuous connection to its origins. In such a theater, the dramas might arrive thick and fast, perhaps overwhelmingly so.

U.S. constitutional framer James Madison called democracy's worst weakness "the mischiefs of faction." It's worth listing the many factors that can play into faction formation. Factions can be

- Geographic
- Class-oriented
- Occupational
- Racial / ethnic / clan-based / tribal
- Enterprise- or industry-oriented
- Ideological

The following sections take factionalism as the biggest threat to democracy in a generation starship. The stakes are high. There will be relatively little territory for a winning faction to conquer, and no interstellar Ellis Island relief valve - no place to which disgruntled, hapless subjects might emigrate in the event that starship democracy becomes a sham, or is replaced altogether by tyranny. Where there's no escape, internal safeguards should be strong.

6.1 Idealized Democracy — an Inventory

In the midst of America's bloodiest war, President Lincoln defended the bloodshed in the name of preserving government "of the people, by the people, for the people." This is still one of the pithiest summaries of a form of government aiming to feature the virtues, as outlined by Cohen & Rogers,

- "popular sovereignty"
- "political equality"
- "distributive fairness"

- "civic consciousness"
- "economic performance"
- "state competence"

Factionalism - over the issue of slavery, chiefly - had led the U.S. into the war in progress during Lincoln's speech. A resource-constrained starship might return to slavery - even civil war - under conditions we can't yet imagine, repeating a history that people had learned yet were forced inexorably to repeat because of systemic polity design errors and their unintended consequence. Perhaps the neglect of only one of these virtues would be enough for the whole house of cards to collapse. Let's anatomize each in turn.

6.1.1 Popular sovereignty

Briefly, the people are the ultimate determiners of authority. Either the people, directly, or their elected representatives, are empowered to --

- Pick goals
- Propose plans
- Choose a plan
- Oversee/enforce it

This notion is probably the most basic concept underlying democracy. Factionalism obviously undermines belief in this concept, insofar as the prevailing factions wield more more power than most people can. A starship society might be more exposed to the risk of faction than most others, except for small island societies. Small islands face little ecological extinction risk, even if they may undergo some species loss under human population pressure. Small islands face outward onto unthinkably larger biomes: oceans. Interstellar hydrogen is a poor substitute. Easter Island's population finally crashed, but it did not wink out of existence. Even if had been reduced to a diet of fish and seaweed, it might have gone on. In space, you'll find neither.

6.1.2 Political Equality

As Cohen & Rogers describe it, political equality is what John Rawls called "the fair value of political liberty." If the goal is equality under the law, then laws regarding political participation must also treat all equally. In particular:

- Everybody has a chance at public office
- Every vote counts the same
- All citizens can vote
- The system actively compensates for individual limits

As an example of that last, there might be a law requiring that the polls stay open for a range of hours so that even those who work graveyard shifts can vote.

The perennial controversies over ballot access for minorities in the U.S. show that these issues of political equality still burn. It's difficult to imagine a starship society evolving a caste system, or a society featuring second-class citizenship, though at least one writer has persuasively imagined that external threats might kick global society into the latter form.[Heinlein1959] Nevertheless, we are trying to hedge against the unimaginable. Only design-for-evolvability can do that, and any threat to representational equality could result in a fragile "monoculture" in starship governance.

6.1.3 Distributive Fairness

Cohen & Rogers hold that no system is truly equitable unless it compensates for individual advantages that are unrelated to moral character. Among the factors contributing to inequities to be addressed, they list:

- Inherited wealth
- Inborn talent
- Luck

At the very least, this suggests there should be no "winner take all" society.

Note that wealth is relative, and the tokens of it sometimes arbitrary. In certain insular Polynesian societies, carving cash 'coins' out of stone meant that the conspicuous consumption of the very rich sometimes involved hiring other islanders to carry their (very heavy) money around for them. Islands can breed odd extremes, as Darwin discovered. This is perhaps no less true of an evolving social order, on an island in interstellar space. A starship might actually need to breed some odd extremes. The question is: which ones might be fatally destabilizing, and which ones only harmless (or even healthy) adaptations?

163

6.1.4 Civic Consciousness
The quality of civic consciousness entails a general agreement that formalizing a due regard for the society as a whole can yield net benefits for the individual. Rogers & Cohen list the minimum requirements:
- Some stable idea of the public interest
- … shared by most citizens …
- … and providing a basis for popular deliberation.

Peons and feudal subjects needn't talk about what their social order should be; they need merely bow before what they cannot change, and hope for the best from lords to whom they never raise their eyes. Religion (taken as Marx's "opiate of the people" rather than as a spiritual resource for staring down life's more withering challenges) can blind us to the "elephant in the room" - uncomfortable and dangerous to mount, much less to steer, especially when the rider is wilfully blind. That a starship society could descend into feudalism - even theocracy - might seem a stretch. But it is dangerous to simply take it for granted that it won't. After all, the assumption itself could be the first turn onto a road to serfdom. Education in how a practical democracy should work at its best is essential to keeping real democracy merely adequate (at least) to practical demands. Such education gives people a standard against which to measure their state. Their civic education should not be left to chance. It should be an irrevocable part of the starship's government mandate.

6.1.5 Economic Performance
Cohen & Rogers emphasize productivity, which might seem a misplaced priority as we look to the later 21st century. Surely, by then, technologically-enabled cornucopian abundance for all will have rendered the issue of labor productivity (even, to a Marxist, of property) entirely moot? Manufacturing is likely to be completely automated, and most information-intensive services would be automated as well. These trends are already in place. Life aboard a starship should be sybaritic. But is it really that simple?

As a closed system without an enormous and varied economy to draw on,, a starship must be able to reproduce its own factors of production. Many of those factors might be biological. Some of those biological means might revert to being human: a labor force, trading its time for wages. Accordingly, Cohen & Rogers advise that a democratic state needs to:
- Foster growth, or, at least …
- Maintain acceptable prosperity

But this seems to raise yet more questions. The idea that economic growth could ever be a priority for a starship also seems misplaced. Wouldn't a starship not only naturally have but also need a steady-state economy? Experimental economics raises the question of whether steady-state is even possible.

In recent years, it's understood that economies can boom and slump on their own, with entirely endogenous drivers, and that pulling an economy out of a slump is not always an easy task. We can't simply assume that a complex economy in a starship won't be subject to business cycles. The business cycle problem was assumed solved during the Great Moderation, until two bubbles in a decade-long span (the second bubble's bursting being very severe) put an end to that assumption. Experimental economists now understand more about the conditions under which bubbles can form. They are less sure about what to do to prevent them without economic strangulation, though there are some intriguing thoughts on the matter. [Miller 2001]

More intriguing, however, is the prospects for growth even as the material substrate of a starship shrinks. As Sam Dinkin points out[Dinkin2013], a starship could continue to receive information about mass-saving innovations as the gap grows between the home system and the craft, and as the total spacecraft mass dissipates and erodes. These innovations might improve productivity not just on the basis of human time, but also spacecraft mass.

6.1.5 State Competence
It would seem to go without saying: distributing common-pool resources not just fairly but efficiently can make all the difference in people choosing a democracy over more authoritarian forms of rule. As Gérard Chaliand pointed out long ago [Chaliand1989], the developing world tends to alternate between military juntas and democracy. At this writing, South America seems to have escaped this dreary cycle, while the Arab world appears to be entering it with a vengeance, and sub-Sahara Africa seems never very far from it. In these cycles, democratic leadership tends more toward greater corruption - and coups are often greeted with relief. Accordingly, a competent state would
- foster public confidence
- stabilize democracy

Note the strong connection here with distributional fairness and other elements of the democratic ideal. Whatever the limits of the military, it is often the most egalitarian, demographically representative and meritocratic institution in developing-world societies. We cannot simply assume a starship society without a need for armed force. That junta rule could emerge from democracy in a starship - for lack of more competent alternatives - cannot be safely ruled out. A sufficiently civic-minded cabal of colonels might even fake an external alien-intelligence threat on a starship, confabulating on-board fifth columns, in the interest of "turning this ship around," politically. This is a particular source of concern if some ennui or existential malaise growing aboard the starship gives rise to a UFO cult, a threat of theocracy by cynical sociopaths, a threat that could perhaps only be countered by coup leaders by accepting the irrational belief but then turning it against its originators.

6.1.6 The Faction Problem Reformulated

Let's see if we can say it all in one (long) sentence:
- Let no faction become parasitically dominant, but …
- … don't let the controls stifle freedom, diversity or prosperity either, while …
- reproducing a legitimate, well-understood government for generations.

The civic understanding part is especially important for vitality in a democracy. This is not to slight leadership, which will always be essential. But the idealized democratic virtues should help produce long-view leaders who see virtue as its own reward. As Lao Tsu put it, "When the best leader's work is done, the people say, 'We did it ourselves!'" A starship society, upon arrival at a habitable planet (if that's actually the goal), should be able to say "We got here," not "They got us here." A we-got-here society will provide a much firmer basis for healthy colonial government.

Note that 'arrival' can be a metaphor that extends even to an Earth that has transcended its crises of resource depletion and species loss, through whatever cybernetics we evolve to reach that new equilibrium. A Terran planetary citizen who's saying "We got here" would be more likely to aid in the work needed to stay at that point for as long as necessary. A "they-got-us-here" subject will always be a distracted contributor, looking out suspiciously for where "They" might take us next, and eyeing the exits in the meantime. A starship will have no exits to eye. The social gaze will fall on the distrusted cybernetician elite faction, magnifying every flaw, with even some elite virtues ending up framed as flaws. This is tinder for the most dangerous kind of populism - the wolf in sheep's clothing who drives away the shepherd.

6.2 Democracy - Its Main Forms

Rogers & Cohen provide a rough taxonomy of solutions to the problem of approaching the ideal form and avoiding factional dominance. Their list:
- "neoliberal constitutionalism" (Hayek)
- "civic republicanism" (Hamilton)
- "egalitarian pluralism" (Dahl)

Each has its own approach to the "mischiefs of faction." As Rogers & Cohen analyze them, each approach has its own strengths and weaknesses. Starship society designers might try to add more approaches, but they are likely to fall within the same overarching categories.

6.2.1 Neoliberal Constitutionalism: Limit Faction by Limiting the State

Hayek is probably the exemplar for neoliberal constitutionalists. Their faction management strategy: limit state power, so that there's not much power for any faction to abuse. Among the features:
- Avoid limiting associational liberties
- Anti-pluralist to avoid bargaining
- Limit the state to limit faction
- Promote divided government
- Use competition: free markets, elections
- but also use anti-trust, and limiting unions is OK

Rogers & Cohen see in this approach the risk of increasing returns to the already advantaged, with growing inequality an affront to the civically conscious. They believe that, politically, we "can't get there from here" anyway. Worse, to try would only give birth to, or further empower, factional power bases that either oppose or circumvent the change. Finally, they see it throwing the baby out with the bath. That is, associations that could become abusive factions might, in some more inclusive polity, become benign sources of information and regulation for government. Absent such opportunities, their virtues could end up stunted or squandered. A starship democracy, being small in global terms (city-sized), will need all the cognitive diversity it can manage. So this squandering of the perspectives of diverse interests is perhaps the highest opportunity cost that a starship would pay in adopting the Hayekian state.

6.2.2 Civic Republicanism: Limit Factions By Insulating The State From Factions

The core strategy for civic republicans: tolerate, even promote, a strong state, but insulate that strong state from factions.

- Strengthen the state vs. factions (Hamilton)
- Also anti-pluralist to avoid the bargaining of "bazaar politics"
- Foster "juridicial democracy" (Lowi)
- Insulate deliberative public-good institutions
- Accept lobbying, guardedly, as education
- Value precision in government over "vague delegations" of powers

Rogers & Cohen are rather unsparing in their criticism of this model as well. As they point out, it shares some of the weaknesses of neoliberal constitutionalism, by missing the potential for win-win/non-zero-sum games with associations, and by underutilizing associations for their educational value.

The most troubling weakness, however, is that the more resourceful will circumvent the insulation; and once they are on top of it, there's nothing to be done. In this objection, Rogers & Cohen might have their best counter-argument. After all, it's thought that Saddam Hussein achieved domination of Iraq because he gained the power to appoint judges - and favored those who adjudicated in favor of his own Ba'athist faction while otherwise handing down fair decisions to everyone else. In short, he cornered the market on what little fairness there was, in a corrupt system where judges were being bought left and right. Under a more benevolent dictator, this might have actually helped grow more fairness in Iraqi society. We know the upshot: Whatever civic republicanism Ba'athism might have originally embodied, it ended up largely undermined. A starship society can't afford to let a particularly wealthy faction buy its judiciary. Down that palatial hallway, we might find only torture chambers.

6.2.3 Egalitarian Pluralism: Limit Factional Dominance By Making All Factions Equal

If every identifiable grouping gets a seat at the table, no group can claim to be voiceless. In a society where under-representation and non-representation are serious problems, this approach holds great appeal - at least to those who feel left out. The egalitarian pluralist strategy for avoiding factional dominance is to accommodate all factions on an equal footing. Among the ways to restate this strategy::

- Oppose special interests "with a vengeance"
- Give all factions seats at the table
- Don't enshrine freedom - it leads to some factions gaining more power
- Define the "common good" as the bargaining of groups
- Foster an egalitarian "bazaar"

As Rogers & Cohen point out, dethroning liberty, shedding insulation, and allowing no limits on the state doesn't really solve any problems. It merely enshrines political process with no universalistic civics in the shrine - or civics only as pro forma incense. Around the shrine: the bazaar. Eventually, as in most bazaars, bargaining will become more bilateral and less transparent. In the system's growing disorganization, information useful for globally optimizing benefits to society will be lost, and dangerous factions might arise out of the resulting information asymmetries. A starship society, being very resource-limited (except perhaps in energy, which you can't eat) will need globally optimizing benefits more than most insular societies.

6.2.4 Overview: Strengths And Weaknesses

The following table should help visualize the trade-offs in choosing among the three models of democracy.

	"Hayek"	"Hamilton"	"Dahl"
popular sovereignty			
political equality			
distributive equity			
civic consciousness			
economic performance			
state competence			

Table 2: the democratic models compared

It might come as no surprise that some of the more economically and politically successful societies have arrived at something close to civic republicanism as the "least worst" system. Scandinavia is nominally egalitarian pluralist, but Rogers & Cohen argue that it's a special case. Its dependence on exports for growth in the "economic miracle" of post-war European reconstruction compelled factional unanimity around economic performance goals. This unanimity was achieved in societies that were none too pluralist to begin with: small, and with high ethnic homogeneity. Starship societies will be small, but they won't be export-oriented at all, much less exporting into a thirsty growth market. High pluralistic diversity would probably be a good feature for starship societies. They'll need more cognitive diversity to democratically solve problems that nobody can rescue them from. Egalitarian pluralism on a starship might too easily dissolve into factional bickering, with one faction ultimately triumphant.

On the face of it, something like civic republicanism might be the "least worst" choice for starship societies as well - but only if this is truly how the choices are limited. A starship project presupposes a society on Earth that has become (or at least enjoys strong representation in) an inner-planet spacefaring civilization. We have good reason to wonder whether such a state of affairs in space isn't achieved by moving on from -- or at least radically extending -- the available choices for democracy.

7. A Space-Faring Civilization

To attend a conference like 100-Year Starship Symposium makes it a virtual certainty that you're a partisan for becoming a spacefaring civilization. The nagging problem, four decades after the last bootprints on the moon, is this: How do we get there from here?

There seems to be little doubt about a necessary condition for civilizational expansion into space: we will need much better economies of scale in Earth-to-orbit launcher production and launch operations. Schisms have formed over what would be the cheapest way to provide this scale, given adequate demand. Some simply assume (or at least suggest) that adequate demand would materialize if only the scale were provided.[Walker1993] Some say that Space-Based Solar Power is the "killer app" for space transportation demand. Others advocate Mars colonization. Most thinking on the subject falls afoul of naivete about what's been called the Political Economy of Very Large Space Projects.[Hickman1999]

Earth-to-orbit transportation that's theoretically cheaper does not, in itself, address the necessary condition for its use: some big, new source of launch demand. A starship won't be that source of demand any time soon. We still don't know how to build a starship, and it's unlikely to be funded until there's more certainty about that. A century seems the right time-scale for talking about these things. A starship's time is unlikely to come, however, unless getting to Earth orbit has been made cheap in the meantime.

7.1 Demand-Scale Solutions So Far Proposed

Drawing on historical analogies to the U.S. frontier, John Hickman proposes that demand will materialize with some new militarization of space.[Hickman2010] If there's a new space race between the U.S. and China, he may well be deemed prophetic. Such a future is far from certain, however. Diplomatic moderation, a general liberalization of the PRC regime, and new arms treaties are all possibilities that could foreclose this option for increased launch demand.

Keith Lofstrom proposes that microelectronic satellites in an enormous orbital cloud would be a very economical way to meet humanity's apparently unslakable thirst for computing and data centers. He makes an excellent case in commercial terms, in humanitarian terms (cheap telecom for the developing world), and in terms of husbanding our diminishing energy resources on Earth. However, even he admits there might be technological showstoppers.[Lofstrom2009-2013]

Orbital space tourism could draw upon a virtually inexhaustible supply of customers, as the developing world begins to produce billionaires in numbers we've mainly seen in the West so far. Admittedly, launch of tourists is currently monopolized by Russia, with its *Soyuz* being the only manned craft for reaching ISS and returning from it; the rumored prices have only increased since Dennis Tito's landmark flight. At this point, however, a number of commercial launcher initiatives show promise for competitively serving this market before the decade is out. Unfortunately, with such an illiquid market, demand is far from certain. In particular, the true demand elasticities farther out along the curve remain mysterious: would much cheaper launch mean many more launches for this market? This chicken is still pecking its way out of the shell, and whether it will succeed, grow, and lay more eggs is uncertain.

Finally, there is the strategy of Build It and They Will Come. John Walker, in a popular essay, proposed that some nation simply fund a high rate of rocket launch, citing the German V-2 program as a precedent for beating costs down through sheer volume. Perhaps some new market would emerge.[Walker1993] (Peter Diamandis alluded to this essay's analysis and conclusions in remarks that were widely reported, but unfortunately misunderstood for lack of more delicate framing.) Perhaps such an experiment might actually be conducted, as part of a program of economic stimulus, in an authoritarian nation where a (Saddam-like) dictator needed nobody's permission to give a radical space program a shot. The weakness of this approach is in answering a question with a question.

7.2 Exovivaria - A New Space Recreation?
According to the Project Persephone website, one of the organization's goals is:

... to see if exovivaria - ecosystems in orbit, collectively governed but also hosting private property and commerce - can become an economical pastime for those of us who can't go. Teams on Earth would tend these ecosystems through video links and teleoperation, using the Internet to update each other on "the state of our worlds." Some members (mostly in the developing world) might be paid for their efforts. Others (mostly in the developed world) would pay to take part. Much of the "game value," whether it derived from earnings or just sheer fun, would be in feeling part of a team and in competing with other teams. However, the problem of keeping an ecosystem alive would also make this a Serious Game, one requiring some cooperation from all. You might think of it as a microcosmic Spaceship Earth.

Project Persephone takes encouragement for the idea of exovivaria from the very existence of one orbital recreation: space adventure travel, which remains an idea that's breathtaking and inspiring in its simplicity. That is, instead of appealing to ostensibly rational reasons for space development, appeal to purely affective motivations: many people want to experience spaceflight, and a few can even afford it. The question here is whether there's a much cheaper substitute for actually going, with reasonable demand for that substitute. The exovivarium concept requires a market test. Project Persephone aims to provide initial testing on a non-profit basis. Concurrently, it might provide a testbed for experiments in the cybernetics of starship societies.

7.3 Exovivarium User Demand? Unknown
Without knowing in advance what the user experience will be like for exovivarium "exopolitans", it's impossible to assess how sustainably appealing it could be. At the moment, the best one can do is argue for a market along the lines of the Drake Equation for guessing at extraterrestrial populations:

- Only 1% interested at all
- Only 1% of those can afford it
- Only 1% of those choose it as pastime
- Is the market glass half-empty or half-full?
- Half-empty: "Only" one-in-a-million
- Half-full: 9,000 "early adopters"!

9,000 out of 9 billion is a tiny fraction, but it does provide a basis for "split-testing" on virtual exovivaria, since split-testing has been done on much smaller user bases. (The basis for financing a virtual exopolitan governance that can generate a rainy-day surplus might enjoy a somewhat less venerable provenance.[Krugman2010]) Virtual exovivarial experiences that prove compelling can then be tried in terrestrial prototypes, which would incur more expense per experimental subject because they are made of atoms, not bits. Experiences that remain compelling in prototypes can be further evaluated for the risks they might pose to real (orbiting) exovivaria. Those that make that cut can be accommodated in the design of the actual spacecraft. At that point, with a substantial mindshare, launch might be financed in large part by auctioning off yet-to-be-created "land" and other resources (non-monopolistically) in the future exovivarium.

7.3 Exovivarium Costs? Unknown

It seems obvious enough that being telepresent in orbit would be a lot cheaper than actually going. But how much cheaper? Without learning from experiment what sorts of ecosystems or spacecraft would sustainably host exovivaria, precise estimation is a fool's errand. Nevertheless, a general case might be made that one minute (or one decade) of orbital telepresence in an exovivarium could be thousands of times less expensive than the same amount of real presence in orbit, whether in a space station or in a private "space hotel."

Once an ecosystem+telebot "starter yeast package" has been derived, Project Persephone would be launching what might be only an inflatable shell that wraps a "mud ice cube" studded with small silicon and metal telebot components. The mass might be only a hundred kilograms or so. Being disposable and durable, exovivaria starter packages could be launched

- as low-cost payloads
- on low-reliability rockets (ICBMs slated for destruction anyway?)
- with potentially very high accelerations

All three of these factors, in combination, suggest much lower launch costs. In the long run, if the experiment succeeds in radically boosting launch demand, a more projectile style of launch might be ideal for further reducing costs and widening the market. As argued in a NASA launch technology roadmap: [NASA 2012]

> Ground-based, hypervelocity accelerators for low-cost delivery of large numbers of small, high-g tolerant payloads to LEO are a near-term technology that can provide significant payoff for a relatively small technology investment.

7.4 Exovivaria As Social/Ecological/Political Cybernetics Labs

The Project Persephone website suggests a number of experiments in economic and political mechanisms for achieving policy goals, most of them intended to address known market failures, known democratic deliberation failures, or both. Among them:

- Emissions trading systems for environmental management
- Hanson/Abramowicz Predictocracy for policy decisions
- Roemer's Equal Shares for citizen equity in firms
- Mark Klein's Deliberatorium for moderated discussion
- Fishkin's Deliberative Poll as model for preparing and framing discussion
- Vernon Smith's bubble-dampeners for smoothing business cycles

The word-count limits on 100YSS Symposium papers forbid going into more detail on these, each of which might merit a paper in itself. Let this suffice: if there were upwards of 9,000 users of virtual exovivaria, there would be considerable scope for experimenting with combinations of these mechanisms, modifying the mechanisms, and simply disposing of mechanisms that either don't work or prove to be redundant with better approaches.

7.4 Virtual Population? Can It Work?

Telepresence in a society where others are telepresent resembles virtual presence in MMORPGs. This similarity raises the very reasonable objection that exovivaria would be vulnerable to the social pathologies found in such games - pathologies one would not want to see on starships. These issues are rendered even more serious by the dim prospects for online democracy, especially in such games. Among two relevant research results, we have those of Cass Sunstein[Sunstein 2002] and of John McKnight[McKnight 2012].

Sunstein: "The Law of Group Polarization"
- deliberation often only polarizes the participants
- … and it gets worse on-line

McKnight: "The Failure of Convivencia"
- democracy is unpopular in virtual worlds
- … and attempts at democracy only produce intense factionalism

Only experiment can confirm whether these phenomena are better (or perhaps worse) in virtual exovivaria and terrestrial prototypes. I argue that there are reasons for hope on both counts. But first: what's going wrong in these contexts?

7.5 Diagnosis: Not Much At Stake

Incentives matter in market behavior. They matter for democracy too. Vital interests matter very much: some incentives take the form of the threat of loss. (Indeed, it's been argued that the prospect of loss, all else equal, is more compelling than the prospect of gain.)

With these motivational themes in mind, let's look at how being online offers only a kind of fun-house mirror of real-world incentives:

- Virtual worlds: one can kill with real-world impunity
- Virtual worlds: virtual reincarnation on the cheap
- Online debate: nobody knows you're a dog
- Online debate: Talk is cheap
- Online debate: Trolling is fun
- Online debate: Anti-trolling enforcement is expensive

In short, the usual social and physical inhibitions preventing us from descending into savagery (or other forms of social infantilism) have diminished force, if any, in virtual worlds. Could exovivaria offset these tendencies somehow? It might be argued that they already do, almost by definition.

7.6 Life Itself To The (Moral/Ethical) Rescue?

E.O. Wilson has hypothesized that biophilia is an in-born trait in human beings: living things command our attention and our affection in ways that inanimate objects can't. On-orbit experimentation with growing plants suggests that this attention might be especially profound.[Hirsch2013] With a "Second Self"[Turkle1984] telepresent in space with truly vital interests there, we might feel strong personal attachments to:

- family/child proxies: pets
- employee proxies: livestock
- general social proxies: "charismatic microfauna"

Nevertheless, it's reasonable to ask just how civilizing "owned non-human life" can be, regardless of whether the ownership is private or in a well-managed commons. After all, Earth still hosts anarchic pastoral cultures that are significantly oriented around cattle-raiding.

Here, perhaps we can only invoke a kind of path-dependence: an exovivarium (not to speak of a starship) would be no politico-economic tabula rasa. We will assume initial conditions that at least include property rights and the rule of law. Exovivaria should not be required to recapitulate civilizational evolution to reach their optimal social organization; perhaps they couldn't anyway, no matter how much time they were given. Starships, with their much higher capital investment, should likewise start from a more reasonable point. The governance problem is not so much "how to get there from here." It's more to see if "there's a there, there." And, once there, whether you can stay there.

7.7 Telebots as "Second Self"?

Another type of embodiment that might lend itself to the incentives of true loss - and therefore to salient social norms for framing a democratically legitimate legal system - springs from the fact that animals can't do it all. There will be tele-operative equipment - "telebots" - in the exoviviarium to help carry out ecosystem maintenance, spacecraft maintenance, and some purely recreational functions. Telebots could have the following features:

- Personal (or small-group) property
- Customizable - a visible personality
- A Turklean "second self" when they are personalized property
- A heroic "avatar" (better: avatar team vehicle) on the cheap, in emergencies.

We can't leave this question without acknowledging the problem of how people would "know what they know" - the "epistemics of telebotics." There has been work on telerobotics and botanicals, investigated by Ken Goldberg, et al., in the Telegarden experiments.[Goldberg2001] Since that time, webcams have become much less exotic technology. Until photorealistic real-time rendering of persuasively simulated natural nvironments becomes equally cheap and commonplace, the "telepistemological" questions raised (i.e., what's real if it's ostensibly happening somewhere else?) might seem only quirkily academic. If such questions are ever raised with respect to real (i.e., orbiting) exovivaria, they might be decisively settled by relatively indefeasible means. The existence of such a spacecraft could be verified with optical telescope observations and narrow-beam communications. Its contents could be verified by inspecting artifacts made in orbit and conspicuously returned from orbit (some of which might have commercial collector value) These artefacts (which might include biomaterials with DNA) could be cryptographically signed to prevent fakery.

7.8 Exovivarial Cybernetics Compared

The following table should help in assessing how close the exovivaria cybernetic design problem approaches the starship cybernetic design problem.

	Papuans	Earth itself	Juche	ISS & Mir	Worldship	Exovivaria
Energy Source	Sol	Sol+fuels	Sol+petro	Sol+fuels	Fusion	Sol
Population	~1K	~5B	~20M	v. low	~10K?	~1k-~3k?
Pop Density	low			urban	urban	
Technology	lithic	uneven	mix tech	V. hi-tech	U. hi-tech	V. hi-tech
Ecosystem	wild					
Time Scale						(See caveat)
Gen. Diversity						
Cult. Diversity						
Cybernetics					????????	?????????

Table 3. Exovivarium matching attempt

The most dramatic departure that could matter here seems to the time-scale: exovivaria will probably have relatively short lifetimes, on the same order as those of the space stations lofted so far. However, this is appropriate: exiovivaria would initially be "test tubes", and (in business terms) ultimately more like theme parks than whole civilizations.

Note, however, that the decommissioning and deorbiting of an exovivarium need not be the end of the social aspects of such a simulacrum. Since its human denizens are telepresent in the first place, "exopolitans" could certainly "migrate" easily to newer exovivaria, as citizens with all of their cultural learnings intact. At some cost, they might also arrange for their livestock, pets and favorite ornamental plants to be transported. If human lifespans can be significantly extended, a kindergartener playing in a virtual exovivarium in 2015 might board any starship that comes to fruition in 2115 as a wise, seasoned and senior member of a starship polity that originally grew from an exovivarial seed, one that the member had known continuously - and helped evolve - since childhood.

8. Exovivaria - For Aerospace Engineers And Life Scientists

There is work to be done on exovivaria well before any are fully designed and lofted. Terrestrial prototypes - admittedly limited in simulating exact configurations and artificial gravity levels -- would help provide a degree of reality for the "Second Self" factors of interest. This analog lab work will require aerospace engineers and ecologists, and perhaps even synthetic biologists where existing terrestrial organisms just can't meet the requirements.

In software, a more physically realistic simulation could be achieved. However, until there are orbiting exovivaria, the questions raised by Goldberg et al. are more salient here: Achieving a degree of gravitational realism in MMORPG exovivaria, for, say, 1/6th g in order to match what the moon could offer an ecosystem but doesn't yet, only tells the user that the briefly airborne hopping turtle on the screen can't be real. Such simulations may help hone skills for use in real exovivaria, and expose unsuspected problems that they'll suffer, but they will also limit the degree to which the user can "fall into" a Second Self projection.

In both kinds of experimental arenas, it will be important to study failure, and refine.

8.1 Exovivaria - For Social Scientists

Although it might resemble "doing plumbing with the water running," exovivaria terrestrial prototypes and virtualizations should provide a rich field of exploration for social scientists. One field of application is the engineering effort itself. Resource trading systems as applied to spacecraft design would form but one class of examples, one that offers an inspiring precedent or two. Economist Robert Ledyard et al. implemented the Cassini Resource Exchange in which teams designing various components of this very complex interplanetary probe communicated with each other in large part by trading various limited resources - mass, power, etc. - that were freed up or allocated during their individual teams' design iterations.[Ledyard1994] The exchange is believed to have had very salutary effects on the schedule, on the budget, and especially on final spacecraft mass. We should have more such experiments, applied to more space applications.

Another fertile field for social scientists on Project Persephone is the developing-world "telepresent" labor force. If a democratic polity can be designed for exovivaria, it might be the first effective democracy that many of these workers have ever participated in. Studying how they adopt it, adapt to it, or simply reject it could be grist for the mill of quite a few dissertations and research papers.

8.2 Exovivaria - For Anybody Who Cares

If Project Persephone reaches any scale at all, it will involve quite a few stakeholders who aren't engineers, bioscientists, social scientists or developing-world experimental subjects. Employees, volunteers, donors and beneficiaries will all be essential for the organization, even when they can only serve as encouraging bystanders in the exovivarium design process. For them, understanding how and why Project Persephone pursues its agenda scientifically is important to the overall enterprise. This same consideration is vital in starship polity: clearly conveying how and why the government was designed the way it was speaks to the general question of democratic legitimacy.

9. Conclusions

As John Carter McKnight likes to put it (following Kim Stanley Robinson), "As above, so below." In other words, we're already a generation starship society. Those of us who know it bear a special onus to make the metaphor work for those who don't. Starship Earth could yet founder, with Madison's "mischiefs of faction" being the Chief Demon in the boiler room.

In this, exovivaria might offer grounds for hope. The "boiler explosions" in real polities are lethal. In virtual exovivaria, terrestrial prototypes and even the orbital ones, finger-pointing would be inevitable, but very unlikely to turn deadly. Exovivaria might enable us to do something like human social experiments via non-human proxies.

Science has a funny way of failing upward. So has civilization - so far, anyway. Exovivaria might be a good starting point for "failing upward" to a space-faring civilization - maybe even to the stars. There's a world to win if exovivaria succeed. In what's learned even if they fail, however, we might avoid losing the one world we have.

Acknowledgements

This paper has benefited by comments and suggestions from Aragon St.-Charles of Japan Aquaponics, and Sam Dinkin of Power Auctions. Over the years, John Carter McKnight has been an indispensable sounding board for the ideas behind Project Persephone

References

1. Abramowicz, M. *Predictocracy: Market Mechanisms for Public and Private Decision Making*, Yale University Press, 2008

2. Castronova, E., "Virtual Worlds: A First-Hand Account of Market and Society on the Cyberian Frontier", CESifo Working Paper Series No. 618, December 2001

3. Cohen, J, Rogers, J., *Associations and Democracy*, Verso, 1995

4. Dahl, R.A, *A Preface to Democratic Theory*, University of Chicago Press, 1956

5. Dinkin, S, pers. comm., Sep 2013

6. Fuller, R.B. *Operating Manual for Spaceship Earth* , 1969.

7. George, H., *Progress and Poverty* (1879)

8. Gibson, W. "NPR Talk of the Nation", National Public Radio, 30 November 1999 discover.npr.org/features/feature.jhtml?wfId=1067220

9. Goldberg, K. ed, *The Robot in the Garden: Telerobotics and Telepistomology in the Age of the Internet*, MIT Press, 2001

10. Hanson, R. "Shall We Vote on Values, But Bet on Beliefs?", to appear in *Journal of Political Philosophy*, 2013

11. Hickman, J., "The Political Economy of Very Large Space Projects", *Journal of Evolution and Technology*, Volume 4, November 1999

12. Hickman, J. *Reopening the Space Frontier*, Common Ground Publishing (November 23, 2010)

13. Hirsch, J, "Space Farming: the Final Frontier", *Modern Farmer*, http://modernfarmer.com/2013/09/starship-salad-bar/

14. Krugman, P, "The Underpants Gnomes Theory of Reform" in *The Conscience of a Liberal* (blog entry), www.nytimes.com, January 21, 2010

15. Landemore, H. *Democratic Reason: Politics, Collective Intelligence, and the Rule of the Many*, Princeton University Press (2012).

16. Ledyard, J.O., et al., "Using computerized exchange systems to solve an allocation problem in project management", *Journal of Organizational Computing*, Volume 4, Issue 3, 1994

17. Lofstrom, K. Server Sky: Orbital Data Centers (website), 2009-2013

18. McKnight, J.C., "A Failure of Convivencia: Democracy and Discourse Conflicts in a Virtual Government", *Bulletin of Science, Technology and Society*, October 2012 vol. 32 no. 5 361-374

19. Meadows, D.H. et al. *The Limits to growth: A report for the Club of Rome's Project on the Predicament of Mankind*, Universe Books, 1974

20. Miller, R.M. "Can Markets Learn to Avoid Bubbles?", Miller Risk Advisors, 2001

21. NASA, April 2012. Launch Propulsion Systems Roadmap: Technology Area 01, p.2

22. Stevenson, A., Speech, to the Economic and Social Council of the United Nations, Geneva, Switzerland, July 9, 1965. quoted from —*Adlai Stevenson of the United Nations*, ed. Albert Roland, Richard Wilson, and Michael Rahill, p. 224 (1965).

23. Sunstein, C. "The Law of Group Polarization", *Journal of Political Philosophy* 10 (2):175–195 (2002)

24. Turkle, S. *The Second Self: Computers and the Human Spirit*, MIT Press, 1984

25. Turner, M.E. "Exovivaria" (wiki article), www.projectpersephone.org: Project Persephone, 2009.

26. Walker, J., "A Rocket a Day Keeps the High Costs Away", Fourmilab (website), September 27, 1993

27. Ward, B. *Spaceship Earth*, Columbia University Press, 1st ed. (1966)

28. Wiener, N, *The Human Use of Human Beings*, Houghton Mifflin, 1954

29. Wilson, E.O., *Biophilia: The Human Bond with Other Species,* Harvard University Press, 1984

Michael Turner

A Holistic Approach for Including Social, Ethical, and Cultural Sensitivities for an Interstellar Civilization

Edythe E. Weeks, Ph.D.

Washington University, Webster University and Outer Space Education Alliance, L.L.P.,

1737 Q Street NW, Washington, D.C. 20009

outerspacedevelopment@gmail.com or eweeks@artsci.wustl.edu

Cameron Ashkarkhizani

Outer Space Education Alliance, L.L.P. and SIT Graduate Institute for World Learning,

1737 Q Street, Washington, D.C. 20009

cameronashkar@gmail.com

Abstract

This paper presents an outline for a holistic approach for including social, ethical and cultural sensitivities to enhance peaceful relations between the inhabitants of a 100 Year Starship. It also addresses the issue of knowledge about aspects of human life which will need to be adjusted to suit the purpose of interstellar travel, and the needs of an evolving global spacefaring civilization. This paper allows the symposium participants to imagine producing monumental innovations and enhanced human capability for aeronautics & astronautics, diversity, international relations, human rights, intercultural competencies, identity development models and interpersonal relations. A key assumption is that by factoring in these types of considerations we can encourage a wider range of people to engage, heighten and contribute their talents and abilities towards enabling humankind to achieve sustained interstellar travel. This aims to include an ideal type quality of life, amidst an interstellar voyage. We argue that, in addition to complying with the Outer Space Treaty requirements, inviting all members of the human family to participate in the 100 Year Starship endeavor will ensure best efforts are put forth to attract rare minds and abilities, which may otherwise be left behind.

Keywords

interstellar, social-behavioral, space law, intercultural competencies, identity development, interpersonal relations, international relations

1. Introduction

Interstellar spaceflight will be a reality of the future. Thinking ahead and planning must include making sure people function well together on a long duration space mission beyond our solar system. It's not too soon to think about the broad range of social, ethical and cultural issues likely to arise between diverse groups of people, living and working together on a long duration space mission to another star system. The selection process will need to involve a method for choosing people on the basis of their ability to learn and speak various languages, and a flexible respect for various religions, cultures, ethnicities, gender, races and class backgrounds. Few people are aware, or care, that the Outer Space Treaty of 1967 deemed outer space as the "province of mankind". In an effort to allow the participants to conceptualize and articulate ways to consider the impact that outer space development will have including people in various fields of study, professions, races, ethnicities, creeds, gender, regions, religions, classes, nations and ages. It further seeks to demonstrate that through education, a broad range of people can prepare themselves to qualify for opportunities arising as newly emerging industries begin to expand and become established. Recent advances in space science and technology have made it possible for humankind to begin the process of outer space development and colonization. Space studies traditionally have involved the STEMS (science, technology, engineering and math) fields. As more people and diverse groups of people begin to travel into outer space what are the social and behavioral sciences issues that humankind should consider? We envision a holistic approach for creating a peaceful environment in which the inhabitants of a 100 Year Starship can flourish. This includes considering social, ethical and cultural sensitivities to enhance peaceful relations between the inhabitants of a 100 Year Starship. Knowledge about aspects of human life will need to be adjusted to suit the purpose of interstellar travel, and the needs of an evolving global spacefaring civilization. We must ask what is it that we believe we "know" about ourselves and each other. What aspects of everyday human life will need to be adjusted to suit the purpose of interstellar travel, and the needs of an evolving global spacefaring civilization?

2. Inevitability of the Interstellar Journey

In August, 2012 NASA announced the Voyager I spacecraft had traveled outside our solar system. A few months later NASA confirmed reports indicated that it had traveled beyond the heliosphere, making it the first probe to go interstellar [1]. It's inevitable, if these types of consistent milestones continue, humans may one day also be traveling beyond our solar system into interstellar regions too. Increasingly, researchers are providing credible suggestions focused proposed suggestions for on interstellar travel [2]. Naysayers often seem to forget the many decades of successful research and development, along with many instances of successful implementation methods, have led humanity to possess the capability to produce advanced space transportation systems, new types of spaceships, space habitats, space stations, space settlements, space mining enterprises and spacecraft trajectory optimization techniques for landing on near Earth asteroids and spaceports. Interstellar travel may become as real as Skype on a big screen television – something once only envisioned in scifi. Science and technological discoveries are making it possible to move forward towards exploring our universe in new ways. The Hubble telescope has new maps of the outer space terrain, and the Kepler spacecraft sent back images of a multitude of previously undiscovered celestial phenomena, including Earthlike planets.

3. Mapping Out A Holistic Quality of Life

To increase the likelihood of peaceful social and behavioral practices of crew members and participants of the 100 Year Starship voyage, it is important that each individual experience happiness, joy, pleasure, peace, fulfillment, excitement and motivation during this long mission. We examine several factors which might help to create a more ideal type quality of life and existence amidst an interstellar voyage.

3.1 Human Capabilities

Pre-mission training to prepare an international interstellar crew to deal with each other for extended periods of time, peacefully. Imagine producing monumental innovations and enhanced human capability for aeronautics and astronautics, diversity, international relations, human rights, intercultural competencies, identity development models and interpersonal relations. We are proposing a checklist of possible actions to be taken towards optimizing human beings capability. This section provides a blue print for what humanity could be evolve into.

3.2 Intercultural Competence

We argue that, in addition to complying with the Outer Space Treaty requirements, inviting all of humanity to participate in the 100 Year Starship endeavor will ensure best efforts are put forth to attract rare minds and abilities, which may otherwise be left behind. With this, intercultural competence training will be critical for ensuring peacefully interpersonal relations. Intercultural competence is a concept typically defined as involving the ability to understand, gage and make sure not to violate the norms, rules of behavior, and values of people from distinctly different backgrounds [3]. Our world is increasingly becoming evermore complex and globalization and increased frequency of international interactions is a key characteristic of the twenty-first century. Social media, the Internet, online classes, new trade technologies and many other technological advances have provided people with multiple channels for carrying out relationships, business, knowledge gathering and communication. At the same time, segregation structures are eroding, thereby freeing up interactions within multicultural societies, between people of diverse races, ethnicities, gender, class, nationality, religion, creeds and cultures. With all of these interpersonal forms of communication occurring, intercultural dimensions are likely to arise. Thus intercultural competence is at a heightened state of importance. Interpersonal issues can be identified and people can be trained to cope, manage, handle and shift potential sources of conflict over to cooperative endeavors. Preflight communication and interpersonal skill training can be instituted so that interpersonal issues can be identified and people can be trained to cope, manage, handle and shift potential sources of conflict over to cooperative endeavors.

Literature exists setting forth the pedagogy [4] on how to teach intercultural competencies, along with literature providing extensive rationales on why and in what situations intercultural competence is important [5]. Scholars have emphasized the critical need for intercultural competence development to enhance learning for university students in the twenty-first century [6]. Others have stressed the value of intercultural competence in the workplace, beyond the classroom learning environment [7]. For example, Liu & Dall'Alba (2012) make the point that intercultural competence is becoming increasingly important beyond the learning sphere into the workplace and that the experience of intercultural competence training enhances learning and knowledge building.

Howitt, Richard et al., 2013 attribute various land and sea natural resource management failures and international conflicts to the lack of intercultural competence, particularly with respect to indigenous belief systems, environmental stewardship, and clashes caused by contrary practices [8]. Cajander, Daniels and McDermott, 2012 explain the importance of intercultural competence to peer training programs [9]. We agree with these assertions expressing the importance of intercultural competence in a broad array of patterned human interactions. We would like to extend these assertions over on to the realm of astronautics and interstellar space travel. Intercultural competence is especially critical during a long duration mission with international and diverse participants inhabiting an interstellar starship for 100 years. Requiring flight participants and crew members to undergo intercultural competence awareness training could be the key to reducing or preventing instances of social, ideological, psychological and interpersonal conflict during a long duration space mission. We further suggest concentrating on universal themes, which exist across various cultures as a starting focal point for merging belief systems, ideological stances and comfort levels for the diverse, international crew members prior to embarking on their interstellar journey. This can be accomplished by identifying similarities in interior design, architecture, music, fashion, cuisine, art and linguistics and using these links as part of the design structure and interior design for the spaceship, clothing, meals, entertainment, and other things that will impact the senses of crew members during the voyage. Mathematics and numbers have the ability to do this - unify people's ability to function.

Crew members can also be trained to develop new abilities or enhanced abilities to persevere and to cope to improve behavioral health, social skills, interpersonal skills, coping mechanisms, mistrust and other social and behavioral issues that may arise while traveling in outer space with a diverse groups of crew members. training to enable them to deconstruct biased information regarding people's culture, nationality, race, gender, religion, ethnicity and age, since, so much of this is inherited thought from the mass media and other discourses, crew member will need to undergo pre-mission training to learn how to deconstruct hidden exercises of power, hegemony and ideology likely to infect interpersonal communications in ways likely to offend, harm or otherwise prevent cooperation.

3.3 Language Based Identities: Multilingualism as a Potential Glue to Bond Crew Members

Data exists suggesting that, like intercultural competence, speaking more than one language can increase the likelihood of expanded identity consciousness. Similar to intercultural awareness, we argue that multilingualism is an additional critical skill set for crew members aboard a 100 Year Starship. Yegin (2013) uses the term "intercultural communication competence", which is useful for our analysis here blending various skills which are argue are necessary in order to increase the likelihood of social and behavioral success for the 100 Year Starship [10]. Salaberry (2009) suggests that "language alliances" are formed and "language based" identities, this includes being able to identify with specific beliefs, reactions to ideology [and discourses], legal litigation, educational agendas, cultural identifies, political strategizing and other phenomena. Although Salaberry focuses on the United States, key points are applicable to our analysis. For example, deep bonds tend to develop between people who can speak the same language. Understanding and interpretations are more likely to be similar between people because of the identity-language connection that Salaberry illustrates [11]. Multilingualism has also been linked to enhanced brain function. In addition to furthering communicative bonds between more people, multilingualism has also been attributed to enhanced mental abilities. Recent reports indicate that speaking more than one language makes people "smarter" [12]. Kluger (2013) informs us that "[n]ew studies are showing that a multilingual brain is nimbler, quicker, better able to deal with ambiguities, resolve conflicts and even resist Alzheimer's disease and other forms of dementia longer" [13].

3.4.1 A Heightened State of Consciousness
There is support for the perspective that bursts of creativity, genius, inventions, artistic expressions, novel ideas are caused by elevated consciousness [14]. It is important to consider proven techniques for accomplishing elevated states of consciousness to help further prepare crew members and participants for the interstellar mission aboard the 100 Year Starship.

3.4.2 Meditation and Visualization
Throughout history, the heavens above have been a source of spiritual reverence by all peoples. Beyond preparing for a successful interstellar starship mission, humankind must take this opportunity to evolve into a higher self expression. To be engaged in interstellar travel, must we allow ourselves to enter into a heightened state of consciousness? Meditation techniques are a form of coping strategies to relieve boredom, stress, fear, anxiety and to enhance inner peace during long term space missions. Spirituality can be encouraged to spark heightened states of intelligences. As we move closer to a space faring civilization, a universal and applied look into meditation practice will improve the ability for interstellar travelers to cope with long duration space missions.

Meditation has been known to help alleviate pain, anxiety, infection, unpleasant physical and psychological experiences, and other medical conditions which could debilitate crew members. Crew members should be trained or skilled in meditation techniques for various foreseeable circumstances likely to hinder a person's performance. In long duration space missions, sense deprivation, lack of environmental diversity, and vertigo are all issue that meditation can mitigate. Meditation, yoga and other practices have been linked to the ability of people to engage higher states of consciousness, which have allowed many to tap into increased storehouses of abilities [15]. Mediation encourages creativity and genius as well as the day to day ability to function and to find purpose in everyday tasks or work [16]. Some studies suggest that meditation may enable people to experience an enhanced ability love unconditionally and to practices kindness and compassion or "unrestricted readiness and availability to help living organisms" [17]. These practices could be critical during an interstellar mission.

3.5 Health
3.5.1 The Concept of "Holistic Nutrition"
Foods and nutritional supplements capable of "boosting" [18] the brain, might also increase people's ability to achieve an increased level of creativity. This might help people to rise beyond the challenges likely to emerge during and after an interstellar voyage. Colbin's (2002) [19] dissertation, Holistic Nutrition: From Biochemistry to Chaos, Complexity, and Quantum Physics proffers a theoretical framework for seeing connections between nutrition and how it can impact our state of consciousness. This analysis adds to the study of holistic nutrition by applying concepts from contemporary science, including systems theory, complexity theory, quantum physics, and chaos theory to offer an understanding about how food and nutrition affects health along with the "physical, mental, emotional, and spiritual" aspects of human being. Colbin demonstrates that food and nutrition can help maintain and recover health. Beyond food to sustain life and health, we must be cognizant of nutritional components capable of enabling people to maximize their ability to create, innovate and to achieve unthinkable feats and to overcome impossible barriers and challenges currently understood.

3.5.2 Alternative Medicine

It may not be possible to carry the wide range of medicines to cover most of the ailments and illnesses likely to plague the 100 Year Starship crew. Alternative medicine may be a way to ensure cure triggers for ailments and illnesses most likely to impact the crew. Attitudes concerning alternative medicine are beginning to change and more information and research are available [20].

3.5.3 Sexual Health: Drives, Deprivation, Impact on Optimism and Mental Well Being

Whether we assume sexual needs are driven by biological forces, or socially learned, we can anticipate that some of the participants and crew members aboard the 100 Year Starship voyage may experience real or perceived needs for sex. What is likely to happen if beliefs, attitudes, thoughts, fantasies about sex do arise? Will everyone be able to restrict any thoughts and feeling related to sex? Will everyone have a spouse or sex partner during the 100 year journey? Is sex deprivation likely to cause depression many or some of the crew members aboard the Starship? Will needs, feelings, and desires create tension between the people aboard the starship? Is sex necessary for people's well being? How will values, roles, religion, ethical, cultural, sexual orientation and eroticism play out in the interstellar journey scenario? Relying on knowledge in the field of sexual health and sex psychology will help enable us to prepare crew members and participants for these human aspects of the interstellar mission [21]. In addition, there are other concerns that sex in space may be logistically difficult to perform [22].

4. Unchecked Potential for Interpersonal or International Conflict
4.1 Interpersonal Conflict Could Spark War

International partnerships for new types of space missions to new destinations are becoming a new trend. The 100 Year Starship project is planning to carry a diverse crew, including multiple international partners. However, as new missions, both human and robotic, begin to occur more frequently, and as key actors practice partnering across international boundaries, we should also plan for cultural conflicts to potentially arise between crew members traveling throughout outer space during long duration missions. Spaceships, navigation systems and telecommunications devices may operate just fine, yet a mission may be doomed if people clash. Maximizing the enjoyment and freedom of diverse space travelers will require sensitive, intelligent planning that takes into account the potential for interpersonal human conflict. People are likely to take with them historical, ideological, religious, social, moral, ethical, economic, psychological, institutional social and behavioral patterns, and varying perceptions regarding civil rights and human rights, with an eye towards understanding and explaining potential sites of soft conflict.

4.2 The Outer Space Treaty and Peace: International Space Law and Including Everyone

Few people are aware, or care, that the Outer Space Treaty of 1967 deemed outer space as the "province of mankind". It also states that as outer space develops, we must be sure to do so in a way that benefits all humankind. Promoting and ensuring peace as we travel to the stars in required by law. The preamble of the Outer Space Treaty of 1967 (the Constitution for space activities) states:
- INSPIRED by the great prospects opening up before mankind as a result of man's entry into outer space,
- RECOGNIZING the common interest of all mankind in the progress of the exploration and use of outer space for peaceful purposes,
- BELIEVING that the exploration and use of outer space should be carried on for the benefit of all peoples irrespective of the degree of their economic or scientific development,
- DESIRING to contribute to broad international co-operation in the scientific as well as the legal aspects of the exploration and use of outer space for peaceful purposes,
- BELIEVING that such co-operation will contribute to the development of mutual understanding and to the strengthening of friendly relations between States and peoples …

4.3 Remembering History

Stoessinger in Why Nations Go to War (2010) relies on case studies of various wars to support his argument that wars are started by people and their personalities. He demonstrates numerous instances wherein wars between nations were initially triggered by interpersonal conflict, ill will, resentments and emotion. Stoessinger highlights how individual dissent can lead to international conflict. His detailed analysis includes facts surrounding World

War I, World War II, the Korean War, the Vietnam War, the war in Bosnia and "the war over the remains of Yugoslavia", the series of wars between India and Pakistan in 1947, 1965, 1971, and 1998, the wars between Arabs and Jews, Israel and Palestine (The Palestine War of 1948, The Sinai Campaign and the Suez Crisis of 1956, the Six-Day War of 1967, the October War of 1973, the Lebanese Tragedy, and the 1988 Arab-Israeli Conflict); the Iran-Iraq War, the Desert Storm conflict concerning Saddam Hussein's invasion of Kuwait, and the "new war" against terrorism prompted by the 9/11 bombing of the Twin Towers in New York City's World Trade Center. Using his analysis of various conflicts, we can boil it down to two basic reasons for these conflicts emerging: 1) the conquest of new territory and/or 2) conflicting ideologies. The framers of the Outer Space Treaty of 1967 understood these reasons for conflict. Thus, it is consistent with the law. International space law treaties and declarations are replete with articulations requiring peaceful relations in space.

5. Including a Broader Audience of People to for the 100YSS Mission: What is Might Entail

A key assumption is that by factoring in these types of considerations we can encourage a wider range of people to engage, heighten and contribute their talents and abilities towards enabling humankind to achieve sustained interstellar travel. This paper allows the symposium participants to imagine the likely outcomes arising as people are encouraged to contribute their best abilities to enable humankind to achieve sustained spacefaring.

5.1 Sensitivities and Key Concerns

Even in nations with stringent diversity policies and affirmative action laws, measurable discrepancies still continue to exist, interrupting full equality being experienced in real time by people. Excuses are typically made to explain away observable patterned inequality. Individuals are usually blamed. Yet, scholars have provided frameworks for demonstrating systemic forces and how they tend to operate to produce, maintain and manufacture inequality. Labeling practices, representations, discourses, ideologies and existing subtle subjugation patterns (international and within nations) have been named as possible sites for conflict. Language – written, spoken, nonverbal forms of communication, images, poems, lyrics, commercials, jokes, themes operate in ways "to reinforce certain hierarchies in social practices" [23]. Through language we come to understand how to comprehend and interpret each other. Language has "remarkable power" [24]. Ideologies and labels are often accepted at face value to be politically correct, right and fair. We must be willing to perform a critical analysis of discourses, for example, to locate sites where power and language are linked. This requires that we interpret the use of language within historical contexts [25]. This can happen by factoring in and remembering past patterned labeling practices, representations, discourses, ideologies and subtle silent ways in which these phenomena tend to play out, automatically, to help undermine peace and equality between people. In most societies and subcultures there are measurable race-based, nationality-based, gender-based, religion-based, cultural-based, class-based, ethnicity-based, hierarchies.

Training crew members for the 100 Year Starship journey can involve teaching people how systemic inequalities can be observed, noticed, discussed and justly or fairly remedied. For example, what types of psychological-social emotions, sentiments and automatic patterned social and behavioral belief systems and reactions might be associated with a crew participant who is labeled and referred to as "White", "Native American", "Black", "African American", "Chinese", "Bosnian", "Iranian" and so on. As part of creating a living environment, we must be brave enough to address these issues. Various factors, including ideology, discourses, social structures, gender, class, religion, ethnic and race relations and culture tend to be rooted in an understanding of existing sensitivities within the hearts and minds of people. A laser like focus on tensions associated with the above described social constructions, could enhance the peaceful relations between the inhabitants of a 100 Year Starship.

5.2 Becoming Global Citizens for Interstellar Travel

There are themes which exist in a wide variety of cultures such as architecture, music, fashion, cuisine, art and linguistics, which serve to highlight humankind's ability to create, enjoy and need similar things. Interstellar travel can serve as a precursor for a new paradigm shift. Enabling people to combine and focus on similarities more so than on differences is a necessary step in becoming a spacefaring civilization. There are universal themes throughout all cultures such as architecture, music, fashion, cuisine, art and linguistics. Science has been universalized and so can social and behavioral sciences. The goal of global citizenship, in the context of interstellar travel would be to encourage diversities and synthesis in music, fashion, art, cuisine and architecture for a new age of human expression - the space age. Once we can conceive the earth as our home, then we will be able to understand the universe as our world. Adams & Carfagna (2006) explain that in order to survive and to succeed in today's world, people need to understand the trends that go along with globalization so that they can shape their lives as "global citizens" [26].

Cabrera (2010: 13) defines global citizenship as involving "sets of moral understandings that give emphasis to attributes common to all individuals regardless of their national or other group affiliations" [27]. Similarly, Shultz, Abdi & Richardson (2011: 82) suggest that it is "urgent to discover a type of education capable of shaping a citizen able to live in this globalized world in a more ethnical, humane, and emancipated manner" [28]. O'Byrne (2003) sees global citizenship as a possible solution to many of the world's problems. He argues that global citizenship is not a utopian unrealistic fantasy, rather it has been around throughout history, and that world citizenship is a real concept [29]. The trend poses questions of culture in the content of national identity and being able to relate to others beyond their nation-state identity. However, a deeper aim of global citizenship would be for an individual to perceive their citizenship as part of a world, and to perceive each nation as an integral part of their own citizenship. Literature on global citizenship has focused on global citizenship as a possible cultural bridge to promote human rights, promote peace, justice and equality, or to create a nonviolent world. We assert that cultivating global citizenship is a way to produce super intelligence and abilities by way of the synthesis of cultural information and perspectives. Using the global citizenship concept serves as a reminder of the divisions which exist within individuals from different nations, which can be bridged in a way that unites humanity as we seek existence beyond our star system. This might help to foster positive relations and ensure smooth sailing on an interstellar voyage to neighboring star systems.

6. Conclusion

The successful fulfillment of a manned interstellar 100 Year Starship voyage which can trigger the beginning of a new period of Enlightenment – a space age enlightenment. Humankind does not have to repeat ineffective, destructive patterns of the past. Our model of considerations can inform and provide a tool for people to use new dimensions of thought and to tap into their genius and creativity to solve problems related to survival and prosperity in an interstellar human voyage to a neighboring star system. The key to maintaining peaceful international relations is realizing progress in the areas outlined herein. As destinations beyond out solar system become more common, social and behavioral scientists must prepare key actors to become skilled at interpersonal-international relations.

Endnotes

1. Matson, John, "Voyager 1 returns surprising data about an unexplored region of deep space", Scientific American (June 28, 2013). Accessed November 2, 2013 at: http://blogs.scientificamerican.com/observations/2013/06/27/voyager-1-returns-surprising-data-about-an-unexplored-region-of-deep-space/?WT_mc_id=SA_CAT_SPCPHYS_20130627; and NASA, JPL, "NASA spacecraft embarks on historic journey into interstellar space" (September 12, 2013). Accessed November 2, 2013 at: http://www.nasa.gov/mission_pages/voyager/voyager20130912.html#.UnWgvlNhD3M

2. Barnes, Marshall, "Solutions for Factors of Time and Space Distance Challenges Outside of Proposed Models Based on General Relativity", paper presented at the 100 Year Starship Symposium White, Houston, Texas, September 2013; Harold G., "A Discussion of Space-Time Metric Engineering", General Relativity and Gravitation, 35(11): 2025-2033 (2003). Accessed on November 7, 2013 at: http://adsabs.harvard.edu/abs/2003GReGr..35.2025W.

3. Association for the Study of Higher Education (ASHE). "the need for intercultural competency development in classrooms," ASHE Higher Education Report. 38: 2 (2012) 1-21.

4. Association for the Study of Higher Education (ASHE), "Developing a pedagogy that supports intercultural competence," ASHE Higher Education Report. 38: 2, 45-63 (2012).

5. Johnson, James P., Tomasz Lenartowicz and Salvador Apud, "Cross-cultural competence in international business: toward a definition and a model," Journal of International Business Studies 37 (2006) 525-543.

6. 6. Association for the Study of Higher Education (ASHE), "understanding intercultural competence and its development," ASHE Higher Education Report. 38: 2, 23-43 (2012).

7. Liu, Shuang and Gloria Dall'Alba, "Learning intercultural communication through group work oriented to the world beyond the classroom", Assessment and Evaluation in Higher Education 37:1, 19-32 (2012).

8. Howitt, Richard, Doohan, Kim, Suchet-Person, Sandie, Cross, Sherry, Lawrence, Rebecca, Lunkapis, Gaim James, Muller, Samantha, Prout, Sarah and Veland, Siri, "intercultural capacity deficits: contested geographies of coexistence in natural resource management", Asia Pacific Viewpoint 54:2, 126-140 (2013).

9. Cajander, Åsa, Daniels, Mats and McDermott, Roger, "On valuing peers: theories of learning and intercultural competence," Computer Science Education, 22:4, 319-342 (2012).

10. Yegin, Han. "research on fostering intercultural communication competence of foreign language learners", Cross-Cultural Communication 9:1, 5-12(2013).

11. Salaberry, Maximo R. (ed.) *Language Allegiances and Bilingualism in the US* (UK: Multilingual Matters, 2009).

12. Bhattacharjee, Yudhijit, "Why bilinguals are smarter", New York Times, Sunday Review, The Opinion Pages March 17, 2012.

13. Kluger, Jeffrey, "How the brain benefits from being bilingual", Time Science & Space (July 18, 2013).

14. O'Brien, Griff, *Enlightened Consciousness: Entering New Dimensions of Spiritual Awareness* (Bloomington, Indiana: Authorhouse, 2008).

15. Perry, Elaine K. (ed.), Daniel Collerton (Editor), Fiona E.N. LeBeau (Editor), Heather Ashton (Editor), *New Horizons in the Neuroscience of Consciousness* (Amsterdam; Philadelphia: John Benjamins, 2010).

16. Emmons, Robert A., "Spirituality and intelligence: problems and prospects", International Journal for the Psychology of Religion, 10:1 (2000). Special issue: The spiritual intelligence: 57-64.

17. Lutz, Antoine, Lawrence L. Greischar, Nancy B. Rawlings, Matthieu Ricard, Richard J. Davidson, Burton H. Singer, "Long-term meditators self-induce high-amplitude gamma synchrony during mental practice"

18. Proceedings of the National Academy of Sciences of the United States of America, 101 (46): 16369-16373 (Nov. 16, 2004).

19. Potter, Beverly and Sebastian Orfali, *Brian Boosters: Food and Drugs that Make You Smarter* (Ronin Publishing, Inc., 1993).

20. Colbin, Annemarie, "Wholistic nutrition: from biochemistry to chaos, complexity, and quantum physics" Union Institute and University, ProQuest, UMI Dissertations Publishing (2002).

21. National Science Board, "Science and technology: public attitudes and public understanding, belief in alternative medicine", Science and Engineering Indicators – 2002 (Arlington, Virginia: Division of Science Resources Statistics, National Science Foundation, 2002) at: http://www.nsf.gov/statistics/seind02/c7/c7s5. htm#c7s512a and http://en.wikipedia.org/wiki/Alternative_medicine accessed November 7, 2013.

22. Wellings, Kaye, Kirstin Mitchell and Martine Collumbien (eds.), *Sexual Health, A Public Health Perspective* (New York: Open University Press, 2012); Buehler, Stephanie, What Every Mental Health Professional Needs to Know About Sex (New York: Springer Publishing Company, 2014); Rhawn, Joseph (ed.), Neuropsychiatry, Neuropsychology, and Clinical Neuroscience: Emotion, Evolution, Cognition, Language, Memory, Brain Damage, and Abnormal Behavior (Baltimore: Williams & Wilkins, 1996).

23. See http://www.youtube.com/watch?v=IQBZbwuW3Y0.

24. Chouliaraki, Lilie and Norman Fairclough, *Discourse in Late Modernity: Rethinking Critical Discourse Analysis* (Edinburgh: Edinburgh University Press, 1999).

25. Fanon, Franz, *Black Skin White Masks* (New York: Grove Press, 1967).

26. Said, Edward, *Covering Islam: How the Media and the Experts Determine How We See the Rest of the World* (New York: Vintage Books, 1997).

27. Adams. Michael J., and Angelo Carfagna, *Coming of Age in a Globalized World: The Next Generation* (Bloomfield, CT: Kumarian Press, Inc., 2006).

28. Cabrera, Luis. *The Practice of Global Citizenship* (Cambridge: UK, 2010).

29. Shultz, Lynetta, Ali A. Abdi & George H. Richardson, *Global Citizenship Education in Post-Secondary Institutions: Theories, Practices, Policies* (New York: N.Y.: Peter Lang Publishing 2011).

30. O'Byrne, Darren J., *The Dimensions of Global Citizenship: Political Identity Beyond the Nation-State*, O'Byrne (Portland, Oregon, 2003).

Devising the "Prime Radiant": The Virtual Starship Program as a Strategy for Achieving the K0→K3 Transition

Paul Ziolo, PhD

Senior Research Fellow, University of Liverpool

m.p.f.ziolo@gmail.com

Abstract

Transition from terrestrial civilisation's current Kardashev level (c. K0.8 or pre-planetary) to K3 (interstellar – the permanent habitation of deep space) - may prove to be an evolutionary step of greater significance than that once taken by our distant ancestors from sea to land. Such an advance would involve confrontation both with our very identity as a species and with our relationship to the 'machinic phylum' (Johnston 2008) that is now such an integral part of terrestrial civilisation. That the 'outward urge' is stronger than ever is clear from the number of space advocacy groups currently in existence – of which the 100YSS is currently one of the most promising. Nevertheless, the individual goals and political affiliations of these groups are highly diverse, such that the precise methods and steps by which the avowed common goal of space colonisation is to be achieved are by no means clear. Since this goal involves co-operation at an international level, can an overarching plan be devised in which all participants in the space endeavour can participate? An initial step in this direction was the Integrated Space Plan or ISP, formulated in the context of the NASA-Rockwell co-operation towards the close of the 1980's. This study examines how the basic premises of the ISP vision could be re-vitalised as a participatory 'Virtual Starship' program realised through distributed computation on the SETI@home model. Due to the diversity of vision among potential participants, such a program would not necessarily adopt any specific goal architecture as yet, but would employ a metagenetic programming strategy to seek out optimal compromise solutions – i.e. through the process of program induction (Koza 1992) . In this manner the 'machinic phylum', by acting on independent evolutionary principles, may be engaged as a politically-neutral ally in assisting us towards the realisation of our common goal.

1. Prologue: Kardashev Levels and Metasystem Transitions

The original scale proposed by Kardashev (1964) ranked civilisations according to their energy sources and consumption levels such that:

- a Type I civilisation would be "at a technological level close to the level presently (1964) attained on Earth, with energy consumption at $\approx 4 \times 10^{19}$ ergs/sec (4×10^{12} watts)" – restated by Lemarchand (2013) as equivalent to that of the total solar insolation on Earth, i. e. $\approx 10^{16} \leftrightarrow 10^{17}$ watts,

- a Type II civilisation would be "capable of harnessing the energy radiated by its own star, with energy consumption at $\approx 4 \times 10^{33}$ ergs/sec" – restated by Lemarchand as equivalent to that of the total luminosity of the Sun i. e. $\approx 4 \times 10^{26}$ watts and

• a Type III civilisation would be "in possession of energy on the scale of its own galaxy, with energy consumption at ≈ 4 × 1044 ergs/sec" – restated by Lemarchand as equivalent to that of the total luminosity of the Sun i. e. ≈ 4 × 1026 watts.

Sagan & Agel (2000) further refined the original scale by interpolating and extrapolating between the above values according to the formula:

$$K = log10(MW/10)$$ Eq. 1,

where K is a civilisation's Kardashev rating and MW its energy consumption in watts.

For purposes of this discussion, types II and III may be subdivided in ways that reflect what the cyberneticist V. F. Turchin has termed metasystem transitions (1977). A metasystem transition describes the process by which a complex biological system effects a transition from a given quasistable state to one of higher complexity. This process is accompanied by an increase in the collective sentience quotient (SQ) of the system, defined as:

$$SQ = log10 (I/M)$$ Eq. 2,

where I = information-processing capacity in bits/sec and M = brain mass in kg [6]. Eq. 2 is the same as Eq. 1 in that SQ could be expressed directly in terms of energy efficiency. Information processing is not the same as intelligence however. If the latter is defined as the inherent tendency of a biological system towards further self-structuring and expansion in pursuit of a desired goal, transition would imply changes not only in infrastructure and technology but also in the ideational systems that catalysed the evolution and transformation of the system as a whole [12]. The original Kardashev scale might therefore be subdivided in terms of human history as shown in Fig. 1.

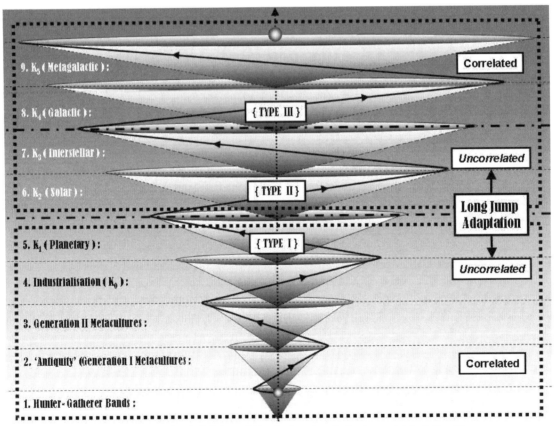

Fig. 1. Proposed subdivision of Kardashev levels for terrestrial civilisation

In this diagram, levels 1 - 5 represent historical convergences of smaller groups into larger associations whose stability required specific social, economic and ideational adaptations on the part of the newly-associated groups. Levels 6 – 9 mark future transitions in the posthuman (post-biological) domain where the specific imperatives of

Darwinian selection and random genetic mutation may no longer be relevant. The 'fanning out' of these levels does not necessarily mean 'imperial expansion' or 'colonisation' on the Star Wars/Star Trek model, but rather a progressive augmentation of the spacetime domains within which such advanced civilisations would necessarily operate, whether virtually or in physical actuality. Kardashev Type II is therefore subdivided into levels 3 (K3 - interstellar) and 4 (K4 - galactic), since assuming a K2 → K3 transition to be possible, further transitions to K4 (galactic) and K5 (metagalactic) may involve further radical advances and deliberate evolutionary choices, the nature of which cannot be foreseen at present. The most radical transition would be a 'long-jump' adaptation from a planetary (biological) environment at K0 to a space (posthuman) environment at K2. Transitions from K0 – K1 occur on a correlated adaptive landscape, as do the transitions from K2+ onward. The transition between both sequences (K1 – K2) however, takes place on an uncorrelated landscape and will involve a radical series of innovations plus a re-structuring of the genome itself, i.e. speciation. A valuable tool in a more accurate quantification of SQ may be the Calculi of Emergence of Crutchfield (1994) where species are defined as "metastable, invariant languages – … temporary (hyperbolic) fixed points in the evolutionary dynamic" (p. 49). Radical advances in computational complexity therefore imply physical re-structuring since innovation necessarily defines speciation. Such a radical step is proposed by the 100YSS in its proclaimed goal of transition from K0 (pre-planetary)→ K3 (interstellar).

2. Issues of Prediction in the Social Sciences

If the 100YSS envisions the creation of a 'platform' for interstellar expeditions by the year 2111 (the 100th anniversary of the first symposium), a plan of action spanning this time-frame might be advisable, in which we may ask: what will 'the world' look like in 98 years? Do we tend to envision this future exclusively in terms of a 'present' which seems to change radically with each decade? A cursory inspection of Fig. 2 (below) may reveal more clearly the problems faced by any attempt at long-range prediction in the social sciences.

Fig. 2. Charles de Gaulle Airport (Paris) in the year 2000 as envisaged in the year 1900.

A popular exercise for beginning psychohistory students is shown in Fig. 3 (a-d) below. This shows four scenes of the imaginary English town of Drayneflete as conceived by Sir Osbert Lancaster (Lancaster 1949). The four figures show: a) Drayneflete during the Roman Era (c. 150 AD – the most prosperous period of Roman Britain), b) Norman Drayneflete (c. 1090, shortly after compilation of the Domesday Book in 1086), c) 17th century Drayneflete (c. 1640 – clearly just prior to the Civil War) and finally d) modern Drayneflete (actually, a surprisingly accurate conception for 1949). The students' 'task' is to analyse what elements of the fictional town change over the centuries, and what elements do not – i.e. the question of 'deep structure' vs. 'invariance' in history.

a) Roman Drayneflete (c, 150 AD)   **b) Norman Drayneflete (c. 1090 AD)**

c) Drayneflete in the 17ᵗʰ century (c. 1640 AD)   **d) Contemporary Drayneflete (Present)**

Fig. 3. The hypothetical English town of Drayneflete at four stages in its history. (after Lancaster (1949))

The main 'lesson' to be learned here is that while technologies may change radically (architecture, modes of transport etc.), social systems and 'deep-level' town planning do not, or if they do, at a much slower rate (e.g. social stratification, places of worship etc. – the scene of Fig. 3 (d) is on far too wide a scale to show the panhandler probably lurking in the shopping mall ('spare any change?')). Humans are an inherently conservative species, appropriately characterised by many anthropologists, and evolutionary psychologists as 'stone agers in the fast lane'.

MacIntyre (1981) lists four main problems that delimit the possibilities for accurate prediction in the social sciences:

1. the unpredictability of radical innovation in relation to science and technology,
2. the game-theoretic character of human behaviour
3. non-linearity – i.e. the unpredictable consequences of unforeseen decisions, and
4. historical contingency – the fact that we live in a non-ergodic world.

To these four we might add the collective fantasies, wishes and desires (what De Greene (2000) calls 'macropsychological parameters') that constrain future choices. 'The future is a canvas on which we paint our desires' as quoted from the Dune Encyclopedia (McNally et al. (1984). In the physical sciences, the isolation and 'idealisation' of a physical system in the laboratory environment might permit prediction to the nth decimal point of accuracy, but in the social sciences, embedded as we are deeply within our own socioeconomic matrix, all human affairs will have 'fuzzy edges' (fractal dimension). We are essentially dealing with complex dynamical systems ('chaotic attractors') and therefore to approximate ecologically valid models, we can work only with probabilities, not certainties.

For the 100YSS to at least approximate its goal, it must devise strategies to protect that goal against a) deflection or deferment, b) dilution, c) compromise, d) dissipation or e) appropriation of the group's goal for ulterior purposes. A key strategy to this end would be to construct, not the type of predictive, deterministic plan envisaged by Asimov in the Foundation Trilogy (the 'Seldon Plan'), but an interactive program that would evolve through distributed computing on the SETI@home model, one that takes into account the political and socioeconomic instabilities likely to dominate the course of the 21st century. Such a program would act as a searchlight to guide the efforts of all those concerned with the permanent colonization of space towards the common goal of establishing a firm platform for future interstellar exploration.

This study proposes that such an instrument would be constructible and computable given current (and immanent) computational technologies. – and may be the nearest thing to the Asimovian 'Prime Radiant' that we can realistically create at the present time. An attempt to formulate such a plan was made by employees of the Rockwell Corporation in 1989 during the era of NASA-Rockwell co-operation. This is the Integrated Space Plan, or ISP.

3. The Integrated Space Plan (ISP)

The only version of the ISP known currently to exist is shown in its original form in Fig. 4 below. This plan appears today as a counterfactual history in which major deviations are known to have set in almost immediately after the plan's completion - i.e. the end of the Cold War, followed by major reductions in funding that ultimately limited 'permanent' human habitation of space to low Earth orbit. The ISP is constructed around a central axis with the flow of time from top to bottom with the 'parent goal' being the launching of an interstellar expedition, The boxes to either side mark the various contributory advances in technology (the 'child goals') and the manner in which they 'patch in' to the central axis as landmark stages in the program as a whole. Although estimates of 'Near-Earth Extraterrestrial Resources' and an 'LEO ET Resource Base' are listed at the upper left, there is little indication of how terrestrial resources would be obtained, distributed or managed nor any input regarding how the world economy and resource base might fluctuate over this timespan (even though world systems-dynamic models such as Forrester's World Dynamics of 1974 were already available). There is no indication of how the dynamics of long-wave economic cycles might affect the generation and development of new technologies, nor the contributory effects of the various macropsychological parameters (De Greene 2000) that are always neglected in long-range predictive modelling and which inevitably undermine the ecological validity of such models.

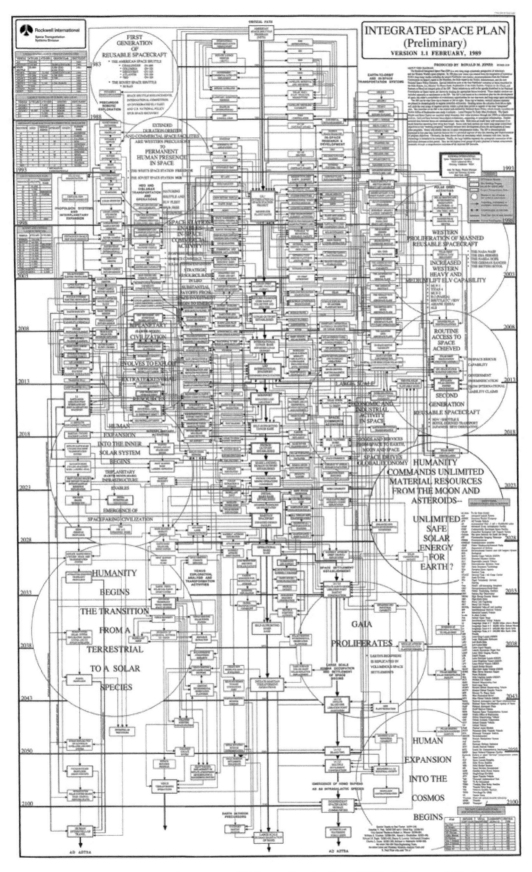

Fig. 4. The Integrated Space Plan (ISP). Credited to Ronald M. Johnson of Rockwell International (1989). Rediscovered and uploaded by Sean Ragan at http://blog.makezine.com/2012/09/13/the-rockwell-international-integrated-space-plan

Fig. 5. below shows the range of Kardashev transitions spanned by the ISP/

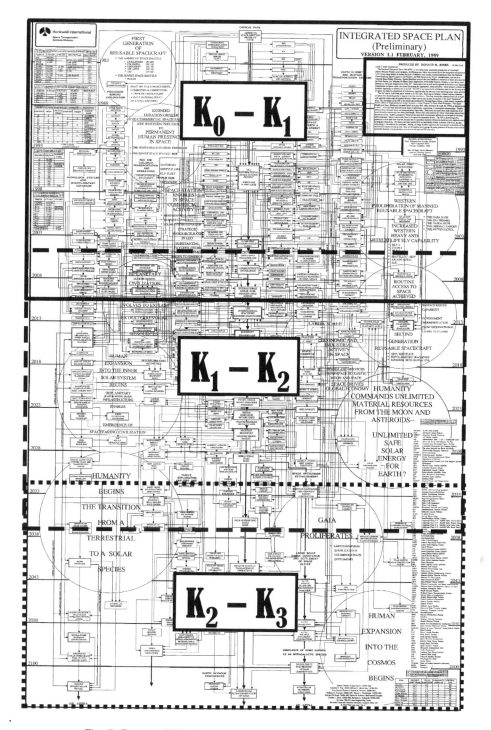

Fig. 5. Range of Kardashev transitions spanned by the ISP

It will be seen that eventuation is fairly sparse at the initial phase of the ISP (the history is all too familiar), that it trails off as the plan extends farther and farther into the future (by reason of uncertainty) and that the phase bracketing the immediate present (at time of writing - 2013, i.e. from 2003 – 2023) is embedded in the densest eventuation period – that of the critical 'long-jump adaptation' from K0 → K2. By expanding this area (Fig. 6) and magnifying the central axis, we can see the stage we 'should be at' according to the counterfactual estimates of the ISP.

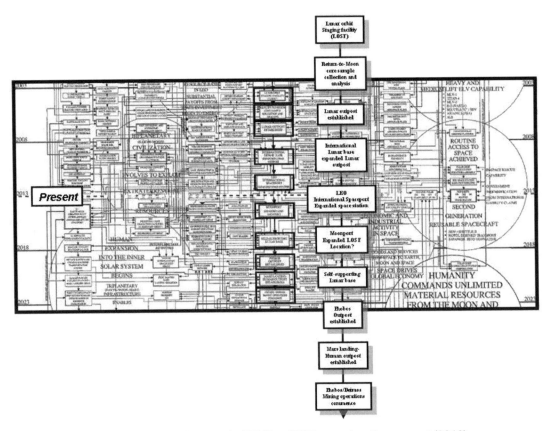

Fig. 6. Expansion of the period(2003 – 2023) covering the present (2013)

If the shuttle accidents, funding cuts, shifts in priorities and general fragmentation of aims had not occurred, by the year 2013 we should have had an "LEO International Spaceport and Expanded Space Station', a Lunar outpost (to become fully self-supporting by 2020) and steps would already have been taken to exploit the resources of Phobos and establish a base on Mars. That we are nowhere near this point should not depress us – the 'lessons' to be learned from the ISP are the consequences of formulating even the most detailed technical plans without consideration the socioeconomic matrix in which they are embedded – i.e. the 'messy people stuff'. Fortunately this can, to a certain extent, be remedied.

The ISP could serve as a prototype if it were reworked through an active system-dynamics modelling of a set of domains and agents co-evolving on a 'fitness landscape' created by the world's shifting political, economic and psychosocial climate. Such a reworking would be an interactive combination of program and database incorporating linear optimisation, Bayesian decision theory and other methods which lie well within the capabilities even of current computing technology. It would permit a regular updating of 'child goal' trajectories based on continual inputs of new data, whether economic, environmental, political or psychosocial. In addition to the political and socioeconomic environment in which the Plan must evolve, a further dimension would be added - the macrospychological parameters that govern the behaviours of participatory domains and agents. We might call such a Plan the 'Virtual Starship Program' – or the 'Prime Radiant' in honour of Isaac Asimov's conception in the Foundation Trilogy. Whereas Asimov's 'Seldon Plan' covered 1000 years, ours would span a mere 100 – or more precisely 98, now that 'countdown' has begun. Ironically, Asimov's conception of the 'Prime Radiant' 3D 'circumferential presentation technology may well prove quite feasible within 10-15 years. Let us begin therefore by examining the first major parameter of the 'Virtual Starship' (or 'Prime Radiant') program - the fitness landscape or environment upon which the Plan must evolve.

4. The World3 Model: 'Sustainable Development' or Systems Collapse?

Continuous updates of data sourced from the World Resources Institute or World Economic Outlook may serve as input to a general systems analysis program such as World3 (the software for which is commercially available through the Institute of Ethical Engineering (IEE)). The World3 model itself, developed from Jay Forrester's original World Dynamics program initiated at MIT during the 1960's represents a 50-year-old tradition of systems-dynamics modelling (Forrester 1974). In identifying five key parameters that would govern any expanding industrial civilisation – non-renewable resources, population, agriculture (food supply), industrial output and pollution – the model can be generalised to refine the calculation of that civilisation's position on the Kardashev scale. The term 'non-renewable resources' includes (in addition to coal and oil) all precious metals or rare earths essential for today's sophisticated technologies. These five parameters and the main ways in which they are interlinked are shown in Fig. 7 below.

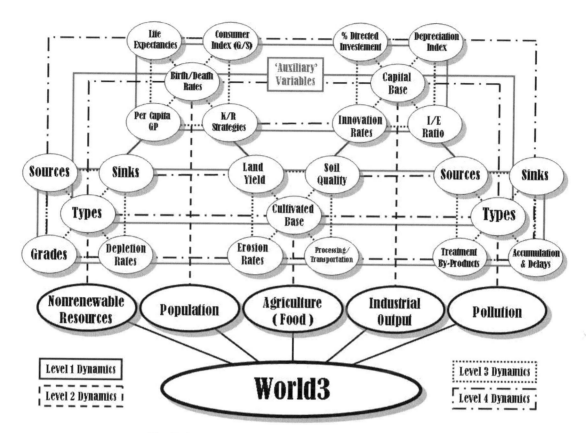

Fig. 7. A tree-structured overview of the World3 model

Current updates of the model (based on Meadows et al. 1993) present 13 scenarios with varying sub-parameters based on data initialisation from 1995. The scenarios of most concern are nos. 1 and 10 (Figs. 8 (a) and (b) below). Scenario 1 (Fig. 8 (a)) presents the 'Standard' or 'Reference' model – the most likely outcome if 'business as usual' strategies are followed. Scenarios 2-9 assume double resource availability and add sequences of remedial strategies such as pollution control, resource-efficient technologies, population controls and the cutting of implementation delays etc. In all these scenarios unforeseen 2nd- or 3rd-order dynamics precipitate a catabolic systems collapse within 100 years. Scenario 10 (Fig. 8 (b)) assumes the implementation of all ameliorative strategies simultaneously and in so doing offers a model of 'sustainable development' - the only drawback being that these strategies should have been implemented at least from 1975 for systems collapse to be averted. Full implementation of these strategies before the model's 'cut-off' date of 2015 seems highly unlikely. Without being unduly pessimistic it may be safe to assume that the 100YSS ISP is likely to evolve on a highly 'rugged' fitness landscape.

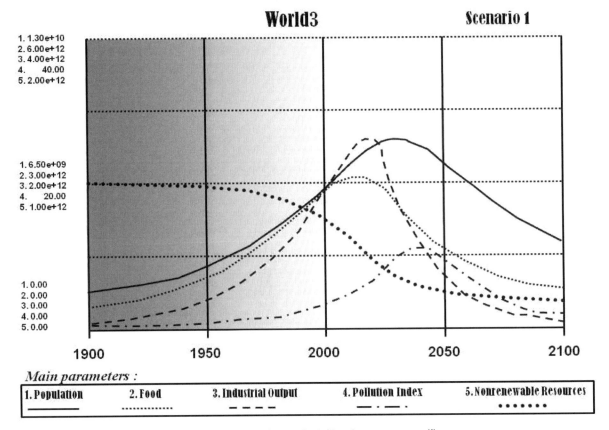

Fig 8 (a). World3: Scenario 1 ('business-as-usual').

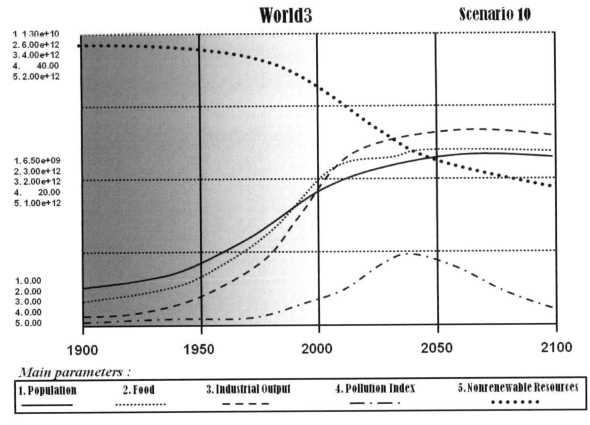

Fig. 8 (b). World3: Scenario 10 ('sustainable development').

While some (but not all) of the Scenario 10 controls have been partially implemented since c. 1995, the World3 model, described by its opponents as 'unduly pessimistic', is, if anything, too conservative. It does not take into account for instance a) war and social unrest/insurrection, b) political and financial corruption, c) natural disasters or d) denial and other macropsychological parameters (indicated in Fig. 7 as 'auxiliary variables') those that most seem to trouble the model's critics. Factors a) → c) have increasingly come to the fore since 1995, effectively threatening to counter (through negative feedback) any advances in control technologies that have been achieved since that time. Scenario 1 is therefore the best 'default' scenario to retain for the present, especially since ongoing re-assessments of the model appear to confirm its ecological validity (Cole et al. 1973). In this respect it is the model's very 'overgeneralization' that makes it robust. .

The 1500 input equations of World3 can be summarised for present purposes by the following simplified model (which we may call the 'Micawber Model' by analogy with the character in Charles Dickens' novel David Copperfield).

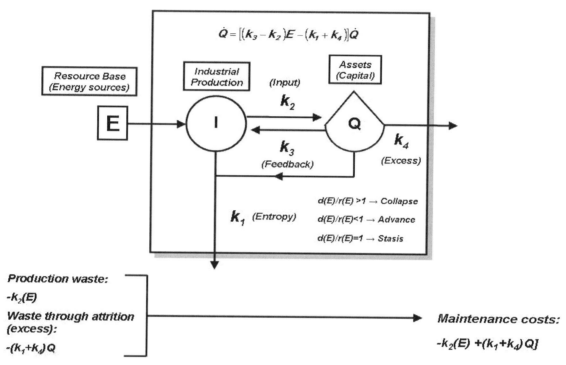

Fig. 9. The 'Micawber Model' of world systems dynamics

The rectangle in Fig. 9 above stands for the human 'Ekumen'– the adaptive landscape within which the Plan will evolve. Energy (E) is imported from the natural environment and transformed through industry (I) into assets or capital (Q) according to flow rates k2 (input) and k3 (feedback). The resource base from which E is created includes every kind of resource, both natural and manufactured, including all human resources plus information in the broadest sense, both actual and potential (e.g. technological innovation). Capital (Q) includes all resources that have been incorporated though flow rates kn into the ecumenical dynamic and consist not only of physical capital (food, fields, tools, buildings etc.) but all human systems (individuals, groups, organisations, economic systems, hierarchies etc.) plus informational capital (scientific knowledge, technical know-how etc.). Money as such represents the transport of capital flow rather than 'capital' itself (as commonly understood), and therefore is part of the flow system (k2 - k3) analogous to blood circulation. Waste is both entropic (k1(E) – i.e. 'waste as commonly understood' and 'system endemic' or dissipative waste generated though excess ((k1+k4)Q), including, for instance, wasted human resources (the unemployed, the underemployed, the disadvantaged etc.). To maintain 'sustainability' (stasis), new production from capital (Q) must equal maintenance costs arising from both entropic and dissipative waste, i.e.

$$\dot{Q} = \left[(k_3 - k_2)E - (k_1 + k_4)\right]\dot{Q} \qquad \text{Eq. 3}$$

Resources are consumed at a certain rate d(E) and replenished at a certain rate r(E). Essentially, the socio economic evolution of a society is critically determined by the balance between these rates, i.e.

$$d(E)/r(E) > 1 \rightarrow \text{Collapse (catabolic or anabolic)}$$

$$d(E)/r(E) < 1 \rightarrow \text{Advance} \hspace{4cm} \text{Eq. 4}$$

$$d(E)/r(E) = 1 \rightarrow \text{Stasis}$$

or to paraphrase the words of Mr. Micawber in David Copperfield : "Income one dollar, expenditure 99 cents, result = happiness. Income one dollar, expenditure one dollar and one cent, result = misery".

'Collapse' as such means simply 'a reduction in socioeconomic complexity', (not necessarily the dramatic 'Mad Max' or extinction scenarios visualised in apocalyptic fiction), and can be either catabolic (sudden and large-scale such as the 'fall' of the former Soviet Union) or anabolic (a 'stepped' collapse or 'decline' process). It makes little difference to the future of the 100YSS however, whether the next 98 years is likely to unfold as a 'stepped anabolic' (partial) or a 'catabolic' (total) collapse – any fragmentation or dissipation of knowledge capital is likely to impede the development of critical technologies.

5. Consequences of Limiting the Model to K1 (Planetary) Convergence.

Why (as we so often hear) should we not "sort out our problems here on Earth before we go soaring off into the wild blue yonder"? The simple answer is that 'our problems' will never be 'sorted out' while the human genome remains unmodified. Heilbroner (1995) presented 6 core arguments that suggest why convergence to a planetary culture (K1) carries certain existential risks. Similar arguments (with references to the Heilbroner studies) were also made by Gerard O'Neill in his pioneering study of space habitats (O'Neill 1977)

1. *Approaching limits.* In times of crisis, conventional rationality operates within very narrow limits. While 'business as usual' may lead to collapse, arresting or reversing growth is both equally futile and dangerous. If 'limits to growth' are reached, the focus should be on quality of life (global optimisation) rather than the satisfaction of 'goods hunger'.

2. *Increasing wealth disparities.* In accordance with 'downswing' or B-phases in long-wave economic theory (Van Duijn 1983, Reijnders 1990; Tylecote 1983), technological acceleration may only serve to delimit and constrict the market area available for saturation, widening disparities between 'core' and peripheral areas of the globe. Redistribution may be a desirable strategy, but even in the face of massive threat the scale would be prohibitive, since strategies of resource switching demand long implementation periods.

3. *Spread of conflict.* Increasing scarcities precipitate acute anxieties, leading to a compensatory 'goods hunger' and struggle for what remains. Localised conflicts (instabilities) threaten to expand in scale, the consequences of which are aggravated by increasing access to dangerous weapons. It might be noted that areas of chronic conflict tend to be those where environmental degradation is most acute (Diamond 2005; Friedman 2010).

4. *Threat of totalitarianism.* Periods of uncontrollable anxiety increase human proclivities towards dependence and foster totalitarian solutions. Post-collapse, neo-totalitarian régimes are likely to be collective in spirit, based on archaic, regressive theologies and hostile towards all 'open' scientific research.

5. *Social science paralysis.* The social sciences, dependent as they are on resource-controlling institutions and power structures, are only likely to collaborate with any emergent 'new world order' (Prilleltensky et al. 1997).

6. *Crisis of envisionment.* The fragmentation and dissolution in today's world of any 'bond with the future'.

In the case of digital technology, the 'co-evolution of humans and machines' (Mazlish 1993) has a long history – that of the machinic phylum (Deleuze & Guattari 1980; Johnston 2008). The question is whether this co-evolution may lead to 'in-volution' (closure) or 'e-volution' outwards. "The Machine will not dominate the human – humans and machine will become One" [Sandberg q.v.] – yet fears of eventual 'domination by the Machine' may not be entirely groundless. The reasons for this arise less from the putatively emergent superhuman powers of any 'rogue' AI than from the evolutionary fact of innate human proclivities to dependence (spending, as we do, the first third of our lives in this state). If 'God created Adam to love Him' so we create our machines to love us, constructing a 'womb-surround' to protect us from the chthonic forces of the 'outer darkness'. The proliferation of digital social media may tend to reinforce social 'in-volution' rather than 'e-volution' such that we would prefer to 'imagine' a risk-free interstellar voyage via YouTube than to make it happen in reality. The highly versatile applications of the programming language C++ for instance, with its many versatile properties (including the capacity for re-writing – though not originating – its own source code), may strongly influence the cognitive processes of the greater multitude of users neither sensitive enough nor sufficiently trained to perceive such influence. Involution of this type is an example of what is called 'niche construction' in evolutionary biology (Lalande et al. 2001). Instead of undergoing selective modification in response to its natural environment, an organism may endeavour to transform its immediate environment to suit itself. The main problem with this strategy is that its success is guaranteed only as long as the fitness landscape itself remains stable. If the latter undergoes sudden and/or severe deformation, the organism, though over-adaptation to its constructed 'niche', may find that it cannot adapt to such changes in time and faces the risk of extinction. There is little doubt that human beings are the 'master niche constructors' of Planet Earth and it is this 'in-volution' leading to psychosocial closure that constitutes a major (if unrecognized) existential risk at present – indeed, all others can be shown to derive from it (Ziolo 2013). A cautionary parable in this respect is E.M. Forster's story The Machine Stops (1909) – a remarkably accurate example of social prescience at a distance of c. 100 years.

6. The Psychodynamic Dimension: Experiential Bayesian Programming

Within the Plan's rugged fitness landscape (which we may call the 'Ekumen' after Ursula K. le Guin's novel The Left Hand of Darkness), agents and domains co-evolve. Domains are defined strictly as those areas of scientific research within which starship technologies will eventually be developed, while agents are the (organisation, companies, institutions) working within them. Both domains and agents have specific topologies (connective structures) and bandwidth (communication weightings). Domains evolving within the global Ekumen must achieve an equilibrium between three competing forces: 1) the military-industrial complex, which seeks specified applications, 2) academia, which by and large remains theoretically conservative and 3) the innovative research-technology sector (described below). Agents may be considered as autonomous, goal-seeking programs evolving on two adaptive levels: 1) within a particular domain and 2) as independent agents (e.g. private initiatives) within the general context of the Plan. More concise identification of the domains will follow shortly, but for the present, both domains and agents are referred to as 'agents' in Fig. 10 below due to a basic similarly of structure.

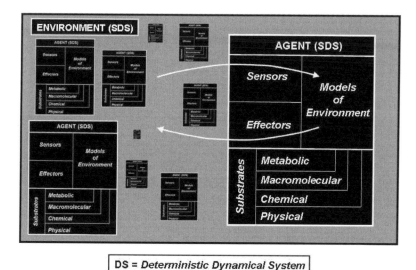

Fig. 10. The co-evolution of agents within a deterministic Universe (After Crutchfield (1994))

In Crutchfield's Calculi of Emergence (1994) 'agents' are considered to be stochastic dynamical systems (SDS's) that co-evolve within a biosphere (the Ekumen - also an SDS) which in turn evolves within a deterministic dynamical system (DS) – the known Universe. All agents in the terrestrial context (whether individuals or nucleates) share a similar embodied substrate – physical, chemical, macromolecular or metabolic. What differentiates them are the classes of model each agent creates in order to make sense of its environment and to interact with other agents in a manner that best serves its own interests.

If we consider domains as nucleations of agents (groups, organisations, institutions etc.) that form collective environmental models, and assume that 'the individual is embedded in the social and the social in the individual', a hierarchy of experiential Bayesian algorithms for adaptive group behaviour can be created based on concepts originated in Ashby's cybernetic models (Ashby 1947, 1960), and developed further in Haken's synergetics (Haken 1996) and the neurodynamic models of Friston et al. (2008, 2009, 2010). Fig. 11 below offers a simplified generalisation (for present purposes) of this algorithm set.

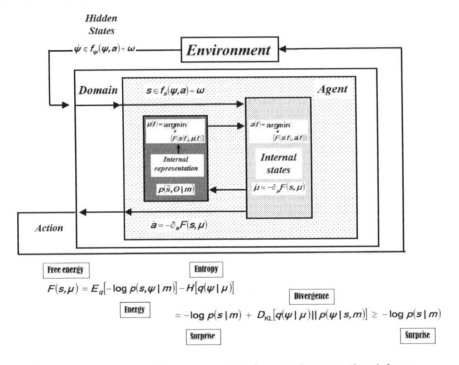

Fig. 11. An experiential Bayesian model of a agent's perception, information processing and action within the context of a domain

In Fig. 11 the 'hidden' (unclassified) environmental states $\psi \in \Psi$ impinge upon a domain's collective sensory systems $s \in S$ according to

$$\dot{\psi} \in f_\psi\left(\psi, a\right) + \omega$$
Eq. 5,

where a signifies 'action', $\omega \in \Omega$ represents a parameterization of random fluctuation of these states and

$$s \in f_s\left(\psi, a\right) + \omega$$
Eq. 6.

These input states are bijectively mapped onto 'internal representations' μ of environmental knowledge (the 'working paradigm' of the group or domain), the 'relevance' of which is determined through a minimisation of 'free energy' (Shannon entropy or 'surprise'), i.e.

$$\mu(t) = \arg\min_\mu \cdot \left\{ F\left(s(t), \mu(t)\right) \right\}$$
Eq. 7.

This bijective mapping then initiates the process of selecting a course of action :

$$a(t) = \arg\min_a \cdot \left\{ F\left(s(t), a(t)\right) \right\}$$
Eq. 8,

the choice of which is weighted by the collective mood and reaction of the group to the input, i.e. the group's instantaneous internal state at its 'task-sentient boundary' (Czander 1995) defined here by :

$$\dot{\mu} = -\partial_{\mu} F(s, \mu)$$

Eq. 9,

and which impacts in turn upon how the group 'interprets' its internal model or paradigm at that moment, i.e.

$$p(\tilde{s}, \Theta \mid m)$$

Eq. 10.

where Θ represents the perspective or 'angle' from which the range of possible internal model representations $m \in M$ is viewed at that moment. The final decision as to course of action, i.e.

$$\dot{a} = -\partial_{a} F(s, \mu)$$

Eq. 11.

is a consequence of what Haken (1996) terms 'order parameter emergence' and this course of action further impacts upon the environment, affecting subsequent sensory input. This cyclic process strives constantly to minimise free energy or Shannon entropy, i.e.

$$F(s,\mu) = \underbrace{E_q[-\log p(s,\psi \mid m)]}_{\text{Energy}} - \underbrace{H[q(\psi \mid \mu)]}_{}$$

Free energy   Entropy

$$= \underbrace{-\log p(s \mid m)}_{\text{Surprise}} + \underbrace{D_{KL}[q(\psi \mid \mu) \| p(\psi \mid s, m)]}_{\text{Divergence}} \geq \underbrace{-\log p(s \mid m)}_{\text{Surprise}}$$

Eq. 12.

A similar process unfolds in the case of any individual element of an agent-as-group (Fig. 12).

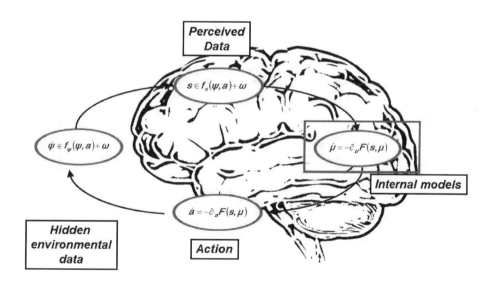

Fig. 12. Experiential Bayesian reasoning in the case of the individual agent.

A crucial aspect of this process is the formation of internal models. How does this come about? In the case of the individual, internal models are formed through experience and learning, modified by the formation and evolution of personal constructs. In the case of both domains and agents (the activities of groups, organisations or institutions) the collective paradigm is influenced by the dominant projective construct or belief system prevailing in a given culture (North 1997). Both these cases will be discussed in more detail in Religious Engineering for the K2 Transition (this volume). For now, experiential Bayesian programming offers the possibility of quantifying the more abstract concept of SQ (section 1) – especially in conjunction with Crutchfield's (1994) ε-machine reconstruction (see below).

Free energy minimisation is a conservative process in that 'innovation' is traded for security. Historically this has proved to be an evolutionarily stable strategy and therefore accounts in some degree for the 'disturbing' character of innovation. Innovation has also shown itself to be an essential survival strategy however, especially under deformation of a fitness landscape, even if loosening the upper bounds of entropy minimisation causes temporary instabilities in the cognitive system – hence the link between 'schizophrenia' and 'creativity' (Spinks et al. 2004).

7. The Identification of Domains and Transversal Linkage through Research Technologies

A (proposed) set of eight scientific-technological domains relevant to the development of interstellar flight is shown in Fig. 13 below. These include the GRAIN technologies (Genetics, Robotics, Artificial Intelligence and Nanotechnology) that drive the current long-wave economic cycle and are likely to be instrumental in catalysing posthuman evolution.

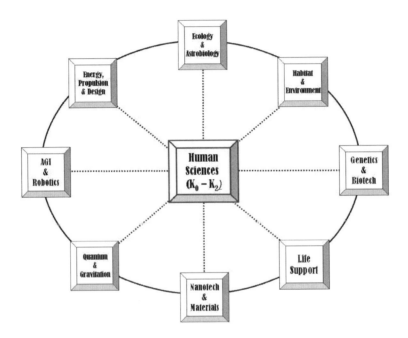

Fig. 13. The 8 domains, linked by a social science 'nexus'.

This identification is for present purposes only – i.e. to illustrate the concept of a domain within the context of a Plan for the 100YSS Project and to distinguish it from the usual IT meaning of the term. The final identification of domains relevant to the Plan remains open for the present, A key strategy for all domains contributing to the 100YSS Project (and the organisations, firms and institutions comprising them) would be that of developing a co-ordinated plan of research-technology or transversal research as described by Shinn (2010). Transversality first emerged as a theorem in algebraic topology developed by René Thom (1954). Topological transversality and the sociological analysis of engineering transversality are linked through their emergence from within the same conceptual milieu - the Institut des Hautes Récherches Scientifiques, and GEMCAS (Groupe d'Étude des Méthodes de l'Analyse Sociologique). The relevance of what Shinn defines as research-technology pertains to generic instrumentation, i.e. the development of instrumentation and technologies that are applicable in many different fields simultaneously. Examples cited by Shinn and others include: the electric motor, the digital computer, the ultracentrifuge, the electron microscope, Fourier transform spectroscopy, the microchip and the C++ programming language. As William Bechtel wrote in 1993: "The emergence of a new sphere of learning is achieved precisely through a strong convergence and meshing of already existing domains. The centripetal logic of integration prevails over the centrifugal logic of differentiation". (Bechtel 1993).

The ability of research-technology to integrate and catalyse simultaneously many domains of industry lies behind the succession of Kondratyev or economic long-wave cycles that have brought terrestrial civilisation to its present level. Transversal initiatives offer a means of escaping Bechtel's 'centrifugal logic of differentiation' while preserving the essential integrity of participatory domains, They are usually located at the interstices between their conventionally-defined boundaries, and according to Shinn, promote:

1. a flow of ideas and information from the research-technology (transversal) sector to participatory domains,

2. a reverse flow from the participatory domains back to the research-technology sector, further refining the development of generic instrumentation,

3. a technical lingua franca between both sectors, further enhancing the commitment, communication and aims of participatory domains and

4. greater personnel mobility between participatory domains.

Marcovich & Shinn (2011) suggest that research-technology initiatives tend to operate most significantly in the context of specific projects which, by their very nature, would catalyse co-operation of many disciplines in pursuit of a common objective or 'parent goal'. The 100YSS offers just such a project. Fig, 14 (a) and (b) below illustrate how a domain, with its network of organizations, companies or institutions (the 'secondary' agents comprising a group of primary or individual agents) might operate within a research-technology 'nexus'. A secondary agent would map into the wider as shown in the upper half of Fig. 14 while the eight key domains identified for purposes of the present paper, would form the interlinking structure shown in the lower half of the figure. The Petrie diagram of an n-dimensional polytope appearing in the lower half of Fig. 14 represents 'linear optimisation' (convergence to a goal) and is proposed as an 'icon' of the 'Virtual Starship' program over the next 98 years.

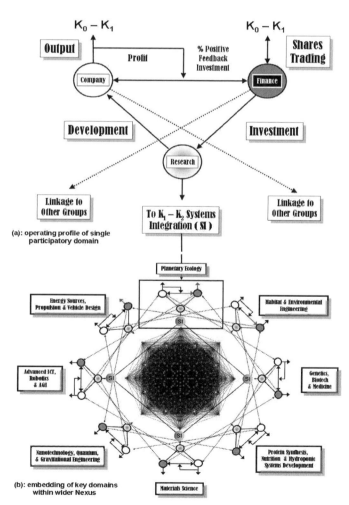

Fig. 14. operating strategy of an individual domain (upper half) and the embedding of that domain within the wider 'Nexus' (lower half)

8. Research Technologies and the Calculus of Innovation.

Advance to K2+ will require radically innovative approaches not only in technology, but also in mental and physical being. This is the essence of an evolutionary advance – a step that involves speciation and the advent of the 'posthuman' (Braidotti 2013). Bearing in mind Crutchfield's dictum that 'species [pl.] 'correspond in realization space to metastable invariant languages; they are temporary (hyperbolic) fixed points in the evolutionary dynamic' (1994 p. 49), a species' computational capacity is would therefore be determined by its mode of embodiment (structure) such that 'structure (both physical and mental) would correspond to a species' mode of adaptation and fitness measure within a specific environment. Advance to K2+ will require that human physical structure (and mental capacities) be augmented though partnership with the machine – the merging of both evolutionary lines within the 'machinic phylum'. Innovation begins with the creation of better models, and a study of Shinn (2010) reveals that a history of the research-technology sector is, by and large, the history of metrology – how the environment is measured so as to facilitate the development of better models.

Innovation corresponds to a process of increasing abstraction, which may often reveal hitherto undetected levels of deep structure, and in order to catalyse any advance to K2+ increasing advances in abstraction will ultimately prove necessary for survival in the context of a shifting, non-ergodic environment. Such advances expand the possibilities of 'ε-machine reconstruction' where ε represents the level of accuracy of measurement in a given model i.e. the degree of discrete quantization. Crutchfield's ε-machine hierarchies are shown in Fig. 15 below (for a fuller discussion see The Astrobiological Matrix – this volume).

Level	Model class	MACHINE	Model size if class is appropriate	Equivalence relation
...	...	...	...	
3	String Production	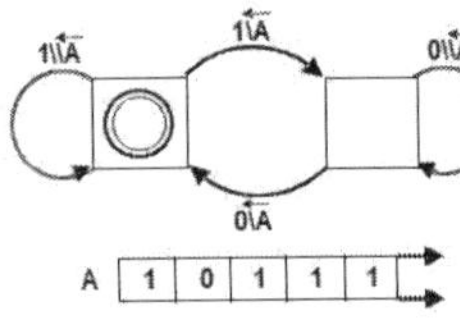	$O(\|V\| + \|E\| + \|P\|)$ Compute probabilities for state transitions	Finitary-Recursive Conditional Independence
2	Finite Automata	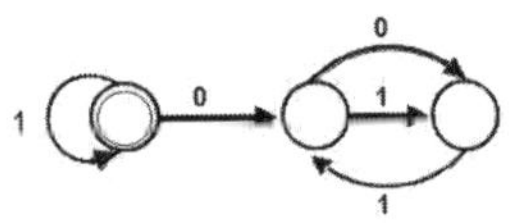	$O(\|V\| + \|E\|)$ Group tree nodes into state transition sequences	Conditional Independence
1	Tree Structures	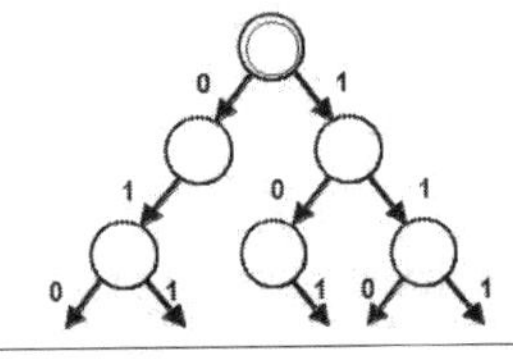	$O(\|\mathcal{A}\|^D)$ Group eventuation sequence into appropriate tree structures of depth (D)	Block Independence
0	Data Stream	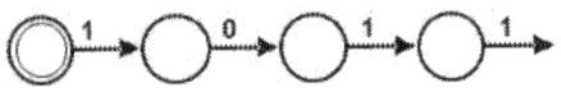	(m) Disconnected eventuation sequence	Measurement

Fig. 15. The. ε-machine hierarchies (after Crutchfield 1994)

In this model innovation corresponds to the 'deconstruction' of simple but inadequate computing machines at Level N and the 'reconstruction' of a new, more advanced computing machine model at Level N + 1. When the complexity of an agent's internal model $\|M\|$ approaches that agent's modelling capacity $\|A\|$, i.e. when a threshold is reached at

$$\|M\| \approx \|A\|$$

Eq. 13

innovation becomes mandatory for further adaptation. Let $C_\mu^l(\varepsilon)$ represent the statistical complexity of model $M_l(\varepsilon)$ in the ε-machine hierarchy1 where l represents the length of a bit string. The innovation rate Il at this threshold is given by

$$I_l = \lim_{\varepsilon \to 0} -\frac{2^{C_\mu^l(\varepsilon)}}{\log_2 \varepsilon} \qquad \text{Eq. 14.}$$

Thus $I_l \|M_l(\varepsilon)\|$ monitors the increase in model size. If Il > 0, $\|M_l\|$ diverges, and a new model class must be evolved at the first threshold of accuracy ε' where

$$C_\mu^l(\varepsilon') > \|A\| \qquad \text{Eq. 15.}$$

Of course such an 'advance' is by no means imperative – hence the persistence of life-forms at many levels of complexity within the terrestrial biosphere. Eq. 14 may be re-written as

$$I_l = \lim_{\varepsilon \to 0} \left(2^{C_\mu^l(\varepsilon/2)} - 2^{C_\mu^l(\varepsilon)} \right) \qquad \text{Eq. 16}$$

and expanded as

$$I_l = \lim_{\varepsilon \to 0} \sum_{\substack{v \in V(\varepsilon/2) \\ v' \in V(\varepsilon)}} p_l \log_2 \frac{p_v}{p_{v'}} \qquad \text{Eq. 17}$$

where V(ε) is the set of states of $M_l(\varepsilon)$. Under ε-machine reconstruction the states $v \in V(\varepsilon/2)$ of the more 'advanced' (accurate) model result from the subdivision or 'splitting' of the states of $v' \in V(\varepsilon)$ in the less accurate model (through increasingly fine subdivision of ε). Research-technology therefore 'works' by increasing the scope and precision of the ε-factor in generalised ε-machine reconstruction and thereby broadening the possibilities for convergence between disciplines.

9. Programming Strategies: the Genetic and Metagenetic Approach

Since we are dealing with an evolutionary long-jump adaptation, genetic programming as described by Koza (1992) might be an ideal programming approach. Genetic programming involves the creation of a set of autonomous, goal-seeking programs that are released within the 'primordial ooze' of a defined database with the injunction to seek out and optimize programs for reaching a prescribed target or goal (program induction). Genetic programs operate though Darwinian strategies of mutation, crossover and optimisation through selective extinction. There are five key stages: 1) selection of terminals (including zero-argument functions) → 2) the mathematical encoding of these terminals → 3) the setting of fitness values → 4) definition of the global parameter space → 5) termination point. Recent applications of these techniques to a wide array of problems have shown them to be successful in finding solutions that are not only human-competitive, but frequently surpass human capabilities. The code evolved by a genetic program in these instances often may appear incomprehensible to human software engineers (Langdon & Poli 2002). This may have less to do with any absolute limit on 'human' intelligence than with the fact that such programs can evade the constraints of those 'biases and heuristics' that arise from specifically human- evolved models and therefore seek independent pathways towards innovation. The overall flow chart of a genetic program is shown in Fig. 16 below.

---

1. This measure of 'statistical complexity' differs from the more common notion of Kolmogorov complexity in that while the latter measures the minimum bit length required to encode a given model and disregards the remaining entropy, statistical complexity measures the quality and degree of structure within a process along a scale from minimum to maximum (Shannon) entropy.

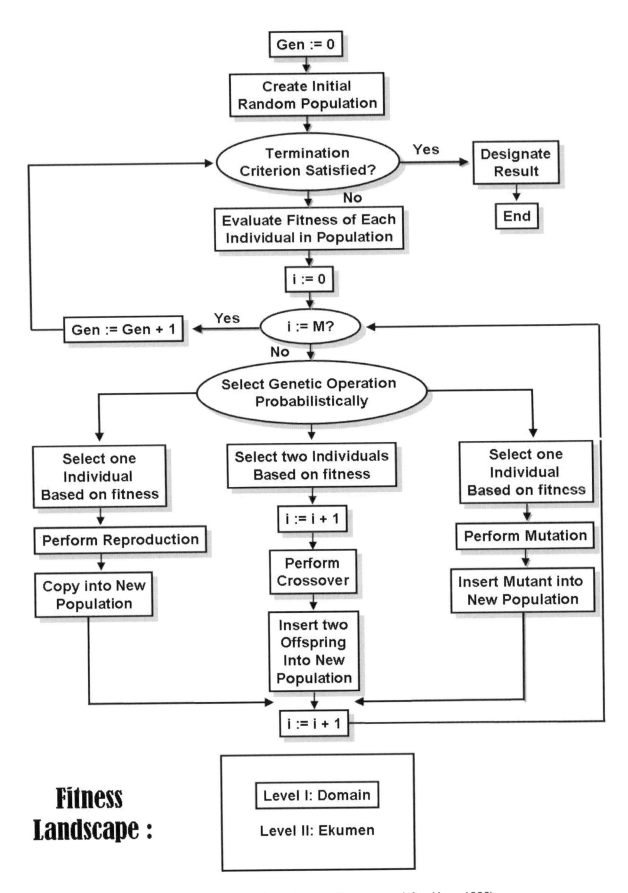

Fig. 16. General flow chart of a genetic program (after Koza 1992)

In terms of a more specific genetic algorithm:

1. the eight research domains would be the initial terminals (goal-seeking programs),
2. their efficiency index and modes of operation would be the encoded functions,
3. world economic data processed through a World3-type systems analytic program would provide a continuously updated parameter space (fitness landscape),
4. the fitness function would be a general measure of convergence (see below) and
5. the termination point would be defined either as the first fully self-sustaining space arcology – the seed for transition to K3 - or launching of the first interstellar expedition.

The 100YSS 'agents' operate on two adaptive levels: Level I – within an 'immediate' adaptive landscape of the domains, and Level II – within the 'general' adaptive landscape of the Ekumen. This would imply a recursive structure in which the basic algorithm shown in Fig. 16 above is embedded in a large-scale metagenetic program (Schmidthuber 1987) as shown in Fig. 17 below:

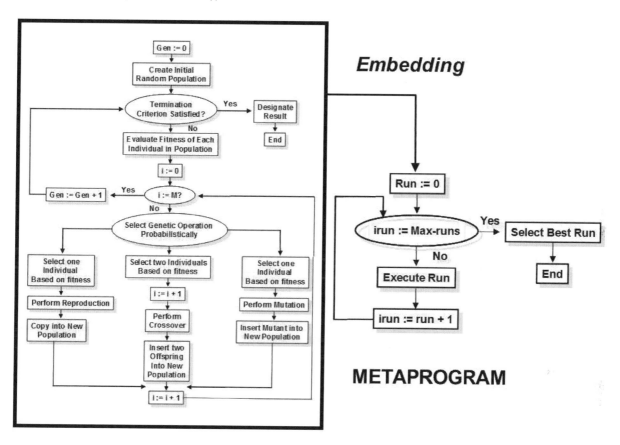

Fig. 17. Recursive structure of a metagenetic program (after Koza 1992)

10. Setting the Fitness Function

A suitable fitness measure may be defined through an appeal to Holland's schema theorem (Holland 1975), whereby if we let f(H,t) be the average fitness of schema H over a number of generations (t0, t1 …, tn) – i.e. the average fitness values of a set-valued function in the population belonging to the schema

$$f(H,t) = \frac{\sum_{x_i \in H} f(x_i, t)}{m(H,t)}$$

Eq. 20

where M(H,t) is the number of occurrences of schema H at generation t (which has an associated variance that depends on the number of items being summed to compute the average), the fitness ratio would be given by

$$FR(H,t) = \frac{f(H,t)}{f(t)} \qquad \text{Eq. 21}$$

where $\overline{f(t)}$ is the average fitness of the population at generation t. For genetic algorithms based on fitness-proportionate reproduction, the expected number m(H, t + 1) of occurrences of every schema H in gen (t + 1) is approximately

$$m(H,t-1) = \frac{f(H,t)}{f(t)} m(H,t)(1 - \varepsilon_c)(1 - \varepsilon_m) \qquad \text{Eq. 22}$$

where εc is the probability of disruption by crossover and εm the probability of disruption through mutation. If we assume H to be a string-based schema (as in many basic LISP expressions) then if δ(H) is the defining distance between the outermost specific (i.e. non-null) symbols of a string of length L and L − 1 is the number of interstitial points where crossover may occur, then the probability εc of disruption due to crossover is

$$\varepsilon_c = \frac{\delta(H)}{L-1} \qquad \text{Eq. 23}$$

in which εc will be small when L is small.. The probability εm of disruption through mutation is

$$\varepsilon_m = (1 - p_m)^{O(H)} \approx 1 - p_m O(H) \qquad \text{Eq. 24}$$

where O(H) is the specific order of the schema in question and in which εm will be small when O(H) is small.

An overall flow architecture involving convergence to K2 itself is shown in Fig. 19, with the flow of time from bottom to top. In this flow chart the various 'mixed-strategy' domains within the total Ekumen (educational, research and scientific institutions, the military/industrial complex, dominant financial & corporate interests) national space organisations such as NASA and ESA, the eight technological domains, private ventures and unaffiliated space advocacy groups) all carry positive, negative or 'mixed' reinforcement weightings.

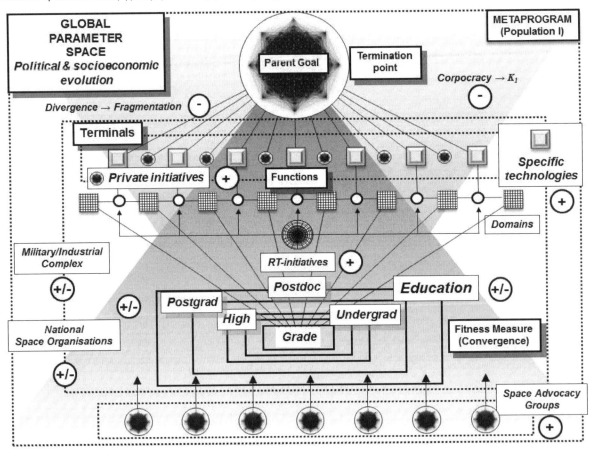

Fig. 19. More detailed flow architecture for convergence to K2

Those sectors that carry 'mixed' weightings will tend to exert both positive and negative influences depending on context. The educational sector for example is subject to highly diverse interests in which the 'centrifugal logic of differentiation' favoured by a late capitalist economy exerts a negative influence over the training necessary to encourage fruitful RT-initiatives. National space organisations with the unmatched experience and expertise of NASA for instance are central to the K"-transition, yet as recent history has shown, their efforts may often be compromised by the political and military/industrial sectors on which they rely for support and funding. The 'corporate' sector tends to favour convergence to K1 ('corpocracy') and may resist any further expansion to K2: money is conservative and will only follow where a firm beachhead has already been established.

The establishment of an independent and self-reliant 'beachhead' may therefore raise questions concerning national security and interests in space as well as the 'balance of power' between terrestrial governments and 'extraterrestrial' colonies. The history of the colonisation of the N. American continent affords clear historical examples of a 'nation-based' speciation process. Henceforth we have a 'mixed strategy' game in which the 'winning' outcome is convergence to K2 as opposed to a 'divergence of interests' strategy that will inhibit convergence to K2 while promoting 'convergence' to a state of stasis at K1 – a corpocracy, in which space interests remain strictly bounded and limited (The Economist). A simplified digraph of this 'mixed-strategy' game is shown in Fig. 20 below.

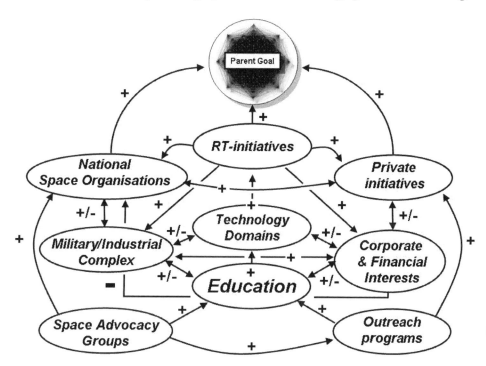

Fig. 20. Digraph showing 'mixed-strategy' interests

Given such a 'mixed strategy' situation, can the possibility of convergence of set-valued functions to a weak Nash equilibrium favouring a K2-transition be guaranteed from the input data? By an appeal to the Kakutani fixed-point theorem (Kakutani 1941), Nash (1950) proved that such an equilibrium should exist. According to Nash (op. cit.) if $r_i(\sigma_{-i})$ is the optimal response of agent i to the strategies of all other agents, then

$$r_i(\sigma_{-i}) = \arg\max_{\sigma_i} u_i(\sigma_i, \sigma_{-i})$$

Eq. 25

where $\sigma \in \Sigma$ and ($\Sigma = \Sigma i \times \Sigma\text{-}i$) is a mixed strategy profile in the set of all mixed strategies and ui the payoff (fitness) function for agent i. Define the set-valued function:

$$r = \left(r_i(\sigma_{-i}), r_{-i}, (\sigma_{-i})\right)$$

Eq. 26

such that r : $\Sigma \rightarrow 2\Sigma$. The Nash Equilibrium will be found at the fixed point of r provided that a) Σi is compact, convex and non-empty and b) r(σ) is convex, non-empty and hemicontinuous. Since Σi is a simplex it is compact and is also non-empty given the agents' mixed set of strategies. Thus we could define the overall fitness function for the Plan as a 'Nash-Kakutani convergence'. The necessity of minimising possible future conflict between those favouring convergence to K2 and those favouring convergence to K1 (which by the end of the century may become a conflict between 'human' and 'posthuman') requires that a Nash-Kakutani convergence be found that favours transition to K2 without posing threats to terrestrial interests. and can, in addition, guarantee significant benefits to Earth

12. Future Advances in Computation: Distributed Architectures

The recombinant abilities of a genetic program would enhance the search for transversal (research-technology) initiatives and would prove highly adaptive in terms of Moore's First Law (increasing computational power), Wirth's Law (corresponding increase in software 'density') and, through the eventual incorporation of quantum algorithms, overcome Moore's Second Law (the increasing costs of microchip engineering). Further advances in quantum computation would accelerate the plan's development over the coming decades. Genetic programs can be employed to devise quantum algorithms (which pose a number of problems given their counterintuitive nature) and the genetic programs themselves run on a quantum substrate (minimising the search space). Aided by advances in nanotechnology, the 'genetic-quantum interface' may ultimately prove to be the source of the anticipated 'singularity' (Nielsen & Chuang 2000) and become a central tool in the design of K2 arcologies (Fig. 21 below). It is within this context – the emergent and autonomous 'machinic phylum' – that a truly 'posthuman' culture may come into its own.

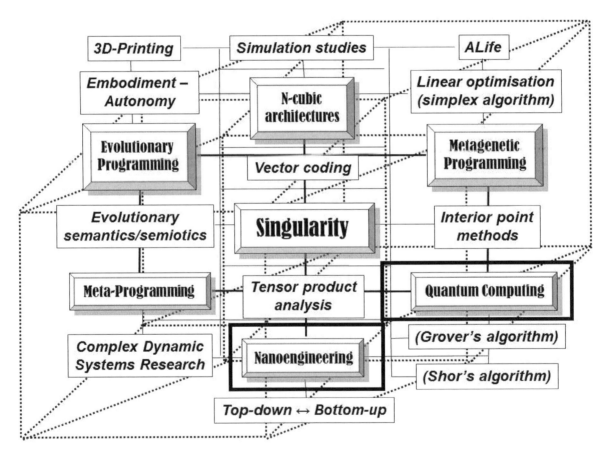

Fig. 21. Future advances in computation

The general architecture of the program is conceived by analogy with the SETI@home distributed computing model (Korbela et al. 2001) with some structural differences. In Fig. 22 below, raw (or perhaps 'half-cooked') state-of-the-world data is collected via such sources as the World Resources Institute, World Economic Outlook or other Cloud-derived sources (1). This data is 'split' in 2 ways: the total set is passed to the central program for initial processing by W3-type systems-analytic software (2) and streamed into channels appropriate to the various domains (3). These pass to a server linked to a user profile database and to the 'central program' interface (4). The data channels are then routed (5) to the listed users (the agents) who, after collating their own activities in relation to the program's 'fitness estimates' (6), relay updates of their current and projected activities back for re-processing (7) by the central program. This 'W4 synthesis', obtained by matching this input with the previously-processed W3 version, is then made available for inspection by the agents (8).

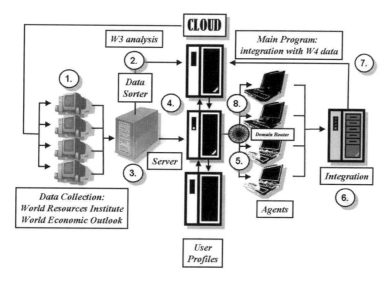

Fig. 22. Distributed computing architecture

The question arises as to whether a cloud- or grid-based architecture would be most suitable for such a project. The issue as to which form - cloud or grid – may predominate in the near future or, as is most likely, how they will integrate, remains open at the present time. According to Foster et al. (2013), both architectures currently exhibit a variety of 'trade-offs' with regard to such issues as interoperability, data provenance and segregation methods, security, virtualization and monitoring. They see future developments in computing and future modes of energy distribution as evolving ever more parallel structures in terms of economies, scales and utilities, thus drawing both domains closer on the Kardashev scale (Eq. 1). 'Major players' in these advances, Foster et al. predict, will include not only the 'usual suspects' (Silicon Valley, Amazon, Google, Yahoo, Microsoft & IBM) including academia, military and government labs, but also communities dedicated to specific, large-scale projects such as 100YSS. It is in this context – the future evolution of the 'machinic phylum' – that the cautions articulated in Section 1 regarding the unpredictability of radical advances in technology become most relevant.

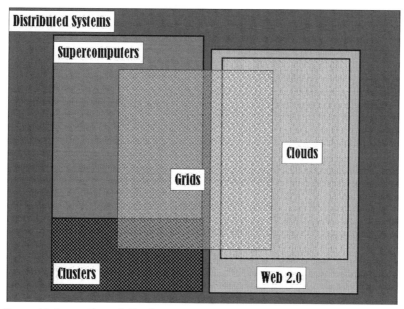

Fig. 23. Current intersection of distributed computing architectures (after Foster et al. 2013)

13. Further Advances in Computing: Tracking Critical Transition Points

"The Future is all around us
waiting
in moments of transition
to be born
in moments of revelation…"

(Babylon 5)

In some traditional mental disciplines these 'moments of revelation and transition' occur when five elements intersect – the person, the teaching, the place, the time and the teacher. We may translate these in terms of dynamic systems theory as vectors in social space, i.e.

- *Who* is involved in the transmission of information?
- *What* information is transmitted?
- *Where* is this information transmitted?
- *When* does this happen? and
- *How* and in what context does this transmission occur?

The conjunction or intersection of these 5 vectors form a 'sweet spot' or point in a dynamical system where minimal leverage (intervention) can create maximal 'rippling' effects (Fig. 21 below). Any general conference (such as the 100YSS Symposia) constitutes such a 'sweet spot', but there are many other possibilities. Can their occurrences be predicted?

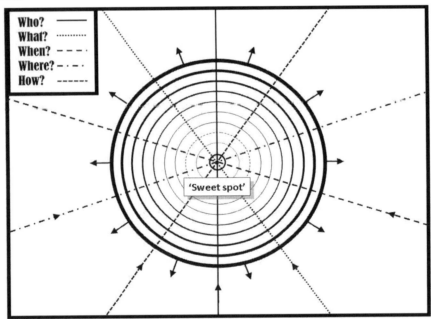

Fig. 26. The 5-vector convergence point

These 5 vectors continually intersect across the fabric of social space-time within a matrix that is continually flexing and twisting in the manner of a complex attractor in phase space. This attractor represents the prevalent macropsychological parameters of the society in question, which shift between paranoid-schizoid and depressive positions (Klein) depending on generational maturity and the political and socioeconomic context. Tracking a probability succession ($p1, p2, …, pn$) of critical intersection points ('sweet spots') in so-called polynomial time would be a formidable task using standard methods – but this task may be facilitated with the advent of quantum computers. In quantum computation, the quantum analog of a bit is the quantum bit or qubit which is implemented physically as the energy state of an electron in one of its two superimposed states $|0>$ and $|1>$ (Sgarbas 2013). These states are also the orthogonal states of a 2-dimensional Hilbert space – the basis states of a qubit - the composition of which can be written in matrix form as

210

$$|q\rangle = a|0\rangle + b|1\rangle = a\begin{bmatrix}1\\0\end{bmatrix} + b\begin{bmatrix}0\\1\end{bmatrix} = \begin{bmatrix}a\\b\end{bmatrix} \qquad \text{Eq. 27}$$

in which a and b are complex numbers representing the probability amplitude $|a|2$ of the qubit being in state $|0>$ at the point of observation and that of $|b|2$ of being in state $|1>$ at that point. A succession n of such qubits forms an n-qubit quantum register denoted as

$$|Q_n\rangle = c_0|0\cdots000\rangle + c_1|0\cdots001\rangle + \cdots + c_2|1\cdots111\rangle$$

$$= \sum_{i=0}^{2^n-1} c_i|i\rangle \qquad \text{Eq. 28}$$

which has 2n observable states, each with a probability of $|ci|2$ when measured, and may be considered as a vector in n-dimensional Hilbert space with

$$\sum_{i=0}^{2^n-1}|c_i|^2 = 1 \qquad \text{Eq. 29}$$

If a single qubit is considered as a trivial quantum register with n = 1, a quantum register with n > 1 is a series of qubits whose tensor product may be written as

$$|Q_n\rangle = |q_{n-1}\rangle \otimes |q_{n-2}\rangle \cdots |q_i\rangle \cdots |q_1\rangle \otimes |q_0\rangle$$

$$= |q_{n-1}q_{n-2}\cdots q_i \cdots q_1q_0\rangle \qquad \text{Eq. 30.}$$

A quantum register remains in a condition of superimposed states until observation triggers a quantum collapse into one or other of the superimposed states. Not every qubit need be measured for collapse to a basic state to occur, thus the search can be scaled according to the desired outcome. The construction of a suitable gating architecture and the application of Grover's algorithm (Grover 1997) permits resolution in polynomial time of NP-type problems with massive input data such as estimation of the 5- vector intersection points over a specified time range (Childs et al. 2003), Such a (hypothetical) track is shown in Fig. 27 below where each vector 'net' is slightly offset regarding its own spacing and with respect to the others.

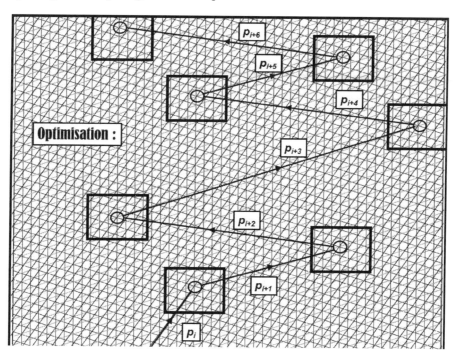

Fig. 27. Tracking the 5-vector intersection points ('sweet spots')

Game theoretic applications of quantum methods have also been shown to be highly suitable for computing probability outcomes of the type of mixed-strategy situations depicted in Fig. 27 above (Piotrowski & Sladowski

2004; Miakisz et al. 2006; Huberman & Hogg 2003), in which quantum-based algorithms have proved far more successful in dealing with the uncertainties of 'messy people stuff' than have 'classical' methods (Mendes 2005).

14. Path Dependencies in Economic and Social Evolution

An effect that cannot be underestimated in attempting prediction in the social sciences is that of 'path dependencies' – i.e. the 'conservative' effect of belief systems or, as will be argued in Religious Engineering for the K2 Transition (this volume), of dominant projective systems, or constructs. It is neglect of this very factor (in a so-called 'secular' age) that so often vitiates prediction. The Nobel Prize-winning economist Douglass North has shown that the main catalysing force in a civilisation's genesis and growth is the institutional/organisational matrix governing its political economy, and that the dominant ideational or belief system of that civilisation is the primary determinant of that matrix (North 1997).

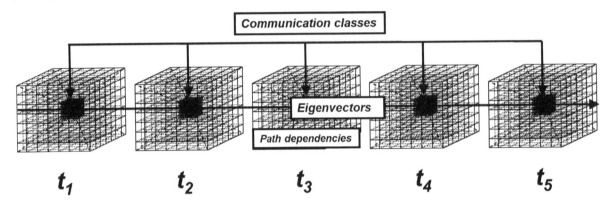

Fig. 28. Path dependencies in stochastic transition matrices

Given a series of Markovian stochastic transition matrices modelling the evolution of a social group (Fig. 28 above), the dominant projective system of that group is represented by the eigenvectors in that series, exercising a strong but often 'hidden' conservative force. The origin and evolution of these systems – and those that prevail in the present epoch – are discussed in more detail in Religious Engineering.

15. Summary Of The Overall Program Structure

An overall flow chart of the program on 'game-theoretic' models might cover 3 stages as shown in Fig. 29 below (the flow of time is from top to bottom). Stage I would consist of determining the initial conditions: terminals, functions, parameter space, and setting the fitness measure. Stage 2 would monitor the program flow through various 'child goals' towards Stage III: convergence to a pre-defined termination point. If this termination point is 'convergence to K2' (the self-sustaining arcology), then upon achieving this state, a further program might be initiated for 'convergence to K3' (the Starship).

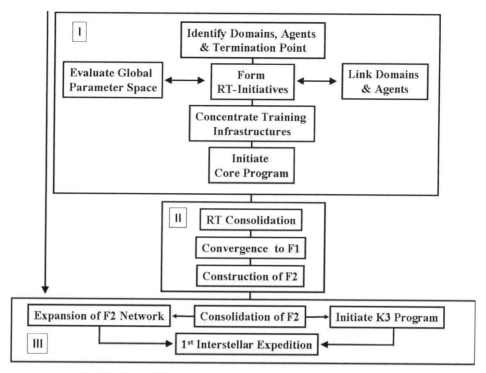

Fig. 29. Overall flow architecture as a game-theoretic model

Any species' psychology rests upon three foundations: 1) evolutionary history, 2) morphology and 3) epigenetic development. Based upon these foundations, any complex technological civilisation may be represented as a set of seven nested hypercubes that form the civilisation's developmental matrix (Fig. 30). Each hypercube represents in turn 1) the species' genome, 2) the primary drives arising from the genome, 3) the controls (defences) set in place to contain those drives and enable social co-operation, 4) the projective system or constructs that stabilize these controls, 5) the institutional structures that emerge from these constructs, 6) the modes of activity permitted within the range of these institutions and 7) nesting of the civilization within its planetary ecology (Fig. 31). We may deduce from this the extent to which the developmental pathways of a species are constrained by its 'core morphology'– the structure that determines a species' computational capacities and specific ways of modelling the environment to which it has become adapted (Section 8 above).

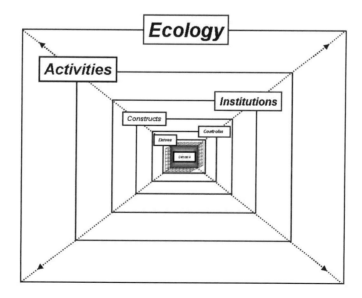

Fig. 30. Developmental matrix of a technological civilisation

213

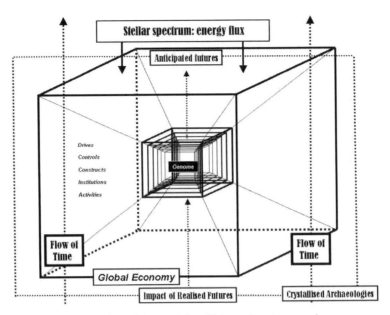

Fig. 32. Nesting of the matrix within a planetary ecology

The seven developmental levels correspond to those of the program as follows: 1) genome → genome, 2), drives → drives, 3) controls → Σ-calculus (see Religious Engineering), 4) constructs → program (as overall controlling instrument), 5) institutions → domains, 6) activities → RT-Tracks (as specific technologies of convergence) and 7) the governing ecology → K2-Base (or the finally-decided termination point).

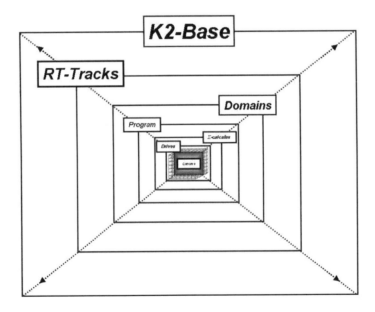

Fig. 32. The Ekumenic program as a set of nested hypercubes

This structure is conceived as a secondary or ancillary program designed independently as a monitoring instrument for the first program. Built on quite different principles (the hypercubic calculus), it is intended to monitor more closely the path dependencies described above and to situate the developmental matrix more precisely according to its position on the Kardashev scale (section 1).

16. Conclusion

For the 100YSS goal to remain stable – without deflection, dilution, , dissipation or appropriation, the program suggested above would serve as a pilot or searchlight to guide the project through the next nine turbulent decades. Without it, the 100YSS could well become 'history' in as little as 10-15 years – as has happened to the original NASA-Rockwell ISP and numerous other 'space renaissance' initiatives that have become fossilised at the level of chat forums. The essence of 'The Plan' is a distributed, interactive program that feeds continually updated data concerning global political and social ('Ekumenic') evolution and psychosocial evolution into a central 'axis' program that seeks convergence to the specified goal (Fig. 33). The ultimate choices of overall architecture and terminals, modes of initiation, monitoring, security procedures and above all, the final goal, must be reached consensually by members of the 100YSS community.

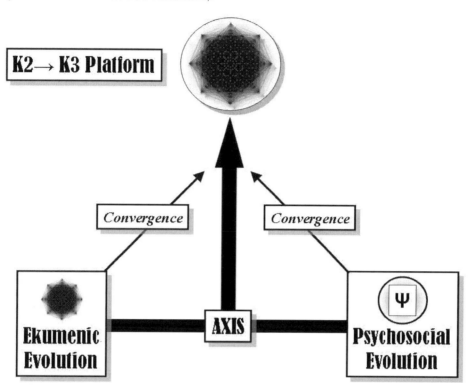

Fig. 33. The Prime Radiant: Summary

In this exploratory study the nature of this goal has purposely been left ambivalent. Whether this goal should take the form of an O'Neill type arcology at L5, a permanent Lunar Base, a permanent Martian Base or even an actual starship, is beyond the present author's competence to speculate. What really matters is that this goal, by its nature, should be a bridge to a new era, a decisive and irrevocable advance to K2, a stage that is both stable and autonomous, one that is no longer dependant on Earth for resources, personnel or governance. Whatever material form this goal may take, it is imperative that it be attained before the constraint and error catastrophes affecting global civilization precipitate a catabolic systems collapse to the point were any future recovery to our present level would be seriously compromised by key resource depletion. A balance must be struck at this stage between essential levels of security on one hand and full inclusivity of participation on the other. All usual barriers which foster 'electronic tribalism' should be eliminated since it is this, above all, that leads to fragmentation, sidelining, deflection, dilution or dissipation of the final goal.

The 100YSS projects an 'iconic' machine as both image and purpose - a machine that seems for so many to symbolise liberation, not only from the 'bonds of Earth', but from the 'human condition' itself. Will this machine remain 'virtual' or can we actualize it? Jean Petitot's discussion of the Thom-Pomian 'historical chreod' (Petitot 1978) analyzes a model tracing a 500-year period of convergence to globalisation beginning with the Dutch Revolt of 1568. This convergence process is shown to be an inner dynamic of human history, even if not consciously directed. With our accumulated historical experience and advanced computer technologies, would we not be capable of engineering, through broad participation, a 98-year convergence to a stable technological goal?

The seemingly 'insurmountable' complexity of such a task is illusory. Being as we are in media res – 'in the thick of things' – we tend to accept the dense levels of eventuation in our immediate environment as the one, true 'reality' and are all too ready to sacrifice 'dreams' on the altar of a more expedient 'practicality'. Historical perspective however has a way of 'filtering out' these details and revealing the larger, very real structures and processes which underlie them. Psychohistory, which takes an exclusively materialistic and evolutionary approach to both history and human psychology (what may be called a 'hylomorphic-hylopathic' approach), concerns itself precisely with these deeper processes. Looking at history with the 'eyes of psychohistory is like looking through a radio telescope as opposed to an optical telescope. The latter instrument magnifies what we 'normally' see in the visual spectrum, but when looking through the former, big things become small, small things become big, and the true sources of cosmic energy are revealed for the first time.

While emphasising abstraction, psychohistory does not concern itself with any 'ultimate questions' of origins or teleologies but remains at 'street level', pinpointing and distilling those factors of lived and embodied historical experience which may help us at the present time to get 'from here to there'. For instance, at least four distinct human generations will come to maturity and pass away in the course of the next 98 years. In the 'eyes of psycho-history', the so-called 'Hegelian dialectic' has precious little to do with 'intellectual history' and everything to do with intergenerational/psychoclass conflict and the demographic weightings that bias them.

We have identified the 'machinic phylum' – the co-evolution of humans and machines – as a potentially powerful ally in the realization of the parent goal provided that we are aware of the dangers of 'in-volution' vs. 'e-volution'. "The Machine will not dominate the Human, Human and Machine will become One" – provided our understanding of 'machine' and 'machinic' do not refer to any computational 'device', program or 'contraption' familiar to us at present, but is re-conceptualized in terms closer to the Calculus of Emergence, and utilized as a means of quantifying 'emergence' in the context of bringing the 100YSS goal to fulfilment.

The permanent colonization of space necessarily involves speciation, and the 'machinic phylum' may enable us to 'speciate' sufficiently to achieve an interstellar civilization provided that we retain a thorough understanding of the machines we create and the ability to guide them with foresight. The language of the machinic phylum and the way it will evolve over the next 98 years will prove central to all 'outreach' programs. It will constitute the 'battleground' on which the hearts and minds of those crucial four future generations will be lost or won. What, after all, is a 'dream' if not a 'goal' without a concrete plan formulated to achieve it? By involving these generations in the evolving 'Virtual Starship Program' as outlined in this study. We will create a powerful instrument for converting the 100YSS 'dream' into a practical goal.

References

1. Ashby, W. R. (1952.) Design for a Brain. Chapman & Hall, London.

2. Bechtel, W. (1993). 'Integrating Sciences by Creating New Disciplines: The Case of Cell Biology.' Biology and Philosophy,, vol. 8 (3), pp. 277-99.

3. Braidotti, R. (2013). The Posthuman. Polity Press, Cambridge, UK.

4. Childs, A. M., Cleve, R. E., Deotto, E., Farbi, E., Gutmann, S. & Spielman, D. A. (2003). 'Exponential Algorithmis Speedup by Quantum Walk'. Proceedings of the 35th ACM Symposium on the Theory of Computing, pp. 50 – 68.

5. Cole, H. S. D., Freeman, C., Jahoda, M. & Pavitt, K. L. R. (eds.) (1973). Models of Doom: A Critique of Limits to Growth. Universe Publishing.

6. Crutchfield, J. (1994). 'The Calculi of Emergence'. Physica D. Proceedings of the Oji International Seminar: Complex Systems – from Complex Dynamics to Artificial Reality.

7. Czander, W. M. (1993). The Psychodynamics of Work and Organizations: Theory and Applications. The Guilford Press, New York.

8. De Greene, K. B. (2000). 'Field-Theoretic Framework for the Interpretation of the Evolution, Instability, Structural Change and |Management of Complex Systems'. In Chaos Theory in the Social Sciences: Foundations and Applications. L. Douglas Kiel & Euel Elliott (eds.). Univ. of Michigan Press, Ann Arbor, pp. 273-94.

9. Deleuze & Guattari, F. (1987). A Thousand Plateaus. University of Minnesota Press.

10. Diamond, J. (2005). Collapse: How Societies Choose to Fail or Succeed. Penguin Books, New York.

11. Dune Encyclopedia, The. (1984). McNally, W. Corgi Books.

12. Forrester, J. (1974). World Dynamics. Wright-Allen Press, Cambridge, Mass.

13. Foster, I., Yong Zhao., Raicu, J. & Shiyong Lu. (2013). Cloud Computing and Grid Computing 360-Degree Compared. (N. D).

14. Friedman, G. (2010). The Next 100 Years: A Forecast for the 21st Century. Allison & Busby Ltd. London.

15. Fristion, K. & Kiebel, S. (2009). 'Cortical circuits for perceptual inference'. Neural Networks 22, pp. 1093-1104.

16. Friston, K. (2008). 'Hierarchical Models in the Brain'. PloS Computational Biology, vol. 4: 11, pp. 1-23.

17. Friston, K. (2010). 'The free-energy principle: a unified brain theory?'. Nature Reviews | Neuroscience AOP doi: 10. 1038/nrn2787.

18. Grover, L. K. (1997). 'Quantum Mechanics Helps in Searching for a Needle in a Haystack'. Phys. Rev. Lett. vol 78, pp. 325-78.

19. Haken, H. (1996). Principles of Brain Functioning: A Synergetic Approach to Brain Activity, Behaviour and Cognition. Springer-Verlag, Berlin & Heidelberg.

20. Heilbroner, R. (1995). Visions of the Future: The Distant Past, Yesterday, Today and Tomorrow. Oxford University Press, New York & London.

21. Holland, J. (1998). Adaptation in Natural and Artificial Systems. MIT Press, Cambridge, Mass.

22. Huberman, B. A. & Hogg, T. (2003). 'Quantum Solutions of Coordination Problems'. Quantum Information Processing, vol 2 pp. 421-32.

23. Johnston, J. (2008). The Allure of Artificial Life: Cybernetics, Artificial Life and the New AI. MIT Press, Cambridge, Mass., London.

24. Kakutani, Shizuo (1941). "A generalization of Brouwer's fixed point theorem". Duke Mathematical Journal 8 (3): 457–459.

25. Kardashev, N. (1964). "Transmission of Information by Extraterrestrial Civilizations". Soviet Astronomy 8: p. 217.

26. Korpela, E. Wertheimer, D., Anderson, D. Cobb, J. & Lebofsky, M. (2001). 'SETI@home – Massively Distributed Computing for SETI'. Computing for Science and Engineering, Jan.-Feb. 2001, pp. 79-83.

27. Koza, J. R. (1992), Genetic Programming: On the Programming of Computers by Means of Natural Selection, MIT Press.

28. Lalande, K., Odling-Smee, J. & Feldman, M. W. (2001). 'Cultural niche construction and human evolution'. J. Evol. Biol. 14, pp. 22-33.

29. Lancaster, O. (1949). Drayneflete Revealed. John Murray, London.

30. Lemarchand, G. A. 'Detectability of Extraterrestrial Technological Activities'. http://www.coseti.org/lemarch1.htm. Accessed: 13/02/2013 16:00 GMT.

31. MacIntyre, A. (1984). After Virtue. University of Notre Dame Press, Notre Dame, Indiana.

32. Marcovich, A. & Shinn, T. (2011). 'Where is disciplinarity going? Meeting on the borderland'. Social Science Information 50 (3-4), pp. 582-606.

33. Mazlish, B. (1993). The Fourth Discontinuity: The Co-Evolution of Humans and Machines. Yale University Press, New Haven & London.

34. Meadows, D. H., Meadows, D. L. & Randers, J. (1992). Beyond the Limits: Confronting Global Collapse, Envisioning a Sustainable Future. McClelland & Stewart Inc. Toronto.

35. Mendes, R. V. (2005). 'The Quantum Information Game'. Quantum Information Processing, vol. 4 pp. 1-12.

36. Miakisz , K., Piotrowski, E. G., & Sladowski, J. (2006). 'Quantization of Games: Towards Quantum Artificial Intelligence.' Theory of Computer Science, vol. 358 pp. 15–22.

37. Nash, J. (1950) "Equilibrium points in n-person games" Proceedings of the National Academy of Sciences 36 (1): pp. 48-49.

38. Nielsen, M. & Chuang, I. (2000). Quantum Computation and Quantum Information. Cambridge University Press.

39. North, D. (1997). Understanding the Process of Economic Change. Princeton University Press.

40. O'Neill, G. (1977). The High Frontier: Human Colonies in Space. William Morrow & Company, New York.

41. Petitot, J. (1978). 'Sur le Modèle Historique de Thom-Pomian'. Mathématiques et Sciences Humaines, 16e année no 64, pp. 43-70.

42. Piotrowski, E. G. & Sladowski, J. (2004). 'The Next Stage: Quantum Game Theory'. Mathematical Physics Frontiers, Nova Science Publishers Inc.

43. Reijnders, J. (1990). Long Waves in Economic Development. Edward Elgar Publishers, Aldershot & Brookfield, Vermont.

44. Sagan, C. & Agel, J. (2000). The Cosmic Connection: An Extraterrestrial Perspective. Cambridge University Press.

45. Sandberg, A. (2013) 'We Borg: Speculations on Hive Minds as a Posthuman State'.: http://www.aleph.se/Trans/Global/Posthumanity/ WeBorg.html. Accessed 21/02/2013.

46. Schmidhuber, I (1987). 'Evolutionary principles in self-referential learning, or on learning how to learn: The meta-meta-... hook'. Diploma thesis, Institut für Informatik, Technische Universität München, 1987.

47. Sgarbas, K. N. (2013). 'The Road to Quantum Artificial Intelligence'. Proceedings of the 11th Panhellenic Conference in Informatics, pp. 473-77.

48. Shinn, T. (2010). Research-Technology: Instrumentation, Genericity, Transversality. GEMAS Studies in Social Analysis.

49. Spinks, R., Harinder, K. S., Andreasen, N. C. & Philibert, R. A. (2004). 'Association of the HOPA12bp allele with a large X-chromosone haplotype and positive symptom schizophrenia'. American Journal of Medical Genetics Part B: Neuropsychiatric Genetics: May 15 2004, 127 (1): pp. 20-7.

50. Thom, R. (1954). 'Quelques propriétés des variétés différentiables'. Commentarii Mathematici Helvetici Vol. 28: 17–86,

51. Turchin, V. (1977): The Phenomenon of Science. A cybernetic approach to human evolution. Columbia University Press, New York.

52. Tylecote, A. (1992). The Long Wave in the World Economy: The Current Crisis in Historical Perspective. Routledge, London & New York.

53. Van Duijn, J. J. (1983). The Long Wave in Economic Life. George Allen & Unwin, Boston & Sydney.

54. Ziolo, P. (2013). 'Seeding the K2 Transition'. JBIS (under review).

Religious Engineering for the K0→ K3 Transition

Paul Ziolo, PhD

Senior Research Fellow, University of Liverpool

m.p.f.ziolo@gmail.com

Abstract

What is the strength of steel compared to that of the hand that wields it? While science and technology will provide the material tools for getting us o the stars and helping us live there, only the appropriate ideational system can sustain that vision long enough for us to get there. An ideational system is defined here as a cognitive-emotional construct that shapes, harnesses and directs the evolutionary drives of a group towards a 'transcendental' according to the challenges of the presenting environment. Examples of how transgenerational task-oriented groups catalysed major social and technological transitions in the past are provided by the role of the medieval monastic institutions and knightly orders in the genesis and growth of Western civilisation. This paper examines how the structure and character of such foundations and the strategies employed by them might be translated into the terms of the present and thereby assist the 100YSS in achieving its goal, Following practical approaches to 'religious engineering' such as those studied by Kuah Khun Eng (Khun Eng 2009), this study would recommend, not the invention de novo of some new 'Galactic religion', but a discrete and subtle emphasis on and gradual synthesis of, those elements in existing ideational systems most likely to foster the 'outward urge' and gain a broad international base of support for the 100YSS vision.

1. Projective Systems as Cultural Determinants.

> "It is the work of Science to describe the physical order of the Universe – and
> the work of Religion to place humanity within that context..."
> (The Dune Encyclopedia: Bene Gesserit Training Manual,)

> "Οἴων την μέν ουσίαν θεολογίας διδάσκαλων"
> ('Being is the Teacher of Theology')
> (Maximos the Confessor: Ambiguum X, PC. p.1134, 148b).

The Nobel Prize-winning economist Douglass North has shown that the main catalysing force in a civilisation's genesis and growth is the institutional/organisational matrix governing its political economy, and that the dominant ideational or belief system of that civilisation is the primary determinant of that matrix (North 1997). Even

219

studies that claim primacy for environmental determinism such as Diamond's Collapse (2005) make it clear that similar environmental conditions can evoke different responses from human groups at comparable technological levels. Challenges posed by an Oceanic ecology evoked radically different responses from the societies of Tikopia and Rapa Nui (Easter Island) respectively, as did an Arctic ecology from the Inuit and the Greenland Norse, the semi-desert ecology of Utah from the native Paiute-Shoshone groups and Mormon settlers and the South African veldt from the Bantu-Xhosa groups and Dutch 'voortrekkers'. On every continent, small 'traditional' societies with quite different social systems have co-existed in close proximity to one another. The variance in these systems has been traced primarily to differences in the mythic structures of each group and the intrademic transmission of those myths.

The 'strength' of a dominant projective system or construct is defined as its capacity to inspire its adherents towards collective action. Construct strength was termed asabiyya' (group solidarity) by the Tunisian historian Ibn Khaldun (1332– 1406) and the evolution of asabiyya' in relation to social complexity is analysed in the dynamic models of P. Turchin (Turchin 2003), who shows that constructs can be effectively regarded as homeostatic mechanisms, much as in the models of the cyberneticists (Ashby 1952; Haken 1996; Friston et al. 2008, 2009, 2010). Fig. 1 below shows a simplified, unidimensional model of this type, omitting delay factors for negative feedback and translating parameters of physical space into those of social space.

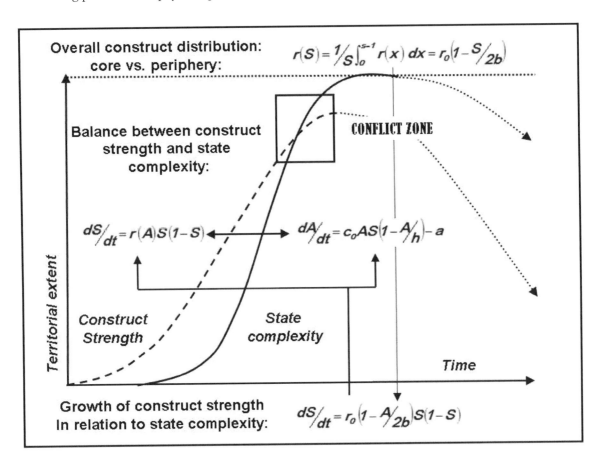

Fig. 1. Co-evolution of construct strength and state complexity

After initial consolidation and expansion, a construct becomes the foundation or Spenglerian 'prime symbol' (Spengler 1928) of cultural genesis and state formation. While the society is in its nascent, exploratory stage and the construct still 'open', almost any external challenge (barring extreme physical catastrophe) can be overcome. In Fig. 1 construct strength S grows in conjunction with state complexity A according to:

$$dS/dt = r(A)S(1-S)$$

Eq. 1

where r is the growth rate of state complexity. As wealth increases, construct strength falls off within the 'élite' social core due to 'habituation' while remaining high at the more 'deprived' periphery. 'Habituation' (Ibn Khaldun's term) signifies the withdrawal of projective significance from objects in the construct's 'transcendent' frame of reference and their condensation onto the 'realities of daily life' as those 'realities' grow more complex - hence Quigley's description of institutional decay (Quigley 1979) and Weber's observation that following the Reformation, medieval 'grace' became translated into 'money' (Weber 1958). Construct strength has the overall distribution:

$$r(S) = \frac{1}{S}\int_0^{s-1} r(x)\,dx = r_0\left(1 - \frac{S}{2b}\right)$$

Eq. 2

where b = the residue of construct strength at the periphery in relation to that at the core. Inputting this term into Eq. 1, the relations between construct strength and infrastructural complexity are given by:

$$\frac{dA}{dt} = c_0 AS\left(1 - \frac{A}{h}\right) - a$$

Eq. 3

and

$$\frac{dS}{dt} = r_0\left(1 - \frac{A}{2b}\right)S(1 - S)$$

Eq. 4

where a = habituation level, h = implementation force of the construct ('power to inspire') and c_0 = a constant reflecting the inherent state complexity at the time of its foundation (or at a time t0 from which the model is calculated), When social infrastructure is extended beyond a critical point (the 'Conflict Zone' in Fig. 1) the construct, having largely validated that infrastructure, can no longer contain the anxieties precipitated by the resulting instabilities and becomes brittle and fragmented. A challenge that at a point prior to a society's entry into the Conflict Zone might have been successfully overcome now proves fatal. Thus, as Will Durant stated, "before a civilisation is destroyed from without, it first destroys itself from within" (Durant 1944). The aggressive, expansionist 'imperial phase' that follows this inner breakdown may last for centuries, but in time the cultural system, as infrastructure complexifies and marginal returns diminish, eventually succumbs to erosion and collapse.

Dynamics of a similar order relating to the interaction of behavioural codes (constructs), stress levels, task complexity and group numbers, can be shown to operate at the level of smaller groups (Ziolo 2004) – where the scaling factors are group size, profile, construct strength and time. These factors will be of critical importance for future starship crews.

2. The Origin and Function of Myth

The myths of a group determine that group's relationship to its environment and are the structural foundation of all ideational (or 'projective') systems. They are not 'fairy stories' or 'fables' but poetic evocations intended to contain the psychic conflicts arising from epigenesis, and in forming the roots of a culture's 'prime symbol' (Spengler 1928) generate that culture's 'Orphic response to the evolutionary sources of Awe' (Danesi 1995). As Binion (1997) remarks: "Myths are the vehicle of Revelation: as such they possess a coherent structure that evolves in response to sociohistorical events. Since myths are continually re-experienced, the truths they contain must be re reinterpreted in each generation".

Over time, the myths of a group become codified within a shared projective system or construct. A 'dominant' projective system (or construct) is normally identified as 'major world religion', but it can also be a philosophy, a political or economic ideology (such as National Socialism, Marxist-Leninism or 'Liberal Capitalist Democracy'). 'Mainstream' science has all the characteristics of a 'religion' – orthodoxies, heresies, rituals ('conferences'), priests and bishops (academics'), saints ('eminent' scientists) and demons (practitioners of 'pseudoscience'). A psychohistorical analysis makes no judgement as to whether a given construct is 'rational' or 'irrational', or to be classified as 'science' or 'superstition'. It is not the proclaimed, overt character of a construct that matters so much as its deep structure and the manner in which it catalyses individual or collective action. Neither is it the job of psychology (nor of physics nor philosophy for that matter) to 'prove' or 'disprove' the 'existence of God'. It is a legitimate point of psychohistorical inquiry to ask why people believe the things they do in any given era or culture, why the things they believe in take the forms they do at these times and above all, how and why these forms make a population act in certain ways as opposed to others. Such an approach requires a language that is specific yet sufficiently abstract in relation to 'traditional' theological or philosophical discourse so as to avoid irrelevant controversies. Only in this way can it be seen how specific constructs become instruments whereby the primary evolutionary drives and residues of generic trauma are refined and shaped so as to result in specific desires and goals. 'Religious' engineering can become a far more subtle and efficient tool of social change than more explicit types of 'social' engineering. The study conducted by Kuah-Pearce Khun Eng (Khun Eng 2009) is a modern example of this, while historical examples are provided by the sermons and letters of St. Bernard of Clairvaux (1090-1153 AD) and the prophecies of Joachim of Fiore (1135-1202 AD).

The 'complex' consciousness of so-called 'higher' mammals forms one end of a continuum originating with the sucrose gradients of unicellular organisms such as Paramecium (Froese & Di Paolo 2009). The structures of organic life determine the models different organisms construct in order to interpret their environments (Crutchfield 2008), and the prescriptives of evolution require a degree of plasticity and swiftness of adaptive response such that in more complex cognitive systems, more basic cognitive and perceptive mechanisms are necessarily relegated to the level of the 'subconscious' in a fitness landscape, the understanding of which is far from complete. We consciously operate with little more that 15% of our brain capacity, the remainder includes 'free energy' or environmental stimuli that 'transgress the boundaries' of models based on everyday experience. The 'supernatural' can be therefore be considered as a 'reification' of all that transcends conscious experience – a projection in bodily form of the 'as-yet-unknown' and a naming of the unnameable in the terminology of a group construct whereby the thing named assumes a concrete reality delimited by the operational mentalities of the group. Such a fixation of what is essentially fluid permits temporary co-ordination of the group's shared perceptions and enables a collective response to the shifting challenges of an environment whose hidden features therefore remain mysterious.

All sources of transcendent experience therefore undergo projection in terms of human embodiment and become 'in-corporated' into constructs that serve a binding function ('religion' > Lat. 're-ligāre' – to 'bind together' or 'reconnect') so that members of a group can live and work in co-operation for that group's survival in a world whose origins and purpose are imperfectly understood. Religion is thus an essential tool of survival, with specific 'religions' remaining subject to the same rules of mutation and evolution that govern organic life in response to shifts and deformations in the fitness landscape.

3. Probing the Matrix

"The symbolism of uterine ecology is the Rosetta Stone of all world religions"
(Terence Dowling – personal communication)

Despite the diversity of human groups and cultures throughout history, all human constructs derive from the same morphogenetic 'core'. As Giambattista Vico (1668-1744) has stated: "The mental vocabulary of human social institutions, which are the same in substance as felt by all nations but are diversely expressed in language according to their diverse modifications, is exhibited to be such as we conceive it" (The New Science (1744) [355]).

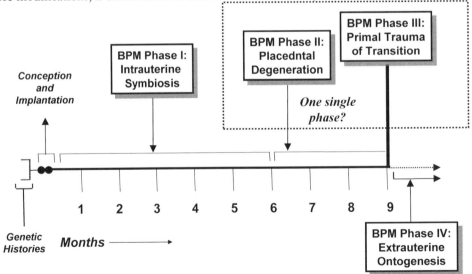

Fig. 2. The Basic Perinatal Matrix (BPM) (Grof 1975)

Where does this 'mental vocabulary' come from? The generic 'archetype' of all human experience is birth and early morphogenesis (growth of form). Evidence for the centrality of this experience and its foundational character for all later mental development is abundant in the gynaecological, clinical and fetal psychiatric literature (e.g. Rank 1924; Ferencsi 1929; Fodor 1949; Peerbolte 1957; Lake 1966; Mott 1968; Ployé 1973; Janus 1977; Verny & Kelly 1982; Wasdell 1985; Ziolo 2004 etc.). Fig. 2 above shows the sequential stages of the Basic Perinatal Matrix (BPM) charted out with temporal succession running from left to right. According to Grof's (1975) clinical identification stages in the BPM, each stage is the generic substrate for the following 'mythic' archetypal situations (stages III and IV are sometimes 'telescoped' into a single phase):

- BPM I : Symbiosis within the womb, a state of peace, of timelessness, of Paradise, of 'union with God' and of being in touch with the 'ground of Being', during which the environment is ever bountiful, limitless in resources and endlessly supportive of unfettered growth.
- BPM II: The beginning of antagonism, conflict and of subjective time. This phase runs from the onset of placental degeneration to that of labour, hence first evoking a sense of increasing confinement and suffocation, and of shrinking lebensraum, eventually leading to   powerful sensations of constriction and crushing, of cardiac distress and intense suffering, and finally to the feeling of being sucked towards a whirlpool - of being between Scylla and Charybdis - or of being swallowed by some monstrous placental avatar - a dragon, octopus, giant squid or many-headed Hydra. A confrontation with, and fear of engulfment by, the infinite abyss of Being.
- BPM III: The titanic struggle of birth, the 'Mother of all Battles', archetype of all wars, of Armageddon and Götterämmerdung, of all sadomasochistic orgies, of cataclysmic volcanic eruptions, nuclear detonations, rapes, mass murders, suicidal frenzies and orgies of destruction - the ultimate conflict between Life and Death.
- BPM IV: After birth - liberation, relief, salvation, the sensation of having been forgiven, purged, absolved, yet also of being exhausted, helpless and exposed - the anticlimax of 'what now?'

The recovery of birth experiences by analytic memory is difficult due to their prelinguistic character and the transmarginal stresses induced by perinatal transition. Stress becomes 'transmarginal' when the stress quotient exceeds the boundaries of previous experience, becomes dissociated or split off from active consciousness and then bound within a defensive psychic construct whose function is to contain and control the potentially explosive power of the residual anxiety generated by it (Ziolo 2004). Perinatal stress is a direct concomitant of morphogenesis: "experience can change the mature brain, but experiences during the critical periods of perinatal transition and early childhood organize brain systems" (Perry et al. 1995). This is why so many perinatal studies often tend sooner or later to verge on the 'mystical' – a tendency we might regard as further evidence in support of Dowling's statement at the beginning of this section. The uterine ecological sequence involves the transition from a water-breathing entity to an air-breathing entity. Such transition –a true metamorphosis - necessarily involves the psychological death of the former state of the organism prior to its 'rebirth' into a new form. In this way the BPM becomes the archetype of the death experience and, being imprinted in subconscious memory, exacerbates the human fear of death and longing for immortality (Lifton 1974) that lies at the root of the 'human condition'. Failure to achieve 're-birth' implies death by suffocation. The BPM, linked as it is to sexuality and death, is thus the 'core matrix' for all myths and, by extension, of all projective systems, whether 'rational' or 'irrational' (Fig. 3 (a) and (b) below). For this reason it is not necessary to abide by a dominant projective system in order to follow its precepts, consciously or unconsciously. One can even be actively opposed to such a system, yet be compelled to follow its precepts, at least externally, in order to conform to and flourish within, a given society.

It is therefore important to realize the extent to which the BPM serves as the root metaphor for transition from K0-K1 (confined existence within a planetary atmospheric environment) to K2 (permanent adaptation to a vacuum environment) whenever we speak of 'emerging from the womb of Earth'. For many if not most, the 'Starship' is a symbol of liberation, not only from the 'mortal bounds of Earth', but from the human condition itself. Such a protean symbol should be exploited intelligently. Any myth-based construct that exceeds the boundaries of the 'core' shown in Fig. 3 (a) is felt not to be of concern to 'real people' and hence somehow 'bizarre', 'alien' or 'incomprehensible'. This does not prepare us well for the eventual posthuman challenge, for the possibilities of a technological singularity, or for what we may encounter when we finally leave the boundaries of the Solar System (Lem 1984).

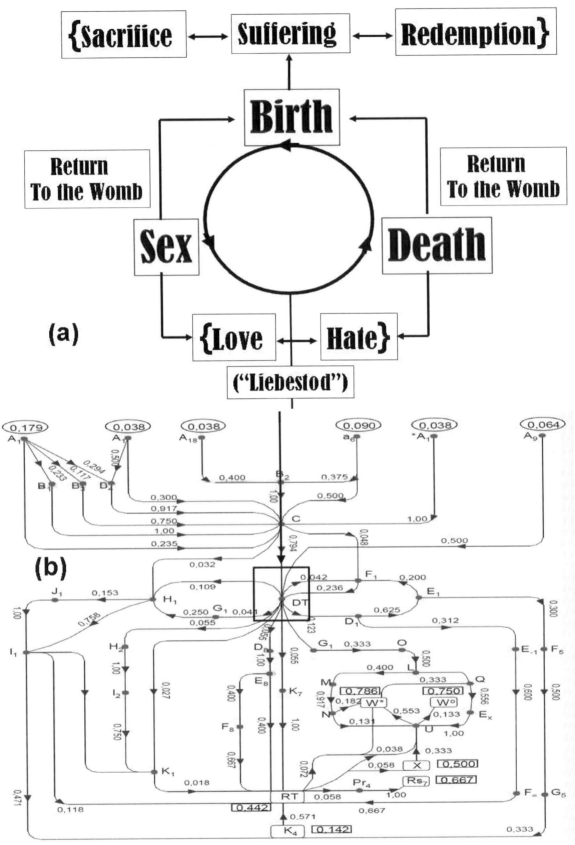

Fig.3. (a) The 'core matrix' as source of all mythic structure and (b) neural net for the generation of myths and stories based on Prop's Analysis of the Folktale(1968).

4. The Mapping of Ego Defences onto Dominant Projective Systems.

Human beings, confronted with the basic evolutionary drives (survival, sex and status), have evolved a number of so-called 'ego-defences' or 'involuntary coping mechanisms' both to maintain psychic equilibrium in a social context (homeostasis) and to facilitate social co-operation (Freud 1921). The transcultural ubiquity of these defences is well established in the clinical and ethnopsychiatric literature (Devereux 1967, 1980) so no extended discussion is required here. Suffice it to say that these 'defences' are an integral part of human epigenesis, that they grow in sophistication over the lifespan, their stable features defining 'personality traits' and that their transformations mark out critical 'life stages' (Erikson 1956). Figs. 4 and 5 below summarize these processes.

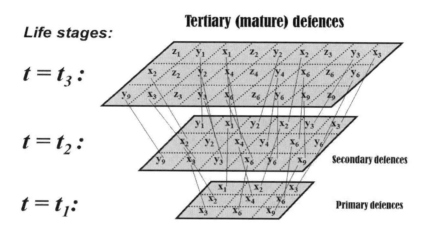

Fig. 4. Evolution of 'personality traits' at three arbitrary points in personality development.

Since ego defences serve a homeostatic function (to maintain dynamic equilibrium) their moment-to-moment functioning is quasistable – hence the flux of 'mood changes'. An 'ego-defence' or 'involuntary coping mechanism' only becomes pathological when equilibrium cannot be maintained due to excessive stresses, whereupon some form of therapy is mandated,

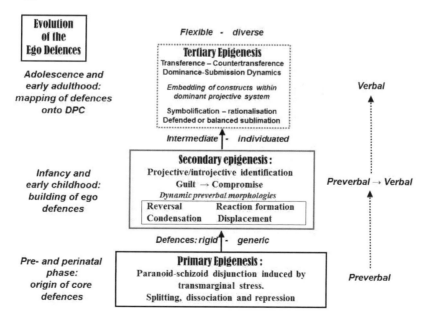

Fig. 5. Hierarchic development of the ego defences over the lifespan

Under 'normal' circumstances, ego defences are stabilized through bijective mapping onto a dominant projective system or construct. A construct evolves within a group in order to assist this function and bind the group together ('religion' > Lat. re-ligāre = 'to bind together' or 'to reconnect') by becoming the group'totem'. By means of mapping her/his inherently unstable defences onto the mythic structures of a construct, an individual confers stability (equilibrium) on these defences, and maintains this stability by sharing personal conflicts with other group members in terms of the semantic and syntactic structures of the construct (Stromberg 1993; Breck 1994; Brueggemann 2000). Individual mappings are bijective in that although the mapping may be one-to-one or, on occasion, one-to-many, the construct itself evolves the capacity to absorb high degrees of individual variance. Should the construct rigidify and fail to evolve new semantic and syntactic structures in response to a changing psychosocial environment, fragmentation or radical reform will result (as was the case of the historical 'Reformation' in Western Europe). This 'mapping and diffusion' process is illustrated in Fig. 6 below.

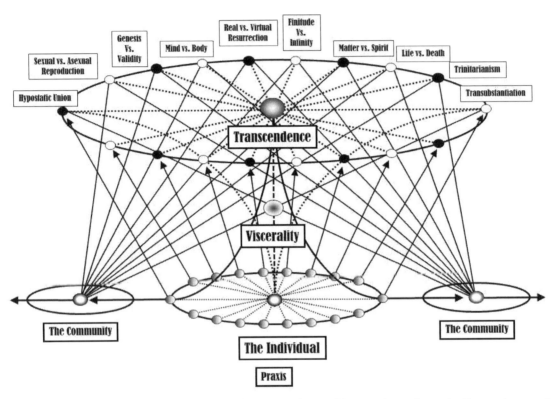

Fig. 6. The mapping of individual conflicts onto the mythic structure of a projective system and the stabilization of this mapping through sharing this system with other members of the group.

5. General Structure of the West European Construct

For a construct to be an effective catalyst for action, it must evolve the capacity to contain a wide range of conflicts and the flexibility to adapt over time to changing psychosocial circumstances. This capacity depends on three basic qualities a construct must acquire during its generative phase if it is to become 'dominant'. These are:

1. *transcendence*: the system (or construct) must confer on the individual and the group a firm understanding of personal and collective existentiality in relation to the wider cosmos,
2. *viscerality*: the system (or construct) must make a direct appeal to the basic drives and emotions – the 'evolutionary sources of Awe' and
3. *praxis* ('action'): the system (or construct) must provide a clear guide as to how to behave and act in relation to self and others.

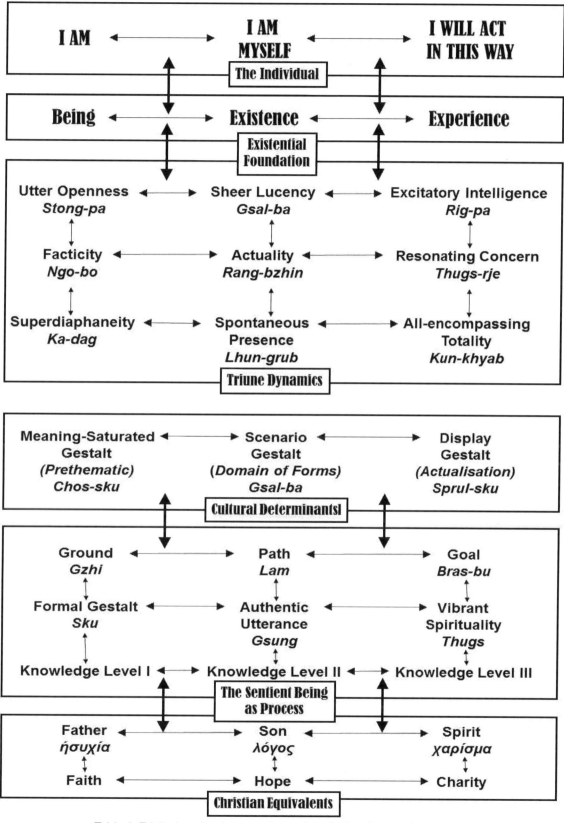

Table 1. Trinitarian structures and meanings in the rDzogs-chen tradition of Tibetan Buddhism and their Christian equivalents

These qualities are reflected in the 'trinitarian' theologies of advanced religious systems as shown in Table 1. From this comparison of trinitarian structures in the Tibetan rDzogs-chen and Christian patristic traditions, it will be seen that in essence, the quality of transcendence corresponds to the experience of 'being-as-such', that of viscerality to individual embodied identity and that of praxis ('action') to the ethics of personal and collective behaviour. The 'psychological' character of the rDzogs-chen terminology reflects the emphasis of that tradition on apophatic (non-symbolic or non-theistic) cognitive development in contrast to the more specifically cataphatic (dogmatic) terms of Christian patristic theology. Nevertheless the latter, construct, in its course of development, acquired certain specifically 'visceral' features and a historically dynamic embedding which, in the European West was to effect a profound social transformation. Many studies (e.g. Weber 1958; Eisenstad 1982;, Toulmin 1992; Galgan 1992; Jaki 1986; Holton 1988; Woods 2005; Gray 2007; Hannam 2009 etc.) show conclusively that it was the very ambiguities and contradictions inherent in the Judaeo-Christian construct which, in forcing a creative response to 'living in the world', catalysed the development of a recursively self-enhancing scientific and technological culture. These features are:

1. one single Universe, finite in time, created once and once only by a single Creator,
2. a final and all-embracing eschatology,
3. a patristic theology of space and time which teaches the doctrine of synergy (co-creation) with the Creator and the doctrine of individual and collective progress towards this final eschatology,
4. a trinitarian theology which hypostasizes ('personalizes') Being, Identity and Action and, by combining the Augustinian theology of time with the Filioque doctrine, becomes embedded in the historical process itself.
5. a resolution of existential dualism (matter vs. spirit) through the doctrine of the two co-equal natures of Christ,
6. a final synthesis of dynamic trinitarianism and existential dualism within a framework of historical immanence through the 12th century Joachimite prophecies and
7. the Johannite doctrine of apocatastasis (the final and universal redemption of all Being).

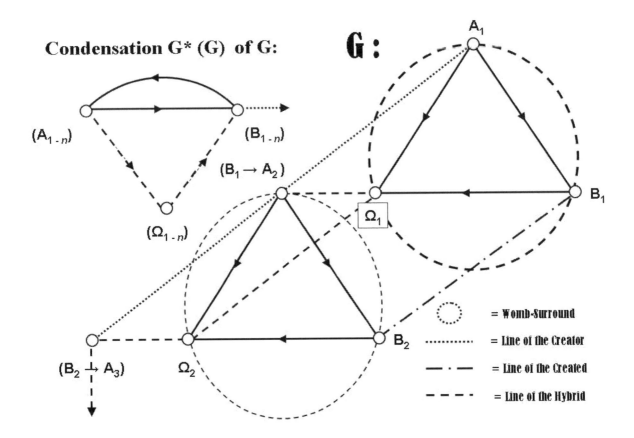

Fig. 7. Digraph (G) and condensation G*(G) of the Judaeo-Christian construct in its Western form showing transformations. An = 'Creator', Bn = 'Created' and Ωn = 'Hybrid'.

Of especial importance is the combination of 5) (the bridge between matter and spirit) with 3) (synergetic creation) and 4) (embedding of both in historical time, i.e. sanctification of the historical process itself). It is this combination that catalysed the sequences of apocalyptic cycles in European history (Fig. 6 above) and which differentiates the construct from all other world religions. Each cycle begins with a Creator, who creates the Created, both fuse to form a Hybrid, which in turn becomes the new Creator – a form of 'Hegelian dialectic' that in psychosocial reality represents the conflict between successive generations that may be represented symbolically as:

$$\left[(A_n \rightarrow B_n) \rightarrow \Omega_n\right] \xrightarrow{\ C_{n+1}\ } \left[(A_{n+1} \rightarrow B_{n+1}) \rightarrow \Omega_{n+1}\right] \xrightarrow{\ C_{n+2}\ } \dots \qquad \text{Eq. 5.}$$

where Cn represents the dominant construct and its states of transformation. Fig. 7 below provides a more 'literal' representation of this process, starting from "biblical' foundations and extending into the future.

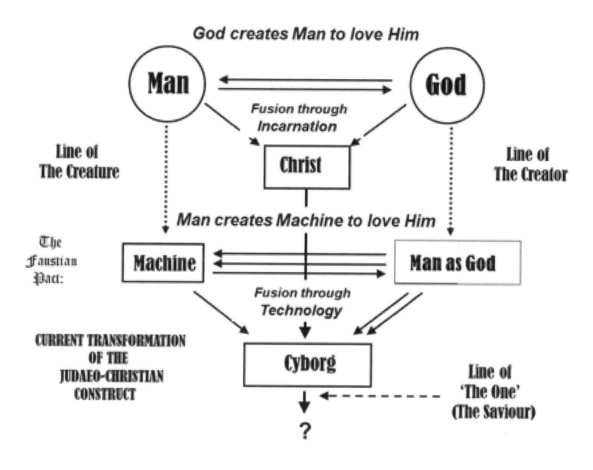

Fig. 8. Creative cycles in the Judaeo-Christian construct

6. Monasticism and the Joachimite Prophecies.

It took over 1,000 years for the West European construct to evolve – the main stages in its evolution being marked by the first seven Ecumenical Councils (Wilken 2012). The critical point of 'crystallization' occurred just prior to and during the Cistercian Reformation which preceded what is now identified as the 12th century Renaissance. The critical role of monastic institutions, both male and female, in the genesis of Western civilization should never be underestimated (Knowles 1949; Silber 1995; Ziolo 2002). The foundational contributions of this erstwhile 'deeply reticent world' (Davies 1997) include:

1. the preservation of classical learning,
2. the creation of school and university infrastructures,
3. through the disciplined integration of work and liturgical cycles ('laborare est orare' – work is prayer), the foundational concepts of goal-directed rationality and enterprise,

4. radical innovations in animal breeding, metallurgy, architecture and civil engineering,
5. the creation of conditions for the later 'Industrial Revolution' and the prototypes of modern corporate institutions and
6. through the novitiate formation process, the foundations of psychoanalytic and psychological training.

Various forms of ascetic practise have existed since the earliest periods of recorded history, but the institutionalisation and formalisation of a specifically Christian asceticism dates from the mid 4th century AD and is female in origin (Elm 1994). In this context, monasticism may be considered a precursor of the modern transhumanist/posthumanist movement. Against the fundamental drives governing human society (the 'World') -- pride, lust and greed, or 'status, sexuality and resource acquisition' – the monastics set the counter-behaviours of poverty, chastity and obedience (humility). Any association of these latter terms with 'virtue' tends to obscure the fact that 'asceticism' in itself carries no intrinsic moral imperative but is in essence a behavioural tool refined in the service of specific ends. No moral systems are absolute. All of them are behavioural codes specifically tailored to assist a given group in achieving its goals. History has shown that no weapon is deadlier than the 'jihadist' mentality schooled in a rigorous ascetic practice.

'Poverty' does not mean 'rags and begging', but the subjection of one's own personal economic advantage to the needs and welfare of the group. 'Chastity' was regarded as a liberation of mind and body from the demands of human sexuality – a deliverance from 'human bondage' rather than 'human bonding' - while 'humility' did not mean slavish subservience to any particular individual, but submission of one's own will to the overriding needs of the group's long-tern goal or 'Plan'.

Monastics chose 'to resign from their unique human identities in order to transcend the collective limits of that identity' (Elson & Moore 1981). The various 'habits' adopted by monastics as standard dress represented a funeral shroud – a virtual death with respect to the 'human World' of the passions – while the adoption of a new 'monastic' name signified the loss of a previous worldly identity. As a monastic, one underwent 'metamorphosis' in the manner of a chrysalis, and was virtually 'reborn' into a new life. One was no longer a 'person' but an element of the power one served. Through subjugation of the passions ('apathy' in its patristic sense) to a 'higher' purpose, one achieved a positive state of synergy between emotional drives and cognitive insight – "the fires of apathy' writes Maximos the Confessor "illuminate the eyes of the heart".

Medieval monastic codes of behaviour closely approximate to what modern psychology would term 'anhedonic" – i.e. 'pleasure-denying' – a type of behaviour normally associated with what is loosely termed 'schizophrenic' or at least, 'schizotypal'. Historically, many pre-industrial societies retained special niches for 'schizotypal' members in order to profit from the potentially creative abilities that are so often linked to such personality types (Nichols 2009; Spikins 2009; Crespiu et al. 2007; Brüne 2004; Polimeni et al. 2003). The Middle Ages was an era in European civilization – the era of stabilization – when such a niche appears to have spontaneously emerged. Given the 'borderline' personality type (in modern terms) prevalent in this epoch (Leclercq 1973; McLaughlin 1976; deMause 1982) and the ability of monastic institutions to absorb such personality types, it is hardly surprising to find almost one third of the population of Western Europe in religious orders for most of this period (Davies 1997; Knowles op. ,cit.).

The psychodynamic genius of Bernard of Clairvaux (1090 – 1153 AD) contributed greatly to this phenomenon. This genius consisted in Bernard's ability to divert the erotic impulse away from primary goals and into the service of 'sublimated' cultural goals through the use of the biblical Song of Songs as a 'neurolinguistic' metaphor in his sermons and letters (Leclercq 1973; Evans et al. 1987 (see esp. pp. 54-55); Leclercq 1989). Bernard was also well aware that human sexuality is intimately linked with aggression – one cannot 'make love' without 'making war' since then latter always arises from the ultimate frustration of the former. In order to stabilize the annexation of the erotic impulse to the service of cultural goals, Bernard was compelled, as so many leaders before and since, to locate an 'enemy' as a focus social aggression. Then, as now, the Muslim world was deemed appropriate, hence Bernard's call for the Second Crusade. Modern opinion has not been kind to Bernard on this account – yet by what other means was he to persuade a quarrelsome group of feudal barons and as yet only superficially-converted 'barbarian' war- band leaders to unite and create the conditions for a strong Christian civilization? For homo sapiens in our present, genetically-unmodified state, morality relative is, unfortunately, relative.

An understanding of these 'functional' principles lying behind the monastic ideal is essential both for an understanding of how and why the monastic and military Orders sought and achieved power in the Middle Ages and of the complex roles they played in medieval history. Much can be learned here that would facilitate long-term survival and prosperity. Anyone familiar with modern Japanese corporate culture will have a good idea of the 'corporate' dynamics involved here. For an application of these principles to modern Western business practise see Dollard et al. (2002).

The founder of Western monasticism is considered to have been St. Benedict of Nursia (c. 480-550 AD) whose Rule became the rock on which the edifice of Western monasticism was built and is in its own right a work of profound psychological insight. By the end of the 11th century however, the Cluniac Order of the Benedictines (so-called after the Order's central abbey at Cluny in France) had acquired vast wealth and was in danger of absorption by the very social matrix whose formation it had so successfully catalysed. It was at this point in time that the Cistercian Order was founded, originally by Robert de Molesmes (c. 1027 – 1111), Stephen Harding (ob. 1134) and Alberic of Cîteaux (ob. 1109) about the year 1098, but it was the reception into the Order of Bernard of Clairvaux around the year 1110 that inaugurated the Cistercian Reformation (Benson et al. 1982; Tobin 1995l; Burton & Kerr 2011). The 12th century witnessed a rapid expansion of Cistercian abbeys throughout Europe, many of which, such as Rievaulx Abbey in Yorkshire, becoming major centres of technological innovation in such domains as architecture, civil engineering, animal breeding and metallurgy (Fergusson & Harrison 2000) and by the middle of the century, the Order had come to dominate the main centres of learning in Western Europe.

The most significant, if 'hidden' event of this century however, may have been the dissemination of the prophetic visions of Joachim of Fiore (1135 – 1202). Born at Celico in the diocese of Cosenza in Calabria, Joachim was educated for diplomatic service at the Sicilian court and sent to Constantinople c.1167 as part of a diplomatic mission to the Byzantine Emperor Manuel I (Comnenus). Before the conclusion of this mission Joachim travelled to the Holy Land where he received 'a vision of the fullness of knowledge' on Mount Tabor (the legendary Mount of the Transfiguration). The results of these revelations were the Liber Concordiae Novi ac Veteris Testamenti (The 'Book of Concordance between the Old and New Testaments'), the Expositio in Apocalypsim ('Exegesis of the Book of Revelation') and the Psalter Decem Chordarum (The Ten-Stringed Psalter) all written from 1183-4. In addition, Joachim spent the remainder of his lifer working on the Liber Figurarum - a collection of images and geometrical figures intended to elucidate and summarise the theses contained in his written work. The complex illuminated codices of the Liber Figurarum present a philosophy of history geometrised in terms of a graph-theoretic 'topology of the mind' and from the psychohistorical perspective therefore. constitute an invaluable analytic resource, far exceeding in political significance and historical impact anything along the lines of the so-called 'Da Vinci Code'.

The 'Prime Directive' behind the prophecies is shown in Fig. 9 below – a tripartite scheme of past, present and future history called the Triplex Aetatum or 'Triad of the Three Ages'. Its significance is as follows:

1. Human history is divided into three successive Ages (in Joachimite terms, the Ages or Status (Lat. status (pl.) in the sense of epochs, aeons or psychospiritual 'conditions') of the Father, of the Son and of the Holy Spirit).
2. The 'First Age' – that of the Father – is that of genesis and 'tradition'. Humanity is currently situated in the Second Age - the age of struggle and transition, while the Third will be the 'New Age', ('Novis Ordo') bringing the resolution of all conflict and an endless 'spiritualised' state of human perfection.
3. The New Age will heralded by the victorious struggle of the God-anointed 'World Emperor' in alliance with the 'Angelic Pope' (i.e. the Jedi 'Force') over the 'Beast of the Apocalypse' and the Antichrist (the 'Sith' representing the 'Dark Side of the Force').
4. The New Age will be ushered in or 'catalysed' by two new monastic orders - one engaged in the active life, the other in the contemplative. Life.

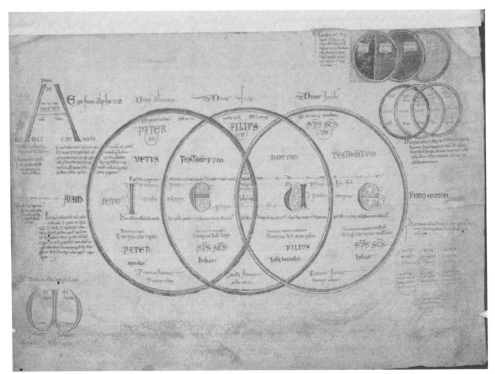

Fig. 9. The TRIPLEX AETATUM. Trinitarian Circles enclosing the Tetragrammaton from the Liber Figurarum of Joachim of Fiore (1135-1202 AD).

(Archives of Corpus Christi College, Oxford MS. 255A, f.7v).

In this way, Joachim created a synthesis of dynamic trinitarianism and existential dualism within a framework of historical immanence. The tripartite program clearly fulfils the foundational requirements of the dominant projective system, successfully embedding it in lived time and causing it to be re-experienced in every age by every individual who comes under its influence. The First Age is the 'age of the past', the past we all inherit at every moment, the 'Second Age' is the 'today' – the moment of struggle and transition, while the 'Third Age' is the eternally hoped-for future – the age of 'Utopia'. The structure corresponds to the 'ecological sequence' of the BPM, so every generation is primed to experience it. A graphic 'deconstruction' of the Triplex is shown in Fig. 10 below.

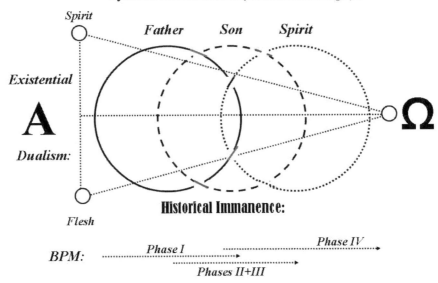

Fig. 10. Graph-theoretic interpretation of MS. 255A, f.7v

After Joachim's death, the prophecies were disseminated in the form of what became known as the Eternal Evangel - a reference to Rev.14: 6 and to an actual 're-interpreted' compilation and abridgement of Joachim's works issued under this title by Gerardo di Borgo Santo Donnino in 1252. At this time dissension and strife within the Church were on the increase and Joachim had become a controversial figure - a fact that eventually led to the condemnation of his works by the Protocol of Anagni in 1256. This did not diminish the emotionally felt canonical power of his ideas - a power that was consciously imitated by later writers of the apocrypha. The 'vector' for dissemination of the prophecies were the various Orders of Friars that emerged over the course of the 13th and 14th centuries as symptoms of passive or active resistance against ecclesiastical authority. The Franciscans, the Minorites, the Spirituals, the secretive Fratricelli and the more explicitly terrorist Apostoli founded by Seguarelli and Frà Dolcino - all saw themselves as representing the 'New Order' prophesied by Joachim which was to initiate the New Age. These Orders wandered far and wide over northern and southern Europe preaching to the common people and thus were crucial agents in the dissemination of pseudo-Joachimite ideas. The Friars themselves, anxious to justify their own canonical authority in the face of ecclesiastical disapproval, appealed to the prophecies in Revelation and to Joachim's supposed interpretations of them in order to endorse their own activities. Hence the intense preoccupation with the Joachimite prophecies on the part of later German Reformation thinkers. Explicit identification of stages in the Joachimite program with specific historical events led successive groups to re-interpret their program according to their own political ambitions. During the Enlightenment and Industrial Revolution, as the static and etherealised immanence of the medieval Civitas Dei receded from Western consciousness, the Joachimite 'embedding' of the construct within the context of lived time led to a quest for a sociopolitically-immanent 'New Jerusalem' realisable in the here and now. This became the 'germ' for all Western concepts of unilinear progress, the core catalyst of the emergent European nation-states and the foundation for all utopian and apocalyptic movements, including the Nazi and Comnmunist ideologies and, paradoxically, Al-Qaeda and all 'radicalised' Islamist movements (McGinn 1985; Ziolo 2001; Reeves & Gould 2001; Gray 2007).

7. Construct Evolution through Semiotic Permutation

The construct 'lies beneath' modern philosophies of both science and history thanks to the process of 'semantic permutation' that occurred following the 30-Years War of 1618-1648 and which permitted the construct itself to evolve. Through semiotic permutation the basic structure of the medieval dominant projective system was preserved through a mutation of its forms of discourse from the 'theological', through the 'metaphysical' to the 'scientific'. The 'Enlightenment' was never a question of 'Science vs. Religion', but rather a power struggle between two groups – the clergy and the 'philosophers', both appealing to the basic mythic forms of the same construct while veiling them in contradictory semiotic structures. The process is shown in Table 2 below. The first semiotic permutation occurred during the Enlightenment, while the second represents the 'background' assumptions current in much futuristic thinking today.

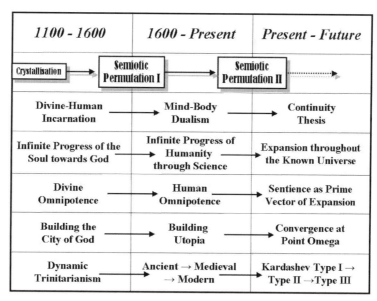

1100 - 1600	1600 - Present	Present - Future
Crystallisation →	Semiotic Permutation I →	Semiotic Permutation II ┈┈┈→
Divine-Human Incarnation	Mind-Body Dualism	Continuity Thesis
Infinite Progress of the Soul towards God	Infinite Progress of Humanity through Science	Expansion throughout the Known Universe
Divine Omnipotence	Human Omnipotence	Sentience as Prime Vector of Expansion
Building the City of God	Building Utopia	Convergence at Point Omega
Dynamic Trinitarianism	Ancient → Medieval → Modern	Kardashev Type I → Type II → Type III

Table 2. Semiotic transformations of the Western dominant projective system from its inception to the near future

233

Transformations of this type are especially possible in the West due to the predominantly analytic character of Western European languages. The chief 'fallacy' engendered by analytic languages is that of nominalism, where because a 'name' is given to some concept, it is assumed that that concept has thereby acquired real material existence. Rates of linguistic evolution proceed much faster than those of cognitive evolution. Signifiers of a construct therefore change (surface variance) while the signified (deep structures) remain constant.

Successive levels of semiotic permutation are interpreted cognitively by analogy with the Hausdorff transform, where if $\{\mu_p\}$ (p = 0. 1, 2, …) is an arbitrary sequence of numbers, the double sequence $\{\Delta n \mu p\}$ is defined by:

$$\Delta^n \mu_p = \sum_{r=0}^{n}(-1)^r \cdot \binom{n}{r} \cdot \mu_{p+r} \quad (n, p = 0, 1, 2, \ldots) \qquad \text{Eq. 6,}$$

these quantities being termed the 'differences' of the sequence $\{\mu p\}$ since they satisfy the recurrence relations:

$$\{\Delta n \mu p\} = \mu p \quad (p = 0, 1, 2, \ldots) \qquad \text{Eq. 7}$$

and

$$\{\Delta n \mu p\} = \Delta n - 1 \mu p - \Delta n - 1 \mu n + 1 \quad (n = 0. 1, 2, \ldots : p = 0, 1, 2, \ldots) \qquad \text{Eq. 8,}$$

then the Hausdorff transform

$$t_p = \sum_{q=0}^{p}\binom{p}{q} \cdot \left(\Delta^{p-q}\mu_q\right) \cdot s_q \qquad (p = 0, 1, 2, \ldots) \qquad \text{Eq. 9}$$

is the transformation of the sequence $\{sp\}$ generated by the sequence $\{\mu p\}$ (Jakimowski 1956). In the case of the generalised transform (Hausdorff 1921; Leviatan 1968), if the sequence (λi) $(i \geq 0)$ satisfies:

$$0 = \lambda 0 < \lambda 1 < \ldots < \lambda n < \ldots,$$

$$\lim_{n \to \infty} \lambda_n = \infty,$$

$$\sum_{i=1}^{\infty}\frac{1}{\lambda_i} = \infty \qquad \text{Eq. 10,}$$

and if $\{\mu n\}$ $(n \geq 0)$ is a sequence of real or complex numbers, the generalised transform $\{tn\}$ $(n \geq 0)$ of a sequence $\{sn\}$ $(n \geq 0)$ is given by:

$$t_n = \sum_{m=0}^{n}(-1)^{n-m} \lambda_{m+1} \cdots \lambda_n [\mu_m, \ldots \mu_n] s_m \qquad \text{Eq. 11,}$$

where for $0 \leq m \leq n = 0, 1, 2, \ldots,$

$$[\mu_m, \ldots, \mu_n] = \sum_{i=m}^{n}\frac{\mu_i}{(\lambda_i - \lambda_m) \cdots (\lambda_i - \lambda_{i-1})(\lambda_i - \lambda_{i+1}) \cdots (\lambda_i - \lambda_n)} \qquad \text{Eq. 12.}$$

Thus in the Western construct, while global and continuous symmetry transforms operate horizontally across the trinitarian hypostases ('personifications') of the three Ages (Father, Son and Spirit), they are simultaneously projected downwards through the ver etween discrete number series, but between n-dimensional matrices bounded only by the creative potentialities peculiar to the psychic ecology of the universality class that embodies them – in this case, a historically contextualised humanity.

$$i \xrightarrow{C_p} j : C_p = \{S_n\} \xrightarrow{\delta} \{t_m\}; t = (\delta(\mu)\delta)s \qquad \text{Eq. 13,}$$

where

$$t_m = \sum_{n=0}^{m}(-1)^m [m! \, n! \, (m-n)!] \qquad \text{Eq. 14.}$$

These permutations are also embedded in the history of science, where the function of the underlying construct is to protect the dominant paradigm and to contain innovation within acceptable bounds. As Jean Petitot states:

"There are certain problems in the history of science which are as yet unrecognised. Often, instead of simple steps from approximation to greater rigour, major scientific breakthroughs were in fact acts of containment which repressed key aspects of reality by binding them within webs of symbolic elaboration". (Petitot (1978) translated by the present author).

Thus if 'mainstream science' itself has all the properties of a projective system, its so-called 'controversies' are organized so as to create webs of this type – webs whose primary function is not to access 'reality-as-such' but rather to keep existential anxieties at bay and create an acceptable 'playing field' for the competitive pursuit of status and resources – the Darwinian 'imperatives' – that all too often absorb and neutralize the creative energies of emergent generations. This is why radical innovation, which 'transgresses the boundaries' of the construct, provokes so much conflict. A 'Kuhnian paradigm shift' forces a deep 'reconstruction' of this construct in the same way as the medieval construct was forced to transform and adapt during the transition from 'Renaissance' to 'Enlightenment'.

8. From Cathedral to Starship

As J.R.R. Tolkien has pointed out in his Introduction to the Elder Edda (Tolkien 2009), it is the archaic, preliterary oral forms of a culture's epic poetry that contain the essence of that culture's 'prime symbol'. During its period of genesis therefore (its first thousand years) the Judaeo-Christian construct was adapted to the deep mythological structures of Northern Europe. It has been suggested (Cohen et al. 2011) that only in the building of the great medieval cathedrals do we find an instance where human beings have proved capable of undertaking major transgenerational projects – and this point is well made. The medieval cathedral and the starship represent material projections of the same 'prime symbol' – an evolving image that began with the genesis of Western Gothic architecture in the 12th century and may culminate in an era yet to come. A continuity can be observed from images of primeval forest groves where the hunter-gatherers of Northern Europe assembled to celebrate their ancient rites, through to the masterpieces of Gothic architecture where the trunks, branches, leaved canopies and filtered sunlight of the sacred groves mutate into the ribbed and fan vaultings, flying buttresses and rose-windows of the great cathedrals (Fig. 11 below).

a) *Forest grove* b) *Fan vaulting: Wells Cathedral*

c) *Black Spruce* d) *Notre Dame (Paris): East elevation*

Fig. 11. From sacred forest grove to Gothic cathedral architecture

This continuity of architectural evolution was sustained through to the present where the 'cathedral' appears to prefigure the 'starship' itself Fig. 12 below) and the sanctuaries and altars where priest and people came face to face with the 'Transcendent' morph into the 'starship bridge' where 'captain' and 'crew' come face to face with the Cosmos (Fig. 13). Indeed as we have seen, rather than 'rejecting' the physical world, the medieval Christian construct above all sought direct engagement with 'matter' and its purposeful transformation through praxis – with the doctrine of the Incarnation forming the bridge between Matter and Spirit, or between Earth and the transcendent realm. As we have seen, the deeply rooted psychological structures of this construct were conserved throughout the Renaissance, Reformation and Enlightenment through a transmutation of discourse from the realm of the theological to that of the scientific.

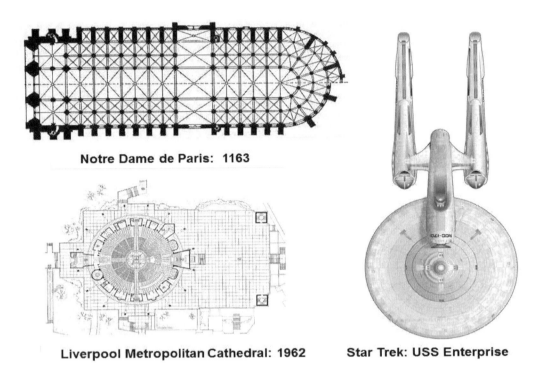

Notre Dame de Paris: 1163

Liverpool Metropolitan Cathedral: 1962   **Star Trek: USS Enterprise**

Fig. 12. From Gothic cathedral architecture to Starship

Fig. 13. From Gothic cathedral altar to Starship bridge

9. Conclusion

Let us consider two contrasting visions of the human future:

I.   "Those who live and work permanently in space will be distinguished by self-discipline, their ability to meet the requirements of the Machine, to repress fear, desire, all emotion. They will belong to a breed apart, cut off from family, the consolations of love and sexuality. After they have endured the initial ordeals of training, their physicality will be measured by the requirements of the Machine. Life in space ships will be as closely regulated and lonely as life in a monastery: the greatest virtues will be those of restraint, not excess. They will voluntarily cut themselves off from earthly satisfactions in order to approach closer to the infinite". 127]

(Elson, P. & Moore, C. (1981). Parallel Lines: The Science Fiction Illustrations of Peter Elson & Chris Moore. Quote from the Introduction by Pat Vincent, p. 16).

II.   "The cultural era is past. The new civilization, which may take centuries or a few thousand years to usher in, will not be another civilization – it will be the open stretch of realization which all the past civilizations have pointed to. The city, which was once the birth-place of civilization, such as we know it to be, will exist no more. There will be nuclei of course, but they will be mobile and fluid. The peoples of the earth will no longer be shut off from one another within states but will flow freely over the surface of the earth and intermingle. There will be no fixed constellations of human aggregates. Governments will give way to management, using the word in a broad sense. The politician will become as superannuated as the dodo bird. The machine will never be dominated, as some imagine; it will be scrapped, eventually, but not before men have understood the nature of the mystery which binds them to their creation. The worship, investigation and subjugation of the machine will give way to the lure of all that is truly occult. This problem is bound up with the larger one of power – and of possession. Man will be forced to realize that power must be kept open, fluid and free. His aim will be not to possess power but to radiate it."

(From Henry Miller's Sunday After the War, cited in Brown (1985) p. 305).

Both these visions aspire to the prophetic and are unquestionably 'religious' in tone. The first quotation represents the philosophy of space exploration while the second represents the 'Earth-Child' philosophy. Which is more 'Utopian'? We are often told that we should 'solve all our problems here on Earth' before we go 'bombing off into the wild blue yonder'. But 'natural', i.e. genetically unmodified, humanity will never 'solve its problems here on Earth' since dominance, submission, aggression and the struggle for resource control, status and sexuality are all core aspects of a 'natural' human psychology. If we had our 'utopia' we would destroy it through sheer boredom. Radical modification of the genome would appear to be a prerequisite for any realistic 'peace on Earth' – and this is not a solution likely to find favour with the majority.

Permanent habitation of space on the other hand will require an even greater 'long-jump adaptation' on the part of humanity. As the first of the above quotations makes clear, transcending the constraints of one evolutionary trajectory will simply require us to deal with unknown constraints of the newly-chosen trajectory. Such a transition will present fierce challenges – challenges that only be overcome with the aid of a suitably modified construct. Whether those who accomplish this transition are destined to exult or weep in their transcendence – this will be their own affair, and no concern of 'the rest of us'.

The human future in deep space (as opposed to LEO) will require a pioneer society that will be polycentric, metacomplex and cyborganic. 'The Machine will not dominate the Human: Human and Machine will become One' (Sandberg 2013). For now at least, the Machine is capable of a virtually unlimited (from our present context) range and rapidity of computation - but lacks motivation and the power to take large-scale evolutionary decisions. The Human on the other hand, thanks to a long evolutionary and morphogenetic history, possesses an intense motivational drive. Although 'computational power' for the human is slower and more restricted in range than that of the Machine, the massive parallelism of the biological brain and the evolutionary sources of motivational drive make an alliance with the Machine – i.e. 'merging' with the machine as the construct dictates – a powerful alliance for the permanent colonisation of space.

What strategy is best adopted by those 100YSS members whose 'outreach' territory includes religious organisations? Certainly not that of 'inventing' some new 'Galactic religion'. Rather, we might follow the example of Kuah Khun-Eng's 2009 study (and that of the Bene Gesserit as outlined in the Dune Encyclopedia (McNally) and selectively emphasise those elements of whatever religious field we are involved with that promote teleology, transcendence, and human 'synergy' with the Creator.

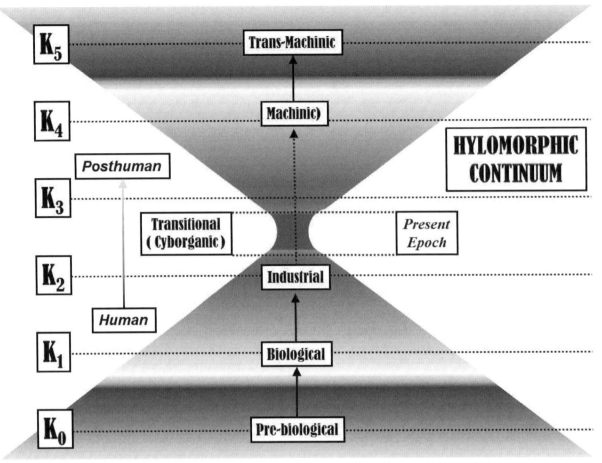

Fig. 14. Projected Kardashev levels in the evolution of a sentient species

As a species, we are in no position at present to make any final statements about the 'meaning of life' - but the directionality of evolution is evident, even from a cursory study, even if that directionality appears chaotic and frequently destructive. It is possible that from a far more 'advanced' perspective, such chaos and destruction is simply part of the statistical process necessary for the emergence of advanced intelligence throughout the cosmos – 'many are called but few are chosen' (Matt. 22:14). Fig. 14 above shows a sequence of possible Kardashev levels a hypothetical sentient species would traverse from the point of its emergence from within a planetary biological matrix to the most 'advanced' level – K5 –that we could realistically imagine at present. The most radical transition is the 'long-jump' adaptation from a planetary (biological) environment at K0 to a space (posthuman) environment at K2 – the 'bottleneck' of Fig, 14. If we succeed in making this transition, well and good, but should we fail, this failure would be of no ultimate consequence for the overall 'Galactic Plan'. And what is this Plan? We cannot guess at present, but it may be safe to assume from the evidence we have (as do many hylomorphic-hylopathic philosophies) that the ultimate 'fate' of sentient life may be bound up with that of the Universe itself (Fig. 15 below). No moral prescriptive is implied here – participation in an evolutionary advance of this type is a matter of species choice.

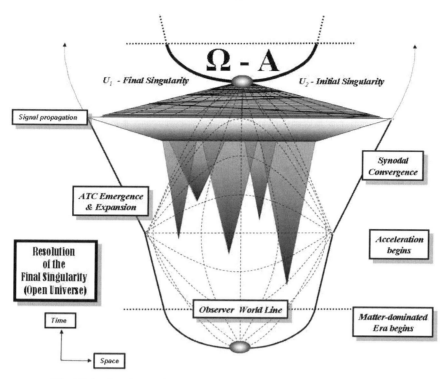

Fig.15. Is the 'fate' of sentient life bound up with that of the Universe?

A 'dominant projective system' may be regarded as a 'metaprogram' guiding the evolution of a population or a biological species, and the Judaeo-Christian construct in its Western form has brought us to the edge of the K0 – K2 transition, but this construct will be insufficient to carry us through. To this end, a synthesis with other constructs will be essential and inevitable– a voluntary evolutionary jump on the species level requires an existential and experiential synthesis from all participants in that jump.

The main 'opposition' between the philosophies of East and West appears to derive from each tradition's approach to the question of the fundamental impermanence 'matter' (> Lat. 'mater' = 'mother'). In the West, this impermanence is denied through an attempt to fixate transient phenomena within the bounds of an analytic language. In the East, 'impermanence' is denied simply by denoting all material manifestations as 'illusion' or 'maya' (Fig. 16).

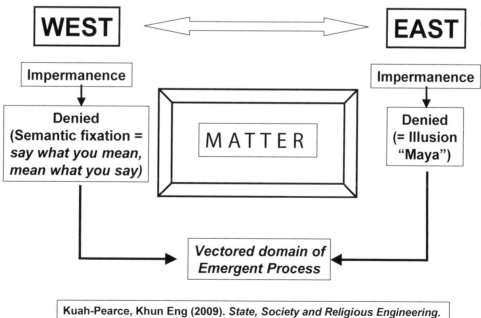

Fig. 16. Possibilities for future construct evolution

To combine the deep cognitive-emotional disciplines of the East with the West's commitment to the dynamic transformation of matter-as-lived process would result in a psychological 'thermonuclear bomb'.

From the Joachimite prophecies, a dramatic history leads us from the North Yorkshire moors to the mountains of Sicilian Calabria, from the forests of Northern Germany to the archives of Corpus Christi, Oxford and thence to the sands of Cape Canaveral. The historical record serves only to demonstrate the moral neutrality of a construct as construct, discussed above. 100YSS members, like most space advocates, are heirs to the Joachimite prophecies, even if few are explicitly aware of the fact. Since this inheritance has come to us, the question is – do we have the intelligence to benefit from historical experience and use such an instrument to best advantage.

Future interstellar pioneers will not be 'natura;', unmodified humans. At present our constructs reflect our evolutionary history, our morphology and modes of epigenesis, but posthuman or cyborganic evolution will challenge the most basic bonds the define our 'humanity' – those between male and female, between parent and child, between biosphere and species, between genes and culture – and between life and death (Braidotti 2013). Cyborganic evolution will force us to redefine these bonds and require that we come to terms with the infinite mutability and contextuality of Being. Genetics is the real 'language of God' and constructs are the metaprograms written in that language that direct the currentrs and flows of matter across time and through space. The time may come when we no longer need to rely on the salvific promise of constructs and can engage consciously and confidently with those vectored domains of emergent process of which we are so intimate a part. That time, however, is not yet.

References

1. Ashby, W. R. (1952.) Design for a Brain. Chapman & Hall, London.

2. Benson, R. L., Constable, G. & Lanham, C. D. (1982),(eds). Renaissance and Renewal in the Twelfth Century. Harvard University Press, Cambridge, Mass.

3. Binion, R. (1997). Sounding the Classics: From Sophocles to Thomas Mann. Praeger, Westport CT.

4. Braidotti, R. (2013). The Posthuman. Polity Press, Cambridge, UK.

5. Breck, John (1994). The Shape of Biblical Language: Chiasmus in the Scriptures and Beyond. St. Vladimir's Seminary Press, Crestwood, New York.

6. Breck, J. (1994). The Shape of Biblical Language: Chiasmus in the Scriptures and Beyond. St. Vladimir's Seminary Press, Crestwood, New York.

7. Briend, A. (1979). 'Fetal Malnutrition - The Price of Upright Posture?'. British Medical Journal 1979, 2 pp. 317-19.

8. Brown, N. O. (1985). Life Against Death. Wesleyan University Press, Middletown CT.

9. Brueggemann, W. (2000). 'The Prophetic Word of God and History'. Texts That Linger, Words That Explode: Listening to Prophetic Voices. Fortress Press, Minneapolis.

10. Cohen, M., O'Donnell, D. J., Becker, R. F. & Brody, A. (2011). 'Interstellar Sweat Equity'. http://www.astrotecture.com/Interstellar_-_Exoplanets_files/20110708.Abstract.Update.Interstellar_Sweat_Equity.Public%20Symposium.pdf. Accessed 22/02/2013: 15.23 GMT.

11. Crutchfield, J. (1994). 'The Calculi of Emergence'. Physica D. Proceedings of the Oji International Seminar: Complex Systems – from Complex Dynamics to Artificial Reality.

12. Danesi, M. (ed.) (1995). Giambattista Vico and Anglo-American Science. De Gruyter Mouton. Reprinted in 2011.

13. Davies, N. (1997). Europe: A History. Pimlico, London.

14. Durant, W. (1944). The Story of Civilization. Vol.3: Caesar and Christ. Simon & Schuster, New York. Quotation from the Epilogue: Why Rome Fell.

15. Deleuze & Guattari, F. (1987). A Thousand Plateaus. University of Minnesota Press.

16. Diamond, J. (2005). Collapse: How Societies Choose to Fail or Succeed. Penguin Books, New York.

17. Dollard, K., Marett-Crosby, A. & Wright, T. (2002). Doing Business with Benedict: The Rule of St. Benedict and Business Management: A Conversation. Continuum Press. London & New York.

18. Eisenstadt, S. N. (1982). 'The Axial Age: The Emergence of Transcendental Visions and the Rise of Clerics'. Archives Européenes de Sociologie 23 (1982) pp. 294-314.

19. Elm, S. (1994). Virgins of God: The Making of Asceticism in Late Antiquity. Oxford University Press.

20. Erikson, E. (1956). 'The Problem of Ego Identity'. Journal of the American Psychoanalytic Association, 4, 1 pp. 56-121.

21. Evans, G. P., Leclercq, J. & Cousins, E. (1987). Bernard of Clairvaux : Selected Works. Paulist Press, Mahwah, New York.

22. Ferenczi, S. (1989). Thalassa: A Theory of Genitality. Maresfield Library, Karnac Press, New York.

23. Fergusson, P. & Harrison, S. (2000). Rievaulx Abbey. Community, Architecture, Memory. Yale University Press.

24. Fodor, N. (1949). The Search for the Beloved: A Clinical Investigation of the Trauma of Birth and Prenatal Condition. University Books, New Hyde Park, New York.

25. Freud, S. (1921). Group Psychology and the Analysis of the Ego (1921). SE vol. 18 (1955). Penguin Freud Library vol. 12 pp. 91-178.

26. Friston, K. & Kiebel, S. (2009). 'Cortical circuits for perceptual inference'. Neural Networks 22, pp. 1093-1104.

27. Friston, K. (2008). 'Hierarchical Models in the Brain'. PloS Computational Biology, vol. 4: 11, pp. 1-23.

28. Friston, K. (2010). 'The free-energy principle: a unified brain theory?'. Nature Reviews | Neuroscience AOP doi: 10. 1038/nrn2787.

29. Froese, T. & Di Paolo, E. A. (2009). 'Sociality and the life-mind continuity thesis'. Phenomena in Cognitive Science, DOI 10.1007/s11097-009-9140-8.

30. Galgan, G. (1982). The Logic of Modernity. New York University Press, New York.

31. Gardner, J. (2007). The Intelligent Universe: AI, ET and the Emerging Mind of the Cosmos. New Page Books, NJ.

32. Gray, J. (2007). Black Mass: Apocalyptic Religion and the Death of Utopia. Penguin Books.

33. Grof, S. (1975). Realms of the Human Unconscious: Observations from LSD Research. Viking Press, New York.

34. Haken, H. (1996). Principles of Brain Functioning: A Synergetic Approach to Brain Activity, Behaviour and Cognition. Springer-Verlag, Berlin & Heidelberg.

35. Hannam, J. (2010). God's Philosopher's: How the Medieval World Laid the Foundations of Modern Science. Icon Books.

36. Hausdorff, F. (1921). 'Summationsmethoden und Momentfolgen I umd II'. Math. Zeit. vol. 9 (1921), pp. 74-109, 280-288.

37. Jaki, S. (1986). Science and Creation: From Eternal Cycles to an Oscillating Universe. Scottish Academic Press, Edinburgh.

38. Jakimowski, A. (1956). 'A Note on Hausdorff Transforms'. Proceedings of the American Mathematical Society vol. 7 no. 5 (Oct.) pp. 803 – 7.

39. Janus, L. (1997). The Enduring Effects of Prenatal Experience: Echoes from the Womb. Jason Aronson, Northvale NJ & London.

40. Knowles, D. (O.S.B) (1949). The Monastic Order in England: A History of its Development from the Times of St. Dunstan to the Fourth Lateran Council 943-1216, Cambridge University Press.

41. Khun Eng, Kuah, (2009). State, Society and religious Engineering: Reformist Buddhism in Singapore. Institute of South-East Asian Studies (2nd Edition).

42. Leclercq, J. O.S.B (1973). 'Modern Psychology and the Interpretation of Medieval Texts'. Speculum, vol. 48 (1973) pp. 476-490.

43. Lem, S. (1984). Microworlds. Harcourt Brace & Co., New York.

44. Leviatan, D. (1968). 'Moment problems and quasi-(Hausdorff) transformations'. Can. Math. Bull. vol. 11 (1968), pp. 225-36. DOI.10.4153/CMB-1968-026-7.

45. Lifton, R. J. (1974). 'The Sense of Immortality: On Death and the Continuity of Life'. Explorations in Psychohistory: The Wellfleet Papers. (Lifton, R & & Olson, E. (eds.) (1974). Simon & Schuster, New York pp. 271-87.

46. McGinn, B. (1985). The Calabrian Abbot: Joachim of Fiore in the History of Western Thought. MacMillan Publishing Company, New York.

47. McLaughlin, M. M, (1976). 'Survivors and Surrogates: Children and Parents from the Ninth to the Thirteenth Centuries', in The History of Childhood: The Evolution of Parent-Child Relations as a Factor in History, DeMause, L. (ed.), Souvenir Press (Educational & Academic) Ltd. London, 1976, ch.3 pp. 101-181, p. 171 n.182 and n.186.

48. McNally, W. (1984). The Dune Encyclopedia. Corgi Books.

49. Mott, F. J. (1948). The Universal Design of Birth: An Analysis of the Configurational Involvement of Birth and Its Relation to Emergence Generally. David McKay Co., Philadelphia.

50. Mott, F. J. (1964). The Universal Design of Creation. Mark Beech, Edenbridge, UK.

51. North, D. (1997). Understanding the Process of Economic Change. Princeton University Press.

52. Peerbolte, L. (1951). 'Psychotherapeutic Evaluations of Birth-Trauma Analysis'. Psychiatric Quarterly 25, pp. 596-600.

53. Perry, B.D., Pollard, R., Blakely, T., Baker, W. & Vigilante, D. (1995). 'Childhood trauma, the neurobiology of adaptation and 'use-dependent' development of the brain: how 'states' become 'traits'. Infant Mental Health Journal, Vol. 16 no. 14 (Winter), pp. 271-91.

54. Petitot, J. (1978). 'Sur le Modèle Historique de Thom-Pomian'. Mathématiques et Sciences Humaines, 16e année no 64, pp. 43-70.

55. Ployé, P. M. (1973). 'Does Prenatal Mental Life Exist?'. International Journal of Psycho-Analysis 54, pp. 241-246.

56. Propp, V. (1968). Morphologyof the Folktale. Second Edition, University of Texas Press.

57. Quigley, C. (1979). The Evolution of Civilizations: An Introduction to Historical Analysis. Liberty Fund Inc. (2nd. Edition).

58. Rank, Otto (1923). The Trauma of Birth. Harper & Row, New York, 1973.

59. Reeves, M. & Gould, W. (2001). Joachim of Fiore and the Myth of the Eternal Evangel in the Nineteenth and Twentieth Centuries. Oxford University Press.

60. Sagan, C. & Agel, J. (2000). The Cosmic Connection: An Extraterrestrial Perspective. Cambridge University Press.

61. Sandberg, A. (2013) 'We Borg: Speculations on Hive Minds as a Posthuman State'.: http://www.aleph.se/Trans/Global/Posthumanity/ WeBorg.html. Accessed 21/02/2013.

62. Silber, I. F. (1995). Virtuosity, Charisma and Social Order: A Comparative Sociological Study of Monasticism in Theravada Buddhism and Medieval Catholicism. Cambridge University Press, Cambridge.

63. Spengler, O. (1928). The Decline of the West (Die Untergang des Abendlandes). Alfred A. Knopf Inc. Abridged Edition - George Allen & Unwin Ltd., London 1961.

64. Spinks, R., Harinder, K. S., Andreasen, N. C. & Philibert, R. A. (2004). 'Association of the HOPA12[bp] allele with a large X-chromosone haplotype and positive symptom schizophrenia'. American Journal of Medical Genetics Part B: Neuropsychiatric Genetics: May 15 2004, 127 (1): pp. 20-7.

65. Stromberg, P. G. (1993). Language and Self-Transformation: A Study of the Christian Conversion Narrative. Publications of the Society for Psychological Anthropology, Cambridge University Press.

66. Tobin, S. (1995). The Cistercians: Monks and Monasteries in Europe. The Herbert Press, Ltd.

67. Toulmin, S. E. (1992). Cosmopolis: The Hidden Agenda of Modernity. University of Chicago Press. Reprinted. 2nd Edition.

68. Turchin, P. (2003). Historical Dynamics: Why States Rise and Fall. Princeton University Press.

69. Verny, T. & J. Kelly (1982). The Secret Life of the Unborn Child. Sphere Books Ltd., London.

70. Vico, G. (1744). The New Science of Giambattista Vico: Unabridged Translation of the Third Edition (1744) with the addition of "Practice of the New Science". Bergin, Thomas G. & Fisch (trans.), Max H. Cornell University Press. Ithaca & London 1948. Revised 1968, 1984. Reprinted, 1986.

71. Wasdell, D. (1985). Towards a Unified Field Theory of Human Behaviour: A Collection of Four Papers. URCHIN (Unit for Research into Changing Institutions), Meridian House, London.

72. ---, (1990). The Roots of the Common Unconscious. URCHIN (Unit for Research into Changing Institutions), Meridian House, London.

73. ---, (1992). The Pre- and Perinatal Grounds of Capitalism and the Free Market Economy. URCHIN (Unit for Research into Changing Institutions), Meridian House, London.

74. Weber, M. (1958). The Protestant Ethic and the Rise of Capitalism. Scribner, New York.

75. Wilken, R. L. (2012). The First Thousand Years: A Global History of Christianity. Yale University Press. New Haven & London.

76. Woods, T. E. (2012). How the Catholic Church built Western Civilization. Regnery History.

77. Ziolo, P. (2001). 'Joachim of Fiore and Apocalyptic Immanence'. Journal of Psychohistory 29 (2) pp. 186-224.

78. ---, (2002). 'The Psychodynamics of the ECF-Nexus: Monasticism and Psychospeciation in Western Europe, c.500-1500 AD'. The International Journal of Psychotherapy vol. 7:. 3, pp. 221-48.

79. ---, (2004). Psychohistory: Emergence, Theory and Applications. PhD. Thesis, University of Liverpool, ch. 5: 5, pp. 101-107.

100 YEAR STARSHIP™

Key Factors
in Time-Distance Solutions

Key Factors in Time-Distance Solutions

Chaired by Eric W. Davis, PhD

Senior Research Physicist, Institute for Advanced Studies at Austin

Track Description

In considering potential time-distance solutions, what are the possible paths to leap from current knowledge and capabilities to those needed to meet the interstellar challenge?

Track Summary

Interstellar travel and exploration are not possible without starship propulsion and power. How quickly ("time") and how far ("distance") a starship can deliver its mission payload is uniquely determined by the fastest type of propulsion system that achieves the shortest flight time over interstellar distances, and by how much power can be generated to drive the propulsion system. It is the purpose of the Key Factors in Time-Distance Solutions Track to present the latest research and development on starship propulsion and power concepts. There are also the associated issues of interstellar communications, starship command-control computers, robotic starships or manned starships, optimized flight trajectories from Earth to destination stars, starship structural design, materials used for constructing starship systems and subsystems, radiation and debris shielding, etc., which must also be considered.

Session A of the track had presentations on Nuclear, Beamed Energy, and Exotic Physics Propulsion. These topics included recent theoretical and experimental progress on advanced nuclear fission fragment and fusion rocket propulsion, an interstellar laser propulsion network, and faster-than-light warp drive propulsion. Such topics, while sounding like science fiction themes, are actually credible concepts from today's (peer-review) published propulsion physics theories and experiments.

Session B of the track had presentations on Exotic Physics and Interstellar Communication. Presentations dealt with the problem of understanding how galactic and cosmic radiation behave when encountered by starships moving through space at significant fractions of the speed of light, and how gravitational waves and quantum theory could be used to implement an interstellar communication system. Other presentations were speculations that proposed using compact condensed quark matter inside of asteroids to power starships, and examining time-distance solutions outside of general relativity theory.

Session C of the track had presentations on Interstellar Communications, Starship Probes, Exploration Strategies, and Navigation. It will be important to design and construct command and control computers that are robust and autonomous enough to handle the rigors of multigenerational interstellar voyages. Two presentations showed that such computers based on artificial intelligence and artificial brain technologies can be designed and tested to implement autonomous control of unmanned or manned starship probes, and run optimized, efficient self-diagnosing/self-repair algorithms that will ensure that the complexities of operating a starship do not overburden computer systems or human crews. A novel concept was presented that exploits the focal point of the Sun's gravitational lens to collect and amplify very weak interstellar radio or optical signals to a very high gain, and apply a highly effective new signal processing algorithm, to implement very effective interstellar communications regardless of the starship's distance from Earth. A final presentation was given on several solar system mission architectures and escape trajectory profiles to support advanced interstellar flyby science probes that use advanced solar sails for propulsion.

Most of the presentations given in this track were superb and of very high professional quality. Many of them contributed valuable design studies and data that add to the ever-increasing knowledge base of interstellar flight science, as well as add to the foundations that will help guide mankind to the stars.

Track Chair Biography

Eric W. Davis, PhD
Senior Research Physicist, Institute for Advanced Studies at Austin

Dr. Eric W. Davis is a Senior Research Physicist at the Inst. for Advanced Studies at Austin (EarthTech Int'l, Inc.). His research specializations include breakthrough space power & propulsion physics, beamed energy propulsion, space nuclear power & propulsion, directed energy weapons, future and transformational technology, general relativity theory, quantum field theory, quantum gravity theories, quantum optics/metamaterials/complex light/photonics, and SETI contact/xenoarchaeology. Since 1984, Dr. Davis has worked in academia and industry and has also been a contractor/consultant to the U.S. Air Force, Air Force Research Laboratory (AFRL), Department of Defense (DoD), Department of Energy, and NASA. His professional experience and contributions include: develop megawatt-class laser propulsion physics, systems design, and mission applications for the Air Force laser Lightcraft launch vehicle; design ultrahigh-power laser experiments to explore the structure/properties of the quantum vacuum, and corresponding production of antimatter from the vacuum; conduct theoretical studies on the potential for producing ultrahigh-power coherent light from the vacuum using quantum vacuum generators; design quantum optics experiments using ultrahigh-power lasers to produce negative vacuum energy for faster-than-light (general relativistic) space propulsion; design quantum tomography experiments to measure negative vacuum energy; design tabletop experiments using metamaterials to simulate warp drives and traversable wormholes; and perform feasibility studies on laser inertial confinement and ultrahigh-pulsed power Z-pinch/ DPF/hybrid fusion for rocket propulsion. Dr. Davis is the co-editor/author of the peer-reviewed academic research monograph *Frontiers of Propulsion Science* (American Inst. of Aeronautics and Astronautics Press, 2009). He also authored/co-authored several AFRL and DoD technical reports, peer-reviewed symposium and technical journal papers, chapters in books, conference papers, and award winning STAIF-2006 and 2012 AIAA Joint Propulsion Conference papers. He was twice recognized by the American Inst. of Aeronautics and Astronautics for outstanding contributions to national defense and space public policy. He earned an A.A. in Liberal Arts from Phoenix College (1981), a B.Sc. in Physics-Mathematics (1983) and Ph.D. (1991) in Astrophysics from the University of Arizona. Dr. Davis is a Fellow of the British Interplanetary Society, Associate Fellow of the American Inst. of Aeronautics and Astronautics, member of the New York Academy of Sciences, member of the Directed Energy Professional Society, member of SPIE, member of the American Astronomical Society, member of the Assoc. For Intelligence Officers, and was a lifetime member and Vice-President of the now-defunct American Inst. of Beamed Energy Propulsion. He is a practitioner and advisory board member of the Tau Zero Foundation, a member of the 100-Year Starship Study (Jemison Foundation of Excellence) science advisory board, and a member of the Icarus Interstellar technical advisory board and advanced projects group. Dr. Davis has appeared in or consulted/contributed to many American and BBC television and documentary film projects as well as many online/print news and magazine articles on interstellar flight and breakthrough propulsion physics.

Solutions for Factors of Time and Space Distance: Challenges Outside of Proposed Models Based On General Relativity

Marshall Barnes

R&D Eng

AET RaDAL, 500 Dublin Ave. S. 103

Columbus, OH 43215

aet.radal.hq@technologist.com

Abstract

The state of theoretical scenarios for creating loopholes in barriers to interstellar travel reflects the lag that has plagued theoretical physics so far this century, despite attempts at advancement in the last decade or so of the previous century. This lag in progress is in large part due to the culture of peer pressure within the theoretical physics community cited by Kip Thorne of CalTech in his book, "Black Holes and Time Warps: Einstein's Outrageous Legacy". This paper will propose new solutions that will exceed the current discussions on faster than light travel by including the reasons why the current models based on General Relativity are inadequate, the kind of thinking that finding further solutions will require and why that thinking hasn't happened more readily.

Keywords

warp drive, unified field theory, space travel

In the area of advanced concept propulsion, warp drive is the ultimate platform. However, difficulties with solving, the many associated physics and technological issues, have been daunting beyond the realization of not only the public but scientific community as well. Marc Millis, the former director of the NASA Breakthrough Propulsion Physics Program wrote a paper [1] dealing with the overarching question on the public's mind - why don't we have warp drive yet? The answer to that question can actually be seen to have four parts:

1. Lack of knowledge
2. Lack of Funding
3. Lack of will
4. Fear of Peers

Each of these parts plays a significant role in hindering the attainment of the goal in question. Let me explain, step by step.

1. Lack of knowledge: Clearly there is a lack of knowledge. After all, no one yet has figured out how to create enough negative energy or make exotic matter that would be just two of the essential requirements to achieve warp

drive propulsion. There is another major element that also remains a significant question, which I will go into later. So lack of knowledge is a significant issue, but it is not the only one.

2. Lack of funding. There are no grant programs for researchers to work on warp drive concepts. NASA's Harold Sonny White [2], is the only researcher currently getting government funding for warp drive research and that is said to be below $100,000 coming from NASA. If the brightest minds aren't working on the problem, then the problem will remain unsolved.

3. Lack of will: There is no real national agenda to accomplish the development of warp drive in the same way that there was a will to put a man on the moon within ten years. Instead, we are told that it could take 100 years to develop interstellar travel capabilities and then there are no pools of funding to even try to achieve it.

4. Fear of Peers: This to me, is the most insidious of the problems. At a time in our history where the problem of bullying is a nationally recognized issue, I have witnessed more bullying in the science community than I have ever seen on any school playground. But this is not a problem that I'm complaining about personally, rather simply acknowledging what others have complained about. In particular, Kip Thorne, physics professor at Cal Tech, co-author of the book, Gravitation, close friend of Stephen Hawking and the source of the idea of using wormholes for time travel, stated in his book, Black Holes and Time Warps: Einstein's Outrageous Legacy [3] that "while many of us may enjoy reading science fiction or may even write some, we *fear* (emphasis mine) ridicule from our colleagues for working on research close to the science fiction fringe …"

Ridicule from colleagues? Fear because of essentially trying to be too imaginative? The facts are that our entire modern day civilization is filled with the science fiction notions of the past. The role that skepticism plays in all this is also detrimental because it has the effect of dumbing down the field. This is very critical and can be easily illustrated - it takes no intelligence, education, or expert knowledge to say, "No!". All it takes to feign intellectual superiority, within the context of scientific skepticism, is the recognition of certain key phrases and buzzwords which are frowned upon and literally any idiot can raise their self-esteem by looking superior and "scientific" through attacking anyone who dare, as Thorne put it, get too close to "the science fiction fringe". This extends the ridicule factor far beyond the legitimate peer group and into the general public out of which future scientists will emerge who will already be witness to the trend of ignorant skepticism and how it is used to keep individuals who fear ridicule "in line."

This problem is compounded when otherwise reputable scientists are confronted with development situations that do not fit neatly within the typical context of scientific discovery. As a result, they suspect the validity of the developments needlessly, a circumstance in point that I will return to shortly. In applying this situation to the subject of warp drive development difficulties, in 2010, warp drive researcher Richard Obousy said that the number one reason why few physicists are working on warp drive is because of what he calls the "giggle factor" [4] of attempting to develop a propulsion system based on an idea straight from science fiction. This shows exactly how the negative impact of peer pressure - the same condition described by Thorne in ,88, is hindering legitimate scientific development in the area in question, even to this day.

The solution for this situation? Starting a NDRC style organization for warp drive development.

During World War II, many of the best scientific and engineering minds in the United States were gathered together under the umbrella of the NDRC - National Defense Research Committee [5]. They had one singular purpose - to use their creative minds to develop technologies and applications that would defeat the Axis powers. They got all the money they needed as well as the physical resources and all new ideas for technology were not only considered but encouraged. This is the era where Einstein, an active member in NDRC projects related to the Navy, stated that "imagination is more important than knowledge" and Vannevar Bush, the head of the NDRC stated that "If scientific reasoning were limited to the logical processes of arithmetic, we should not get very far in our understanding of the physical world. One might as well attempt to grasp the game of poker entirely by the use of mathematics of probability"[6].

Despite how many of us would wish that such an organization would exist, with the funding and dedication to the purpose of developing the technology required to travel outside our solar system and beyond, such an endeavor on that scale is not on the horizon. Then again, perhaps it needn't be.

In 1960, the father of the atomic bomb, J. Robert Oppenheimer, made a curious statement. He said, "There are children playing in the street who could solve some of my top problems in physics because they have modes of sensory perception that I lost long ago…" [7] No one had really thought much about the quote until I discovered that Kip Thorne had made a train wreck of errors in the book version of his concept for using wormholes to create a time machine, in fact, the idea is flawed at its core. No one in the physics community, that I showed the mistakes to, could see them - until I pointed them out. Only then did they see that the entire idea was a misinterpretation of the application of time dilation to one end of the wormhole. There is no way for the time dilated end to be connected to a reference frame that exists in the past. It just means that the time dilated mouth of the wormhole has aged less.

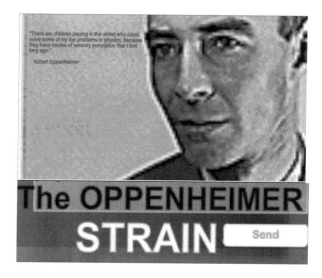

Fig. 1. Official Oppenheimer Strain logo

I recognized that this was an example of a psychological blind spot, a reliance on hidden assumptions, and with this recognition I surmised that high school students in physics might be able to see these errors because their minds are more flexible. I tested the idea, first in 2007 [8] and then again in a number of times between 2008 and 2012. Every time, 20% or more of the students tested were able to see the error in the model I presented to them and these went beyond the Kip Thorne example but also included some by Stephen Hawking, J.R. Gott and Michio Kaku. In 2008, I discovered the Oppenheimer quote and began to apply it to my further testing, even naming the inability of physicists to catch these mistakes, the Oppenheimer Strain. In 2012, I conducted an experiment that matched exactly the Oppenheimer quote when I tasked seven elementary school children from the OSU Wexner Medical Center Math and Science Club [9] with detecting an error in a time travel model that Stephen Hawking used in his Discovery Channel TV special, Into the Universe with Stephen Hawking [10]. Four out of the seven got the correct answer, the highest percentage yet. These were, after all, children of the age that would play in the street as opposed to high schoolers who would be most likely to be driving through them.

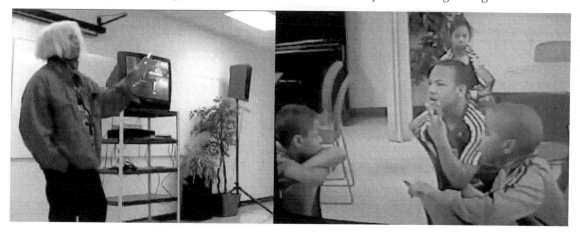

Fig. 2. Testing children from the Math and Science Club

So, although these activities were very interesting and garnered me a number of awards and recognitions, one of the main items of significance from them is the fact that it proved that physicists are not operating at the level that they need to, at least not in the advanced concepts area. They suffer from the exact same condition that Oppenheimer anecdotally described which is certainly not the proper state of affairs desired in the field of trying to develop advanced propulsion platforms such as warp drive. But has this really been the case? The facts, and in some cases, the physicists, speak for themselves.

251

In 1994, Mexican physicist, Miguel Alcubierre, was the first physicist to develop a model for warp drive [11]. It, like all the other versions to follow, was based on solutions from equations derived from Einstein's General Relativity theory. In 2012, Miguel surprised everyone when he told Popular Science magazine that he no longer supported the idea because, although it was his to begin with, he felt that the difficulties in finding the solutions to the energy requirements and exotic matter were too much [12]. Also there was the little thing about there not being a way to get the warp field, which would be the method by which space was being warped to result in faster than light travel, to be controlled by the spacecraft. He literally stated that there was no way, even if he could get the exotic matter and negative energy required to create the warp field, to get it around the spacecraft where he needed it.

Such an admission has more significance than it may appear, at first. This is after 18 years of work, and more than a handful of other physicists working on their own versions of the same model, yet not only Alcubierre, but no one else had noticed the overwhelming significance of not immediately having a solution for how the field would be created around the spacecraft? Let me explain - there is no model for warp drive if there is no method identified for the spacecraft to initiate the warp field. That is the "drive" part of the idea. If you can't do that, then it doesn't matter if you can create the field, as Alcubierre admitted, but that means that for 18 years, physicists looking at solving the idea for warp drive were putting the cart before the horse, literally. The horse is the drive, that's why engines are rated at horse power. In this case, the assumption was that the horse would be able to pull the cart, except no one bothered with figuring out how to get the horse connected to the cart. Oppenheimer Strain, indeed.

Now, this Popular Science article was not written about Alcubierre but Harold "Sonny" White who works for NASA and claims that he has figured out how to reduce the energy requirements calculated by everyone for the warp field to work. As far as I know, he still hasn't figured out how to get the spacecraft to generate the field but he has recently acquired other problems. The idea, that NASA had someone who was actually working on warp drive, has captured the public's imagination as well as the media's attention. Introduce the negative peer factor. A number of physicists have come out claiming that White's work is more fanciful than practical and others, including Alcubierre, have begun to get rather nasty, claiming that White's work is "dubious" [13]. This is all driven in part because there are a few technical details with White's testing apparatus that he's not revealing. Because of this, certain critics see what they believe to be a weakness in White's work and are behaving like sharks when blood is in the water. However, what they don't realize is that there are very good reasons for White not to reveal those technical details. First, because the matter involves specific technology, there are intellectual property issues involved. The idea that scientists must reveal everything about their work, especially in a technology area, is outdated and antiquated. Doing so makes the funding part of the equation more problematic since the private sector is the only area where serious funding might be currently acquired. Remember, he's already underfunded by NASA. If you remove the private sector funding possibilities then in no uncertain terms, you kill any serious chance that there will be a warp drive solution. Let me make this perfectly clear - without private sector funding and initiatives you kill any hope of a successful warp drive development. Look at the results so far - 18 years and no one has even been able to recognize that there was a ‚drive' issue? That means that even if the exotic matter and negative energy problem had been solved then the drive issue would still have to be resolved and without that, solving the negative energy and exotic matter issues are meaningless.

The second issue is that Alcubierre is hardly in a position to say anyone's work is dubious as he was the one who initiated the warp drive idea without a clue as to how to make it work in the first place. Another issue, that no one has ever broached is the fact that any functioning platform for warp drive could also be weaponized and in fact, a complete operating system is not a requirement to do so. So there are very good reasons for White not to reveal certain technical details.

As I mentioned earlier, all the models for warp drive so far are based on Einstein's General Relativity. All, that is except one - a special electromagnetic field that would exhibit gravitational effects. The application of such a field need only effect the front of a vehicle as space would expand back on its own once outside the field's influence. Unlike Alcubierre, I know that the first thing that would have to be determined is if the field can appear around the front end of a craft. If that isn't feasible, the project would end there. Period. Being an engineer and not a physicist, my focus is always, ultimately, will an idea work and that is the proof that a theory is valid. Already I am very familiar with the ideas that were well established in the engineering community about how fields are created around fuselages and craft bodies, ranging from high voltage applied to the leading edge of aircraft wings, to plasma sheaths tested by Russia to reduce the radar cross section of aircraft [14].

Of special importance, however, is the history behind this idea, which is not known to most physicists. First, this effect is not described by General Relativity but by Einstein's unfinished unified field theory [15] which only sought to show a coupling between electromagnetism and gravity. In other words, an electromagnetic field that acts like it is a gravity field of some kind, could be derived from this and thus it can cause the kind of effects that you would normally expect from a gravity field as described by General Relativity. The formal name for this theory is Distant Parallelism or Teleparallelism. The nice thing is that this doesn't require any of the negative energy and exotic matter that would normally be part and parcel of such an idea. People don't talk much about this theory of Einstein's because he failed to complete it, and so the unification theories are all aimed towards unifying all the forces of nature, which of course are not required to achieve warp drive and other interesting ideas. The fact that Einstein failed to complete his theory doesn't mean, however, that it is impossible to get any use out of it. The problem is that few have tried, instead, wasting their time on solutions from General Relativity because it is "safe". Despite the fact that if an attempt were made to find a solution, the outcomes would make everything about warp drive easier, the entire field of researchers into warp drive have placed their bets on a platform that is now sinking, even as some of its proponents turn on each other.

An indication that there is validity to this alternate approach, Soviet astrophysicist, N.A. Kozyrev, mentioned in the 1960s a similar concept in his paper, The Way To Space [16], citing that a way that time could be modified by gravity, as a propulsion method, could result in obtaining speeds best suited for rapid space travel that would exceed practical rocket capabilities and would in effect be a warp drive. This reference shows that I am not alone in my thinking. In fact, others, such as H. David Froning, have an interesting concept with a close relationship to my own. His was the idea of specially conditioned electromagnetic fields, using polarization to get the field to couple with gravity[17]. Froning and others have been working on such research, with limited results, since the 90s, in part as part of the now defunct NASA Breakthrough Propulsion Physics community. Once again, proof that a private sector effort must be part of the solution and not reliance on any government entity that has its funding controlled by bureaucrats, unless it is a top priority, NDRC style effort. Anything less is, well, less and that is not good enough.

So in conclusion, the factors as to why warp drive technology has failed to be developed so far, have been clearly identified. I see absolutely nothing in the immediate future, from within the space science community, that has any chance of changing that. None.

An alternative research method has been identified and so solutions must come from outside the confines of the space science community if significant progress is going to be made within our lifetimes, which means 30 years or less. The space science community will have to learn a difficult lesson - to do extraordinary things requires extraordinary thinking, not just in science but in economics and business. If you can't get a project funded the old way, then to continue to try to get a project funded the old way is, in short, insanity. Although Stephen Hawking and Kip Thorne have both spoken of things, like those covered here, as being those capable of "a sufficiently advanced alien civilization", what no one seems to realize from that idea is that the advancement doesn't have to be due to any arbitrary length of time that said civilization had existed beyond our own - so that they have had enough time to advance beyond us. Rather, that they have those "modes of sensory perception" that have enabled them to see and recognize solutions that we haven't and not make our mistakes in the first place.

References

1. Millis, M., "Warp Drive When?" NASA paper, September 7, 2001

2. White, H., "Warp Field Mechanics 101", 100 Year Starship Symposium, September 2011

3. Thorne, K., "Black Holes and Time Wraps: Einstein's Outrageous Legacy", W. W. Norton & Company, Inc., 1995

4. Obousy, R. "Warpsim", Interstellar Dreams (https://web.archive.org/web/20120130175602/http://www.interstellarjourney.com/blogs.php?title=Warpism), September 3, 2009

5. en.wikipedia.org, "National Defense Research Committee" http://en.wikipedia.org/w/index.php?title=National_Defense_Research_Committee

6. Bush, V., "As We May Think" Atlantic Monthly, July 1945

7. McLuhan, M., "Address at Vision, 65" McLuhan on Maui, June 18, 2011 http://www.mcluhanonmaui.com/2011/06/address-at-vision-65-by-marshall.html

8. Bryant, C., "Science Kids Bust Hawking Mistake", Columbus Messenger, September 12, 2008

9. Barnes, M, "Math and Science Club Students Make Oppenheimer Quote Real", www.physicsintrouble. iwarp.com, 2012

10. Hawking, S., "Into The Universe with Stephen Hawking", Discovery Channel, TV special 2011

11. Alcubierre, M,. "The warp-drive: hyper-fast travel within general relativity", http://arxiv.org/abs/gr-qc/0009013 September 5, 2000

12. Kakaes, K., "Warp Factor", Popular Science, April 1, 2013

13. Alcubierre, M., "Dubious is actually being generous", Twitter, August 23, 2013 https://twitter.com/DrMR-Francis/status/371023044170366976

14. Venik, "Plasma Stealth: Past and Present", Above Top Secret, October 2004, http://www.abovetopsecret.com/forum/thread89869/pg1

15. Goenner, H.F.M., "On the History of Unified Field Theories", Living Reviews in Relativity, February 2004, http://relativity.livingreviews.org/open?pubNo=lrr-2004-2&page=articlesu15.html

16. Kozyrev N. A., "The Way To Space", 1969, Cause Mechanics, http://www.alexfrolov.narod.ru/kozyrev.htm

17. Froning, H. D., Cleveland, B., and G. H., Hathaway, "Specially Conditioned EM Radiation Research with Transmitting Toroid Antennas", American Institute of Aeronautics and Astronautics AIAA-2001-3658 2001

Gravitational Mechanics of First Contact

Alvin Eric Cantrell

National Aeronautics and Space Administration (NASA)

National Space Science and Technology Center, 320 Sparkman Drive, Huntsville, AL 35805

Alvin.e.Cantrell@nasa.gov

Karthik Srinivasan

Universities Space Research Association (USRA) Science and Technology Institute

National Space Science and Technology Center, 320 Sparkman Drive, Huntsville, AL 35805

karthik.srinivasan@nasa.gov

James Jeff Richeson

ERC, Incorporated, 320 Sparkman Drive, Huntsville, AL 35805

James.J.Richeson@nasa.gov

Abstract

Future intergalactic travel requires the ability to communicate over vast distances, through asteroid fields, various forms of radiation, and solar systems, well beyond the capability of current communication technologies. The shortcomings of electromagnetic communications include unavoidable damping, interference and noise. Unlike electromagnetic waves used in today's technologies, gravitational waves are not attenuated by these phenomena. The gravitational equivalent of electromagnetic impedance of free space was first theorized by JD Kraus in 1991. This non-zero gravitational impedance of free space implies that there may indeed be a way to harness this energy for the purpose of communicating through any mass or energy, unimpeded. Kraus also suggested a method for gravitational modulation. By improving upon the well-established theories of impedance matching techniques, it will be shown that there may potentially be a way to utilize gravitational effects for the purpose of communications via gravitational modulation. A series of simple, yet inherently complex set of equations are introduced in this paper that proposes a method for gravitational impedance matching. An experiment is proposed that may determine the feasibility of using gravitational impedance matching as a means of detection.

Keywords
gravity, gravitational, interstellar, communications, impedance matching, communication systems

1. Introduction
Contact mechanics is the study of the stress and deformation which arises when surfaces of two solid bodies when they are physically in contact with each other. In his groundbreaking book, "The Principles of Mechanics [1]," Heinrich Hertz describes in detail his theory of contact mechanics. However, Hertz did not hypothesize the mechanism for the force that is experienced by each object before they make contact with each other. In the preface of Hertz's book, Hermann von Helmholtz states that for these invisible forces, Hertz "has not given examples illustrating the manner in which he supposed such hypothetical mechanism to act." A new hypothesis is being proposed that attempts to fill in the void by introducing a set of relationships that describe "first" contact between two bodies. One potential application is introduced that may lead to the possibility of a gravitational communications system or potentially new astronomical observatories.

2. Gravitational Impedance
The equation for the gravitational force of attraction between two objects is

$$Force = G * \frac{Mm}{R^2}$$

(1)

where M and m are the gravitationally interacting masses, R is the distance between the two objects, and G is the gravitational constant, which has a value of approximately

$$G = 6.673 * 10^{-11} \frac{m^3}{kg*s^2} \ .$$

(2)

An object at rest will remain at rest until an external force acts upon it. This is the Law of Inertia. In Philosophiæ Naturalis Principia Mathematica Newton gave a succinct definition of inertia as "The vis insita, or innate [inherent] force of matter, is a power of resisting by which every body, as much as in it lies, endeavors to preserve its present state, whether it be of rest or of moving uniformly forward in a straight line [2]."

In a sense, impedance is the "power of resisting." The relationship among force, mass, and acceleration of an object on or near the surface of another mass, such as the Earth, is expressed in mathematical form as

(3)

$$F = ma \ .$$

where *a* is the acceleration due to the force of gravity. According to the law of inertia, as more of this gravitational force of acceleration is acting on an object, the more it will resist moving until such a time as the force exceeds a certain value. As long as the masses of the larger object and the smaller object remains constant, this gravitational force of attraction is a primarily a function of distance. Imagine if the planet Jupiter suddenly began approaching Earth. How close would Jupiter have to get to Earth before its gravitational attraction equaled that of Earth's surface acceleration? At what distant could we literally "jump" to Jupiter?

For radio frequency antennas, impedance matching dictates how much electromagnetic energy is absorbed or reflected between the transmitting and receiving antenna. Impedance also represents the relationship between some force and speed - voltage and current, or, mass and acceleration. Similarly, the gravitational mass impedance can be defined as the ratio of the gravitational force of attraction between two (or more) objects to their velocity relative to each other. Since Albert Einstein postulated that the velocity of a gravity wave is equal to the speed of light, namely c = 3.0 × 10^8 m/s, it seems like a natural assumption that gravitational mass impedance is defined as the ratio of an objects gravitational force of attraction to the velocity of a gravitational wave. The gravitational mass impedance can be expressed as

$$z_{Mm} = \frac{Force}{c_g} = \frac{G}{c_g} * \frac{Mm}{R^2} \tag{4}$$

where c_g is the speed of gravity. Analogous to the intrinsic impedance of free space for electromagnetic waves, JD Kraus postulated that there exists an intrinsic impedance of free space for gravity [3]. The intrinsic impedance of free space for gravity, Z_0, is defined as the ratio of the universal gravitational constant G to the speed of light. That is,

$$Z_0 = \frac{G}{c_g} = 2.2258 * 10^{-19} \frac{m^2}{kg*s} \tag{5}$$

Retaining for now the classical view of gravity, the small value of this constant implies that gravity can travel barely impeded through all matter. Since this impedance is not equal to zero, there may be an underlying phenomenon that can be manipulated. Equation (4) now becomes:

$$Z_{Mm} = Z_0 * \frac{Mm}{R^2} \left(\frac{kg}{s}\right). \tag{6}$$

There also exists intrinsic gravitational impedance for an individual object. For a sphere, its gravitational intrinsic impedance is

$$Z_m = Z_0 * \frac{m^2}{r^2} \left(\frac{kg}{s}\right) \tag{7}$$

where m is the mass of the object and r is its radius. In the preface of the Principia, Isaac Newton wrote "Rational Mechanics will be the science of motions resulting from any forces whatsoever, and of the forces required to produce any motions, accurately proposed and demonstrated [2]."

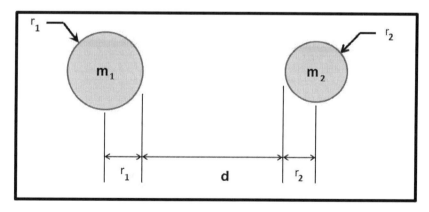

Figure 1: Spherical two-body system.

The hypothesis for the mechanics of first contact lies in the calculation of the mass impedances. More specifically, the calculation of the impedances such that an inherent connection or bond is created so that any change in motion of one object affects the forces acting upon the other. Will this cause the other object to move, change mass or vibrate? The answer is no. What it will do is change the other masses' weight. Consider an elevator. A sphere is resting on an ultra-sensitive weight scale inside the elevator. If the elevator accelerates up, the reading on the scale increases. If the elevator accelerates down, the reading on the scale decreases. Now suppose that the elevator is on its way up. Half way up the building, after the elevator has reached its steady velocity, a very large, dense mass is just outside the door on one of the floors. For brief moment as the elevator passes by, the scales will give an anomalous weight change reading before returning to normal. It may be a very small change in weight, but the change is there nonetheless. This change is because of the pull of the dense mass as the elevator zooms by. The conjecture is that if the sphere is impedance matched with the dense object, then a weight change will be detected. In a sense, this is known as maximum power transfer. If there is a large mass outside of every third floor's door then the sphere will experience a weight change as the elevator passes. The gravitational mass impedances for masses m_1 and m2 shown in figure 1 can be matched by varying the size of either of the masses or by determining an optimum distance between them. Using equations (6) and (7), a set of gravitational mass impedance parameters can be defined as

$$z_{11} = Z_0 * \frac{m_1^2}{r_1^2} \tag{8}$$

$$z_{12} = Z_0 * \frac{m_1 m_2}{d^2} \tag{9}$$

$$z_{21} = Z_0 * \frac{m_2 m_1}{d^2} \tag{10}$$

$$z_{22} = Z_0 * \frac{m_2^2}{r_2^2} \tag{11}$$

Here z_{11} and z_{22} are the gravitational impedances of masses m_1 and m_2, respectively. z_{12} and z_{21} are the gravitational impedances of m_1 and m_2 separated by distance d. Assuming m_1 is the source mass and m_2 is the target mass, an impedance match is obtained when z_{12} and z_{21} are equal to z_{22}. How are the masses impedance matched? If the mass of m_1 and m_2 are unchanging, that leaves the distance d as being the only changeable variable. Thus, the distance is varied until the impedances z_{12} and z_{21} are equal z_{22}.

3. Gravitational Impedance Example

So, how close does Jupiter have to get to Earth before we could we literally "jump" to its surface? Gravitational impedance matching theory might provide a different way to calculate this incredible distance. The primary physical characteristics of Earth and Jupiter are listed in figure 2.

$$M_{Earth} := 5.98 \cdot 10^{24} \cdot kg \qquad \text{Mass of Earth}$$

$$R_{Earth} := 6378.135 \cdot km \qquad \text{Radius of Earth}$$

$$M_{Jupiter} := 1898.3 \cdot 10^{24} kg \qquad \text{Mass of Jupiter}$$

$$R_{Jupiter} := 71492 km \qquad \text{Radius of Jupiter}$$

$$d := 778 \cdot 10^6 km \qquad \text{Avg distance from Earth to Jupiter}$$

Figure 2: Jupiter and Earth physical parameters [4].

Referring to Figure 1, replacing m_1, m_2 and r_1, r_2 with the mass and diameter of Jupiter and Earth, respectively, in equations (8), (9), (10) and (11),

$$z_{11} = Z_0 * \frac{m_{Jupiter}^2}{r_{Jupiter}^2} = 1.57 * 10^{20} \frac{kg}{s} \tag{12}$$

$$z_{12} = Z_0 * \frac{m_{Jupiter} m_{Earth}}{d^2} = 4.18 * 10^9 \frac{kg}{s} \tag{13}$$

$$(14)$$

$$z_{21} = Z_0 * \frac{m_{Earth} m_{Jupiter}}{d^2} = 4.18 * 10^9 \frac{kg}{s}$$

$$(15)$$

$$z_{22} = Z_0 * \frac{m_{Earth}^2}{r_{Earth}^2} = 1.97 * 10^{17} \frac{kg}{s}$$

where d is the separation distance that will give the appropriate value for the gravitational impedance match between the source Jupiter and the target Earth. After some recursive calculations it can be shown that the value for d that gives the distance for which we can "jump" to Jupiter's surface unaided is 113,269.14 km. That's about a third of the way to the moon. One way to verify this is to consider the surface gravitational acceleration of Earth, namely 9.8 m/s². From Jupiter's surface, at a "height" of d, its gravitational acceleration is also 9.8 m/s². Now that both accelerations are the same, it would be easy to "jump" from Earth to Jupiter. This is obviously impossible but it serves as a good example of how impedance matching works for two spheres in space. The calculations for different shapes or number of objects become far more difficult.

4. First Contact Between Two Objects

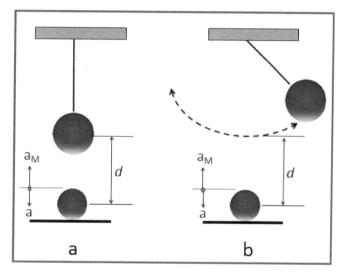

Figure 3: Pendulum System

Consider a pendulum with a large mass on it swinging to and fro above the surface of a smaller stationary mass. As the pendulum's mass moves through the distance (figure 3) required for an impedance match, a measurable change in the "weight" of the target mass will occur. This is because the gravitational acceleration caused by the pendulum "source" mass will act on the smaller, stationary "target" mass. There is no vibration or movement of the target mass, only a change in weight. From the point of view of this system resting on the surface of the Earth, the following equation may help describe this change. From equation (3),

$$(16)$$

$$F_m = m * (a + a_M) .$$

where a is the Earth's gravitational force, 9.8 m/s² and a_M is the additional force of attraction created on the target mass m by the source mass M. Current technology is on the brink of measuring miniscule weight changes in masses of 1 kg or larger [5]. In his textbook, "Antennas," JD Kraus discussed a proposed gravity-wave communications link using rotating spheres on a boom for the transmitter and a Weber Bar as the receiver [6]. This idea would follow up on Kraus' communications system except that instead of using a 3300 pound Weber Bar [7] as the receiver, a new type of sensor designed to measure miniscule changes in weights of objects, such as the National Institute of Standards & Technology's (NIST) Watt balance [5] could be used. The Watt Balance is a moving coil balance instrument used in establishing a value and uncertainty for the fundamental measurement constant of 1 kg. Figure 4 shows Kraus' transmitting "antenna." In addition to rotating the two spheres, having the capability to change the position of either or both masses relative to the length of the boom will create a form of gravity wave modulation. This modulation will have the added benefit of differentiating the "transmitted" signal from the interference of the gravitational effects of incidental masses. Similar to the sphere in the elevator, only a change in weight can be detected. Gravitational impedance matching can be used to determine the distance at which this will occur. The difficulty lies in determining the optimum separation between the "transmitter" and the "receiver."

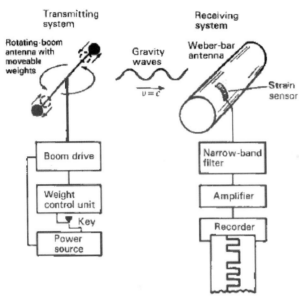

Figure 4: Kraus proposed gravitational communications system [6].

5. Proposed Experimental Measurement

A small-scale test is planned that will validate this theory. The material that will be used for the small-scale test includes a solid steel cylinder as the gravitational source mass and a small sphere as the target mass. The cylinder will be mounted on a rotating platform some calculated distance away from the target mass sphere as shown in figure 5. The target sphere will be mounted on a highly sensitive set of weight scales. As the cylinder rotates about its axis, the sphere will have slight variations in its weight. The weight sensor will output a voltage, which will then go through an amplifier. The amplifier will increase the voltage level such that the signal will be detected by a data acquisition unit (DAQ). The DAQ will be connected to a computer that is recording the data for later analysis. The next section discusses the impedance matching method.

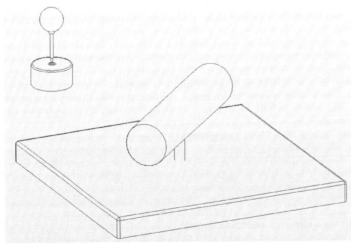

Figure 5: Experiment setup.

The calculation for the impedance and surface acceleration for the sphere is straight forward as outlined in a previous section. For a small lead sphere with a mass of m_s = 1,053 gm and a radius of r_s = 28.55 mm, the gravitational radiation impedance is given as

$$Z_S = Z_M * \left(\frac{m_s^2}{r_s^2}\right) = 3.0289237 * 10^{-16} \frac{kg}{s} \ . \tag{35}$$

The acceleration of gravity for a steel cylinder with a density of 7700 kg/m³, radius a = 5.2 cm and length l = 3.78 m is calculated by equation (37) [9]. Figure 6 displays the parameters for equation (37).

$$g_c(h) = 2 * \pi * G * \rho * \int_h^{h+l} \left(\left(1 - \frac{z}{\sqrt{(z^2+a^2)}}\right)\right) dz \ . \tag{37}$$

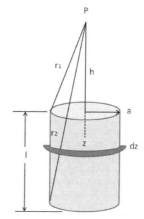

Figure 6: Cylinder parameters [8].

The gravitational impedance of the cylinder can thus be expressed as the ratio of the acceleration due to gravity and the speed of the gravity wave, c,

$$Z_C = \frac{g_c(h)*M_C}{c} \ . \tag{38}$$

The optimum value of h, at which the characteristic gravitational radiation impedance of the steel cylinder is equal to that of the sphere at a point P is derived iteratively, and found to be 0.495m. The gravitational impedance of the cylinder of Figure 6 at the distance of 0.495 m, which is at the location of the center of the target mass, is

$$Z_C = \frac{g_c(h)*M_C}{c} = 3.034 * 10^{-16} \frac{kg}{s} \tag{39}$$

This value gives an impedance ratio of the sphere to the cylinder of

$$\frac{Z_C}{Z_S} = 1.001 \ . \tag{40}$$

This means that the gravitational radiation impedance for both masses has been matched. Equation (28) is a simple manipulation of the power equation (9). The primary difficulty in performing this experiment lies in the accuracy of the measurements of the two masses and the distances involved. Another difficulty will be in eliminating various sources of noise that can interfere with the sensor measurements. The goal here is not to measure the gravitational constant (G), but merely to detect the minute change in the weight of the target mass caused by the cylinder at the predicted distance relative to each other. The signal this experiment hopes to find will be a repeatable signal that will vary with the movement of the source mass in addition to the movement caused be the gravitational attraction of two bodies. This is an easy, inexpensive experiment to perform to validate this theory.

6. Conclusion

Using the gravitational intrinsic impedance of free space as a guide, an expression for the gravitational impedance constant for any mass has been defined. A simple experimental setup to validate this method has been proposed. Future developments in sensor technology will enhance the accuracy of the observations presented here. This paper establishes the theoretical basis for a game-changing communication system using gravitational waves, overcoming the deficiencies of traditional systems that rely on electromagnetic energy. By utilizing gravitational impedance matching and modulation, successful acquisition of gravitational waves greatly increase the probability of communicating over interstellar distances. In addition to communication systems, gravitational modulation techniques offer the possibility of making highly accurate astronomical observations.

References

1. Hertz, H.,1899, The Principles of Mechanics. New York, MacMillan and Co., Ltd, 316 p.

2. Newton, I. and Cohen B., 1972, "Isaac Newton's Philosophiae Naturalis Principia Mathematica, Volume 2," Michigan: Harvard University Press, 916 p.

3. J.D. Kraus, "Will Gravity—Wave Communication Be Possible?," IEEE Antennas and Propagation Magazine, Vol. 33, No.4, August 1991.

4. http://nssdc.gsfc.nasa.gov/planetary/factsheet/

5. Steiner, R.; Newell, D.; and Williams, E., "Details of the 1998 Watt Balance Experiment Determining the Planck Constant," Journal of Research of the National Institute of Standards and Technology, Vol. 110, No. 1, Jan.–Feb. 2005.

6. J.D. Kraus, 1988, Antennas., New York: McGraw-Hill Book Company, 892 p.

7. Weber, J.: "Detection and Generation of Gravitational Waves," Physical Review, V. 117, No. 1, January 1, 1960.

8. Chen, Y.T.; and Cook, A., "Gravitational Experiments in the Laboratory," Cambridge University Press; First Edition, May 28, 1993.

Powering Starships with Compact Condensed Quark Matter

T. M. Eubanks

Asteroid Initiatives LLC, Clifton, Virginia

tme@asteroidinitiatives.com

Abstract

Compact Composite Objects (CCOs), nuggets of dense Color-Flavor-Locked Superconducting quark matter created before or during the Quantum ChromoDynamics phase transition in the early universe[1, 2, 3], could provide a natural explanation for both dark matter and the observed cosmological baryon asymmetry[4, 5, 6], without requiring modifications to fundamental physics. This hypothesis predicts a relic CCO population in the solar system, captured during its formation, and thus both massive strange matter cores in the centers of the Sun and planets, as well as a present-day population of "strange asteroids," bodies with mm-radii quark matter cores and ordinary matter mantles. Methods based on neutrino radiography and solid-body mechanics are developed to detect such strange matter cores in solar system bodies. The CCO hypothesis is directly supported by the observed population of small Very Fast Rotating (VFR) asteroids (bodies with rotation periods as short as 25 sec); the VFR data are consistent with the existence of strange asteroids with core masses of order 10^{10} - 10^{11} kg. If the VFR asteroids are indeed strange asteroids their CCO cores could be mined using the techniques being developed for asteroid mining. Through a process analogous to Andreev reflection in superconductors[7], even normal matter CCOs could be used as antimatter factories, potentially potentially producing as much as 10^9 kg of antimatter per CCO. While of course speculative, this energy source, if realized, would be suitable for propelling starships to a substantial fraction of the speed of light.

Keywords

Asteroids, quark matter, interstellar travel, neutrino radiography

1. CCOs as Dark Matter

Dark matter, first proposed 8 decades ago to reconcile the observed velocities and luminosities of galactic clusters[8, 9], is now thought to make up about 27% of the energy density of the universe[10]. This cosmic element can be shown to be cold (i.e., with low velocity dispersion) in the early universe, and is thus commonly denoted Cold Dark Matter (CDM). There are numerous proposals invoking various forms of new physics to explain CDM (typically through new fields and particles with very weak interactions with ordinary matter) but, despite decades of work, the nature of CDM remains a mystery.

Compact quark objects would represent a bound state of matter left over from epochs near the QCD phase transition, when the density was $> 4 \times 10^{17}$ kg m^{-3} (the nuclear density). The idea that condensed quark matter could form in the early universe and persist until the present has a considerable history, first proposed as strangelets[11] and nuclearites[12] almost 3 decades ago. CCO dark matter is thus a new variant of an old idea. Recent work indicates that at low temperatures and high densities the lowest QCD energy state is Color-Flavor-Locked (CFL) superconducting quark matter[1, 2, 13, 14, 15, 16]. CCOs made of CFL quark matter are thought to be stable at zero temperature, and could in fact be the fundamental state of matter, both more stable than ^{56}Fe and (if CCOs dominate the dark matter) more prevalent than ordinary hadronic matter.

In the theory derived by Zhitnitsky and his colleagues CCOs are created by the collapse of axion domain walls[1, 4, 5, 17, 18, 19] in the first few microseconds after the Big Bang. The axion domain wall theory bounds the primordial CCO mass, M_Q, to a range of a little over an order of magnitude in mass, with the mid-point of the range being set by the value of the axion decay constant, f_a, and the range reflecting the need for a CCO to be both energetically favorable and have greater than nuclear density. The experimental constraints on the axion decay constant are sufficiently broad that they dominate the theoretical uncertainty in the primordial CCO mass; the current experimental f_a limits[20] restrict the stable CCO mass range to

$$10^5 \text{kg} < M^Q < 4 \times 10^{10} \text{kg}, \tag{1}$$

with the actual stable CCO mass range being a sub-range of less than two orders of magnitude in mass located within that range.

CCOs are consistent with the observational constraints on CDM not through new physics and weak interactions with ordinary matter, but through their macroscopic size, very small cross section to mass ratios and high binding energies. Figure 1 shows the most stringent current limits on the masses of compact condensed quark matter (see the Figure caption for more details). The lowest mass limits result from laboratory experiments, the highest mass limits are due to gravitational microlensing and cosmological constraints, while a range of intermediate masses is excluded by seismological constraints, effectively using the entire Earth and the Moon as a detector. Figure 1 shows that the stable mass range of Equation 1 is not excluded by any of these existing experimental constraints. Figure 1 also shows the inferred CCO mass range derived from asteroid observations, as discussed in Section 3.

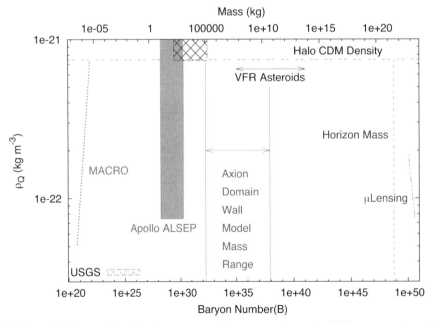

Figure 1: Limits on CCOs as a function of mass, assuming a monochromatic CCO mass spectrum. The experimental "asteroid constraints" and the theoretical "axion domain wall mass range" are included regions, which do not conflict with any of the other, experimentally excluded, mass ranges. The MACRO[21] constraints apply to the left of the indicated curve, and the Horizon Mass[22] and microlensing constraints[23] apply to the right of the indicated curves. (The MACRO limit is a flux limit converted to a minimum mass density assuming that the Galactic Halo dominates the CCO flux, the local Halo CDM density applies to the solar system, and the Halo velocity, v_{Halo}, is 220 km s^{-1}.) The Apollo and USGS seismological constraints[24] exclude the shaded regions. The Halo CDM Density is from local stellar kinematics [25].

2. CCOs in the Solar System

Planetary systems such as the solar system appear to result from the gravitational collapse of cold molecular clouds subject to supersonic turbulence in the InterStellar Medium (ISM), as interacting shock-waves cause density perturbations to exceed the local critical density[26]. The shocked gas then becomes gravitationally unstable and collapses, with stellar systems forming out of fragments of the collapsed material. Dark matter would not be directly perturbed by gas pressure changes during collapse but it would respond to the gravitational potential changes caused by these fluid motions and can become entrained in the collapsing cloud. In particular, a relatively small faction of the dark matter in a molecular cloud would, by chance, be moving slowly enough to be captured by the collapsing cloud as the cloud gravitational potential changes around it, leading to a population of primordially captured dark matter in the resulting planetary systems, including during the formation of our solar system.

While this gravitational capture mechanism would apply to most dark matter candidates, many hypothesized forms of dark matter do not interact much with ordinary matter under any circumstances, and thus would have a negligible influence in the subsequent development of the planetary system. CCO dark matter, however, would actively influence subsequent events, leading to tests of the CCO hypothesis. CCO dark matter would, for example, possibly cause heating and radiation events in the early solar system through mergers and annihilation of quark matter condensates, which would leave detectable signatures in chondrules and other meteoritic material. CCOs at the upper end of the stable mass range could also be important in planetary formation, providing high mass-to-area-ratio planetesimal nucleation sites and thus resolving the "meter barrier" issue[27, 28, 29] in the growth of protoplanetesimals.

Quark matter in the solar system would, after taking part in planetary formation, mostly now reside at the center of the Sun, planets and smaller bodies, leading to at least two further tests of CCO dark matter, through the detection of quark matter cores in large bodies by neutrino radiography and through the detection of quark matter cores in small bodies through their solid-body dynamics. The first test will be briefly described in this section, while the second will be discussed in more detail in Section 3.

Given the relatively small mass of primordial CCO material likely to be captured in the solar system, massive bodies such as the Earth would have only a small fraction of their total mass in CCO cores. If it is assumed that the solar system formed in an Orion-sized molecular cloud with the same density of dark matter as at the Sun's present location in the Galaxy, then (ignoring any subsequent antimatter annihilation) about 3×10^{-5} of the mass of the solar system would be quark matter. If it is further assumed that the distribution of dark matter in the solar system mimics the present-day distribution of ordinary matter then $\sim 3 \times 10^{-5}$ of the mass of the Earth, or $\sim 2 \times 10^{20}$ kg, would be captured quark matter, which would presumably by now have all collected in the center of the planet, forming an ~ 3.5 m radius strange matter sphere. Even though these interior quark matter cores would be physically small, they could actually be detected and studied with existing technology using neutrino radiography, as internal quark matter should be effectively opaque to neutrino beams generated by particle accelerators.

The absorption from the neutrino-nucleon (υN) optical depth [30] is given for an incident beam of energy E by

$$\frac{I}{I_0} = \exp -\frac{\sigma(E)D<\rho>}{M_N},$$

(2)

where I/I_0 is the diminishment in luminosity, σ_E the cross sectional area at the beam energy, E, D the distance of propagation through the body, $<\rho>$ the mean density, and M_N the mass per nucleon. If for simplicity it is assumed that the cross section is the same for ordinary and strange matter, then the optical depth for a 7 m raypath through the CCO core (with $<\rho> \sim 10^{18}$ kg m-3) would be $\sim 10^8$ times the optical depth of a 12,700 km antipodal raypath traversing the entire (ordinary matter) Earth (with $<\rho> \sim 5500$ kg m^{-3}). This difference in optical depths makes neutrino radiography a natural tool for the detection of dark matter cores.

The CERN Neutrino beam to Gran Sasso (CNGS) project [31], which studied neutrino oscillations and propagation speeds using a 17 GeV neutrino beam sent over a 732 km baseline, shows the capabilities of current technology for neutrino radiography. Using the υN cross section for a beam of 10 GeV neutrinos of $\sim 10^{-41}$ m^2 [32], then I/I_0 transiting the Earth while avoiding any quark matter core would be ~ 0.9996 while I/I_0 transiting through the center of the CCO core would be $\sim e^{42,000}$, i.e., zero to a very good approximation. If a 10 GeV neutrino beam was generated by a terrestrial accelerator and aimed directly down at the center of the core the dense quark matter in a 3.5 m radius core would thus cast an ~ 14 m diameter neutrino shadow at the accelerator's antipode, smaller than the 6.7 m x 6.7 m OPERA detectors. Although the length of an antipodal baseline would reduce the expected event rate by a factor of roughly 300 compared to CNGS baseline, the OPERA experiment resulted in 15,223 detections [33]. An antipodal repeat of this experiment would thus be expected to result in

~50 detections (outside of the core's shadow) or 0 detections (fully inside the shadow), which should be sufficient statistics to claim (or deny) the presence of such a core. By having multiple detectors, it would be possible to build up a true neutrino radiograph (projected image) of any quark matter at the center of the Earth.

While both logistical and technical considerations would probably result in an antipodal neutrino telescope being placed in deep water, instead of inside tunnels as for the CNGS, the current long baseline neutrino experiments undoubtedly show that the technology exists to confirm the existence of a CCO core inside the Earth by neutrino radiography. If the existence of a core can be confirmed, the same technology could be used to measure the size of the core and to study the physics of neutrino absorption and oscillation in strange matter, and possibly even to detect CCO core Slichter modes, if these should be sufficiently excited.

3. Observational Constraints on the Mass of Strange Asteroids

CCOs are thought to be stable against shrinkage at low energies, implying a definite lower limit to CCO core masses in the solar system. Sufficiently small asteroids, with radii < 200 meters, would, if they have a CCO core at all, be truly "strange" asteroids, as a large part of their total mass would be provided by their strange matter cores. This additional mass would greatly increase their bulk density, potentially to values greater than the density of Osmium (the densest stable element, with r = 22587 kg m^{-3}). The most straightforward way to conclusively find strange asteroids would thus be to find objects with densities greater than that of Osmium, through the determination of the size and mass of small asteroids.

Although is straightforward to estimate the size of an asteroid from its distance and luminosity, it is hard to remotely determine the mass of small bodies without either the discovery of a natural satellite or in situ spacecraft exploration. There are very few binary orbits known for asteroids smaller than 200 m in radius, and the smallest asteroid visited by spacecraft is the roughly 500 meter long (25143) Itokawa. It is thus necessary to use indirect methods to estimate the mass of small asteroids; one such method is provided by the rotation of the asteroids.

Radiation forcing is important for small asteroids in the Main Belt and the inner solar system, with forcing in linear momentum being described by the Yarkovsky effect[34], and radiative torques by the Yarkovsky-OKeefe-Radzievskii-Paddack (YORP) effect[35]. Many small and medium sized asteroids are apparently spun up by YORP and rotate near or at their limit rotation[36], the rotation rate where objects on the equator are no longer gravitationally bound. For a strange asteroid with a centrally located core, while the mass would be greatly increased compared to that of a similarly sized ordinary-matter asteroid, the increase in the moments of inertia due to the core would be negligible. This implies that strange asteroids should have small orbital changes from the Yarkovsky effect, but could be greatly spun-up (or down) by YORP torques. For bodies where the CCO core dominates the total mass, the core gravity will hold the mantle together against rotational disruption, allowing small strange asteroids to withstand higher spin rates than similar-sized ordinary matter bodies. As the maximum spin rate before rotational disruption depends on a body's density and tensile strength, asteroid rotation data, together with a tensile strength model, can be used as a proxy to determine densities.

Figure 2 reveals something of the complicated relationships[37, 38, 36] between asteroid radii and rotation periods, using the complete set of rotation data available as of November, 2012[39, 40]. The asteroids can be usefully divided into three separate radius ranges with apparently different rotational regimes. Asteroids with radii R_A > 50 km include both Main Belt and outer solar system objects and have, with one exception, rotational periods between 3 and 60 hours. Asteroids with 200 m < R_A ≤ 50 km are predominately Main Belt and Near Earth Objects (NEO) displaying a wide variety of rotation periods, including both very long period rotators and a large number of bodies near a limiting period of about 2.2 hours[37]. Finally, "small" bodies with R_A ≤ 200 m are 85% NEO and include many fast rotating bodies; the shortest rotation period, that of 2010 JL88, being only 25 seconds.

The limiting period of ~ 2.2 hours visible in Figure 2 is generally thought to reflect a "Rubble Pile Limit," (RPL), the period at which the equatorial rotational acceleration cancels the gravitational acceleration on the body's equator, implying the loss of unattached surface mass and the beginning of surface rotational disruption. For a spherical ordinary matter body (denoted by subscript "A") with uniform density ρ_A rotating at a frequency, Ω, mass loss would begin at the rotational RPL frequency, Ω_{RPL}, with

$$\Omega^2_{RP} = \frac{GM_A}{R_A^3} = \frac{4\pi G\rho_A}{3} \tag{3}$$

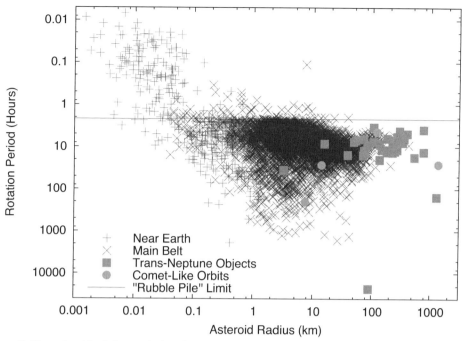

Figure 2: The asteroid rotation period-radius relation for all 5077 bodies with rotation and radius data, based on the November 2012 Asteroid Light Curve Database[39], after the removal of any flagged data. The Hungaria and Mars Crossing asteroids are included in the Main Belt asteroid category in this image. The change in the character of asteroid rotation rates at R < 200 m is obvious to the eye, with many asteroids with R < 200 m having rotation periods < 1 hour and almost all asteroids with R > 200 m having periods < 2 hours. The "Rubble Pile" limit of Equation 3 is also shown.

Equation 3, together with the apparent RPL rotation limit of 2.2 hours, implies a bulk asteroid $\rho_A \sim 2300$ kg m^{-3}, which is within the uncertainty of the average density of the common S type (stony) asteroids [41]. Based on Equation 3 the asteroids can be usefully divided into rotation classes, with "Fast Rotators" (or FR) asteroids being those with periods < the apparent RPL of 2.2 hours, "Very Fast Rotators" (or VFR) being those bodies with periods less than the RPL for a solid sphere with the density of Osmium (0.6 hours), and all other asteroids being considered to be "slow rotators." (Note that while small slow rotators may well have a condensed matter core, there is no way to distinguish between strange and ordinary matter slow rotators purely on the basis of rotation rate.)

Rapid rotation of a rubble pile can be expected to give rise to mass flows and surface deformations, increasing the amount of time the asteroid can evade rotational disruption under radiative torquing. The effects of rotational mass transport are exhibited clearly by, for example, the Alpha component of asteroid (66391) 1999 KW4, which has deformed or flowed into a top-like shape such that the accelerations on the equator cancel to within 1% [42, 43, 44], with a rotation period only 12% longer than the spherical RPL period for its density. Such mass movements will soften the RPL under YORP torquing, keeping bodies rotating near, but slightly below, their formal disruption limit, and delaying complete disruption[45, 46].

In the CCO hypothesis it is straightforward to take the observed radius and rotation frequency and estimate the mass of the CCO core, M_Q, with

$$M_Q = R_A^3 \left(\frac{\Omega^2}{G} - \frac{4\pi\rho_A}{3}\right). \tag{4}$$

(This equation assumes a spherical body, an ordinary matter density of ρ_A and zero tensile strength.) Figure 3 shows a histogram of the number of CCO candidates as a function of the CCO mass inferred using Equation 4, both for all bodies with periods < 2.2 hours, and for the VFR objects only, in both cases assuming $\rho_A = 2300$ kg m^{-3}, together with the theoretically predicted mass range.

Figure 1 shows that the CCO mass range inferred from solar system asteroid data is consistent with both experimental constraints on CCOs and lies within the upper end of the mass range in Equation 1, suggesting the axion decay constant lies within the upper end of its current experimental constraints. It is striking that theoretically predicted and observationally inferred CCO mass ranges overlap: the very size range where CCO cores are predicted to dominate the mass of strange asteroids, and thus bind bodies gravitationally beyond the ordinary matter RPL, is also the range where bodies are actually bound well beyond any ordinary matter RPL. Gaussians are fit to each histogram to estimate the center and spread of the distribution; the two data sets agree with well, with estimated centroid masses of 2.0 and 2.2 x 10^{10} kg, respectively, both towards the upper end but within the range predicted by the axion domain wall model for CCO formation. If this is an indication of condensed matter core masses, and if the CCO hypothesis is correct, these data thus predict that the axion decay constant, fa, should be found near the upper end of its predicted range (i.e., ~ 2.8 x 10^{11} GeV).

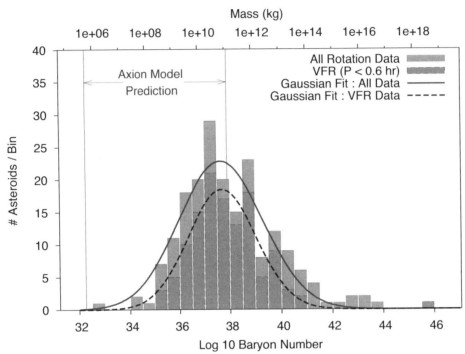

Figure 3: The number of candidate strange asteroids as a function of the CCO core mass required to prevent rotational disruption, assuming gravitational binding only. Estimates are provided from asteroid rotation data referenced to a rubble pile model with a default rA = 2300 kg m-3 for all of the rotation data ("All Rotation Data") and in addition for the Very Fast Rotation asteroid subset ("VFR data"). Also shown (as vertical lines) is the CCO mass predicted by the axion domain wall theory. The displayed Gaussians are fit to determine the histogram centroids; note that these centroids are within the mass region predicted (completely independently) by the axion domain wall theory.

4. Solar System CCOs as a Power Source

Oaknin and Zhitnitsky [4] hypothesized that CCOs could resolve the baryon asymmetry problem (the apparent predominance of normal matter versus antimatter in the universe) if the ratio of antimatter to matter CCOs was roughly 3:2. Such antimatter CCOs should survive to the present; both matter and antimatter CCOs would be protected from environmental interactions by their large superconducting gap energy, Δ ~ 100 MeV. Any incoming baryons would need to possess at least this much kinetic energy to break Cooper pairs and extract quarks from the superconductor [7]. A CCO would thus reflect any incident baryons with energies much less than Δ[4]; antimatter CCOs could thus potentially survive in the interiors of ordinary matter bodies, even at the center of the Sun, as even there thermal energies are much less than 100 MeV. It is not necessary, however, for there to be a substantial fraction of antimatter CCOs for CCOs to be used in the production of antimatter.

CFL superconductivity should support a form of Andreev reflection[7] for interactions with incident baryons with kinetic energy greater than Δ, which would provide a means of CCO energy production. In Andreev reflection, which was first demonstrated in BCS superconductivity, particles impacting on the CCO surface at or above the superconducting gap energy can pass inside the CCO, creating new Cooper pairs inside the superconductor through the creation of particle-antiparticle pairs, yielding one or more antiparticles leaving the CCO boundary (in other words, seen from the outside Andreev reflection consists of the conversion of an incoming particle into its antiparticle). It may thus be possible to create antimatter by radiating CCOs with 100 MeV particles, and it certainly should be possible to extract energy from a CCO by creating new Cooper pairs from 100 MeV particle streams, as these quarks will have a lower total energy after their insertion. Zhitnitsky [1, 2] describes an approximate theory for the growth of CCOs; the energy release from CCO particle insertion can be 10% or more of the total mass energy inserted into the CCO, for a yield of potentially 10^9 kg or more of antimatter from each 10^{10} kg CCO. Strange asteroids would thus be a resource for the future, as their physically small (≤ 1 mm radius) quark matter cores could be extracted by mining operations for subsequent exploitation, with a single 10^{10} kg CCO potentially producing ~ 4 x 10^{25} Joules worth of antimatter, sufficient (ignoring any losses) for ~ 85,000 years worth of current human energy consumption [47], and also sufficient to accelerate a megaton mass spacecraft to close to the speed of light.

5. Conclusion

The CCO theory can be confronted with observations in the solar system in a number of ways (not the least by the independent determination of the density of VFR asteroids), and should be either ruled out or provisionally confirmed within a relatively short period of time. It seems clear that, if the existence of strange asteroids is confirmed, CCOs will be deeply involved in the powering of interstellar travel. This could be done either directly, by incorporating CCOs in the spacecraft propulsion (which, given the likely CCO mass range, would indicate starship masses in the many megaton mass range), or through the production and storage of antimatter. In either case, CCOs could enable interstellar travel at a substantial fraction of the speed of light. CCOs would also have a profound impact on research in gravity and quantum theory (enabling, for example, "laboratory" tests of General Relativity and furthering experimental particle physics without requiring ever-larger colliders[48]), and of course as a general terrestrial and solar system energy source. For all of these reasons, it seems very likely that, if CCOs are confirmed, they will be the subject of intensive spacecraft exploration, and that the future development of starships will depend on the results of that exploration.

References

1. Ariel Zhitnitsky. Dark matter as dense color superconductor. In Nuclear Physics B Proceedings Supplements, volume 124, pages 99–102, July 2003. doi: 10.1016/ S0920-5632(03)02087-5.

2. Ariel Zhitnitsky. 'Nonbaryonic' dark matter as baryonic colour superconductor. J. Cosmology and Astroparticle Physics, 10:010, October 2003. doi: 10.1088/ 1475-7516/2003/10/010.

3. Michael Mcneil Forbes, Kyle Lawson, and Ariel R. Zhitnitsky. Electrosphere of macroscopic "quark nuclei": A source for diffuse MeV emissions from dark matter. Phys. Rev. D, 82:083510, Oct 2010. doi: 10.1103/ PhysRevD.82.083510.

4. David H. Oaknin and Ariel R. Zhitnitsky. Baryon asymmetry, dark matter, and quantum chromodynamics. Phys. Rev. D, 71(2):023519, Jan 2005. doi: 10.1103/ PhysRevD.71.023519.

5. Ariel Zhitnitsky. Cold dark matter as compact composite objects. Phys. Rev. D, 74:043515, Aug 2006. doi: 10.1103/PhysRevD.74.043515.

6. K. Lawson and A. R. Zhitnitsky. Diffuse cosmic gamma rays at 1-20 MeV: a trace of the dark matter? J. Cosmology and Astroparticle Physics, 1:22, 2008.

7. Mariusz Sadzikowski and Motoi Tachibana. Andreev Reflection in Superconducting QCD. Acta Physica Polonica B, 33:4141–4164, 2002.

8. F. Zwicky. Die Rotverschiebung von extragalaktischen Nebeln. Helvetica Physica Acta, 6:110, 1933.

9. J. P. Ostriker. Discovery of "Dark Matter" In Clusters of Galaxies. Ap. J., 525: C297, November 1999.

10. E. Komatsu, K. M. Smith, J. Dunkley, C. L. Bennett, B. Gold, G. Hinshaw, N. Jarosik, D. Larson, M. R. Nolta, L. Page, D. N. Spergel, M. Halpern, R. S. Hill, A. Kogut, M. Limon, S. S. Meyer, N. Odegard, G. S. Tucker, J. L. Weiland, E. Wollack, and E. L. Wright. Seven-year Wilkinson Microwave Anisotropy Probe (WMAP) Observations: Cosmological Interpretation. Ap. J. Supp., 192:18, February 2011. doi: 10.1088/0067-0049/192/2/18.

11. Edward Witten. Cosmic separation of phases. Phys. Rev. D, 30:272–285, Jul 1984. doi: 10.1103/PhysRevD.30.272.

12. A. de Rujula and S. L. Glashow. Nuclearites - A novel form of cosmic radiation. Nature, 312:734–737, 1984.

13. Mark Alford. New possibilities for QCD at finite density. Nucl. Phys. B Proc. Suppl., ...--73:161–166, 1999. doi: 10.1016/S0920-5632(99)85015-4.

14. Jes Madsen. Color-Flavor Locked Strangelets. Phys. Rev. Lett., 87:172003, Oct 2001. doi: 10.1103/PhysRevLett.87.172003.

15. John B. Kogut and Mikhail A. Stephanov. The Phases of Quantum Chromodynamics. Cambridge Monographs on Particle Physics, Nuclear Physics and Cosmology. Cambridge University Press, March 2004.

16. Mark G. Alford, Andreas Schmitt, Krishna Rajagopal, and Thomas Schafer. Color superconductivity in dense quark matter. Rev. Mod. Phys., 80:1455–1515, Nov 2008. doi: 10.1103/RevModPhys.80.1455.

17. Michael McNeil Forbes and Ariel Zhitnitsky. Primordial Galactic Magnetic Fields from Domain Walls at the QCD Phase Transition. Phys. Rev. Lett., 85: 5268–5271, Dec 2000. doi: 10.1103/PhysRevLett.85.5268.

18. Michael Mcneil Forbes and Ariel R. Zhitnitsky. Domain walls in QCD. J. High Energy Phys., art. 013, October 2001. doi: 10.1088/1126-6708/2001/10/013.

19. D.T.Son, M.A.Stephanov, and A.R.Zhitnitsky. Domain Walls of High-Density QCD. Phys. Rev. Lett., 86:3955–3958, April 2001. doi: 10.1103/PhysRevLett. 86.3955.

20. B. Lakic and Cast Collaboration. Status and perspectives of the CAST experiment. Journal of Physics Conference Series, 375(2):022001, July 2012. doi: 10.1088/1742-6596/375/1/022001.

21. MACRO Collaboration. Search for massive rare particles with MACRO. Nucl. Phys. B Proc. Suppl., 110:186–188, 2002.

22. Jes Madsen. Strangelets, Nuclearites, Q-balls–A Brief Overview. Invited talk at Workshop on Exotic Physics with Neutrino Telescopes, 2006.

23. C. Alcock, et al., EROS and MACHO Combined Limits on Planetary-Mass Dark Matter in the Galactic Halo. Ap. J. Lett., 499:L9, 1998.

24. E.T.Herrin, D.C. Rosenbaum, and V.L.Teplitz. Seismic search for strange quark nuggets. Phys. Rev. D, 73(4):043511, February 2006. doi: 10.1103/PhysRevD. 73.043511.

25. Jo Bovy and Scott Tremaine. On the Local Dark Matter Density. Ap. J., 756:89, 2012. doi: 10.1088/0004-637X/756/1/89.

26. R. S. Klessen. Star Formation in Molecular Clouds. In C. Charbonnel and T. Montmerle, editors, EAS Publications Series, volume 51 of EAS Publications Series, pages 133–167, November 2011. doi: 10.1051/eas/1151009.

27. Christoph Mordasini, Hubert Klahr, Yann Alibert, Willy Benz, and Kai-Martin Dittkrist. Theory of planet formation. Proceedings Workshop "Circumstellar disks and planets: Science cases for the second generation VLTI instrumentation", to appear in Astronomy and Astrophysics Review, ed. Sebastian Wolf, 2010.

28. F. Brauer, C. P. Dullemond, and Th. Henning. Coagulation, fragmentation and radial motion of solid particles in protoplanetary disks. Astron. Astropys., 480: 859–877, 2008.

29. Alessandro Morbidelli, William F. Bottke, David Nesvorny, and Harold F. Levison. Asteroids were born big. Icarus, 204:558–573, December 2009. doi: 10.1016/j.icarus.2009.07.011.

30. A. Connolly, R. S. Thorne, and D. Waters. Calculation of high energy neutrinonucleon cross sections and uncertainties using the Martin-Stirling-Thorne-Watt parton distribution functions and implications for future experiments. Phys. Rev. D, 83(11):113009, June 2011. doi: 10.1103/PhysRevD.83.113009.

31. D. Duchesneau.zThe CERN-Gran Sasso Neutrino program. Nuclear Physics B Proceedings Supplements, 123:279–287, July 2003. doi: 10.1016/ S0920-5632(03)02189-3.

32. R. Gandhi, C. Quigg, M. H. Reno, and I. Sarcevic. Neutrino interactions at ultrahigh energies. Phys. Rev. D, 58(9):093009, November 1998. doi: 10.1103/PhysRevD.58.093009.

33. T. Adam and et al. Measurement of the neutrino velocity with the OPERA detector in the CNGS beam using the 2012 dedicated data. Journal of High Energy Physics, 1:153, January 2013. doi: 10.1007/ JHEP01(2013)153.

34. D. Vokrouhlicky, A. Milani, and S. R. Chesley. Yarkovsky Effect on Small Near- Earth Asteroids: Mathematical Formulation and Examples. Icarus, 148:118–138, November 2000. doi: 10.1006/icar.2000.6469.

35. W. F. Bottke, Jr., D. Vokrouhlicky, D. P. Rubincam, and D. Nesvorny. The Yarkovsky and Yorp Effects: Implications for Asteroid Dynamics. Annual Review of Earth and Planetary Sciences, 34:157–191, May 2006. doi: 10.1146/ annurev.earth.34.031405.125154.

36. A. W. Harris and P. Pravec. Rotational properties of asteroids, comets and TNOs. In L. Daniela, M. Sylvio Ferraz, and F. J. Angel, editors, Asteroids, Comets, Meteors, volume 229 of IAU Symposium, pages 439–447, 2006. doi: 10.1017/S1743921305006903.

37. P. Pravec and A. W. Harris. Fast and Slow Rotation of Asteroids. Icarus, 148: 12–20, November 2000. doi: 10.1006/icar.2000.6482.

38. P. Pravec, A. W. Harris, and T. Michalowski. Asteroid Rotations. In W. F. Bottke Jr., A. Cellino, P. Paolicchi, and R. P. Binze, editor, Asteroids III, pages 113–122. University of Arizona Press, 2002.

39. B. D. Warner, A. W. Harris, and P. Pravec. The asteroid lightcurve database. Icarus, 202:134–146, July 2009. doi: 10.1016/j.icarus.2009.02.003.

40. Edward Bowell. Orbits of Minor Planets (Bowell+ 2013), 2012. URL http: //www.naic.edu/ _nolan/astorb. html. The research and computing needed to generate astorb.dat were funded principally by NASA grant NAG54741, and in part by the Lowell Observatory endowment.

41. B. Carry. Density of asteroids. Planet. Space Sci., 73:98–118, December 2012. doi: 10.1016/j.pss.2012.03.009.

42. S. J. Ostro, J.-L. Margot, L. A. M. Benner, J. D. Giorgini, D. J. Scheeres, E. G. Fahnestock, S. B. Broschart, J. Bellerose, M. C. Nolan, C. Magri, P. Pravec, P. Scheirich, R. Rose, R. F. Jurgens, E. M. De Jong, and S. Suzuki. Radar Imaging of Binary Near-Earth Asteroid (66391) 1999 KW4. Science, 314:1276–1280, November 2006. doi: 10.1126/science.1133622.

43. D. J. Scheeres, E. G. Fahnestock, S. J. Ostro, J.-L. Margot, L. A. M. Benner, S. B. Broschart, J. Bellerose, J. D. Giorgini, M. C. Nolan, C. Magri, P. Pravec, P. Scheirich, R. Rose, R. F. Jurgens, E. M. De Jong, and S. Suzuki. Dynamical Configuration of Binary Near-Earth Asteroid (66391) 1999 KW4. Science, 314: 1280–1283, November 2006. doi: 10.1126/science.1133599.

44. A.W.Harris, E.G.Fahnestock, and P.Pravec.On the shapes and spins of "rubble pile" asteroids. Icarus, 199:310–318, February 2009. doi: 10.1016/j.icarus.2008. 09.012.

45. K. A. Holsapple. Spin limits of Solar System bodies: From the small fast-rotators to 2003 EL61. Icarus, 187:500–509, April 2007. doi: 10.1016/j.icarus.2006.08. 012.

46. D. P. Sanchez and D. J. Scheeres. DEM simulation of rotation-induced reshaping and disruption of rubble-pile asteroids. Icarus, 218:876–894, April 2012. doi: 10.1016/j.icarus.2012.01.014.

47. BP. Statistical Review of World Energy 2013. Technical report, BP p.l.c., London UK, 2013. URL http:// www.bp.com/content/dam/bp/pdf/statistical-review/statistical_review_of_world_ energy_2013.pdf.

48. G. Dvali, A. Kusenko, and M. Shaposhnikov. New physics in a nutshell, or Q-ball as a power plant. Physics Letters B, 417:99–106, January 1998. doi: 10.1016/S0370-2693(97)01378-6.

To the Stars with Current Technology?

Pauli E. Laine, M.Sc.

Department of Computer Science and Information Systems, University of Jyväskylä

40014, Finland

pauli.e.laine@jyu.fi

Abstract

If we combine some current or near future propulsion technology we can achieve fraction of light speed. Travel time will still be very long even to the nearest star systems, so for manned space flight some suspension of animation (hibernation) will have to be developed. In this short paper I will review two solutions, one with feasible current propulsion systems and one with current propulsion together with near future technology. The first solution uses Nuclear Thermal Rocket (NTR) and gravitational slingshot for initial acceleration and nuclear-electric propulsion (NEP) using NTR's nuclear reactor for long term (decades) continuous slow acceleration to final speed. In the second solution Fission Fragment Rocket (FFR) is used together with solar sail. It turns out that the latter solution can in principle be used for interstellar travel.

Keywords

interstellar flight, nuclear thermal rocket, nuclear-electric rocket, fission fragment rocket, solar sail

1. Introduction

Can we build star ship with our current technology? There have been some proposals for interstellar probes that use only one kind of propulsion. Within current technology they can use either nuclear-electric propulsion (NEP) or solar sail. Both of these solutions have advantages and disadvantages. Proposed nuclear-electric propulsion systems have very high specific impulse but extremely low thrust. Solar sail requires no propellant but acceleration diminishes while the distance to the Sun increases.

2. Ship with Current Technology

Here I first review a mission that uses combination of Nuclear Thermal Rocket (NTR), NEP, gravitational assist and solar sail technology to overcome each other's disadvantages. Each of these propulsion systems has been proven in either in actual space mission or static test so they are reality today. But are even combined propulsions capable of achieving speeds that makes interstellar voyages, even manned one, feasible? It is commonly accepted that ship capable to speed of 0.1 c, or about 30,000 km/s with some reasonable energy usage can be used for interstellar travel. We can however set the limit to half of this, i.e. 0.05 c or 15,000 km/s for target speed for our mission. With this speed the nearest star system can be achieved in some 90 years.

In this ship, nuclear reactor is attached to one end of a long boom structure to keep it as far as possible from the possible crew. Large propellant tanks (liquid hydrogen) are inflatable, flexible tanks that are filled with several tanker rocket flights (very expensive!). Solar sail is used for reactors heat radiator and to gain more speed from solar wind. Schematic figure of this ship's structure is represented in figure 1.

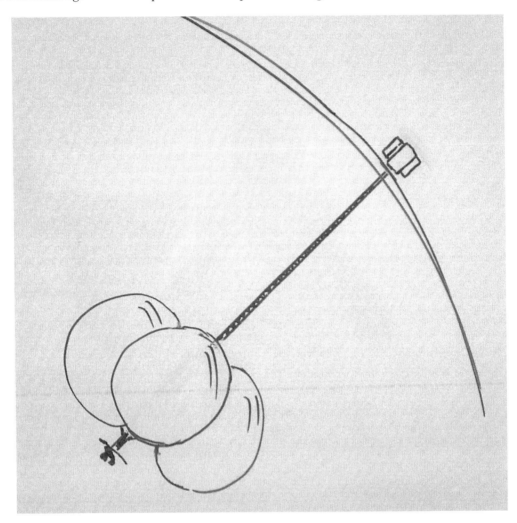

Figure 1: NTR-NEP-Solar sail ship

2.1 Mission Profile

Initial NRT + slingshot + solar sail acceleration will take the ship to the outer limits of the Solar System in some years. Actual end speed depends on how much liquid hydrogen can be transported to Earth orbit and the size of the solar sail.

Ship accelerates from Earth orbit towards Jupiter using NTR and solar sail. NTR can be used for hours and after that solar sail will keep up the continuous acceleration. Gained DV is approx. 100 km/s or more. After this ship gains more speed from Jupiter (gained DV ~ 5.6 km/s, [1]) and fires NTR once more for a slingshot trajectory towards its interstellar target. Here the solar sail has to be turned to horizontal position in order to minimize the ionization effect due the interstellar hydrogen.

After liquid hydrogen is used (solar sail will slow the speed of the ship when it approaches the target star, so no propellant is needed for braking), NRT is converted automatically to conventional nuclear reactor to produce electricity to NEP. NEP will run as long as there is propellant and power in the nuclear reactor, target lifetime is about 20 years. Unfortunately current NEP solutions give only ~100 km/s of DV. Solar sail will still give extra speed to the ship, totally about 40 km/s. In about 20 years ship must accelerate from ~200 km/s to 15,000 km/s. Is that possible? If we plug our values to rocket equation:

$$\Delta v_{tot} = v_{eNRT} \ln\left(\frac{m_a}{m_b}\right) + v_{eNEP} \ln\left(\frac{m_b}{m_c}\right) + \Delta v_{sail} + \Delta v_{sling}$$

we can see that after having accelerated for more than 20 years, our speed is still something like 350 km/s. NRT requires way too much propellant for interstellar travel. This kind of propulsion solution could perhaps be uses for some kind of deep space mission, but its cost-effectiveness will be somewhat low.

3. Ship with Near Future Technology: Fission Fragment Rocket Engine

In the second mission Fission Fragment Rocket Engine (FFRE) [2] is used together with solar sail. FFRE is a proposed and very promising propulsion technology due to its very high exhaust velocity (3-5% c) and I_{sp} (~10^6 sec) [3]. Fission reaction splits atoms into two fragments that will dissipate their kinetic energy by colliding to other atoms. Theoretically FFRE can harness these fragments's kinetic energy directly to produce thrust. In order to fission fragments can escape, fissile material should be very thin or in low density state. This limits usable material to highly fissionable nuclear fuels such as Americium (Am) or Curium (Cm), which are very expensive to produce.

Rodney A. Clark and Robert B. Sheldon proposed 2005 alternative design for FFRE, Dusty Plasma Based Fission Fragment Reactor (DPBFFR), figure 2 [4]. This version of FFRE is used in this second mission.

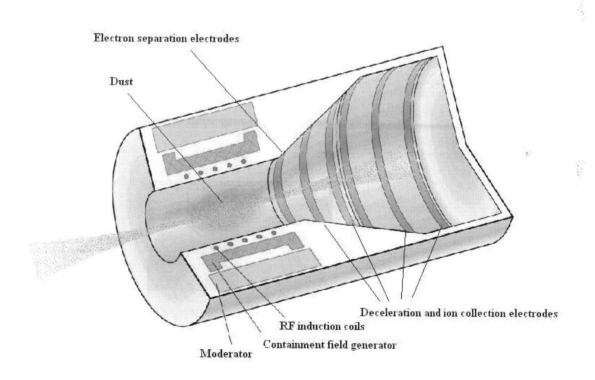

Figure 2: Dusty Plasma Bed Reactor, Credit: modified Wikimedia Commons image

Proposed ship consists of three FFRE stages and a solar sail. Multistage rocket concept is used for highest possible Δv. Solar sail will give extra acceleration near the Sun, will work as heat radiator, and finally will slow down the speed when approaching the target star.

Schematic figure of this ship's structure is represented in figure 3.

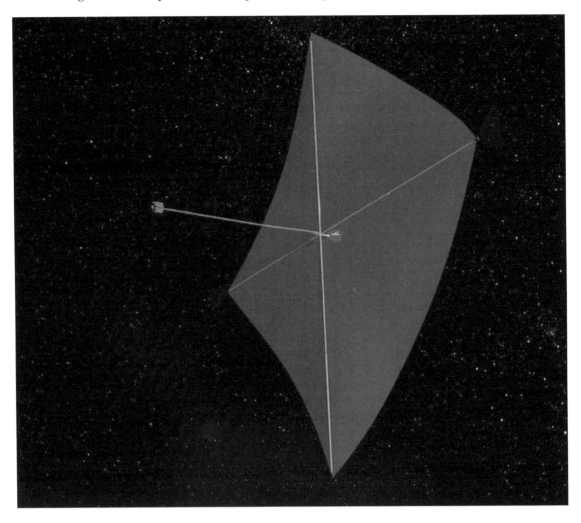

Figure 3: FFRE-Solar sail ship, Credit: NASA, modified Wikimedia Commons image

Here again nuclear reactors are attached to one end of a long boom structure to keep it as far as possible from the crew. Multistage concept is used for longer operational time and efficiency (Δv). However, FFRE has low mass ratio, but used reactors could be jettisoned to reduce the final mass. In our mission each stage contains about 10 metric tons of neutron moderator (lithium hydrite, LiH).

3.1 Mission Profile

With such effective rocket engine as FFRE, single stage ship which starts e.g. half propellant (and jettisoned structures) by mass could theoretically gain Δv about 8000 km/s. In this example mission total mass is 37 metric tons with 900 kg of fuel (Am-242m). Mission profile is somewhat similar than NTR-NEP-Solar sail ship. Initial FFRE + possible slingshot + solar sail acceleration can take the ship to the outer limits of the Solar System in less than a year. FFRE stages will run one after the other, so we can get final speed from the multistage rocket equation:

$$\Delta v_{tot} = \sum_{i=1}^{n} v_{ei} \ln\left(\frac{m_{0i}}{m_{\partial i}}\right)$$

(where v_e is the exhaust velocity, m_0 the initial mass, and m_b the final mass) $\Delta v_{tot} = 0.127$ c, which is considerably faster than our target speed 0.05 c. Realistic Δv will probably be somewhat smaller, but at least theoretically we can gain our limit speed.

4. Conclusion

Interstellar travel is not reality with our current technology, at least in reasonable timescale. However, feasible near future (~10-20 years) propulsion technology (FFRE) could in principle attend speed that makes interstellar travel reality. At least it is an engineering problem, not a theoretical one.

Acknowledgements

The author thanks Dr. Eric W. Davis (Institute for Advanced Studies at Austin) for discussions.

References

1. Zachary, R. G., "Juno and gravity assists", ccar.colorado.edu/asen5050/projects/projects_2011/Grunder_proj/extension.html, (2011).

2. Chapline, G., "Fission fragment rocket concept", Nucl. Instr. and Meth., A271, 207-208 (1988).

3. Werka, R., Clark, R., R. Sheldon, Percy, T., "Final Report: Concept Assessment of a

4. Fission Fragment Rocket Engine (FFRE) Propelled Spacecraft", FY11 NIAC Phase 1 Study, (2011).

5. Clark, R. A., Sheldon, R. B., "Dusty plasma based fragment nuclear reactor", 41st AIAA/ASME/SAE/ASEE Joint Propulsion Conference & Exhibit (2005).

Temperature Inflation Considerations for Ultra-relativistic Subluminal Starships

Jeffrey S. Lee

X-Physics Propulsion & Power Project, Icarus Interstellar

Crescent School

2365 Bayview Avenue, Toronto, Ontario, Canada M2L 1A2

jlee@icarusinterstellar.org

Abstract

Accomplishing subluminal voyages beyond the solar neighborhood on reasonable human timescales will require starships capable of ultra-relativistic speeds. Such starships would be subjected to a forward-directed heat bath from the Doppler temperature inflation of the Cosmic Microwave Background (CMB) radiation.

Keywords

empirical temperature, absolute temperature, relativistic thermodynamics, CMB, occupation number

1. Introduction

The prevalence and extreme isotropy of the Cosmic Microwave Background radiation bestow upon an ultra-relativistic starship on any heading an extremely Lorentz transformed CMB radiation field.

However, the Lorentz transformations of heat and temperature have been problems of long standing in the literature [1], [2], [3], [4], [5], [6]. Contentions have emerged supporting three Lorentz transformations: Temperature Deflation [2], [3]; Temperature Inflation [7], [8], [9], and Temperature Invariance [10], [11], [12], [13].

A ubiquitous approach for determining the transformations of heat and temperature is to consider a finite bounded volume (V_O) of an ideal fluid moving relativistically with respect to the laboratory frame [14], [15], [16]. The clear phenomenological advantage of this methodology is that pressure, p is a Lorentz invariant, and the work done by the fluid is simply pV_O.

Since the CMB does not constitute a fluid, this paper considers the occupation number (number density of occupied states per phase space element), which is also a Lorentz invariant, and is directly applicable to the CMB. This work supports the Temperature Inflation conclusion, as set forth by Ott [7], Arzelies [8], and Møller [9].

2. Empirical and Absolute Temperatures

The confusion that arises regarding temperature in relativistic thermodynamics can be clarified by elucidating the respective differences between empirical and absolute temperatures. The empirical temperature is a frame-independent, relativistic scalar that depicts (for instance) the CMB rest frame and the starship frame as being in thermal equilibrium [17]. It follows from the Zeroth Law of Thermodynamics, and can be ascertained in terms of the absolute temperature in the rest frame of a thermodynamic system.

The absolute temperature of a thermodynamic system follows from the Second Law of Thermodynamics, and is given by the product of the absolute temperature of the rest frame and the Lorentz factor. Although perceptible in non-relativistic thermodynamics, the difference between empirical and absolute temperatures is cogently evident in relativistic thermodynamics.

3. Justification for Temperature Inflation of the CMB

The CMB would constitute a continuous medium in thermodynamic equilibrium with a starship, in which a bounded domain of spacetime with a unit volume ($V_O = 1$) is chosen to move at constant velocity with respect to the starship. The Einstein summation convention is employed. The spatial axes in the CMB and starship frames are assumed to be mutually parallel, and the spacetime metric is given by:

$$\eta_{ij} = \eta^{ij} = \mathrm{diag}(-,-,-,+) \tag{1}$$

By making use of the Lorentz transformation $x^j = \Lambda^j_k x^k_o$, the coefficients of which are given by,

$$\Lambda^\mu_\nu = \delta^\mu_\nu - \frac{v^\mu v^\nu}{v^2}(1-\gamma), \quad \Lambda^4_\mu = \frac{v^\mu}{c}\gamma, \quad \Lambda^\mu_4 = \frac{v^\mu}{c}\gamma, \quad \Lambda^4_4 = \gamma \tag{2}$$

the energy-momentum tensor T^{jk} can be written [18], [19], [20], [21]:

$$T_{jk} = \varepsilon_o u_j u_k + \tau_{jk} = T_{kj} \tag{3}$$

where ε_O is the energy density in the CMB frame, $u^j = \left(\frac{v^\mu}{c}\gamma(v), \gamma(v)\right)$ is the 4-velocity of the starship, and

$\tau^{jk} = \Lambda^j_\mu \Lambda^k_\nu \tau^{\mu\nu}_o$ ($\tau^{\mu\nu}_o$ is the stress tensor).

Although the stress-energy tensor is often rewritten by considering the relativistic motion of an ideal fluid, such an invocation would not be apropos for a starship moving through the CMB. The obvious appeal of an ideal fluid gedanken experiment is the Lorentz invariance of pressure. Since occupation number is directly relevant to the CMB, and is a Lorentz invariant, it is used to rewrite .

The following results:

$$T_{jk} = \left(n_{\alpha\bar{\alpha}} + \varepsilon_o\right)u_j u_k - n_{\alpha\bar{\alpha}}\eta_{jk}$$

$$\tau_{o_{\mu\nu}} = -n_{\alpha\bar{\alpha}}\eta_{\mu\nu} \tag{4}$$

$$\tau_{o_{\mu\nu}} = -n_{\alpha\bar{\alpha}}\eta_{\mu\nu}V_o$$

Since occupation number is a Lorentz invariant and $V = \gamma^{-1}$, the energy differential can be calculated:

$$dE + \sum_{\alpha=1}^{2} n_{\alpha\bar{\alpha}}\frac{hv^3}{c^2}\cos\theta\, dA\, dt\, dv\, d\Omega = \gamma\left(dE_o + \sum_{\alpha=1}^{2} n_{\alpha\bar{\alpha}}\frac{hv_o^3}{c^2}\cos\theta_o\, dA_o\, dt_o\, dv_o\, d\Omega_o\right) \tag{5}$$

The quantity $\dfrac{h\nu_o^3}{c^2}$ is the specific intensity I_ν. It is noteworthy that $\dfrac{I_\nu}{\nu_o^3} = \dfrac{h}{c^2}$ must also be a Lorentz invariant, and instead could have been used to rewrite the stress-energy tensor.

The constraint that the first law of thermodynamics should have its covariant form $(dE_o = \delta Q_o + \delta L_o)$ necessarily results in $\delta Q_o = \gamma \delta Q_o$. Thus, the heat in the starship frame must be greater than the heat in the CMB frame.

In order to determine a relativistic dependence for absolute temperature, the Clausius inequality for cyclic reversible processes, (6), and the stipulations in (7) for a smooth continuous function for temperature, are needed.

$$\oint \frac{\delta Q_o}{T_o} = 0 \qquad\qquad 6$$

$$T = T(T_o, \mathrm{v}) \quad , \quad \lim_{\mathrm{v} \to 0} T(T_o, \mathrm{v}) = T_o \qquad\qquad 7$$

This yields the Ott [7], Arzelies [8] and Møller [9] result of relativistic temperature inflation:

$$T = T_o \gamma \qquad\qquad 8$$

Consequently, the CMB manifests itself as a relativistically beamed (due to relativistic aberration), velocity-dependent radiation field in the direction of motion of the starship.

4. Maximum Starship Speeds through the CMB

Temperature inflation and the relativistic beaming of the CMB radiation impose maximum subluminal speeds, which are dependent on the melting temperature of the material from which the starship is constructed.

In the case of a starship hull constructed from titanium with a melting temperature of 1941 K [22], and defining $\bar{\beta} = 1 - \beta$, the maximum speed of such a starship is $\bar{\beta} = 9.8\mu$. The corresponding proper [starship frame] time and distance [CMB frame] for a sustained proper acceleration of 1g are 5.93 years and 218.3 light years respectively.

At greater speeds, significant thermal degradation of the starship hull is expected.

The Doppler shifting of CMB photons to gamma ray energies will not occur, as $\bar{\beta}$ ranges from 10^{-12} to 10^{-30} for 1 keV to 1 TeV photons respectively. The corresponding CMB rest frame temperatures existed between 3.1 years and 98 picoseconds after the Big Bang respectively.

5. Conclusions

Ultra-relativistic starships on any heading will encounter a highly Doppler shifted, forward-directed CMB radiation field. For the reason that the relativistic motion of an ideal fluid is only analogous and not directly relevant to the CMB, the stress-energy tensor has been rewritten by means of the occupation number. The inflation of heat and temperature from their rest frame values by the Lorentz factor (γ) is supported.

For a starship with a titanium bow, the forward-directed heat bath will achieve the melting temperature of Ti at $\bar{\beta} = 9.8\mu$. Even if the significant energy requirements for ultra-relativistic travel can be achieved, thermodynamically induced speed limits exist, and preclude the possibility of a sustained 1g acceleration for an arbitrary duration.

References

1. M. Przanowski, "Heat, temperature and relativity," *Acta Physicae Superficierum*, vol. XI, no. 43, 2009.

2. A. Einstein, *Jahrbuch der Radioaktivit¨at und Elektronik*, vol. 4, no. 411, 1907.

3. M. Planck, *Ann. Physik*, vol. 26, no. 1, 1908.

4. K. Mosengeil, *Ann. Physik*, vol. 22, no. 876, 1907.

5. W. Pauli, *Relativitatstheorie, Teubner*, 1921.

6. M. Laue, *Die Relativitatstheorie, Friedrich Vieweg und Sohn*, 1921.

7. H. Ott, Z. *Physik*, vol. 175, no. 70, 1963.

8. H. Arzelies, *Nuovo Cim.*, vol. 35, no. 792, 1965.

9. C. Møller, *Det. Kong. Danske Videnskab. Selskab. Mat.-Fys. Medd.*, vol. 36, no. 1, 1967.

10. P. Landsberg, *Nature*, vol. 212, no. 571, 1966.

11. P. Landsberg, *Nature*, vol. 214, no. 903, 1967.

12. P. Landsberg and K. John, *Ann. Phys.*, vol. 56, no. 299, 1970.

13. P. Landsberg, *Europ. J. Phys.*, vol. 2, no. 203, 1981.

14. T. Nakamura, "Lorentz Transform of Black Body Radiation Temperature," 2009. [Online]. Available: arXiv:0910.0164v1. [Accessed 4 November 2013].

15. M. Przanowski and J. Tosiek, 2011. [Online]. Available: arXiv:1010.5701v2. [Accessed 4 November 2013].

16. E. Bormashenko, "Entropy of Relativistic Mono-Atomic Gas and Temperature Relativistic Transformation in Thermodynamics," *Entropy*, vol. 9, pp. 113-117, 2007.

17. D. Cubero, J. Casado–Pascual, J. Dunkel, P. Talkner and P. Hanggi, *Phys. Rev. Lett.*, vol. 99, 2007.

18. C. Møller, *The Theory of Relativity*, Oxford : Oxford University Press, 1972.

19. L. Landau and E. Lifshitz, *Fluid Mechanics*, Oxford: Pergamon Press, 1959.

20. L. Landau and E. Lifshitz, *Theory of Elasticity*, Oxford: Pergamon Press, 1970.

21. S. Weinberg, *Gravitation and Cosmology: Principles and Applications of the General Theory of Relativity*, New York: John Wiley & Sons, Inc., 1972.

22. R. Weast, *Handbook of Chemistry and Physics*, 56 ed., Cleveland: CRC Press, 1975.

Interstellar Communication with Gravitational Lens and KLT

Stephane Dumas

SETI LEAGUE, jgsdumas@gmail.com

Claudio Maccone

Technical Director of the International Academy of Astronautics (IAA),

and Associate of Istituto Nazionale di Astrofisica (INAF), Italy.

Via Martorelli, 43 – Torino (Turin) 10155 – Italy.

clmaccon@libero.it

Abstract

Gravitational lensing is one of the most amazing discoveries produced by Einstein's general theory of relativity. To date, hundreds of gravitational lenses have been observed by astronomers and they led to a number of new results in extrasolar planet search, astrophysics and cosmology. SETI and interstellar communication also could benefit from gravitational lensing.

There is an even more important question, tough, that we face in this paper: how to insure any future interstellar radio links between the solar system and future interstellar probes. We show by calculations that only exploiting the gravitational lens of the Sun as a huge antenna we will be able to achieve such an interstellar link. In other words, we calculate the probability of bit error across interstellar distances both with and without using the gravitational lens effect of the Sun. The conclusion is that only when we will exploit the Sun as a gravitational lens we will be able to communicate with our own probes (or with nearby aliens civilisations) across the distances of even the nearest stars to us in the Galaxy, and that at a reasonable Bit Error Rate (BER).

Furthermore, the Karuhen-Loève Transform makes possible the detection of weak signal buried in noise. This technique may increase the gain of the receiver and help the detection of weak radio signals.

This paper will present the possibility of using gravitational lens coupled with the KLT for interstellar communication.

Keywords

gravitational lens, general relativity, KLT

1. Introduction

The gravitational focusing effect of the Sun is one of the most amazing discoveries produced by the general theory of relativity. The first paper in this field was written by Albert Einstein [1], but his work was virtually forgotten until 1964, when Sydney Liebes of Stanford University [2] gave the mathematical theory of gravitational focusing by a galaxy located between the Earth and a very distant cosmological object, such as a quasar. The focusing effect can be use to amplify a radio signal for a very far source (i.e. interstellar probes).

The second part of this paper introduces the use of the Karuhen-Loève Transform for the analysis of noisy signal the same way the Fourier Transform is used, but with better results. The detection of information in a noisy signal can be interpreted as increase of gain in reception and transmission. The retrieval of very weak signal can be achieved by coupling this analysis method with the gain of placing an antenna at the focal point of the Sun.

2. The Minimal Focal Distance for the Sun

The well-known Schwarzschild solution to the Einstein field equation is the mathematical foundation upon which the theory of the gravitational lens of the Sun rests.

The geometry of the Sun's gravitational lens is easily described. Incoming electromagnetic waves passing outside the Sun and within a certain distance r of its centre are then deviated by the gravity of the star. The basic result following from the Schwarzschild solution shows that the corresponding deflection angle a(r) at the distance r is given by equation 1 [3,4] where G is the gravitational constant, M_{sun} the mass of the Sun and c the speed of light.

(1)
$$a(r) = \frac{4\,G\,M_{Sun}}{c^2\,r}$$

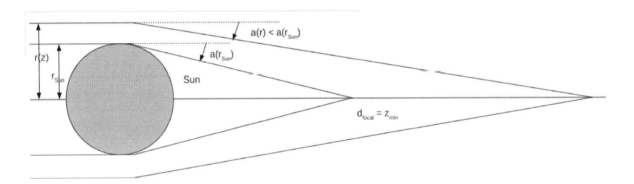

Figure 1: Schematics of the focal point of the Sun.

From figure 1, it should be clear that the minimal focal distance d_{focal} is related to the tangent of the maximum deflection angle by the equation 2. Moreover, since the angle a(r) is very small, the focal distance can be expressed by equation 3 (using equations 1 and 2).

(2)
$$\tan(a(r)) = \frac{r_{Sun}}{d_{focal}}$$

(3)
$$d_{focal} \approx \frac{r_{Sun}}{a(r)} = \frac{r_{Sun}^2}{2\,r_{Schwarzchild}}$$

The minimal focal distance for the Sun is d_{focal} approximately 550 AU or about 8.1×10^{10} km. The orbit of Pluto is between 30 and 50 AU.

3. Computing the Gain in Communication

The standard formula in antenna theory relates the gain [5] to the effective area and to the wavelength is given by equation 4 and assuming an efficiency of 50%.

(4)
$$G_{antenna} = \frac{4\pi A_{eff}}{\lambda^2} = \frac{2\pi^2 r_{antenna}^2}{\lambda^2}$$

The gain of the gravitational lens of the Sun can be proved [3] to be given by equation 5.

(5)
$$G_{Sun} = 4\pi^2 \frac{r_{Schwarzchild}}{\lambda^2} = \frac{8\pi^2 G M_{Sun}}{c^2} \frac{1}{\lambda}$$

4. Using Gravitational Lens for a Communication System

We show that by calculation that only by exploiting the gravitational lens of the Sun as a huge antenna will we be able to achieve an interstellar communication link. We calculate the probability of bit error (i.e. P_e) across interstellar distances both with and without using gravitational lens effect of the Sun.

Consider a radio transmitter that radiates a power P_t isotropically and uniformly over a bandwidth B_t. Then, as a distance d it produces a flux density given by equation 6.

(6)
$$S = \frac{P_t}{B_t 4\pi d^2}$$

Considering directionality of the antenna, the matching of bandwidth between the receiver and transmitter and using the gain of both antennas, the power at the receiving antenna is given by equation 7 where G_r is the gain of the receiver and G_t the gain of the transmitter.

(7)
$$P_t = \frac{P_r G_r G_t}{(4\pi)^2 d^2} \lambda^2$$

In telecommunication theory the bit error ratio is the ratio of the number of bits incorrectly received to the total number of bits sent during a specified interval of time [6]. Equation 8 gives the probability of bit error for a quadrature phased shift keying system (QPSK) commonly used in telecommunication.

(8)
$$P_e = \frac{1}{2} erfc\left(\sqrt{\frac{E_b}{N_0}}\right)$$

where erfc is the complementary function of erf (i.e. erfc(z) = 1 - erf(z)), E_b is the received energy per bit and N_0 is given by the noise temperature of space multiplied by the Boltzmann constant ($N_0 = kT$).

Figure 2 shows the probability of bit error (P_e) as a function of the distance of the source. The transmitting power is P_t = 40 W. The transmission rate is 32 kbits/s. The carrier frequency is 32Ghz. The signal quickly becomes very noisy at a short distance without the gain of the Sun (red curve). The blue curve shows the same scenario with an antenna located at the focal point for the Sun. The probability of bit error is 0.039 for a signal coming from a source at 10 light-years from the Sun.

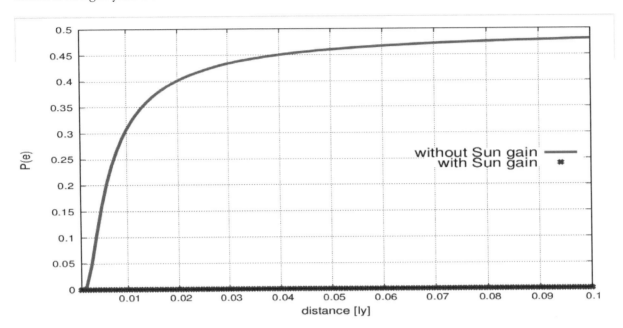

Figure 2 : Gain with and without the contribution of the Sun.

Figure 3 shows the probability of bit error given the transmitting power for a radio link between antennas located at the focal point of the Sun and Alpha Centauri, respectively. A signal transmitted with a power as low as 0.1 mW would be received without too much noise.

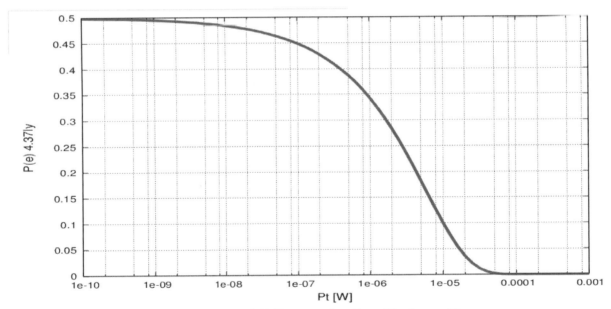

Figure 3 : Probability of Bit Error as a function of the transmitting power.

5. The Karhunen-Loève Transform

The Karhunen-Loève theorem is a representation of a stochastic process as an infinite linear combination of orthogonal functions, analogous to a Fourier series representation of a function on a bounded interval. The importance of the Karhunen-Loève theorem (KLT) is that it yields the best orthonormal basis in the sense that it minimises the total mean squared error.

In the case of a centred stochastic process X satisfying a technical continuity conditions, X admits a decomposition given by equation 9 where Z_k (equation 10) are uncorrelated random variables and the functions F_k are continuous real-valued orthonormal functions. The values of Z_k are found by projecting the vector X to the functions F_k.

(9)
$$X = \sum_{k=1}^{N} Z_k F_k$$

(10)
$$Z_k = \sum_{t=0}^{T} X(t) F_k(t)$$

The functions F_k are also called eigenvectors which define a new orthogonal axis system. They are found by solving what is called the eigenproblems associated to the autocorrelation matrix of X. Let A be a square N by N matrix, x a nonzero N by 1 vector, and L is scalar. L is called the eigenvalue of A, and x is called the eigenvector. Equation 11 summarises the relation.

(11)
$$A\vec{x} = L\vec{x}$$

This situation is true if and only if equation 12 is true, which can be expanded into a system of N equations of N unknowns.

(12)
$$det|A - \lambda I| = \begin{vmatrix} A_{11} - \lambda_1 & A_{12} & \cdots & A_{1n} \\ A_{21} & A_{22} - \lambda_2 & \cdots & A_{2n} \\ \vdots & \vdots & \ddots & \vdots \\ A_{n1} & A_{n2} & \cdots & A_{nn} - \lambda_n \end{vmatrix} = 0$$

Solving this problem with an analytical approach is tedious and not practical for large values of N. It must be solved using numerical methods such as the Jacobi or the QR algorithms.

6. Digital Signal Processing

The usual method of dealing with signal processing is to decompose the raw signal into a series of Sine functions (e.g. the Fourier Transform (FT), equation 13).

(13)
$$X(t) = a_0 + \sum_{n=1}^{\infty} a_n \cos(nt) + b_n \sin(nt)$$

The KLT performs a similar work given that the vector X is describing a time-dependent process. Instead of using a series of Sine functions it uses a series of eigenvectors (i.e. F_k). X must be a wide sense stationary process (i.e. E[X]=const) and a strict sense stationary process (i.e. ergodicity, X(t) and X(t+c) have the same statistics). If the vector does not meet the first criterion then it can be modified by removing the average value.

KLT will look at the structure of the information in the vector X. This is accomplished by creating an auto-correlation matrix R (equation 14) and compute the eigenproblem related to this matrix.

(14)
$$R(t_1, t_2) = E[X(t_1) X(t_2)]$$

The process of discretisation of continuous signal is important to the Fourier Transform (FT). The digital version of FT is known as FFT and it cannot process continuous and infinite signal. X(t) must be a discrete and finite signal to be processed by the Fast Fourier Transform. The original signal must be pre-processed before being used by FFT. The method is called Windowing and involved doing a convolution on the original data to smooth the borders. Processing a signal using FT without doing so will create unwanted small oscillations in the results. KLT does not require such pre-conditioning and can analyse the raw signal directly.

7. Detecting a Pulse with KLT

Figure 4 illustrates the capacity of KLT to find a single pulse in noise. In this example, the signal is defined by single Sine and is buried in a strong noise (i.e. SNR=-16dB). The FT cannot find the signal (red curve) but the KLT can (green curve).

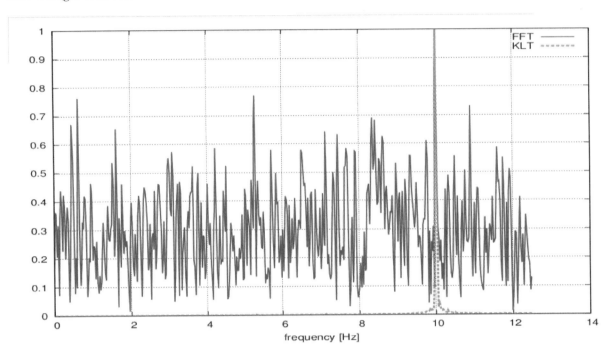

Figure 4 : Illustration of the capacity of KLT to find signal buried in noise (Fs=25Hz, F=10Hz, SNR=-16dB).

The dependence of the FT to the sampling frequency (Fs) is crucial to have a good result. The value of Fs must be several times the value of the signal frequency (Fc). KLT is less sensible to the sampling frequency, which however must be above the Nyquist frequency. Good results from KLT have been achieved with Fs=3Fc. When used for the detection of multiple pulses in a noisy signal, KLT performed better than FT.

8. Rate of Error

In the presence of a very noisy signal, the FT will produce a chaotic output and it will be difficult to detect the frequency of the pulse. When the noise is too much for the KLT, the output will still be a sharp peak but at the wrong frequency. It is important to calibrate the algorithm and understand its limitations given the parameters of the raw signal (i.e. duration and sampling frequency). Figure 5 illustrates the rate of error of KLT for a series of noisy signals. The statistics were produced using 100 iterations per case.

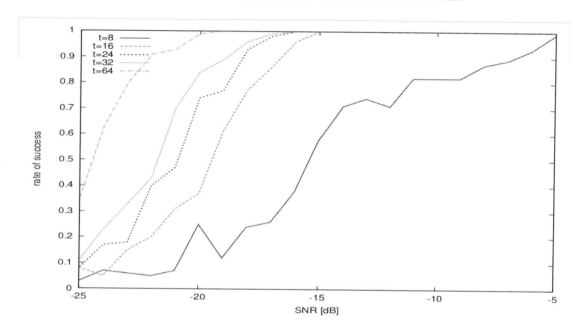

Figure 5 : KLT rate of error for several noisy signal of different length.

The longer the duration of the segment to analyse, the better KLT will perform for the same level of noise. This is not unexpected since KLT work better with more samples to extract the information. This behaviour is not shared be the FT.

9. Chirped Signal

If the source or the receiver is in accelerated motion then the signal will be shifted in frequency. Even if the space probe is not accelerated (in the case of SETI, the nature of the alien transmitter is unknown), the receiver (i.e. Earth) is rotating. This rotation induces acceleration on the receiver. The phenomenon is often called chirped, or Doppler effect.

Figure 6 illustrated the result of FFT and KLT for the same chirped signal. The figures are plots of the frequency vs. time (i.e. waterfall plot). The signal frequency started at F=100Hz and last for T=10s. The rate of chirp is 2 Hz/s. The sampling frequency is Fs=400Hz. The value of SNR is -16dB.

This type of figure should produce a straight vertical line. There is a lot of structure in the FFT output which make it hard to find the signal. In the KLT output, the signal is quite visible (even if not complete).

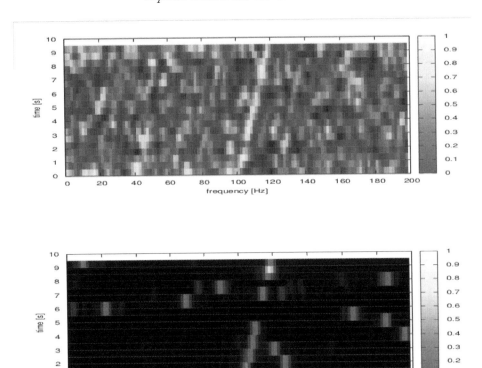

Figure 6 : Comparison between FT (top) and KLT (bottom) for the detection of a chirped pulse in a noisy signal.

10. Non-Sinusoidal Waveforms

Figure 7 illustrates the capacity of KLT to reconstruct a non-sinusoidal waveform as comparison with the FFT. The original square pulse could be approximated using only 18 eigenvectors while the summation of 18 sine functions (from the FT output) does not approximate the original data.

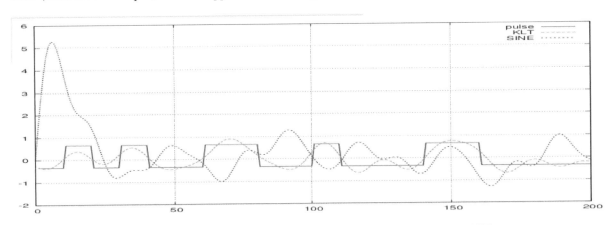

Figure 7 : Reconstruction of a square pulse signal using KLT and FT.

11. Detection of Unknown Signal

The detection of an extraterrestrial signal presupposed a periodic and sinusoidal signal. Following this assumption, one can conclude that the Fourier Transform is the best tool for detection. [7] proposes to use the KLT instead as the tool of detection. Since KLT does not make any assumption on the orthogonal waveforms, it should be more flexible. [7] introduces two measures of the level of information that each methods can extract (equations 15 and 16). Those quantities reflect the capacity of each method of extracting information from the source.

(15)
$$M_{KLT} = 2\,max(L)/\sum L$$

(16)
$$K_{FFT} = max(E_i)/\sum E_i$$

Figure 8 shows the direct comparison between both methods by plotting those measures. For low noise level, the KLT outperforms the FFT. For high noise level, the KLT is still better but the difference is smaller.

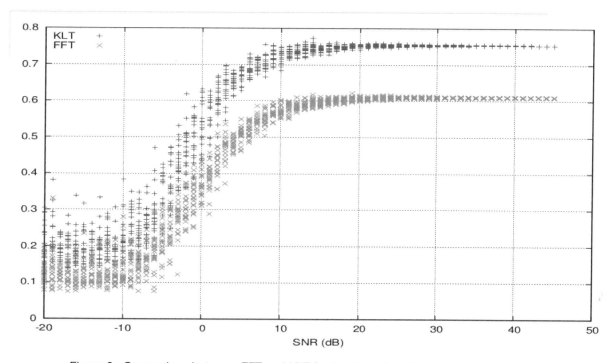

Figure 8 : Comparison between FFT and KLT for the detection of unknown type of signal.

12. How many Eigenvectors

Reference [8] proposes a method to evaluate the minimal number of eigenvectors (F_k) required to reconstruct the original signal. It involves the calculation of an index J_n (equation 17). When $J_n << 1$, then n eigenvectors are sufficient to reconstruct a good estimate of the original data.

(17)
$$J_n = \frac{R(0) - R(T/2N)}{2\,R(0)}$$

where R is the autocorrelation matrix, R(0) is the diagonal value and R(T/2N) is the value at a distance T/2N from the diagonal. This method does not produce a valid result when the data is noisy.

There is another method used to get the number of vectors to be added: a visual inspection of the eigenvalues. Using a plot of L vs. their order, the minimal number of eigenvalues required to rebuild the signal is given where the curve begin to flatten. The values of the first L are generally higher than the rest. Typically, a few L are required to get a good approximation of the original data.

13. Algorithms

Small eigenproblems can be solved using algebra but large one requires numerical approaches since the quantity of calculations is growing very fast. One of the oldest algorithms to solve this type of problem is the Jacobi algorithm. Recalling the equation 12, the process starts with the matrix **A**. The matrix is modified by a succession of operations called Jacobi rotations (equation 18). This process requires access to the whole matrix at each step.

(18)
$$A \rightarrow Q^T A Q$$

The Jacobi algorithm is easy to implement in a computer and it is the most often used. Another popular algorithm is called QR. The process starts by using the following association $A=QR$ where $Q^TQ=I$, Q is orthogonal and R is upper triangular. The eigenproblem associated to A is solved by using a variant of the Householder method. This method also needs the access to matrix A at each step. This algorithm is also relatively easy to implement in a computer code.

A more powerful method of solving the eigenproblem is the Lanczos algorithm [9]. It is not an easy algorithm to implement in a computer code and therefore rarely used. However, it is a very powerful tool.

The Lanczos algorithm can compute only the few first eigenvectors without the others. Jacobi and QR must process all eigenvectors. Since most of the information is stored in the first L, this makes Lanczos faster.

The Lanczos method can be implemented as a parallel algorithm. It does not require the whole matrix A to be stored in memory at each step.

The algorithm can be summarised by a series of operations to construct a matrix T_j which is a tridiagonal matrix. The main diagonal is defined by $a_i = v_i^T A v_i$ where i is the location of the a from 1 to N (rank of the matrix), and v_i are randomly generated unit vectors. The other diagonals (above and below the main) are defined by $b_{i+1} = v_{i+1}^T A v_i$ with $b_1=0$. Another equation is used in the iteration to link a and b, which is $b_{i+1} v_{i+1} = A v_i - a_i v_i - b_i v_{i-1}$.

The matrices T are used to construct the answer of the eigenproblem. A more elaborated explanation of the Lanczos algorithm can be found in [10].

The author has programmed a version of this algorithm and modifies it to increase its performance. The most important change concerned the autocorrelation matrix R which is the core of the eigenproblem, The process of computing the autocorrelation of a vector X(t) is similar to computing the convolution. The discrete correlation theorem says that the discrete correlation of two real functions g and h, is one member of the discrete Fourier Transform pair given by equation 19.

(19)
$$corr(g,h) = \sum_{k=1}^{N-1} g_{j+k} h_k$$

Given a vector X(t) of length M, the autocorrelation matrix requires M^2 values to be stored in a computer memory. Using the convolution method, the storage requirement is now 2M words. This reduction in storage memory makes is possible to handle very large problem on a small computer. The modified version of the algorithm can handle easily a vector of a million items. Storing a autocorrelation matrix of a millions elements vector requires 4×10^{12} bytes (i.e. 3725.3 Gb of RAM). The modified Lanczos program can handle a similar problem using a computer with less than 8 Gb of memory. On a Linux system, the total memory used to process a problem with N=64,000 samples is roughly 42Mb.

14. Performance of the Lanczos Algorithm

Table 1 shows the time (in seconds) to solve the eigenproblem using a vector of N elements. The calculations were performed on a AMD Phenom II X4 955 3.2GHz using 2 cores. Similar calculations were performed on a more recent computer (i.e. Intel i7-3770K) and shows a 2-3 times increase in performance.

Table 1 : Comparison between Jacobi, QR and Lanczos (time is seconds).

N	Jacobi	QR	Lanczos
200	0.129	0.017	0.143
1,000	41.972	7.568	0.282
1,500	190.444	30.938	0.600

Table 2 shows the performance of Lanczos with multiple cores. The calculations were performed on a Intel XEON X5650 2.66GHz. This CPU is a 6 cores CPU with Hyper-thread capabilities (which give a possibility of 12 processes). The linearity of the calculation failed for more than six cores.

N	2 cores	4 cores	6 cores	8 cores
32,000	29.3	15.5	14.5	
64,000	134.4	62.3	42.3	
128,000		157.1	145.0	
256,000		815.8	577.2	473.4
512,000			2497.7	1908.3

15. KLT as Post-Processing of the Focal Point Mission

It was shown that an antenna located at the focal point of the Sun will be able to detect a very low power signal from a distant source. Using the KLT in the analysis of this signal could increase the sensitivity. Figure 9 shows the probability of bit error for a signal received at the focal point using KLT analysis. Any point above a given line P(e)=x indicates that the antenna of radius R will detect a signal of at least Pt W with a P(e) < x.

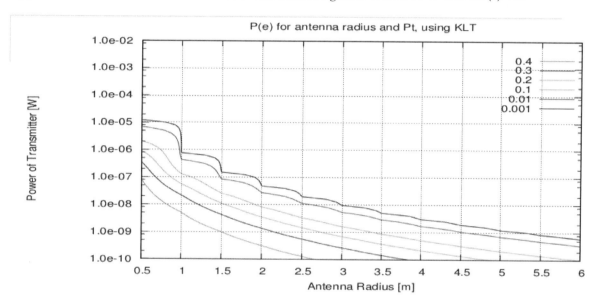

Figure 9 : Probability of bit error for a signal received at the focal point using KLT analysis.

16. Conclusion

It is possible to do Digital Signal Processing with KLT. It is possible to modify the Lanczos algorithm to be fast enough to process vectors of several thousand points in a minute. KLT is still slower than FFT, but provide a better way to find information buried in noise.

The level of sensitivity of any applications dealing with noisy source could be increased.

- Interplanetary RADAR would be able to detect smaller asteroids cruising near Earth, or farther away
- SETI would have a tool to increase its capability of finding ET signal.
- Communication with interplanetary missions would benefice of a better sensibility to communicate with probe
- Commercial communication could use lower power for signal.

Another feature of KLT is its capacity of signal reconstruction, which is better than FFT since it does not assume a shape of the waveform.

References

1. Maccone, C., "Mathematical SETI : Stastistics, Signal Processing, Space Missions", Praxis Publishing, 2012.

2. Cullum, J., Willoughby, R., "Lanczos algorithms for large symmetric eigenvalue computations", SIAM, 2002.

3. Dixon, R., Klein, C., "On the detection of unknown signal", ASP Conference Series. Vol. 47 (1993).

4. Einstein, A., "Lens-Like action of a star by the deviation of light in the gravitationnal field", Science, 84, 506–507 (1936).

5. Fukunaga, K., Koontz, W., "Representation of random process using the finite Karhunen-Loeve Expansion", Information and Control 16, 85–101 (1970).

6. Krauss, J., "Radio Astronomy", McGraw-Hill, 1966.

7. Lanczos, C., "An Iteration Method for the Solution of the Eigenvalue Problem of Linear Differential and Integral Operators", Journal of Research of the National Bureau of Standards, 45, (1950).

8. Liebes, S., "Gravitational lenses", Phys. Rev. 133, B835–B844, (1964)

9. Narayan, R., Bartelmann, M., "Lectures on gravitational lensing", Jerusalem Winter School, (1995).

10. Tomasi, W., "Electronic Communications Systems : fundamentals through advanced", Prentice-Hal, 2001.

Solar System Escape Architecture Revolutionary Science:NIAC 2012-2013 Phase 1 Final Report

Jeffrey Nosanov

Jet Propulsion Laboratory

Brian Trease, Daniel Grebow, Henry Garrett, John West

Synopsis

Our most distance spacecraft, Voyager 1 and Voyager 2, recently reached the boundary of the solar system known as the Heliopause. Beyond this boundary lies interstellar space, and, at tremendous distance, the stars. The Voyager spacecraft have shown us that the Heliopause is a dynamic, rapidly changing environment, varying greatly as the fields and effects emanating from the sun are met by a host of forces pushing in from our nearby galactic neighborhood. This is the region we aim to explore.

Specifically we aim to develop a mission architecture and spacecraft concept capable of reaching the Heliopause (~100 AU) region in multiple directions of interest, with a variety of scientific instrument suites, within a reasonable timeframe (~15 years.) This report details our Phase 1 work including science goal definition, trajectory planning, technology research, mission planning, instrument selection, spacecraft design, and more.

We present an architecture employing a 250m x 250m solar sail with a 175 kg spacecraft. This spacecraft could carry a variety of instrument suites depending on the destination, time, and other factors. The spin-stabilized spacecraft would powered by a small radioisotope power system (~20 watts), makes use of an optical communication system, and carries 3 extensible booms for instrument accommodation as visible in the sketch and rendering below. We conclude that it would be reasonable to implement the architecture described herein in the 2020-2030 timeframe based on likely near-term technological and material advances. We are confident that cruise times of ~15 years could be achieved to science-rich destinations.

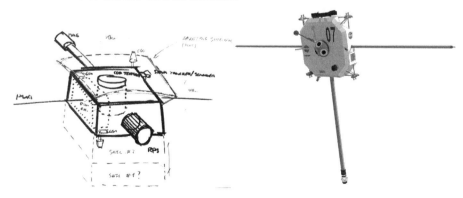

Jeffrey Nosanov, Brian Trease, Daniel Grebow, Henry Garrett, and John West

This report details the approach we used to come to these conclusions and identifies some of the steps along the way. We utilized a variety of methodologies involving our full capability at JPL – from small point studies to large collaborative engineering processes. This paper also describes potential industry partnerships and costing information, and includes the methods used to account for our project's significant deviation from any prior mission in the NASA costing tool database.

Outreach and public engagement is an important part of NASA activities. We engaged in several different forms of this outreach and describe them in this report. We conclude with some open questions and a summary of activities we hope to engage in with Phase 2 funding.

The entire team would like to thank the NIAC program for the opportunity to investigate this fascinating and challenging concept.

Abstract

The Voyager program gives us tantalizing clues as to the nature and behavior of the Heliopause – the boundary between the sun's influence and the interstellar medium. This information comes from forty-year old instruments designed to study the outer planets. A targeted Heliopause investigation would give insight into the formation of the solar system, the role of the sun in the local interstellar neighborhood, and contribute to human exploration planning by helping to predict periods of low galactic cosmic ray (GCR) penetration into the inner solar system.

1. Motivation/Voyager Program Introduction

The Voyager program arose out of a realization in the early 1960s that the mid-1970s would offer a once-in-170-year planetary alignment. This event would allow one spacecraft to fly by multiple outer planets. The primary Voyager Mission was to investigate the Outer Planets, and the Voyager Interstellar Mission (VIM) was confirmed in the late 1980s as it was clear that the spacecraft were functioning well and actually had a chance of reaching the Heliopause boundary intact. As of mid-2013 the VIM is still active and the two Voyager spacecraft continue to return data, and are expected to continue to do so until the mid 2020s when the Plutonium238-based power system no longer produces enough energy to power the communication systems. From that point the Voyager spacecraft will be silent monuments to humanity's technical achievements for roughly one million years until high-speed impacts with interstellar dust grains cumulatively abrade the spacecraft back to the stardust from which they were made.

The SSEARS project concept arose from a conversation with Ed Stone, former JPL director and Voyager project scientist since the inception of the project. At one point Ed Stone was asked how he would continue the Voyager science. His answer was to send multiple spacecraft in multiple directions to study the 3d structure of the boundary. The aim of this project is to develop an architecture that enables this investigation.

2. Heliopause Science

This section will discuss the science goals and rationales for the goal of returning to the Heliopause and traveling beyond. These goals were derived from conversations with Ed Stone (Voyager Project Scientist), the Science Mission Directorate, the Human Exploration and Operations Mission Directorate, the Heliophysics Decadal Survey, and the Planetary Science Decadal Survey.

SSEARS would enable the first comprehensive measurements of plasma, neutrals, dust, magnetic fields, energetic particles, cosmic rays, and infrared emission from the outer solar system, though the boundaries of the Heliosphere, and on into the interstellar medium (ISM). This would allow the mission to address key questions about the distribution of matter in the outer solar system, the processes by which the Sun interacts with the galaxy, and the nature and properties of the nearby galactic medium.

The principal scientific objectives of such a mission would be to:
- Explore the nature of the interstellar medium and its implications for the origin and evolution of matter in our Galaxy and the Universe;
- Explore the influence of the interstellar medium on the solar system, its dynamics, and its evolution;
- Explore the impact of the solar system on the interstellar medium as an example of the interaction of a stellar system with its environment;
- Explore the outer solar system in search of clues to its origin, and to the nature of other planetary systems.
- Significantly reduce human radiation risk for future crewed missions by understanding mechanisms leading to variability of dangerous levels of radiation in the inner solar system

We describe below examples of the scientific issues that could be addressed.

2.0.1 The Nearby Interstellar Medium

Our Sun is thought to be located near the edge of a low-density interstellar cloud (~0.3 cm^3), often referred to as the local interstellar cloud (LIC), that is made up of material blowing from the direction of star-forming regions in Scorpius and Centaurus. Present knowledge of the ISM is based on astronomical observations that average over long lines of sight, measurements of sunlight resonantly scattered back by interstellar H and He, data returned from the Voyager and iBEX spacecraft, and in situ measurements of neutral gas and dust that penetrate the Heliosphere. Direct observations of our local cloud by SSEARS would provide a unique opportunity to derive the physical properties of a sample of interstellar material, free from uncertainties that plague the interpretation of data acquired over astronomical lines-of-sight, and from uncertainties arising from the exclusion of plasma, small dust particles and low energy cosmic rays from the Heliosphere. Direct measurements would be made of the elemental and isotopic composition of the ionized and neutral components of the interstellar gas and of low-energy particle components, and of the composition and size distribution of interstellar dust. These measurements would provide a benchmark for comparison with solar system abundances (representative of the pre-solar nebula) and with abundances from more distant galactic regions, thereby providing important constraints on theories of galactic chemical evolution.

SSEARS would also measure cosmic ray nuclei and electrons, free from the influence of the Heliosphere, and investigate astrophysical processes that include acceleration by supernova shock waves, interstellar radio and x-ray emission, recent nucleosynthesis, and the heating and dynamics of the interstellar medium. Little is known about the properties of magnetic field in the local cloud or in the region beyond the termination shock. SSEARS would enable the first in situ measurements of interstellar magnetic fields and of the density, temperature, and ionization state of the interstellar gas, including studies of their variations over a variety of spatial scales. The possibility of identifying organic matter in the outer solar system and ISM is also an exciting possibility that is under investigation.

2.0.2 The Interaction between the Interstellar Medium and the Solar Wind

The solar wind and the interstellar medium interact to create the global Heliosphere, shown schematically in Figure 1. The size of the Heliosphere is determined by the balance between the solar wind ram pressure and the interstellar pressure. There are presently no direct measurements of the size and structure of the Heliosphere and our present understanding is based on theory and modeling, constrained by a few key measurements. The Voyager spacecraft have detected radio emissions that are thought to be caused by interplanetary shock waves hitting the denser interstellar plasma. Voyager 1 should soon reach the termination shock, providing a first direct test of our current understanding of Heliospheric structure, although some of the Voyager instruments were not designed to explore the boundaries of the Heliosphere and interstellar medium. SSEARS' enhanced capabilities and lifetime would greatly extend Voyager's exploratory studies, answering questions relating to how the ISM influences the solar system and how the solar system influences the ISM.

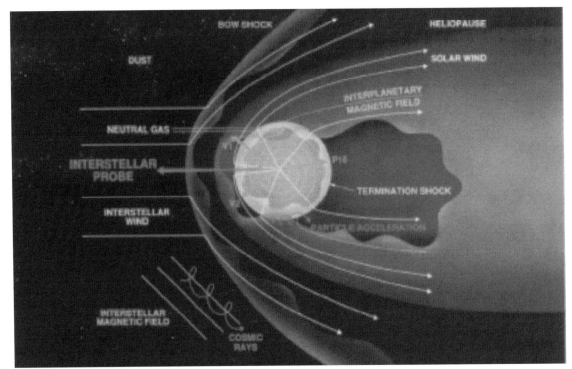

Figure 1: Schematic of the Heliosphere created by the supersonic solar wind diverting the interstellar flow around the Sun. The interstellar ions and neutrals flow at 25 km/s relative to the Sun. The solar wind, flowing outward at 400-800 km/s, makes a transition to subsonic flow at the termination shock. Beyond this, the solar wind is turned toward the Heliotail, carrying with it the spiraling interplanetary magnetic field. The Heliopause separates solar material and magnetic fields from interstellar material and fields. There may or may not be a bow shock in the interstellar medium in front of the Heliosphere.

The termination shock is a powerful accelerator that accelerates particles to energies as high as 1 GeV. In situ studies of shock structure, plasma heating, and acceleration processes at the termination shock will serve as a model for other astrophysical shocks. Past the termination shock, in the region called the Heliosheath, the solar wind flow is turned to match the flow of the diverted interstellar plasma, as illustrated Fig. 1. The spiraling solar magnetic field, frozen into the solar wind, is swept back with this flow. Depending on the unknown interstellar magnetic field strength, there may or may not be a bow shock created in the interstellar medium ahead of the nose of the Heliosphere. Energetic ions created by charge exchange in the Heliosheath can be used to provide an image of the 3D structure of the Heliosphere. Charge-exchange collisions lead to a weak coupling between the neutral and ionized hydrogen in the interstellar medium causing a pile-up of neutral hydrogen at the Heliosphere nose, referred to as the "hydrogen wall." The SSEARS spacecraft would pass through these boundary regions and make in situ measurements of the dust, plasma, fields and flows to answer questions regarding the size, structure and dynamics of the Heliosphere and the processes occurring at the boundaries. Our Heliosphere would serve as an example of how a star interacts with its environment. 1

2.1 Solar System Orientation

The plane of the Solar System is inclined at roughly 60 degrees to the plane of the galaxy, as seen in Figure 2. This helps us identify regions of interest because we can investigate the Heliopause along the solar system plane to avoid interactions with the galactic plane, and specifically study those interactions by sending the spacecraft along the galactic plane.

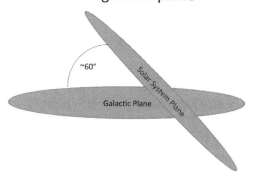

Figure 2: The plane of the solar system and the plane of the galaxy are 60 degrees apart.

2.2 Heliopause/Interstellar Medium Regions of Interest

We began our thinking with the idea of sending spacecraft in the six cardinal directions from the Earth- up, down, left, right, in, and out relative to the sun and the galactic plane. The inclination of the solar system plane to the galactic plane increases the complexity of the ideal investigation by doubling the number of regions of interest. Figure 3 shows the directions of travel along the solar system ecliptic, and Figure 4 shows the directions of travel along the galactic ecliptic.

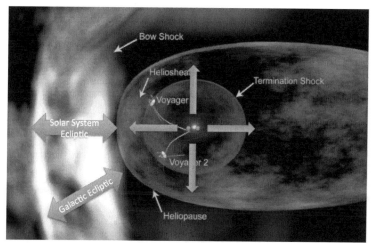

Figure 3: Directions of travel/investigation along the Solar System Ecliptic

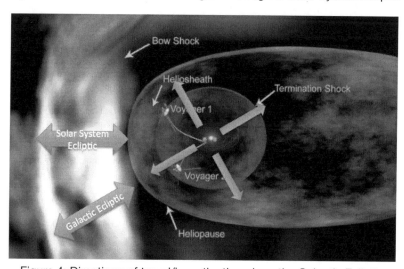

Figure 4: Directions of travel/investigation along the Galactic Ecliptic

Later in the project, after additional analysis, we revised our destinations to better account for the complexity of the sun's magnetic field. The sun's electric currents generate a complex magnetic field that extends far into space with the solar wind. The sun rotates as it emits the solar wind so the magnetic field is "wound" into a spiral known as the Parker Spiral.

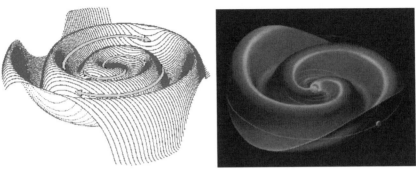

Figure 5: Two visualizations2 of the sun's magnetic field. The spiral structure of the sun's magnetic field as the solar wind carries it past the planets.

This magnetic field is primarily directed outward from the sun in one hemisphere, and inward towards the sun in another. The line between the two field directions is not exactly aligned on the solar equator, so the field becomes "wavy" as seen in Figure 5. As a result of this effect, radiation entering the solar system from the interstellar medium changes significantly with the solar cycle as the sign of the solar magnetic field switches. So, the north and south "hemispheres" of the Heliosphere should be investigated at different times corresponding to the amount of interstellar radiation present. This would necessitate at least two "waves" of spacecraft, one wave planned to reach the Heliopause in one hemisphere at the solar maximum, and another wave planned to reach the Heliopause in the other hemisphere at the solar minimum.

The SSEARS mission proposes to send multiple spacecraft out to the boundary of the Heliosphere to follow up on the Voyagers' recent discoveries and better define the interactions of the Heliosphere and the galactic media. The Voyagers were not targeted for specific locations to measure these interactions and so represent randomly placed snapshots of the Heliosphere—SSEARS would carry out a targeted analysis of the structure of the Heliosphere.

2.3 Specific Helipause Destinations

Specific targets for the SSEARS would be: the Heliosphere's nose (i.e., the point where the interaction is a head on collision due to the combined motion of the solar system and the galactic media), the anti-nose direction, and points perpendicular to the line connecting the nose and anti-nose (both "east and west" and "north and south" to determine the shape of the Heliosphere. Other potential targets are the anti-galactic center so that the center of the galaxy could be imaged using gravitational lensing or the source of neutral particles detected by iBEX (see Figure 6 below). We would also send spacecraft out at various times to measure these interactions during solar minimum and maximum for 2 solar cycles or a complete 22 year Hale solar magnetic cycle 3,4.

An unusual band of high energy neutral particles was detected by the iBEX and Cassini missions. A graphic for the iBEX data is shown in Figure 6—the band is apparently associated with a magnetic merging region where charge exchange between energetic charged particles from the interstellar medium are interacting with slow solar wind neutral particles. The nose is where the large arrow meets the Heliosphere.

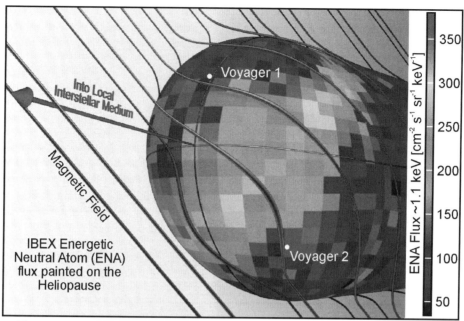

Figure 6: Graphic presentation of the location of the Heliosphere's Nose and the iBEX source of high energy neutral particles. (IBEX Mission, NASA)

Specific destinations along the Heliopause are displayed in two ways. First, a table is presented of approximate coordinates and the associated views from the surface of the earth. Constellations as visible from the surface of the Earth are rendered to aid recognition. The precise location along the Heliopause is at the center of each image. The table lists the destinations in Waves 1 and 2, temporally separated to allow investigation of the Heliopause at different times in the solar cycle. Second, a series of all sky-plots are included in a variety of coordinate systems.

Destination Region Table

Name	Ra	Dec	Nearby Sky
Wave 1			Reach destination regions at solar minimum
Apex	30	270	

Anti apex	-30	90	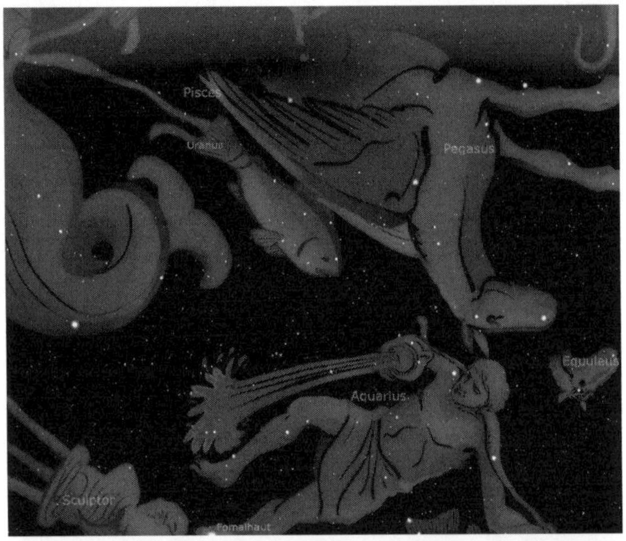
Nose	5	260	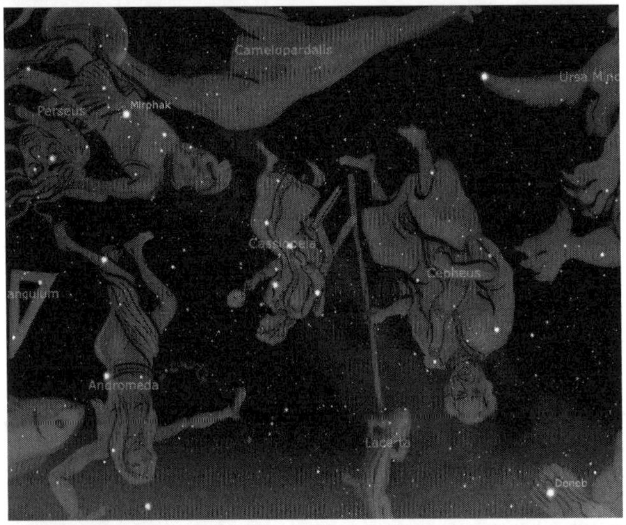
Anti nose	-5	80	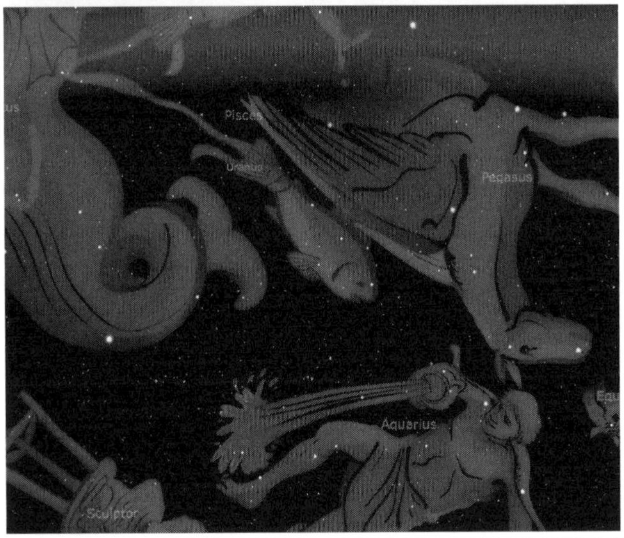

90° from apex	-40	240	
90° from nose	90	270	
Wave 2			(Same destinations as Wave 1, but 11 years later) to study at different times in the solar cycle

2.4 Coordinate Systems

All coordinates presented here are referred to the J2000 epoch. The starting coordinate system is the standard Right Ascension (RA) and Declination (Dec) Earth-based Equatorial system used in most star maps. Right Ascension is a coordinate based on a sidereal day, the time it takes the Earth to make a 360 degree rotation inertially. It is classically broken up into 0 - 24 hours as in a solar day but the sidereal day is 1/365.25 (approximately 4 minutes) shorter than a solar day. The scale is 24 hours to 0 hours as you move from left to right on the map, as time marches on, stars that reach your north-south meridian are assigned a RA corresponding to the sidereal time. The stars are fixed in this coordinate system but the sun moves approximately 1 degree (2 apparent solar diameters) eastward each day in this coordinate system (right to left). These coordinates are dependent on an epoch such as J2000 because they are tied to the Earth and change as the Earth's axis precesses. Dec goes from 0 on the projection of the Earth equator to +/-90° at the poles.

Figure 7 is a segment of a star map showing the RA scale on the bottom. The blue line across the middle is the terrestrial equator, Dec = 0, so the star Regulus has positive Dec while the star Alphard has negative Dec. The diagonal line that passes through Regulus is the ecliptic, the path the sun moves along during the year.

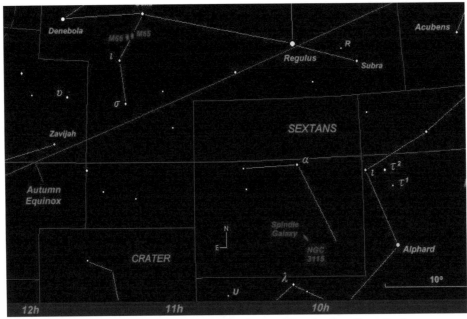

Figure 7: Star Chart in Right Ascension and Declination Coordinates

In our charts, the RA scale is changed to degrees (alpha) to correspond to other coordinate systems longitudes, i.e., RA corresponds to longitude and Dec corresponds to latitude (delta).

The maps are presented in a cylindrical projection, an x-y grid where longitude is x and latitude is y. In these projections, areas near the poles become distorted "beyond recognition". A projection that maps a sphere onto an elliptical area brings the polar areas more into what would be visualized in the real sky.

Figures 8-11 show the above maps with the points of interest for the project marked and a limited number of stars for orientation (dark blue). The Equator is in cyan. Also in cyan are the positions of spacecraft that will leave the solar system, Pioneer 10 and 11, Voyager 1 and 2, and New Horizons (P10, P11, V1, V2, and NH). The Galactic North pole (GNP), Galactic South pole (GSP), Galactic center (GC), anti-Galactic center (AGC) and Galactic Equator are in red. The solar apex, the point in the sky that the sun is moving towards with respect to local stars, the anti-solar apex and apex equator are in black. The ecliptic is in grey. The Nose, Anti-Nose and Nose Equator are in green. The magenta dots are a rough reproduction of the iBEX ribbon. Plots are made with Caltech's FORTRAN plotting package, pgplot.

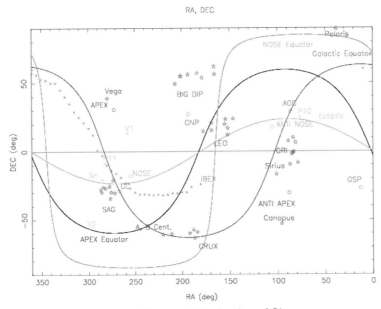

Figure 8: Equatorial Projection of Sky

The next coordinate system is Ecliptic coordinates, based on the ecliptic above. The coordinates are called Lambda and Beta corresponding to longitude and latitude. The 0 degree (beta) latitude is the ecliptic so the sun stays at 0 degrees latitude as it moves across the chart. The ecliptic North pole is at right ascension 18h 0m 0.0s (exact), and declination +66° 33′ 38.55″ Figure 9 shows the Ecliptic projection.

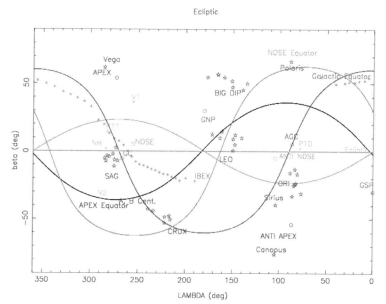

Figure 9: Ecliptic Projection of Sky

The next system is the Galactic coordinate system that is based on the Milky Way (our galaxy's center and poles). These coordinates are called l and b for longitude and latitude. The b=0 line is along the centerline of the Milky Way. The Galactic pole is at RA = 12h 51m.4, Dec = +27°.13 and the galactic center is at RA = 17h 45m.6, Dec = -28°.94. The galactic projection is shown in figure 10

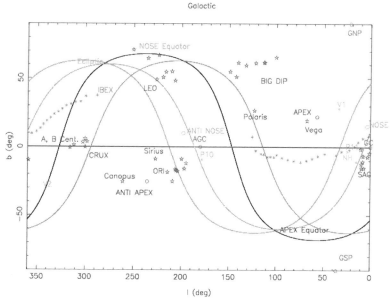

Figure 10: Galactic Projection of Sky

A particular mapping that preserves areas (equal area projection) is a Hammer map. It does not result in excessive crowding around the poles as severely as some other maps but does have a disadvantage that lines of constant latitude are not straight. There is another map (Mollwiede) that conserves areas and produces parallel lines of latitude but it is not solvable in closed form (requires iteration) and produces excessive crowding at the poles. The transformation of any of the above maps into a Hammer map is:

$$x = \frac{2\sqrt{2} \cos b \, \sin \frac{a}{2}}{\sqrt{1 + \cos b \, \cos \frac{a}{2}}}$$

and

$$y = \frac{\sqrt{2} \sin b}{\sqrt{1 + \cos b \cos \frac{a}{2}}}$$

where 1 is the longitude coordinate, b is the latitude coordinate and a is the difference between the longitude of a point and the center longitude for the map (180 degrees used). The calculated x and y coordinates reside within an ellipse in the resulting map.

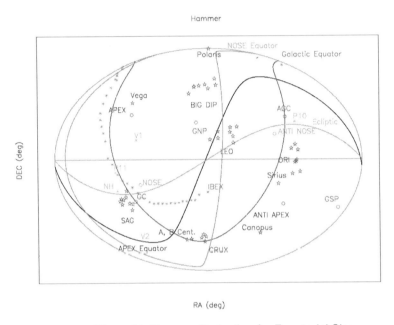

Figure 11: Hammer Projection for Equatorial Sky

Conclusions

Programs to convert between different coordinate systems were developed for the SSEARS mission concept study. This was done to provide coordinates in a variety of systems to improve communication with scientists comfortable with each of the three systems. The table below list points of interest in the various coordinate systems.

Points of Interest in 3 Coordinate Systems, J2000.

Point	Equatorial		Ecliptic		Galactic	
	RA	Dec	lambda	beta	l	b
Galactic North Pole	192.85951	27.1283	180.023	29.8115	122.932	90
Calactic Center	266.4051	-28.9362	266.84	-5.53631	0.00011	-0.0001
Galactic South Pole	12.859508	-27.1283	0.0232	-29.8115	302.798	-90
Anti Calactic Center	86.4051	28.9362	86.8396	5.53631	180	0.0001
Apex (visible)	272	30.5	272.927	53.919	56.9845	22.0802
Anti Apex	92	-30.5	92.9268	-53.919	236.985	-22.0802
Nose	254.73074	-17.5687	255.4	5.1	3.53975	15.2112
Anti Nose	74.730744	17.5687	75.4	-5.1	183.54	-15.2112

3. SSEARS Science Capabilities

The SSEARS architecture is capable of enabling science investigation to the benefit of several major NASA stakeholders. For the Science Mission Directorate (SMD) SSEARS would enable the study of

1. the Interstellar Medium (IM) and its implications for the origin and evolution of matter
2. the influence of the IM on the Heliosphere
3. the influence of the Heliosphere on the IM
4. the dynamics of the coupling of the Heliosphere and the solar system as a model for other planetary systems

For the Human Exploration/Operations Mission Directorate (HEOMD), SSEARS could assist and possibly enable human interplanetary travel by enabling the prediction of periods of low GCR penetration into the inner solar system.

For the Heliophysics directorate, the SSEARS architecture would enable direct, in-situ investigation of two of the four goals of the 2012 Heliophysics Decadal Durvey:

Determine the interaction of the sun with the solar system and the interstellar medium

Discover and characterize fundamental processes that occur both within the Heliophere and throughout the universe.

4. Phase 1 Goals

Our phase 1 NIAC proposal included the following goals for the phase 1 study period:

1. Identify science destination "directions/regions"
2. Develop trajectory modeling tool
3. Determine current material performance limitations
4. Project material trends to ~2030
5. Identify/design concept spacecraft for scaling estimates/modeling
6. Determine mission parameters for 2030 mission assuming current development trends
7. Propose for follow-up funds for further development

We have successfully completed our stated Phase 1 goals on schedule.

5. Propulsion Methods

This section will describe the decisions made that led to the selection of the solar sail as a method of reaching the Heliopause.

Among our first thoughts when planning this project was a recognition of the need to reach the Heliopause much faster than the Voyager spacecraft did. Their 34 year journey was interpreted programmatically by NASA as the Voyager Primary mission (~1977- ~1989) and the Voyager Interstellar Mission (~1989-present). A single 35 year mission to return to the Heliopause strains the imagination as NASA has never in its history approved or directed a mission that, from its inception, was intended to spend over three decades en route. (Some science could be performed during cruise but the primary goals require proximity to the Heliopause.) Thus, we began our study with a review of available in-space propulsion methods.

5.1 Solar Electric vs Solar Sail

In-space propulsion has been extensively studied by various players throughout the space age. Specifically a study at JPL was done in the early 2000s and identified the best available in-space propulsion options at various distances and destinations from the sun. This study shows that solar sail propulsion is clearly superior to solar-electric propulsion for distances of many tens of AU from the sun or greater.

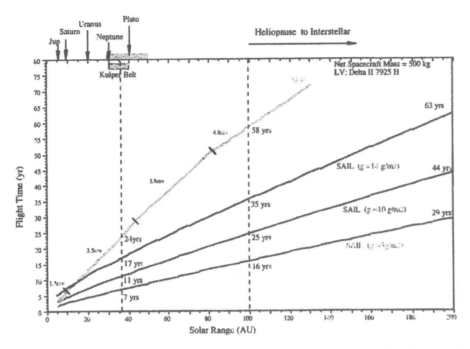

Figure 12: Solar sails are significantly more effective than solar-electric propulsion when applied to solar system escape trajectories. This is largely due to the ability of the solar sail to come close to the sun without using fuel. Here three different sail densities are compared to SEP. (Image courtesy of Chen-Wan Yen)

5.2 Nuclear Electric Propulsion

Nuclear Electric Propulsion (NEP) is not a practical solution to achieve solar system escape for most missions because it does not take advantage of the significant increase in power achieved by going close to the sun. As such, most NEP trajectories to the outer planets are relatively slow while requiring massive power systems.

We concluded early on that a solar sail was the best option for this study at this time. This coincides well with current NASA investments in solar technology demonstrations in the 2014-2015 timeframe. We hope to convey that there are further benefits of that investment.

6. Solar Sail Introduction

A solar sail is a thin film sheet, usually with a very large area, that allows the use of light pressure to exert thrust on a spacecraft. Figure 13 shows the basic components of a solar sail vehicle.

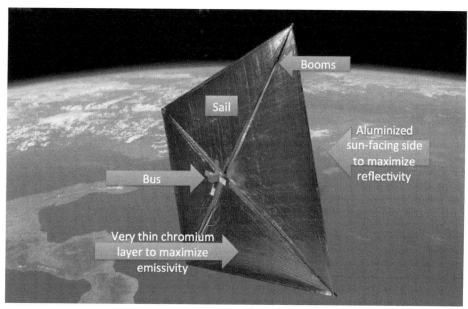

Figure 13: Labeling the top-level relevant parts of a solar sail system.

Key to the operation of a solar sail is to minimize areal density, minimize structural mass, and maximize area. The sun-facing side of the sail must be coated to maximize reflectivity and the opposite side must be coated to maximize emissivity. Usually the sail structural members "booms" extend radially outward from a central bus.

6.1 Trajectory Modeling

The key to using solar sails to escape the solar system is to reach the optimal distance from the sun. The amount of energy received from the sun decreases as 1/r2 and so thrust from the sail increases significantly as the sail approaches the sun. The trajectories involved are hyperbolic escape trajectories from the solar system. In order to achieve these trajectories there are several key design objectives:

1. Maximize sail area
2. Minimize spacecraft mass
3. Minimize perihelion (solar closest approach) distance
4. Maximize speed at perihelion

The following trajectories were developed using an instantaneously optimal steering law (for post solar-close approach). Assuming the Sun's gravity acts as a point-mass force on a sail, where the sail is modeled as a perfectly reflective flat plate, the equations of motion for the sailcraft are

$$\ddot{\vec{r}} = \frac{\mu}{r^2}(\beta\bar{a} - \hat{r}).$$
(1)

In Eq. (1), m is the gravitational parameter of the Sun, r is the distance from the Sun, b (dimensionless) is the sail loading parameter, and $\hat{r}$ is a unit-vector directed from the Sun to the sailcraft. The sail acceleration is defined as

$$\bar{a} = (\hat{r}\cdot\hat{n})^2\hat{n},$$
(2)

where $\hat{n}$ is a unit-vector normal to the surface of the sail. Note that the sail loading parameter b, also called the sail 'lightness number', is the ratio of solar-radiation pressure (SRP) to solar gravity, i.e.,

$$\beta = \frac{2AW_ER_E^2}{c\mu M}.$$
(3)

In the above equation, A is the total area of the sail, c is the speed of light, R_E is one astronomical unit (AU),

and W_E is the solar flux at one AU. The total spacecraft mass M is the payload mass m_p plus the mass of the sail, or $M = m_p + r A$, where r is the density of the sail. It is sometimes convenient to describe the performance of the sail in terms of characteristic acceleration k, or the acceleration provided by the sail at one AU. The characteristic acceleration is then written

$$\kappa = \beta \frac{\mu}{R_E^2},$$

(4)

where κ typically varies from 0.01 mm/s^2 (doable today) to 1.5 mm/s^2 (aggressive).

For fast departure from the solar system, the goal is to maximize the component of sail thrust along the spacecraft's Heliocentric velocity vector $\hat{v}$. This optimization problem is posed succinctly as

$$\max J = \bar{a} \cdot \hat{v},$$

$$\text{subject to } \hat{n} \cdot \hat{r} > 0.$$

(5)

The condition $\hat{n} \cdot \hat{r} > 0$ is present to ensure that the sail acceleration defined in Eq. (2) is always directed away from the Sun. To solve the optimization problem, we begin by defining a transverse vector $\hat{\theta}$ such that $\hat{\theta}$ is in the plane of motion and normal to $\hat{r}$ such that $\hat{\theta} \cdot \hat{v} > 0$. Then $\hat{n}$ can be resolved into radial and transverse components according to

$$\hat{n} = n_r \hat{r} + n_\theta \hat{\theta}.$$

(6)

Making use of $\hat{n} \cdot \hat{r} > 0$ in Eq. (5), we can write Eq. (6) only in terms of n_θ

$$\hat{n} = +\sqrt{1 - n_\theta^2}\, \hat{r} + n_\theta \hat{\theta}.$$

(7)

Now substituting Eq. (7) into Eq. (2), we arrive at the following expression for thrust acceleration

$$\bar{a} = (1 - n_\theta^2)\left[\sqrt{1 - n_\theta^2}\, \hat{r} + n_\theta \hat{\theta}\right]$$

(8)

Note that with Eq. (8), the performance index J in Eq. (5) is

$$J = \bar{a} \cdot \hat{v} = (1 - n_\theta^2)\left[\sqrt{1 - n_\theta^2}\, (\hat{v} \cdot \hat{r}) + n_\theta (\hat{v} \cdot \hat{\theta})\right]$$

(9)

Finally, from the expression provided in Eq. (9), it is easy to show that J is a maximum when

$$n_\theta = \sqrt{\frac{3k^2 - k\sqrt{9k^2 + 8} + 2}{6k^2 + 6}}, \quad \text{where } k = \frac{\hat{v} \cdot \hat{r}}{\hat{v} \cdot \hat{\theta}}.$$

(10)

This locally optimal steering law describes the best direction for orienting the sail normal for fastest departure from the solar system. Following the final perihelion passage, all trajectories are computed by simulating the spacecraft motion with Eq. (1) using the steering law provided in Eq. (10).

6.2 Basic Trajectories – Upper Stage for Earth Escape

We assumed an aggressive sail characteristic acceleration of 1.34 mm/s^2 (assumed because it matched with previous JPL work) and initially analyzed trajectories for four cases. In each figure the blue line represents the trajectory before solar close approach. The red vectors along the blue line show the sail normal angle to the direction of motion, and the green line shows the trajectory after solar close approach with the sail guided by the control law derived in the previous section.

1. using an upper stage rocket to escape earth orbit and escape along the ecliptic (Figure 14)
2. using an upper stage rocket to escape earth orbit and escape off the ecliptic using a Jupiter gravity assist to raise inclination (Figure 15)
3. using the sail to escape earth orbit and escape along the ecliptic (Figure 16)
4. using sail to escape earth orbit and escape off the ecliptic using a Jupiter gravity assist to raise inclination (Figure 17)

Using Upper stage to exit earth Orbit

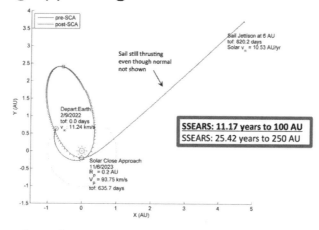

Figure 14: This trajectory shows the spacecraft leaving earth, looping once around the sun to raise aphelion and lower perihelion, and then swinging by the sun again before proceeding radially away from the sun. This method reaches the vicinity of the Heliopause along the ecliptic in 11.1 years.

Using sail to exit earth Orbit

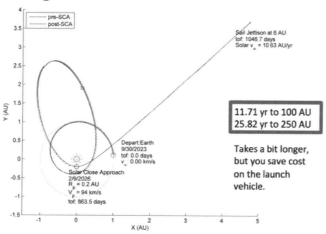

Figure 15: This trajectory uses the sail itself to exit earth orbit and takes slightly longer - ~6 months – to reach the same distance along the ecliptic as that in Figure 14.

Using Upper stage to exit earth Orbit, then Jupiter fly-by before perihelion

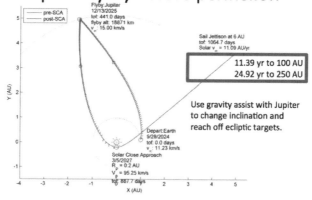

Figure 16: The same distances can be reached at off-ecliptic inclinations by using a Jupiter gravity assist before perihelion. The transit time remains similar to the other trajectories. (3d nature of inclination change not displayed.)

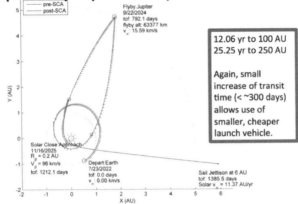

Figure 17: The same technique as in Figure 15 applies to the off-ecliptic destinations, at a modest increase in transit time of ~ 1 year. (3d nature of inclination change is not displayed.)

7. Sunjammer

This section will discuss our heritage with the current NASA Technology Demonstration Mission "Sunjammer." Our proposed flight system is based on the Sunjammer spacecraft, due to launch in 2014. We studied the Sunjammer capabilities and decided to use it as a real-world foundation for the spacecraft design necessary to reach the Heliopause.

7.1 Programmatic Background

Sunjammer is a technology demonstration project scheduled for launch in 2014. It is a sun observing mission with a 34 m x 34 m solar sail propulsion system. The sail is supported by 4 booms extending from the bus and ending in actuated vanes that enable steering of the sail.

Figure 18: An image of the 34m x 34m Sunjammer sail.

Led by industry manufacturer L'Garde Inc. of Tustin, Calif., and including participation by the National Oceanic and Atmospheric Administration (NOAA), the Solar Sail Demonstration mission builds on two successful ground-deployment experiments conducted by L'Garde in 2005-2006 in a vacuum chamber at the Plum Brook Facility in Sandusky, Ohio, a research laboratory managed by NASA's Glenn Research Center in Cleveland. It also leverages the successful deployment of the NanoSail-D sail, a 100-square-foot test article NASA launched to Earth orbit in early 2011 to validate sail deployment techniques [1].

7.2 Mission Summary

The Sunjammer spacecraft was designed to perform a solar weather monitoring mission while "parked" at Sun-Earth L1. The sail will be used for station keeping as the instruments monitor solar activity. Sunjammer should give NOAA and NASA an early warning for certain solar phenomena that might necessitate the proactive safing (switching spacecraft electrical systems into a "safe mode" to prevent interactions with solar phenomena) of certain assets in Earth orbit.

7.3 Scaling Sunjammer

We decided to investigate the capabilities of a Sunjammer-like sail that was 250m x 250m. This is roughly the scaling limit of the Sunjammer sail manufacture, deployment, and control methods.

7.4 Sail Material Choices

7.4.1 Present Sail Materials

The Sunjammer spacecraft will use 5 micron thick Kapton film as a sail material. We performed an investigation into the materials available and determined that 5 micron Kapton and 0.9 micron Mylar are the two leading materials for this application. Mylar however does not survive radiation environments well and further study is required to determine whether this fully precludes the use of Mylar as a solar sail material.

7.4.2 Future Sail Materials

We contacted several manufacturers of Kapton (DuPont, 3M) and were told that 2 micron thick Kapton film is within manufacturing capability. We will see in a later section how this change affects Heliopause cruise times. The 0.5 micron thick Kapton film is theoretically possible but has not been significantly investigated because even 2 micron Kapton has yet to find a commercial application significant enough to justify the necessary modification to manufacturing facilities.

In parallel to the evaluation of DuPont's Kapton® films for the proposed application, we have identified other candidate materials to be studied in phase 2. This study will include CP-1, a potential successor to CP-1 known as CORIN™ XLS, and Thermalbright®2. CP-1 is a space-durable material developed at NASA Langley (LaRC) and exhibits a high resistance to UV radiation. It has currently been fabricated in large sheets and rolls to as thin as 1.5 micron. CP-1 has flown on Hughes HS-702 geosynchronous communications satellite. CORIN™ XLS is a potential next-generation CP-1. Thermalbright® polyimide is a high temperature highly reflective white polyimide film which is expected to be particularly beneficial for thermal control while maintaining good UV and VUV durability.

8. SSEARS Trajectories

With our sail materials in mind, and an assumed spacecraft mass of 110kg, we modeled the transit time for sails with the different materials to 100AU. We also moved to a more realistic characteristic acceleration of 0.5 mm/s^2. We chose two sail sizes to compare, the 250m x 250m size that is the limit of current techniques, and a hypothetical 500m x 500m sail. Material choices are represented by the line color. We also estimated a scaling factor for the boom masses. We assumed two methods of boom mass scaling – linear (here called aggressive) and geometric (here called conservative). This factor is represented by the line style. Solid lines represent a conservative boom mass scaling factor, and dashed lines represent an aggressive boom mass scaling factor. The curve plots in figures 19 and 20 represent these results. Finally, vertical black lines represent the distance to the sun below which the listed material begins to degrade.

The below charts were derived from the initial spacecraft mass assumption of 110kg. When we completed our detailed spacecraft configuration, we concluded that a more realistic spacecraft mass is 175kg. The transit times were relatively insensitive to this change in spacecraft mass.

8.1 SSEARS Model Payload Trajectories with 250x250m Sail

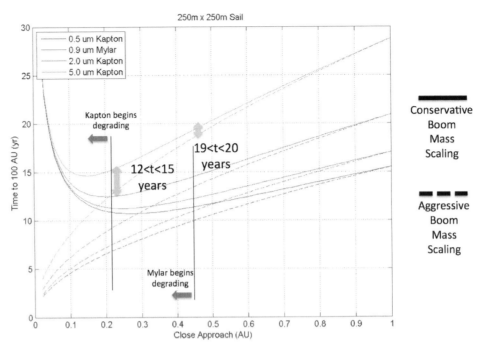

Figure 19: We can see that 5 micron kapton, the material used by Sunjammer, provides the slowest velocity to the Heliopause. It cannot get closer than ~0.22 AU from the sun and so the theoretical cruise time to 100AU is between 12 and 15 years depending on the boom scaling factor. The 0.9 micron thick mylar, which cannot get closer than 0.45 AU from the sun and is a difficult material to use from a radiation tolerance perspective, delivers the same spacecraft to the Heliopause in between 10 and 11 years.

8.2 SSEARS Model Payload Trajectories with 500x500m Sail

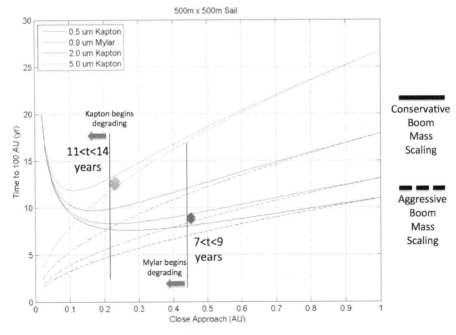

Figure 20: With an even larger sail size we can see the trip times reduced by about a year, each. This result was very insightful because it shows that the additional complexity and cost of a 500m x 500m sail is probably not justified as little is gained by increasing the size of the sail beyond 250m x 250m.

8.3 Optimal Sail Size

Our investigation into the sail material showed us that a significant increase in sail size beyond 250m x 250m does not provide significant velocity improvement. Our flight system design study, then, assumes a 250m x 250m sail size.

8.4 Sail Jettison

The sail would not receive much energy from the sun by the time it crosses Jupiter's orbit. At that time the sail would be turned and then jettisoned (in order to prevent the sail's trajectory from blocking communication from the spacecraft.) The spacecraft would continue alone. A series of renderings follow that demonstrate this process.

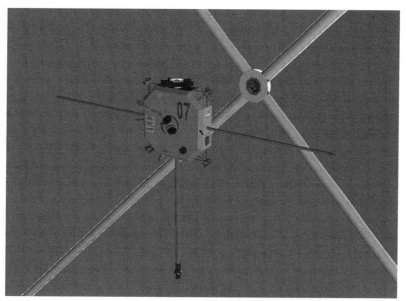

Figure 21: The spacecraft separates from the sail and continues.

Figure 22: Side view of the spacecraft following separation.

9. Spacecraft / Flight System

This section describes the spacecraft architecture that we designed to meet the requirements described up to this point in this report. We being with a discussion of the design approach and show several configuration graphics to demonstrate the stages of the mission.

9.1 Spacecraft Design

The guiding principle of the spacecraft design process was to leverage existing technology as much as possible. This involved scaling up the nominal Sunjammer design concept and using high heritage instruments. The sail would be folded and packed into a modular container. The spacecraft concept itself is visible on the foreground-facing side of the sailcraft container.

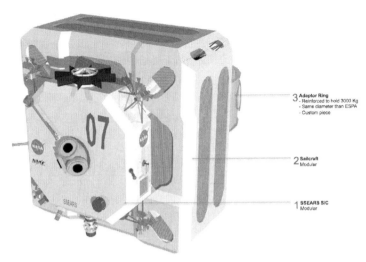

Figure 23: Here the two main components of the module can be seen: the module itself and the sail craft. In the stowed mode 3 complete spacecraft can be stored inside the fairing of an Atlas V launch vehicle (5m in diameter).

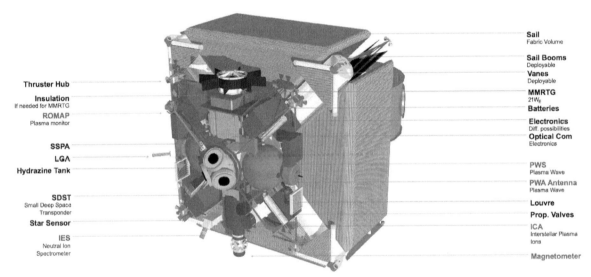

Figure 24: Here the main selection of instruments can be seen as well as the internal structure and configuration. Some of the green volumes represent extra electronic boxes to either support current instruments or to be substituted by extra payload using a better packing ratio.

The sail container deploys in this fashion:

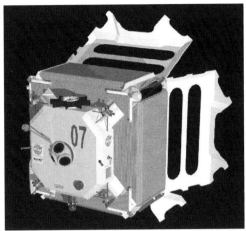

Figure 25: Once SSEARS is detached from the launcher the sail protection covers open and the vanes are deployed. After that the sail is deployed. The next step is to deploy the booms for antennas and instruments.

This component then jettisons after sail deployment leaving the spacecraft and sail separated.

The three major systems are visualized side-by-side for scale comparison below. The left side of the image shows a side view of the spacecraft, sail structure, and mounting hardware (left-to-right) and the right side of the image shows the spacecraft with the booms deployed.

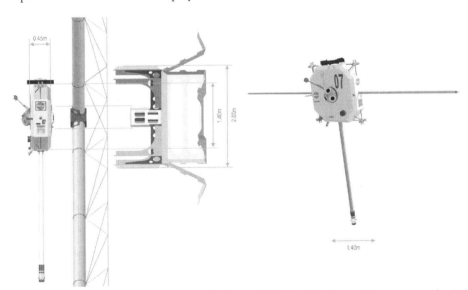

Figure 26: The three spacecraft elements are displayed side by side to provide a sense of relative scale. Launch vehicle compatibility with Atlas 5 501 was shown for 3 units per Atlas 5.

9.2 Communication

We determined early in our study that a large dish antenna communication system would be so massive (as necessary to function from 100AU) that it would severely constrain the design of the rest of the spacecraft. We determined that optical communication can meet our needs.

9.2.1 Downlink

Laser beams at optical frequencies can be transmitted with angular beam-widths of a few microradians (mrads). Coupled with the ability to accurately point narrow laser beams to a fraction of the beam-width, signal power densities required for communication can be delivered over huge distances. To illustrate this further a point design is presented below.

A 20 watt average power 1550 nm laser beam transmitted through a 50 cm diameter telescope will result in an angular beam-width of approximately 3.6 mrad. Pointing jitter control of ~ 0.3 mrad will result in losses relative to the on-axis peak of ~ 1.5 dB. If such a beam with the indicated pointing control were transmitted over a distance of 100 AU with a 12 m diameter collector at the receiving end a 500+/-100 bits/second communication link could be established. This accounts for reasonable transmitter and receiver optical transmission and implementation losses and 3-dB of link margin. Such a link is enabled by the availability of high peak-to-average power ratio (160:1 to 320:1) lasers that permit the use of near-capacity achieving serially concatenated pulse-position modulation (SCPPM) error-correcting coding together with a single-photon-counting sensitivity receiver.

9.2.2 Phase II Plans

A high level summary of the studies for maturing the concept of Optical Communication from a distance of 100 AU to Earth are tabulated in Table 1 below.

	Study Topic	Approach
1	Acquisition and tracking strategy	Sun as beacon combined with knowledge generated on-board of Earth position and phase
2	Concept of operations	Strategies needed to operate with > 1 day round-trip light time
3	Terminal Architecture Requirements	Emphasis on special environmental and lifetime requirements

Link acquisition and pointing strategy based on the remote spacecraft terminal utilizing the Sun as a reference to off-point to Earth using on-board generated position and phase knowledge, will be part of our phase 2 study. Note that off-pointing is mandatory since the Sun-Earth angular separation of 10 mrad from 100 AU is many laser beam diameters. Pointing must also account for point-ahead angles of 100-200 mrad or 30-40 laser beam widths where a beam-width of 3-6 mrad is being considered. Residual 1-sigma errors of 0.3-0.4 mrads must be achieved and maintained for the duration of the link. The objective of these studies will be to show through modeling and simulation that: (a) spacecraft disturbance rejection through passive and/or active means can be achieved and; (b) adequate control bandwidth is available with the sun beacon to maintain offset pointing to Earth within the allocated error.

The field-of-view (FOV) of the acquisition sensor used on the spacecraft would be relatively large in order to overlap the angular separation between the Sun and Earth. Roughly ±10 mrad will be required. At the same time the instantaneous field-of-view (IFOV) should be approximately of the order of the transmitted laser beam-width i.e. close to 10 mrad. This suggests a 1000 x 1000 focal plane array, however, the viability of implementing such a sensor needs further study. Even at 100 AU the sun angular diameter is ~ 90 mrad and this will have to be factored into achieving the targeted residual 0.3-0.4 mrad pointing error. The feasibility and benefits of using other celestial objects will be explored.

On the ground the beam footprint from 100 AU would be approximately 4 Earth diameters, however, the irradiance would be a few femtowatts per square meter. A 12 m or larger collector or an array of large collectors would be required to gather sufficient photons to overcome background and shot noise. In our preliminary analysis a 256 pixel superconducting nanowire array behind a 12 m collector supported 500±100 bits/sec. Ground aperture would very likely utilize a conical scan to acquire and lock on the downlink signal. The use of adaptive optics and aggressive filtering to discriminate the faint signal against prevalent background light will be studied. The performance achieved with the latter would determine how close to the Sun the ground terminal can point and this would also determine the duration of possible outages. For comparison the capability achievable with an orbiting large aperture collector/receiver will be determined where shot-noise limited performance can be achieved.

The concept of operations for a 100 AU optical communication link needs further study. From ranges comparable to where Voyager II spacecraft is at present, round-trip light times of approximately 27 hours (> 1 day) will be encountered. Since bi-directional acknowledgement and re-transmission requests will not be viable with such long ranges, optical communication from 100 AU will involve repetitive data transmission over a sufficiently long duration to ensure signal detection and data reception at Earth. While similar to the strategy used by Voyagers downlinking data to DSN, optical communications would require additional considerations related to cloud-cover, number of available ground stations and their distribution around the globe. In our proposed study these considerations will be addressed and the autonomous capability required by the spacecraft to implement the concept of operations will be evaluated. Emphasis on spacecraft resources needed to support optical communications will also be assessed.

The suitability of space terminal architectures pursued for deep-space optical communication within the solar system will be re-examined for the expected environment at 100 AU, as well as, expected longer lifetime demands. The enhanced acquisition field-of-view mentioned earlier is an example of a needed modification. The spectral characteristics of the sun beacon will also result in optical design modifications. Depending on the concept of operations the command receiving architecture and data-buffering requirements will very likely require modifications. Lifetime demands may impose added redundancy and in some cases re-engineering of components or assemblies. The radiation environment and shielding requirements must also be factored in.

9.2.3 Uplink

For our baseline configuration we assume that the spacecraft would perform autonomously until it fails. In the case of our 100 AU mission this makes sense because there are no encounters, there are no maneuvers, and navigation is moot once the spacecraft has passed the sun. The spacecraft does have a small low-gain antenna for near-Earth communication. We will further investigate the uplink strategy in Phase 2.

9.3 Instrument Suite for Model Spacecraft

The following table shows the baseline instrument suite selected for this spacecraft design. Other instrument suites will be developed and configured as part of the Phase 2 work.

Instrument	Heritage
Magnetometer	Cassini
Plasma Monitor	ROMAP - Rosseta
Plasma Wave	PWS - Voyayer
Neutral Ion Spectrometer	IES - Rosetta
Interstellar Plasma Ion Detector	ICA - Rosetta

This suite primarily focuses on the interactions between the solar wind and the local interstellar medium. Other spacecraft would carry instruments intended for study of the galactic wind, interstellar dust, and galactic cosmic rays as described in the next section. One of the advantages of the spacecraft architecture is that duplicate spacecraft could be built with different instruments. We expect to employ the following instruments in other instrument suites (to be further defined in phase 2:

1. Energetic particle monitor (>500kev)
2. Anomlaous cosmic rays
3. Dust detector
4. Galactic cosmic ray detector (<10 MeV/nuc, 10-100, MeV, and >100 MeV)

9.4 Mass Equipment list (MEL)

The initial estimate of spacecraft mass of 150 kg was close to the mass computed by the detailed spacecraft design: ~150kg. Accounting for margin, a spacecraft mass of 175 kg is used for our trajectory calculations and our spacecraft mass came to less than 170 kg even when fueled and with 10% system margin.

SSEARS Mass Equipment List (MEL)

Spacecraft	Mass (kg)	Units	CBE (kg)	Contin-gency	Expected Mass (kg)	Heritage	Comments
Science Instruments			**6.30**	**30%**	**8.19**		
Magnetometer	0.70	1	0.70	30%	0.91	Cassini	
Plasma Monitor	1.00	1	1.00	30%	1.30	Rosseta	ROMAP
Plasma Wave	1.40	1	1.40	30%	1.82	Voyager	PWS
Neutral Ion Spectrometer	1.00	1	1.00	30%	1.30	Rosseta	IES
Interstellar Plasma Ions	2.20	1	2.20	30%	2.86	Rosseta	ICA
Structure and Mechanisms			**33.00**	**28%**	**42.30**		
Bus structure	15.00	1	15.00	30%	19.50		Composite honeycomb panels
Secondary structure (incl. booms)	7.00	1	7.00	30%	9.10		
Cabling harness	5.00	1	5.00	30%	6.50		
System Assembly Hdw.	4.00	1	4.00	30%	5.20		
Ballast	2.00	1	2.00		2.00		
C&DH			**8.50**	**10%**	**9.38**		
Spacecraft Flight Computer (SFC)	0.60	1	0.60	5%	0.63	SMAP	
Non-Volatile Memory (NVM)	0.70	1	0.70	5%	0.74	SMAP	
MSAP Telemetry Interface (MTIF)	0.70	1	0.70	5%	0.74	SMAP	
MSAP System Interface Assy (MSIA)	0.70	1	0.70	5%	0.74	SMAP	
Local Eng. Unit Digital Card (LEU-D)	0.70	1	0.70	5%	0.74	SMAP	
Local Eng. Unit Analog Card (LEU-A)	0.70	1	0.70	5%	0.74	SMAP	
CDH Elect. Power Conv. Unit (CEPCU1)	1.10	1	1.10	5%	1.16	SMAP	
Critical Relay Controller Card (CRCC)	0.30	1	0.30	5%	0.32	SMAP	
Chassis and backplane (incl. Power cards)	3.00	1	3.00	20%	3.60	SMAP	Holds both C&DH and Power
ACS			**3.65**	**16%**	**4.25**		
Star Tracker/Scanner	2.70	1	2.70	20%	3.24	SMAP	
Sun Sensor	0.10	2	0.20	10%	0.22	SMAP	
LN-200S IMU	0.75	1	0.75	5%	0.79	MSL	
Power			**17.62**	**20%**	**21.18**		
Small MMRTG	10.32	1	10.32	30%	13.42		21 W_e BOL, 250 W_t
Battery	3.00	1	3.00	5%	3.15	MER	150 Wh
Power Switch Slice (PSS)	1.90	1	1.90	10%	2.09	SMAP	
Housekeeping Power Cond. Unit (HPCU)	1.00	1	1.00	5%	1.05	SMAP	
Power Bus Controller (PBC)	1.40	1	1.40	5%	1.47	SMAP	
Telecom			**30.68**	**26%**	**38.61**		
Small Deep Space Transponer (SDST)	2.65	1	2.65	5%	2.78	MSL	
X-Band SSPA	1.35	1	1.35	5%	1.42	MSL	17 W_{RF}
Coax Transfer Switch (CXS)	0.10	1	0.10	10%	0.11		
Filter	0.28	1	0.28	10%	0.31		
Coax Cable	0.30	1	0.30	30%	0.39		
Low Gain Antenna (LGA)	0.50	2	1.00	10%	1.10	SMAP	
Optical Com System	25.00	1	25.00	30%	32.50		75 W_e input power
Propulsion			**8.90**	**14%**	**10.18**		
Hydrazine tank	0.80	2	1.60	30%	2.08	ATK custom	10 liter tank, assume ½ press.
Thrusters	0.40	8	3.20	5%	3.36		4 N monoprop thruster
Valves	0.30	4	1.20	10%	1.32		
Filter	0.50	1	0.50	5%	0.53		
Propellant lines and components	1.50	1	1.50	30%	1.95		
Sensors	0.30	3	0.90	5%	0.95		
Thermal Control			**7.70**	**30%**	**10.01**		
Multilayer Insulation (MLI)	0.38	10	3.80	30%	4.94		
Heaters	0.05	20	1.00	30%	1.30	SMAP	
Sensors	0.01	30	0.30	30%	0.39	SMAP	
Louvers	1.30	2	2.60	30%	3.38		
S/C Dry Mass			116.35	24%	144.09		
Hydrazine Propellant	10.00	1	10.00		10.00		
S/C Wet Mass			126.35	22%	154.09		
S/C Wet Mass with 10% system margin					168.50		
Sail Module	625.00	1	625.00	30%	812.50	Sunjammer	σ=10 g/m², A=62,500 m²
Inflation Module	50.00	1	50.00	30%	65.00	Sunjammer	Incl. adapter & sep'n. hdw.
TOTAL LAUNCH CBE+Contingecy			801.35	50%	1,200.08		

With that spacecraft mass the transit times for different sail materials are provided in Figure 27. Boom mass scaling figures apply as in previous graphs (solid line is conservative scaling, dashed line is aggressive scaling.) 2 micron thick kapton is the material of choice both from a near-mid term (~2020s) feasibility standpoint and a cruise time standpoint. With this material cruise times range between 15 and 18 years. However 2 micron Kapton has yet to find a commercial application sufficient to motive manufacturers to develop it. With enough time .5 micron thick Kapton will emerge as the better choice, further reducing cruise times to between 12 and 15 years.

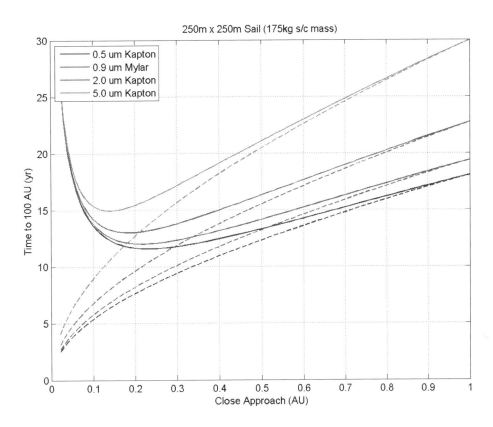

Figure 27: Our estimated spacecraft mass of 175kg raises the transit time somewhat, and shows that 2 micron Kapton is a clear choice for sail material. A phase two task will be to discuss the manufacturing of 2 micron thick Kapton with various manufacturers.

9.4.1 Thermal Control Challenges

The spacecraft would face thermal control challenges both at perihelion and in deep space. The spacecraft concept uses louvers, shielding and insulation as accounted for in the MEL. There is an external wall of aluminum between the sailcraft and the spacecraft itself that would ensure there is a shadow on the spacecraft when the sun is behind the spacecraft. Regarding thermal tolerance as the spacecraft approaches the sun, it is unclear how close the spacecraft can get to the sun, and how long the spacecraft can stay there. Part of our phase 2 study will be to determine specific trajectories, their time spent in the high heat and radiation environment near the sun, and the extent to which the short duration spent at those distances may, to some degree, alleviate thermal and radiation exposure concerns. As a baseline power source, the small RPS would be mounted to the spacecraft near a central position and the waste heat would be used to heat the spacecraft in deep space.

10. Cost

The cost information contained in this document is of a budgetary and planning nature and is intended for informational purposes only. It does not constitute a commitment on the part of JPL and Caltech.

The SSEARS cost estimate for a solar-sail propelled spacecraft, designed to perform fields and particles research at the Heliopause region, was performed using a variety of tools and methodologies. Overall, two distinct flight system cost scenarios were developed, a ten-spacecraft mission concept and a smaller three-spacecraft mission concept, which is considered the descope option. JPL's Parametric Mission Cost Model (PMCM), which uses statistically derived cost estimating relationships in order to estimate the full breadth of the JPL mission work breakdown structure (WBS), was utilized in the estimate. These costs were supplemented with instrument costs, developed using analogous instruments flown on previous missions. L'Garde Inc. provided a ROM (rough order of magnitude cost) for the 250m x 250m solar sail. The launch vehicle cost was determined using ROM costs provided by the Launch Services Program at Kennedy Space Center (KSC). Subsequently, a cost risk analysis was performed using ACEIT to assess a confidence level in the estimate. All estimates were performed in FY13 constant year dollars.

Two mission sizes were considered – the original concept of 10 spacecraft and a descoped concept with three spacecraft.

10.1 Cost Estimate Input Assumptions

Overall Mission: The SSEARS mission is assumed to be Class A mission with dual cold redundancy. Consistent with JPL reserve policy, 30% reserves are assumed through Phase D, and 15% reserves are assumed in Phase E. A team of 6.5 (FTE) scientists is required through launch; 2.5 (FTE) scientists are assumed to be adequate post-launch. The formulation phase (Phases A/B) is assumed to be 18 months; Phases C/D are assumed to be 40 months, followed by a 15 year voyage to the Heliopause.

Spacecraft and Solar Sail: For both the three-spacecraft and ten-spacecraft scenarios, a MMRTG power source and optical communication are the baseline design selections; solar sails and a monoprop hydrazine blowdown configuration serve as the primary propulsion subsystem. Subcontracting of the spacecraft is also assumed in each case. A discount of 50% is taken into account after the first spacecraft unit is produced, as the additional spacecraft are exact replicas of the first unit.

L'Garde Inc provided a solar sail ROM cost based on their experience with costs incurred while building the Sunjammer 1200m^2 solar sail and sailcraft. Their proven expertise with Sunjammer gives the team a high level of confidence in L'Garde's estimate. The $53M cost provided by L'Garde includes the separation and inflation modules, solar sail membrane and structure, as well as their integration. An additional 17% JPL fee is assessed in addition to the quote from L'Garde. A discount of 20% is taken after the first unit.

Instruments: A core payload with five instruments is assumed for both mission scenarios. Cost estimates were developed for the core payload. A Voyager-based magnetometer, plasma monitor, plasma wave, and neutral ion spectrometer are used as analogous instruments for the cost basis. The TIDE instrument on the POLAR mission is used as an analogy base for the interstellar plasma ion instrument. It is assumed that the effort, and thus the cost, will decrease by a factor of 65% after the first unit of each instrument produced, as they are exact replicas of the first instrument units. In the case of the 10 spacecraft scenario, there are 50 instruments in total. There are 15 instruments in total for the 3 spacecraft scenario.

Cost estimates were also developed for two optional instruments, a Channeltron, which will complement the Plasma Monitor, and a Cosmic Ray instrument.

Launch Vehicle: For the ten-spacecraft scenario, an Atlas V 551 throughput cost is used which includes launch services, payload processing, launch vehicle integration mission, unique launch site ground support and tracking, data and telemetry services, as provided in the payload planner's guide from the Launch Services program at KSC. For the three-spacecraft scenario, an Atlas V 501 cost was used.

10.2 Cost Estimate Output

The cost output is based on the input assumptions discussed previously. The relative magnitudes of the ten-spacecraft cost scenario versus the three-spacecraft cost scenario are in alignment. Due to the large amount of fixed cost, one would not expect a direct linear relationship with the number of spacecraft.

Project Total (FY 2013 $M)			
		PMCM Model Output: 10 Spacecraft	PMCM Model Output: 3 Spacecraft
Total Project Costs ($M)		**$3447.0M**	**$1796.7M**
1.0	Project Management	$67.2M	$51.2M
2.0	Project System Engineering	$17.1M	$17.1M
3.0	Mission Assurance	$81.1M	$35.5M
4.0	Science Team	$29.8M	$29.8M
5.0	Instruments	$94.7M	$42.3M
6.0	Flight System	$1426.2M	$515.7M
6.1	Flight System Management	$9.7M	$9.7M
6.2	Flight System Engineering	$15.5M	$14.9M
6A	Starjammer	$876.0M	$318.5M
6B	L'Garde Sailcraft	$516.1M	$163.6M
6.13	Materials and Processes	$0.6M	$0.6M
6.14	Flight System Testbeds	$8.4M	$8.4M
7.0	Mission Operations System	$519.8M	$519.8M
8.0	Launch System	$255.6M	$172.9M
9.0	Ground Data System (Currently included under 7.0)		
10.0	Project Systems I&T	$245.9M	$74.1M
10A	ATLO - Starjammer	$194.8M	$58.1M
10B	ATLO - L'Garde Sailcraft	$51.1M	$16.0M
11.0	Education & Public Outreach	$24.9M	$12.9M
12.0	Mission Design	$8.6M	$8.6M
	Reserves	$676.1M	$316.7M

Figure 28: Cost breakdown by Work Breakdown Structure

Instrument Options: Two instruments were evaluated for inclusion in the SSEARS mission as options, a Channeltron and a Cosmic Ray instrument. The marginal cost of including the Channeltron and the Cosmic Ray instrument on the ten-spacecraft mission scenario is $20.9M and $15.3M, respectively. These are not included in the estimates above; they are merely options at this point.

Cost-Risk Analysis: Uncertainty and risk exist in the estimate, as expected with such a unique mission. The order quantity discounts are aggressive, but fair, given the number of exact replicas of each spacecraft, sail, and instruments required. Additionally, the assumed schedules for both the ten- spacecraft and three-spacecraft scenarios are the same, drawing heavily on the learning curve/repetition assumptions inherent in building multiple units of the same system.

To understand the risk posture of the mission, a mission-level output based s-curve was generated for each scenario in ACEIT. A lognormal cost distribution was assumed, as it has been proven that space system cost typically follows a lognormal distribution. The PMCM total output without reserves was used as the most likely point estimate. A coefficient of variation of 0.4 and 0.45 was used for the three spacecraft and ten spacecraft scenarios respectively, which is higher than the space systems industry standard of 0.35, so that the higher level of uniqueness and risk in the SSEARS mission is captured. Both scenarios attained approximately a 50% cost confidence level, meaning that the probability that the mission actual cost will be less than the cost estimate with reserves is 50%. The risk analysis for the ten spacecraft scenario follows; the three spacecraft risk analysis may be found in the appendix.

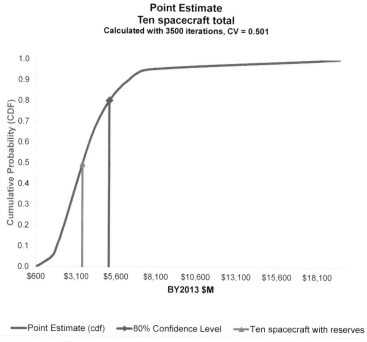

Figure 29: mission-level output based s-curve

Markers	Costs	Confidence
80% Confidence Level	$5,153.189	80.0%
Ten spacecraft with reserves	$3,447.000	49.6%

The cost estimate of $3447M, for a ten spacecraft mission, accounts for a substantial amount of uncertainty and risk, consistent with a space mission at this stage in its definition. The estimate will continue to be refined and risk reassessed as the mission evolves.

Final cost outputs are as follows for both the ten-spacecraft mission and the three-spacecraft mission:

Project Summary (JPL WBS)

		Formulation (Phase A/B) ($M)	Implementation (Phase C/D) ($M)	Development Total ($M)	Operations (Phase E) ($M)	Project Total (FY 2013 $M)	Notes/Models
Total Project Costs ($M)		$109.5M	$935.8M	$1218.2M	$578.5M	$1796.7M	
1.0	Project Management	$6.0M	$31.3M	$37.3M	$13.9M	$51.2M	
1.1	Project Manager & Staff	$1.6M	$4.2M	$5.9M	$9.0M	$14.9M	
1.2	Business Management	$1.6M	$4.7M	$6.4M	$4.4M	$10.7M	
1.4	Project Reviews	$0.3M	$0.7M	$0.9M	$0.5M	$1.4M	
1.6	Launch Approval	$2.4M	$21.7M	$24.1M		$24.1M	
2.0	Project System Engineering	$3.2M	$13.9M	$17.1M	$0.0M	$17.1M	
2.1	Project Systems Engineering	$1.0M	$3.4M	$4.4M		$4.4M	
2.2	Project Software Engineering	$0.8M	$1.8M	$2.6M		$2.6M	
2.3	End-To-End Information System	$0.1M	$1.1M	$1.2M		$1.2M	
2.4	Information Systems Engineering & Communications	$0.4M	$1.2M	$1.6M		$1.6M	
2.5	Configuration Management	$0.3M	$1.2M	$1.5M		$1.5M	
2.6	Planetary Protection	$0.0M	$0.1M	$0.1M		$0.1M	
2.7	Contamination Control	$0.1M	$0.8M	$0.9M		$0.9M	
2.9	Launch System Integration	$0.2M	$1.0M	$1.2M		$1.2M	
2.10	Project V & V	$0.1M	$3.2M	$3.4M		$3.4M	
2.11	Risk Management	$0.1M	$0.2M	$0.3M		$0.3M	
3.0	Mission Assurance	$3.1M	$27.7M	$30.8M	$4.7M	$35.5M	Msn Assurance wrap excludes reserves, LV, and itself
4.0	Science Team	$1.3M	$11.5M	$12.8M	$17.0M	$29.8M	
5.0	Instruments	$4.2M	$38.1M	$42.3M		$42.3M	
6.0	Flight System	$51.6M	$464.1M	$515.7M	$0.0M	$515.7M	
6.1	Flight System Management	$1.0M	$8.7M	$9.7M		$9.7M	
6.2	Flight System Engineering	$1.5M	$13.4M	$14.9M		$14.9M	
6A	Starjammer- 3 copies	$31.9M	$286.7M	$318.5M		$318.5M	
6B	L'Garde Sailcraft - 3 copies	$16.4M	$147.3M	$163.6M		$163.6M	
6C		$0.0M	$0.0M	$0.0M		$0.0M	
6D		$0.0M	$0.0M	$0.0M		$0.0M	
6E		$0.0M	$0.0M	$0.0M		$0.0M	
6.13	Materials and Processes	$0.1M	$0.5M	$0.6M		$0.6M	
6.14	Flight System Testbeds	$0.8M	$7.5M	$8.4M		$8.4M	
7.0	Mission Operations System	$6.2M	$55.8M	$62.0M	$457.8M	$519.8M	
8.0	Launch System			$172.9M		$172.9M	
8.1	Launch Vehicle			$172.9M		$172.9M	
8.2	Upper Stage / SRM			$0.0M		$0.0M	
9.0	Ground Data System (Currently included under 7.0)						
10.0	Project Systems I&T	$7.4M	$66.7M	$74.1M		$74.1M	
10A	ATLO - Starjammer- 3 copies	$5.8M	$52.3M	$58.1M		$58.1M	
10B	ATLO - L'Garde Sailcraft - 3 copies	$1.6M	$14.4M	$16.0M		$16.0M	
10C		$0.0M	$0.0M	$0.0M		$0.0M	
10D		$0.0M	$0.0M	$0.0M		$0.0M	
10E		$0.0M	$0.0M	$0.0M		$0.0M	
11.0	Education & Public Outreach	$0.3M	$2.9M	$3.2M	$9.7M	$12.9M	EPO wrap includes everything except reserves, LV, and itself
12.0	Mission Design	$0.9M	$7.8M	$8.6M	$0.0M	$8.6M	
#.#	Other			$0.0M		$0.0M	
#.#	Reserves	$25.3M	$216.0M	$241.2M	$75.5M	$316.7M	15%

Figure 30: Final mission cost for 3 spacecraft: $1.796B

325

Project Summary (JPL WBS)

		Formulation (Phase A/B) ($M)	Implementation (Phase C/D) ($M)	Development Total ($M)	Operations (Phase E) ($M)	Project Total (FY 2013 $M)	Notes/Models
Total Project Costs ($M)		$265.1M	$2324.2M	$2844.8M	$602.2M	$3447.0M	
1.0	Project Management	$7.4M	$34.3M	$41.7M	$25.4M	$67.2M	
1.1	Project Manager & Staff	$2.5M	$5.1M	$7.6M	$14.5M	$22.0M	
1.2	Business Management	$1.9M	$6.5M	$8.4M	$10.0M	$18.4M	
1.4	Project Reviews	$0.5M	$1.1M	$1.6M	$1.0M	$2.6M	
1.6	Launch Approval	$2.4M	$21.7M	$24.1M		$24.1M	
2.0	Project System Engineering	$3.2M	$13.9M	$17.1M	$0.0M	$17.1M	
2.1	Project Systems Engineering	$1.0M	$3.4M	$4.4M		$4.4M	
2.2	Project Software Engineering	$0.8M	$1.8M	$2.6M		$2.6M	
2.3	End-To-End Information System	$0.1M	$1.1M	$1.2M		$1.2M	
2.4	Information Systems Engineering & Communications	$0.4M	$1.2M	$1.6M		$1.6M	
2.5	Configuration Management	$0.3M	$1.2M	$1.5M		$1.5M	
2.6	Planetary Protection	$0.0M	$0.1M	$0.1M		$0.1M	
2.7	Contamination Control	$0.1M	$0.8M	$0.9M		$0.9M	
2.9	Launch System Integration	$0.2M	$1.0M	$1.2M		$1.2M	
2.10	Project V & V	$0.1M	$3.2M	$3.4M		$3.4M	
2.11	Risk Management	$0.1M	$0.2M	$0.3M		$0.3M	
3.0	Mission Assurance	$7.6M	$68.7M	$76.4M	$4.7M	$81.1M	Msn Assurance wrap excludes reserves, LV, and itself
4.0	Science Team	$1.3M	$11.5M	$12.8M	$17.0M	$29.8M	
5.0	Instruments	$9.5M	$85.2M	$94.7M		$94.7M	
6.0	Flight System	$142.6M	$1283.6M	$1426.2M	$0.0M	$1426.2M	
6.1	Flight System Management	$1.0M	$8.7M	$9.7M		$9.7M	
6.2	Flight System Engineering	$1.5M	$13.9M	$15.5M		$15.5M	
6A	Starjammer- 10 copies	$87.6M	$788.4M	$876.0M		$876.0M	
6B	L'Garde Sailcraft - 10 copies	$51.6M	$464.5M	$516.1M		$516.1M	
6C		$0.0M	$0.0M	$0.0M		$0.0M	
6D		$0.0M	$0.0M	$0.0M		$0.0M	
6E		$0.0M	$0.0M	$0.0M		$0.0M	
6.13	Materials and Processes	$0.1M	$0.5M	$0.6M		$0.6M	
6.14	Flight System Testbeds	$0.8M	$7.5M	$8.4M		$8.4M	
7.0	Mission Operations System	$6.2M	$55.8M	$62.0M	$457.8M	$519.8M	
8.0	Launch System			$255.6M		$255.6M	
8.1	Launch Vehicle			$255.6M		$255.6M	
8.2	Upper Stage / SRM			$0.0M		$0.0M	
9.0	Ground Data System (Currently included under 7.0)						
10.0	Project Systems I&T	$24.6M	$221.3M	$245.9M		$245.9M	
10A	ATLO - Starjammer- 10 copies	$19.5M	$175.3M	$194.8M		$194.8M	
10B	ATLO - L'Garde Sailcraft - 10 copies	$5.1M	$46.0M	$51.1M		$51.1M	
10C		$0.0M	$0.0M	$0.0M		$0.0M	
10D		$0.0M	$0.0M	$0.0M		$0.0M	
10E		$0.0M	$0.0M	$0.0M		$0.0M	
11.0	Education & Public Outreach	$0.6M	$5.6M	$6.2M	$18.7M	$24.9M	EPO wrap includes everything except reserves, LV, and itself
12.0	Mission Design	$0.9M	$7.8M	$8.6M	$0.0M	$8.6M	
#.#	Other			$0.0M		$0.0M	
#.#	Reserves	$61.2M	$536.4M	$597.5M	$78.5M	$676.1M	15%

Figure 31: Final mission cost for 10 Spacecraft: $3.44B

In the beginning of our study we thought we could fit ten spacecraft on one launch vehicle. During our configuration study we learned that we can only fit three per vehicle using currently available vehicles. Future developments in the launch vehicle industry might change this, perhaps with the Falcon Heavy. However for our cost analysis we included a single Atlas 5 501 in both the three-spacecraft and ten-spacecraft scenarios. The three-spacecraft scenario indeed fits onto one launch vehicle. If launched today, the ten-spacecraft scenario would require the addition of roughly $0.5B, the current approximate cost of 2 Atlas 5 launch vehicles. Rather than include those costs (nearly certain to be inaccurate by the time any such mission would be seriously considered) in the formal estimate, we left the acknowledged, under-estimated cost in the model for the ten-spacecraft scenario.

The 10-spacecraft mission could use combinations of launch vehicles at different times. Further several disruptive launch technologies (e.g. SpaceX "Grasshopper" reusable first stage rockets) are nearing the marketplace making accurate predictions more difficult.

11. Phase 2 Activities

Our Phase 2 proposal (developed in parallel with this final report) focuses on three primary technical challenges: demonstrating sail material thermal tolerance for expected perihelion distances, showing that the L'Garde Sunjammer boom design can be scaled up to the size necessary for a 250m x 250m sail, and developing a sail control method suited to such a large structure.

Material	Boom Design	Control
Thermo-mechanical testing of available sail materials at MSFC Solar Thermal Test Facility	~170m design study with team Mechanical Engineer and L'Garde team	Study and simulation of large sail control rates

We will also further develop the optical communications concept of operations and investigate other subsystem issues.

12. Future Applications

The architecture we have described can be applied for other missions besides the Heliopause exploration mission that we have explored in detail. Very large solar sails can enable many types of missions to distant objects.

12.1 Oort Cloud Object / Outer Planet / Moon Impactor

An object discovered in 2010, called 2010WG9, is believed to have originated in the Oort cloud1. It is thought to be a pristine sample of early solar system materiel, as its orbit does not come closer to the sun than the distance to Uranus. This object is a scientifically valuable object as its surface has not experienced the periodic melting and freezing that would occur with objects that come closer to the sun.

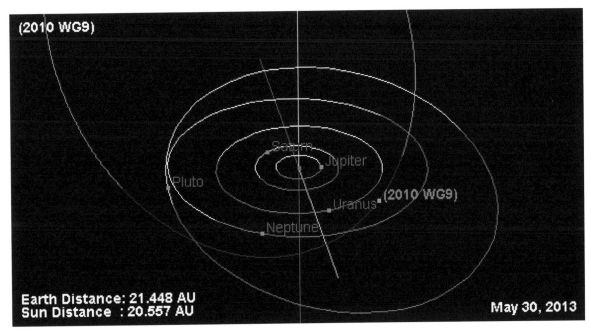

Figure 32: The object 2010 WG9 does not get any closer to the sun than Uranus, protecting its early solar system materials from the cycle of heating and freezing that happens to objects that get closer to the sun.

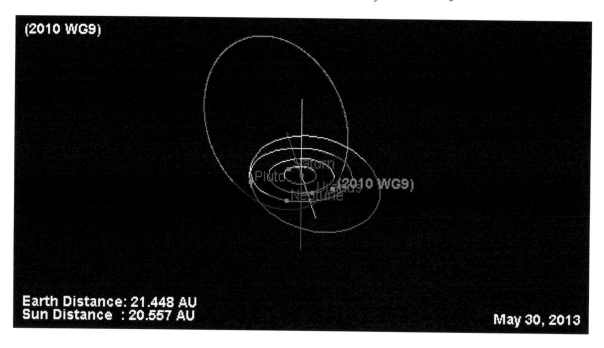

Figure 33: The object has an unusual orbit and likely contains pristine samples of early solar system material.

The SSEARS architecture could be used to deliver an impactor to the surface of this object at high relative velocity, with a second spacecraft following behind to study and pass through the impact plume. This architecture provides great flexibility in mission design and timing due to its use of a solar close approach to "aim" the outbound trajectory. This same concept could apply to Enceladus, Europa, or the other outer planet moons, with expected transit times as follows:

Target Planet (or its moons)	Distance from Sun	Cruise Time
Jupiter	~5 AU	~2 years
Saturn	~10 AU	~3 years
Uranus	~20 AU	~5 years
Neptune	~30 AU	~6 years
Pluto	~32 AU for the next several decades	~7 years

These figures all include variability due to the different lengths of time possible to reach "maximum velocity" depending on the perihelion distance and whether one exits Earth's orbit with the sail itself or with an upper stage rocket. However, the figures represent a significant improvement over current transit times and results in significantly higher arrival velocities well suited for impactor missions.

12.2 Gravitational Lensing (~550 AU)

As early as 1978 it was recognized that a spacecraft at roughly a distance of 550 AU and beyond could take advantage of the sun's gravitational effect to magnify the hydrogen line at 1420 MHz, the so-called ideal frequency for interstellar communications [2]. This concept has been developed further by Frank Drake and Claudio Maccone [3] as well as a study in 1999 at JPL [4].

Figure 34: Gravitational lensing at work. A space probe at 550 AU and beyond could exploit such effects to make detailed studies of other solar systems, among numerous other scientific targets.

In 1999 JPL produced a rough design which estimated the mass of such a telescope at roughly 1000kg. In order to apply our architecture to this mass we conceived of using nine sails as a "Raft" as follows.

12.3 Nine-Sail "Raft" for Gravitational Lensing Telescope Delivery

A concept was developed for nine-sails to be arranged in a tiled formation. The sails would not utilize the Sunjammer-type vanes, but the overall system would use the corner sails themselves as vanes, as shown below:

 Notional 9-Sail Raft Based on Sunjammer

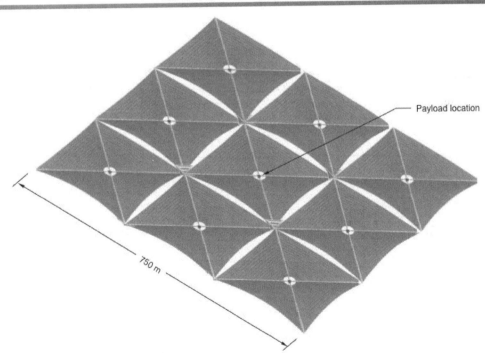

Payload location

750 m

Figure 35: 9-sail raft design to carry payload range between 500- and 1000kg gravity lens telescope.

Analysis showed that we can transport 1000kg to 550 AU in less than a century. Unfortunately, despite the imaginative appeal of this 9-sail approach, one cannot, with this architecture, increase the area of the sail by a factor of 9 without increasing the mass by the factor of 9. This results in essentially the same performance as with just one sail because the payload mass is so small. If the payload was significantly more massive then this "raft" concept would be a useful reduction in transit time over the single-sail version.

So, we conclude that the SSEARS architecture is a reasonable approach to reaching 550AU within a human lifetime, if not during a productive career (at least as such time frames are measured at the beginning of the 21st century.) We leave the feasibility of such biological and medical advances to the imagination.

12.4 Thousand Astronomical Unit Mission (TAU)

JPL developed a mission concept in 1987 that would send a spacecraft to a distance of 1000 AU using then-existing technology. The proposed spacecraft would measure the distance to other stars via stellar parallax, measure conditions in the interstellar medium, and perform tests of general relativity via communications with Earth [5]. This spacecraft was proposed to use a 1 MW fission reactor and ion drive to reach 1000 AU in 50 years. Given that much work remains to develop a flight-ready space fission reactor system, a SSEARS-like solar sail architecture bears further studying for this application.

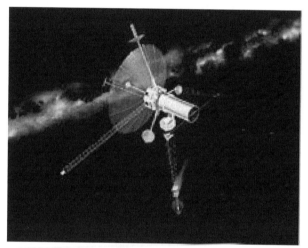

Figure 36: TAU spacecraft concept art

As shown in figures 19 and 20, useful solar sail sizes seem to reach their maximum at about 250 m x 205 m, at least with any currently conceivable support technology. Reducing the transit time to 1000 AU from the 120 years it would take the SSEARS architecture will require applying more energy to the sail rather than increasing the size of the sail. This could be achieved with a reflector or beamed energy system. The SSEARS team intends to propose such a study of such a system to a future call.

12.5 Oort Cloud (~50,000 AU/ 1 LY), Exoplanet Probe (<4 LY)

Our SSEARS concept is theoretically limited only by the amount of power/energy that can be applied to the sail and the ability of the material to withstand that energy. As such we can dream of energy transfer systems and materials capable of the performance necessary to reach another solar system in a human lifetime. We hope to explore this space in the far term and believe that NIAC is the ideal program to support such investigations once the "nearer-term" concepts have been explored.

13. Outreach Activities
13.1 Conferences
Due to the Federal Budget "Sequester" it was impossible to travel to many of the relevant conferences. Attended

NIAC 2012 Fall Conference, Hampton Bays, VA	PI Jeffrey Nosanov attended this conference and presented a poster about the project.
NIAC 2013 Spring Conference, March 2013, Chicago, IL	PI Jeffrey Nosanov attended this conference and presented ongoing work and progress made so far.
Starship Century Symposium, May 2013, San Diego, CA	PI Jeffrey Nosanov attended this symposium and discussed the project with many leaders in the field.

13.1.1 Accepted/Invited but unable to attend due to NASA budget sequestration

International Astronautical Congress 2013, Beijing, China	This final report was accepted but travel will not be permitted.
Starship Congress (Icarus Interstellar)	Abstract was accepted but travel will not be permitted.
100 Year Starship Conference	Abstract was accepted but travel will not be permitted.

13.2 Poster for General Public

The poster graphic for public consumption will arrive separately in an email to program management.

13.3 Reddit AMA (Ask Me Anything)
The popular forum website www.reddit.com hosts exchanges between users called "AMAs" This stands for "Ask Me Anything" and many popular or influential figures have hosted an AMA giving their fans and supporters a chance to post questions. One of us (Nosanov) hosted an AMA under the title "I am a NASA Innovative Advanced Concepts Fellow, developing a mission concept to the edge of the solar system and nearby interstellar space." The post attracted dozens of viewers, many of whom asked insightful and interesting questions. I answered every single serious question and have concluded that an AMA is a valuable component to a broad outreach effort, but I could have expanded my audience significantly (compared to other AMA events) by advertising or posting about the AMA on several other websites beforehand. The entirety of the exchange (~25 pages of questions and answers) will be sent via email to program management.

13.4 Video
We initiated the development of a brief outreach video to convey the mission concept in a 60-second clip. We developed a storyboard concept for the video and hope to produce the video in Phase 2. The storyboards are reproduced below.

1) Establishing shot – Earth

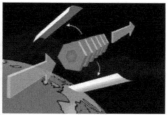

2) Cut to close up – Payload enters frame left as half-shells separate to reveal 6 stacked spacecraft

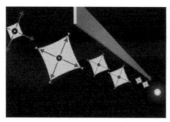

3) Dissolve to – As each spacecraft enters frame left, no solar sail is visible. Solar sails unfurl as each spacecraft travels into frame.

4) Dissolve to – Spacecraft emerge from behind the sun. Camera pans to follow the first craft... [shot continues with next frame]

R. Barkus   SSEARS Storyboard, draft 0501   1

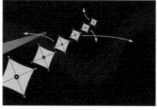

4) [continued from previous frame] Camera continues pan as spacecraft head into distance. Each of the first four spacecraft then begin a graceful move into their respective trajectory.

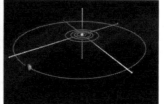

5) Cut to – Animated diagram showing each individual trajectory. The spacecraft, represented by a marker dot and a long fading trail, have just passed Jupiter's orbit.

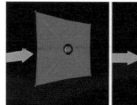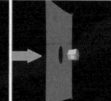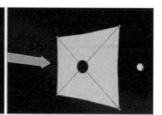

6) Cut to close up – A single spacecraft enters frame left as camera begins follow-pan. Solar sail is released causing a slight speed decrease in the sail and an increase in the spacecraft. Camera pan eases out as spacecraft continues into distance.

R. Barkus   SSEARS Storyboard, draft 0501   2

7) Cut to – Animated diagram showing each individual trajectory. The spacecraft are now beyond Pluto's orbit.

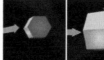

8) Cut to close up – A single spacecraft, now without solar sail, enters frame left as camera begins follow-pan. Camera pan eases out as spacecraft continues into distance.

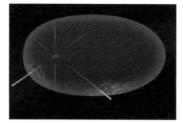

9) Dissolve to – Animated diagram showing spacecraft markers and long trails (but no visible Heliopause). As the first spacecraft passes the Heliopause boundary a bright wavering texture is illuminated. As the spacecraft travels beyond the boundary, the texture becomes still and somewhat dim. The process is repeated as each spacecraft passes the various boundary points. After all six craft have passed beyond the Heliopause boundary, the complete dimensions are visible.

R. Barkus   SSEARS Storyboard, draft 0501   3

References

1. The Peculiar Photometric Properties of 2010 WG9: A Slowly-Rotating Trans-Neptunian Object from the Oort Cloud, David Rabinowitz, Megan E. Schwamb, Elena Hadjiyska, Suzanne Tourtellotte, Patricio Rojo, Astronomical Journal, 2013 Apr 20

2. Von Eshleman, Stanford University

3. Maccone, The Sun as a Gravitaitonal Lens: Proposed Space Missions, Colorado Springs: IPI Press

4. Design Issues for a mission to exploit the gravity lensing effect at 550AU, John West, Acta Astronautica V.44 I2-4, January 1997, Pages 99-107

5. Preliminary Scientific Rationale for a voyage to a thousand astronomical units, Jet Propulsion Laboratory

Propulsion for Rapid Interstellar Travel

T. Kammash, M. Orians

University of Michigan, Ann Arbor, MI 48109 USA

tkammash@umich.edu

Abstract

Using the conservation equations we derive a set of equations yielding specific impulse and travel time as functions of power per unit mass (P/M) of the propulsion system that can be utilized for interstellar missions. We find that for any electrical propulsion technology such as radioisotope thermal generates (RTG's) and present magnetic fusion concepts, a limit of 10 W/Kg is readily obtainable. For such systems, we find that trip time to the sun's gravitational lens and Jupiter lens take 52 and 257 years respectively. However, increasing P/M by an order of magnitude would reduce travel time to the sun's lens to 24 years. Increasing P/M by another order of magnitude which likely is not achievable in fission-driven systems will further reduce the journey time to less than 12 years. A fusion-hybrid concept that can deliver large P/M is one based on the Gasdynamic Mirror where the fusion component serves as a neutron source that deliver neutrons to a surrounding thorium blanket where they breed uranium and simultaneously burn it to produce power. Such a system is shown to be capable of producing tens of megawatts of thermal power per cm of length which translates to several megawatts of electric power per cm with an estimated mass of about 300 MT for the reactor and a much larger total mass to account for other components.

Keywords

Fission, Fusion, Interstellar Destinations, Rapid Travel

Introduction

Man's fascination with space was never limited to explorations within the solar systems but went beyond, deep into interstellar space and perhaps extending to the nearest star, Alpha Centauri. What limited or perhaps prevented those ambitions from becoming a reality is the lack of propulsion systems that can deliver payloads to these challenging destinations. A quick survey of interstellar space places the Kuiper Belt at about 30 to 50 astronomical units [AU], the sun's gravitation lens at >550 AU, Jupiter's gravitation lens at >6100 AU, Inner Oort Cloud 2×10^3 to 20×10^3 AU, and Alpha Centauri at 268×10^3 AU. While it is common knowledge that chemical propulsion is not adequate for such missions, nuclear energy seems to provide the capability for such undertakings. To utilize such a source, and to decide whether it will be fission, fusion or a hybrid system, a criterion in the form of power per unit mass [P/M] is found to be especially useful in evaluating these systems especially in regards to travel time.

1. Conservation laws

To address that point we begin with the conventional conservation equations, namely:

i) Conservation of mass which we express in the form:

$$\dot{m}T = (X - 1)M \tag{1}$$

    a.   Where $\dot{m}$ is the propellant mass flow rate

    b.   (X-1)M is the initial propellant mass

    c.   T, time to destination

    d.   We can write for the total mass of the vehicle at any time "t" the expression with (X-1) M to be determined.

$$M_{Total_{(t)}} = M + (X - 1)M - \dot{m}T = XM - \dot{m}t \tag{2}$$

ii) Conservation of Energy:

$$P = \tfrac{1}{2}\,\dot{m}\,V_{Exh}^2 = \tfrac{1}{2}\,\dot{m}\,I_{SP}^2 g^2 \tag{3}$$

    a.   with I_{SP} being the specific impulse

    b. V_{EXH} the exhaust velocity

    c.   g the gravitational constant.

    d.   equation 3 can be put in the form:

$$\frac{M}{\dot{m}} = \frac{I_{SP}^2 g^2}{2\,[P/M]} \tag{4}$$

iii) Conservation of Momentum:

$$Thrust = \dot{m}\,V_{Exh} = \dot{m}\,I_{SP}g \tag{5}$$

    a.   from which we obtain the acceleration as a function of time, namely:

$$a_{(t)} = \frac{\dot{m}\,I_{SP}g}{XM - \dot{m}t} \tag{6}$$

In addition to the conservation equations it is useful to employ the following kinetic relations:

$$V_{(\tau)} = \int_0^\tau a_{(t)}dt = \int_0^\tau \frac{\dot{m}\,I_{SP}g}{XM - \dot{m}t}\,dt = I_{SP}g \ln\left(\frac{XM}{XM - \dot{m}\tau}\right) \tag{7}$$

$$D_{(T)} = \int_0^T V_{(\tau)}d\tau = \int_0^{\frac{(X-1)M}{\dot{m}}} I_{SP}g \ln\left(\frac{XM}{XM - \dot{m}\tau}\right) d\tau \tag{8}$$

$$D = I_{SP}g \frac{M}{\dot{m}}[X - 1 - \ln(X)] \tag{9}$$

2. Derivation

Using Equations 1 and 4 the above expression becomes:

$$D = I_{SP}g\{T\} - I_{SP}g \left\{\frac{I_{SP}^2 g^2}{2\,[P/M]}\right\} \ln(X) \tag{10}$$

from which we obtain the travel time T as a function of the distance, D:

$$T = \frac{D}{I_{SP}g} + \frac{I_{SP}^2 g^2}{2\,[P/M]} \ln(X) \tag{11}$$

We proceed now to find the I_{SP} that minimizes the travel time by differentiating the above equation with respect to I_{SP}, or more conveniently, with respect to $g\,I_{SP}$ and setting the result equal to zero. The result is

$$I_{SP}g = \sqrt[3]{\frac{D\,[P/M]}{\ln(X)}} \tag{12}$$

and upon combing this with Equation 11, we find

$$T = \frac{3}{2}\sqrt[3]{\frac{D^2\,\ln(X)}{[P/M]}} \tag{13}$$

To solve for the quantity "X", we combine Equation 13, 12 and 4, making use of Equation 1 to obtain

$$3\ln(X) = (X - 1) \tag{14}$$

There are two solutions to this equation, namely X=1, which is not realistic since it implies zero propellant mass, and the second which is given by

$$X = -3W_{-1}\left(-\frac{1}{3\sqrt[3]{e}}\right) \approx 6.71144108 \tag{15}$$

with W being the Lambert function. We now introduce χ to be

$$\chi \equiv \ln(X) \approx 1.90381369444 \tag{16}$$

and with Equation 15, we find from Equation 12 and 13 that

$$T = \frac{3}{2}\sqrt[3]{\frac{D^2\,\chi}{[P/M]}} \tag{17}$$

and

$$I_{SP} = \sqrt[3]{\frac{D\,[P/M]}{\chi}}\,/g \tag{18}$$

The above results were obtained on the assumption of zero gravity, constant thrust, and zero propellant at destination. To validate the zero gravity assumption, we calculate the acceleration [initially, and at time "T"] to compare with local gravity due to the Sun. The assumption of zero gravity is appropriate for missions beyond Jupiter.

$$a_{(0)} = \frac{2}{X}\sqrt[3]{\frac{\chi\,[P/M]^2}{D}} \tag{19}$$

$$a_{(T)} = 2\sqrt[3]{\frac{\chi\,[P/M]^2}{D}} \tag{20}$$

It may also be useful to establish the ion temperature if plasma is ejected to provide the propulsion as may be the case in a fusion system for example. Denoting the ion mass by "m," and the temperature by "kt" where k is the Boltzmann Constant, we see that the mean ion velocity <V> is given by

$$I_{SP}g = \langle V \rangle = \sqrt{\frac{8\,kt}{\pi m}} \tag{21}$$

and using Eq. 18 the above result leads to

$$\frac{kt}{m} = \frac{\pi}{8}\sqrt[3]{\frac{D\,[P/M]}{\chi}}^{\,2} \tag{22}$$

We recall that the initial propellant mass is given by (X-1)M, we readily note that the initial propellant mass is 5.71144 times the dry mass of the vehicle. Using Equation 1, and substituting for "T" from Equation 17 we obtain the mass flow rate as expressed by

$$\frac{kt}{m} = \frac{\pi}{8} \sqrt[3]{\frac{D\,[P/M]}{\chi}}^2 \qquad (23)$$

As a practical matter both "T" and "ISP" are weakly dependent on [P/M] due to the cube root. As a result, we find: that increasing [P/M] by a factor of 10 only reduces T by a factor of 2.15. Moreover, increasing [P/M] by a factor of 1000 reduces T by only a factor of 10. It is generally believed that most electrical propulsion technology concepts including present magnetic plasma devices are limited to [P/M] of 10 W/Kg (1). Clearly this can be higher using solar power but solar works near the sun. A fusion-hybrid device (2,3), to be discussed shortly, is shown to be have the potential to provide a much larger [P/M] so as to reduce significantly travel time into interstellar space. If we restrict our system to 10 W/Kg then travel time and other relevant parameters to interstellar destinations are given in Table 1.

It should be noted that the mass flow rate shown is based on a 10 MT dry mass. Moreover, the results shown are for one way trip without coasting or deceleration. Furthermore, the approach followed will work only if the thrust is much greater than gravity; it is only greater than solar gravity at distances beyond Jupiter, hence chemical or nuclear thermal is needed to start with sufficient velocity to reach Jupiter.

Table 1: 10 W_E/kg System performance

At closest Approach	Distance	I_{SP}	kT	Time		$a_{(0)}$ & $a_{(T)}$ vs Sun Gravity			*
	Au	Sec	ev/ Amu	Days	Years	µg's	µg's	µg's	gram /min
Jupiter**	3.93	1,483	0.861	699	1.9	21	140	25	56.7
Neptune	28.74	2,878	3.2	2,634	7.2	10.8	72	0.68	15.1
Kuiper Belt	50	3,462	4.7	3,810	10	8.95	60	0.23	10.4
Heliopause	100	4,362	7.4	6,048	17	7.10	48	0.0592	6.56
Sun Lens	550	7,699	23	18,843	52	4.02	27	0.0020	2.10
Jupiter Lens	6,100	17,170	115	93,712	257	1.80	12	2×10^{-5}	0.42
Oort Cloud	10,000	20,246	160	130,290	357	1.53	10	6×10^{-6}	0.30
α Cen***	187,000	53,738	1,130	917,919	2,513	0.58	3.9	2×10^{-8}	0.069

*Mass flow rates based on 10 ton probe dry mass.
** This analysis not valid at Jupiter due to the suns gravitational field strength being comparable to acceleration. Shown as a reference point as the lower limit of applicability.
***Alpha Centauri will make its closes approach in 28,000 years; presently it's at 268,000 AU.

3. Antimatter Storage Mass-Radius

In searching for a propulsion system that can provide travel to these distant destinations, one is immediately tempted to explore antimatter-annihilation driven systems because of the enormous energy percent mass available (4). However, a careful examination of the system's mass associated with this approach would reveal another, not necessarily most desirable outcome. It has to do with the magnetic storage of the charged antimatter. To see this, we must first note that the strength of the magnetic field needed to store them is limited. Any collection of like charged particles is in a state of positive potential energy and would strive to relax by moving away from one another and breaking confinement. Clearly, the energy of the confining magnetic field [EMAG] must be greater than the electric potential energy of the charged particles [PEELECTRIC] if this experiment is to be effective. Likewise, the chemical binding energy of the structure holding the magnets [BECHEMICAL] must be greater than the magnetic energy or the magnets would rip the structure apart. To quantify this analysis, we first note that:

$$BE_{Chemical} > E_{Mag} > PE_{Electric} \qquad (24)$$

and since chemical bending energy is generally limited to the order of 10 MJ/kg (megajoules/kg), we can write

$$BE_{Chemical} = Mass * \left[\frac{BE_{Chemical}}{Mass}\right] \approx Mass * \left[\frac{10MJ}{kg}\right] \tag{25}$$

The minimum potential energy of a collection of charged particles with a total charge of "Q," within a hollow sphere of radius "r" can be expressed by

$$PE_{Electric} = \frac{1}{4\pi\epsilon_0}\frac{Q^2}{radius} \tag{26}$$

with ϵ_0 being the permittivity of free space.

The energy released by antimatter [E_A], is given by the well know expression:

$$E_A = 2 * Mass * c^2 = 2Q\left[\frac{m}{q}\right]c^2 \tag{27}$$

with m being the particle mass and q being the particle charge. When Equation 25 and 26 are substituted in Equation 24 the result is

$$Mass * \left[\frac{BE_{Chemical}}{Mass}\right] > \frac{1}{4\pi\epsilon_0}\frac{Q^2}{radius} \tag{28}$$

and upon substituting for "Q" from Equation 27 we find that

$$Mass * \left[\frac{BE_{Chemical}}{Mass}\right] > \frac{1}{4\pi\epsilon_0}\frac{E_A{}^2}{4\left[\frac{m}{q}\right]^2 c^4 radius} \tag{29}$$

which upon re-arranging becomes

$$Mass * radius > \frac{E_A{}^2}{16\pi\epsilon_0\left[\frac{m}{q}\right]^2 c^4 \left[\frac{BE_{Chemical}}{Mass}\right]} \tag{30}$$

Using the 10 MJ/Kg chemical binding energy noted earlier, and the proton mass and charge we obtain from Equation 30 the result:

$$16\pi\epsilon_0\left[\frac{m}{q}\right]^2 c^4 \left[\frac{BE_{Chemical}}{Mass}\right] \approx 3.918x10^{15}\frac{Joule^2}{kg-meter} \tag{31}$$

This result allows us to express Eq. 30 in the form

$$Mass * radius >\approx \frac{E_A{}^2}{3.918x10^{15}\frac{J^2}{kg-m}} \tag{32}$$

or more explicitly as

$$Mass * radius >\approx \left(\frac{E_A}{62.6\ MJ}\right)^2 kg - meter \tag{33}$$

The above equation reveals the concern about using antimatter propulsion due to the fact that the mass and radius of the vessel confining the antimatter go up with the annihilation energy squared. While, theoretically antimatter in quantities of a few 100 MJ which is equivalent to micrograms (μg), can be stored, the fact remains that such quantities are far too small for space exploration. For comparison, it is useful to note that 100 MJ is approximately equal to that obtained from 10 kg of LOX-LOH combustion. Table 2 shows quantities of interest from antimatter annihilation of antiprotons or positrons.

Table 2: Antimatter Containment

Antimatter Quantity	Energy Stored	Containment Size	
	MJ	Kg-m [Antiproton]	Kg-m [Positron]
gram	179,751,036	8.25×10^{12}	2.78×10^{19}
mg	179,751	8.25×10^{6}	2.78×10^{13}
µg	180	8.25	2.78×10^{7}
ng	0.18	8.25×10^{-6}	28

We note from the above table that 1 mg of antimatter would require 8.2 m radius container weighing more than 1000 metric tons (MT), and one gram would require a kilometer radius weighing more than 8.25×10^{6} MT. We can readily conclude from the above brief analysis that we should perhaps ignore using antimatter for space propulsion due to the massive vessel needed for containing it, as well as the scarcity of this substance.

4. Fusion Hybrid Reactor

In view of these considerations, it appears that fission or fusion driven systems provide the reasonable choices for interstellar travel. While fission systems in the form of nuclear thermal rockets and variations thereof have been extensively studied, we focus here on fusion-driven systems and on one in particular, namely the fusion hybrid reactor where fusion component is the Gasdynamic Mirror (GDM) [5]. In this device deuterium-tritium (DT) plasma is heated to a temperature of 10 keV in order to initiate fusion reactions that produce 14.1 MeV neutrons. When these neutrons impinge on a surrounding thorium-232 blanket, they breed uranium-233, and simultaneously burn it to produce power. It has been shown (6) that the thermal power produced per cm (P_L) can be expressed by

$$P_L = \pi r_p{}^2 \left(\frac{1}{1-K_{EFF}}\right) SE \frac{\Sigma_f}{\Sigma_t} \tag{34}$$

where r_p is the plasma radius, E the energy per fission, i.e., 200 MeV, Σ_f the macroscopic fission cross section, Σ_t the total cross reaction, S the neutron source produced by the fusion reactions, namely

$$S = n_P^2/4 * \langle \sigma v \rangle \tag{35}$$

where n_p is the plasma radius, and $\langle \sigma v \rangle$ the fusion reaction rate, and K_{EFF} is the effective neutron multiplication factor in the blanket.

For a plasma density of 10^{16} cm^{-3} at 10 KeV temperature, Equation 35 yields S = 2.5×10^{15} neutrons per cm^2 per second. With careful and deliberate design of the blanket, KEFF can be made close to unity as possible i.e. 0.99 without exceeding it so as to maintain "sub-criticality" for the system. With $\Sigma_f/\Sigma_t \approx 0.4$ and the above noted value, Equation 34 yields for r_p=1 cm, P_L=10 MW/cm, which at a thermal conversion efficiency of 30% yields 3 MW$_E$/cm. A minimum length of GDM is taken to be 4.63 m to satisfy the confinement requirements, and when operated at a "breakeven" condition where fusion power is exactly equal to injection power, P_{inj}, we find from the power balance equation that P_{inj} =1.5 MW/cm. As a result, about 5 MW$_{TH}$/cm will be available for propulsion, and with a length of 463 cm, the result would be 2315 MW$_{TH}$.

Next the [P/M] for the GDM is evaluated. The Thorium Blanket mass is 151 MT, the magnet mass is estimated to be 30 MT. while the injector and the direct converter are estimated to be 28 MT and 0.6 MT, respectively. This gives a total mass of about 210 MT. With current technology the magnet refrigeration is quite massive and consumes a large amount of the available power generated but in the future this may be reduced with high temperature superconducting magnets. In addition, if we allow for tankage and other heat source components a mass equal to that of the GDM reactor we find that the total mass of the heat source is $\approx$ 420 MT. With a thermal power output of 2315 MW we find that [P/M] for our heat source to be about 38.2×10^3 W$_{TH}$ /kg$_{Fue}$. With the mass of the heat engine, radiator and propulsion system included, and assuming a composite heat to electricity to propulsion conversion efficiency of 30%, this system may provide up to the $\approx$10 W$_{Propulsion}$ /kg$_{Total}$.

If we use this value of power per unit mass and refer to Figure 1 or Equation 17, we see that a journey to the sun's gravitational lens will be about 52 years during which the core would be refueled a dozen times. The plot in Figure 1 reveals dramatically the importance of the [P/M] value in the determination of the travel time to destinations in interstellar space. In Figure 2 we can see that even an Ideal Fission-Fusion system operating at 38.2×10^3 W_{TH}/k_{gFuel} with 100% fuel consumption will last only 65 years. With a more realistic fuel burn-up of 60 GWD/MTHM the reactor would have to be refueled every 4.74 years which means the GDM fusion hybrid reactor has a travel distance of only 14.1 AU [doesn't reach Uranus] before refueling is necessary.

5. General Propulsion

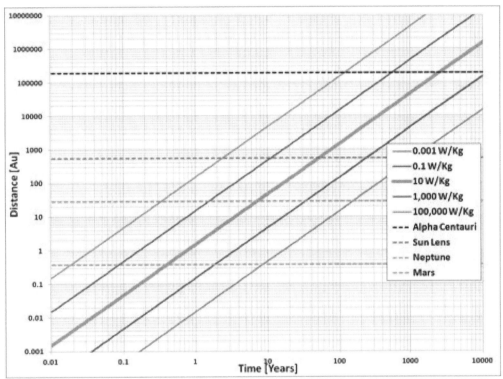

Figure 1: Distance verse time for several values of [P/M] [See Equation 17].

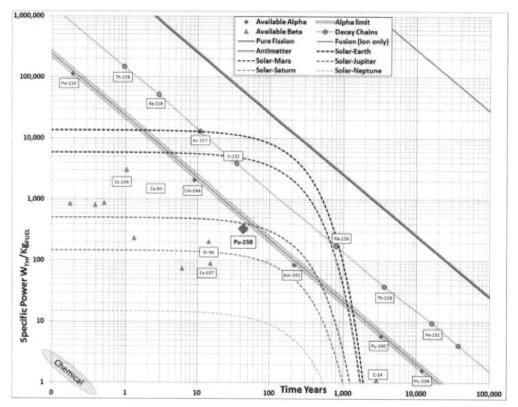

Figure 2: Specific power as a function of time.

Some interesting observations can be made from Figure 1 and 2, particularly in regard to the use of radioisotopes as energy sources. Figure 1 relates the distance traveled to travel time using the specific power of the propulsion system, while Figure 2 relates the specific power in the fuel to the specific energy of the fuel using the time that the fuel will last. To use these figures a few assumptions must be noted the efficiency of converting fuel heat to actual propulsion, and the percent of the dry mass of the vehicle that the fuel constitutes. A good approximation for these assumptions is that the efficiency is 33%, which is perhaps somewhat high but may be achievable in the near future, and that the fuel constitutes about 10% of the dry mass. With these assumptions Figure 2 is employed to produce Figure 3 which gives the specific power of the propulsion system in terms of the total mass of the vehicle.

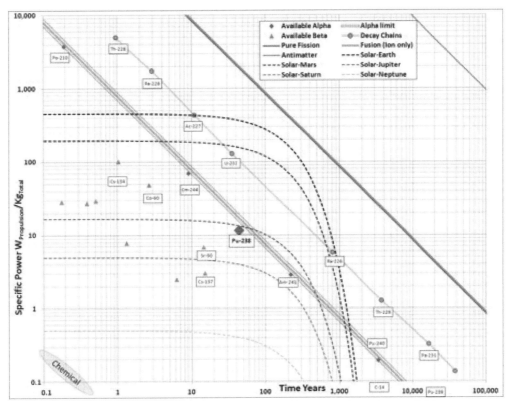

Figure 3: Same as Figure 2 with the left axis shifted down by a factor of 30 to account for the 33% thermal efficiency and the 10% dry mass allocated to fuel.

We note from this figure that for Pu-238 the specific power is ≤11.6 W/kg for 44 years, and from Figure 1, the distance reachable is ≤465 AU. This means that the entire solar system and beyond is possible, all the way out to the sun's lens. Beyond this point, no destination is reachable including, of course, Alpha Centauri. If we focus on another isotope, such as Am-241, we see from Figure 3, that the specific power is ≤2.85 W/kg lasting for 216 years, with a reachable distance of ≤2515 AU. This means that the entire solar system is accessible, but no Alpha Centauri. If we turn to fission and/or fusion, at 1000 W/kg, we see from Figure 1, that an 11,300 AU distance, which reaches the middle of the Oort cloud, is indeed reachable in the 83.5 year lifetime of the system, which is also about a human lifetime. If we lower the specific power of fission/fusion to 10 W/kg, we see from Figure 3, that the lifetime will be extended to about 8350 years, and the reachable distance extended to about 1.13×10^6 AU [≈18 light-years] making Alpha Centauri reachable.

Finally, if we focus on antimatter-driven systems at 10,000 years, Figure 3 shows that the required specific power is 9,500 W/kg, and the reachable distance from Figure 1, would be about 723 light years [747 light years with relativistic effects]. This means that several stars are reachable, but the galactic center or other galaxies are still out of reach. It should be noted, however, that 10,000 W/kg is not necessarily possible with antimatter in view of the storage issues among others discussed earlier.

Conclusion

Man's ambition to travel to interstellar space is tempered by the availability of propulsion systems capable of driving a vehicle that can reach these destinations in a human lifetime. We have examined in this paper several energy sources ranging from radio-isotopes to fission and fusion, and the ultimate source represented by antimatter annihilation. We find that a Pu-238 source with a specific source with a specific power of <11.6 W/kg and lasting for 44 years would allow for a mission to a distance of <465 AU, which would cover the entire solar system and beyond to the sun's lens. Using an Am-241 source at <2.85 W/kg and lasting for 216 years would make distances on the order of 2515 AU, also making the entire solar system reachable but not Alpha Centauri. The most reachable destination in interstellar space is the Sun's gravitational lens which starts at 550 AU. En route this mission could also explore the outer reaches of the solar system [Kuiper Belt, Scattered disk and Heliopause] and then upon reaching the sun's lens and traveling additional thousands of AU while observing the lens, the probe has reached the edge of the Oort Cloud. This mission could utilize fission [best option], fusion or an advanced RTG [Am-241] and at

343

10W/kg could be reached in 52 years which is within a human lifetime. Even without advanced prolusion a small probe may reach this region in 150-250 years with large chemical rockets or several gravitational slingshots in the inner solar system utilizing ion drives and solar power.

References

1. Mason, L.S. "Realistic Specific Power Expectations for Advanced Radioisotope Power System" Journal of Propulsion and Power, 23,1075 (2007)

2. Kammash, T. "Transactions of Fusion Science and Technology." 61,227 (2012).

3. Kammash, T. "Proceedings of the IAEA Fusion Energy Conference." 7 (2012)

4. Kammash, T. "Fusion Energy in Space Propulsion." AIAA, 167,1 (1995).

5. Kammash, T. "Advances in Reactor Physics to Power the Nuclear Renaissance", PHYSOR (2010).

6. Kammash, T. ICENES Conference, San Francisco, CA, (2011).

Artificial Intelligence and Brain Simulation Probes for Interstellar Expeditions

Eray Özkural

Gök Us Sibernetik Araştırma ve Geliştirme Ltd. Şti.

1. Introduction

We are witnessing the dawn of a technological society, in which we will not be merely surrounded by technology, but the very members of the society will have technological components or be comprised of technology altogether. We have ascertained early on that interstellar travel shall be a primary application of human-level AI technology, along with such intelligence requiring applications as unification of general relativity and quantum mechanics, and curing cancer. The renewed interest in interstellar research confirms that boundless amounts of creativity are required to feasibly achieve interstellar flight in a short time. We anticipate that human-level AI technology will be immensely useful both for accelerating interstellar research and for controlling the spacecraft. The present study addresses the latter problem.

We present a high-level design for an interstellar probe built around artificial general intelligence and brain simulation technologies. Due to the communication delay in interstellar missions, an intelligent control system is required for navigation, scientific tasks and emergencies. While biological astronauts fit the bill, the astronauts and life support systems as well as crew space and tools with human interfaces increase the mission mass significantly. Moore's law suggests that around 2025, a laptop computer will have enough processing speed to simulate a human brain at real time. Therefore, fast and small computers that can operate human-level artificial general intelligence agents or brain simulations may be used for interstellar missions in the near future. We outline a one-way mission design for expeditions to Tau Ceti and Gliese 667C systems which house earth-like planets with a hypothetical timeline beginning in 2040. We present a design sketch for the probe, detailing its control, scientific instrumentation, communication, propulsion and shielding components. We detail how a goal-following or reinforcement-learning agent can be designed which will navigate the probe safely to a destination star system, survey the planets, perform experiments and establish communications autonomously. We discuss how the intelligent agent can be trained with sufficient scientific knowledge, and mission simulations. The brain simulation option allows us to create a virtual crew which may rank in hundreds; we detail scenarios of how the virtual crew can be effectively employed inside the interstellar probe. We show the computing and energy costs for such artificial crews The secondary significant cost would be the mass and energy requirements for establishing an interstellar communication link at the destination star system, as well as any scientific equipment. We assume laser based communication for two-way interstellar communication and calculate the costs. We base the scientific instrumentation costs based on existing interplanetary probes, and take into account fuel requirements to survey the entire system. We consider the following extended roles for interstellar probes. We consider whether the probe can refuel or manufacture any equipment such as habitats and robots at the star system using future nanotechnology assembly methods, and we also discuss replicating probes. We consider the cost of carrying a lander module for exploring earth-like planets. For propulsion, we assume advanced propulsion systems such as fusion pulse propulsion to reach a significant percentage of light speed, discuss shielding and navigation requirements for ultra-high speed probes, and discuss the benefits of artificial/virtual crews over human crews in terms of fuel, mass and construction regarding our hypothetical mission.

The recurring themes in our proposal are miniaturization, efficiency and autonomy. A design which optimizes these features is especially fitting for an interstellar probe, whereas miniaturization allows us to use as little propellant as possible, and efficiency lets us get by with little energy and with maximum speed, and autonomy is the cornerstone of our proposal, eventually allowing trans-sapient levels of adaptability and error-recovery to be achieved for spacecraft control.

2. Background
2.1 Target Selection

Name	Distance (ly)	Planets	Planets in HZ	Max. ESI	Confirmed
Gliese 667C [1]	22	6 (7)	3	0.82	Yes
Gliese 581	20.2	5	1	0.81	Yes
Tau Ceti [43]	11.9	5	2	0.77	No
Gliese 163	48.8	3	1	0.74	Yes
HD 40307	41.7	3	1	0.72	No

Table 1: Promising nearby star systems with earth-like planets.

Recent surveys of extrasolar planets have revealed 743 star systems which contain 973 planets, 504 of which are closer than 100 light-years [45]. Most habitable exoplanets are expected to be found around M-class stars in recent studies that refines the concept of habitable zone; reference [18] revises the habitable zone according to atmospheric data, and reference [3] develops an empirical habitable zone definition which suggests prevalence of M stars with habitable planets (36.5) followed by K, A, G, F in order of decreasing percentage. Some of the most promising nearby planetary systems are displayed in Table 2.1, the columns of which indicate the name, the distance from solar system in light-years, the total number of planets, number of planets in the habitable zone, and maximum Earth Similarity Index (ESI), taken from the as of current list in Habitable Exoplanets Catalog [20] with high ESI values which measures the similarity of the planet to Earth incorporating many parameters [5]. Most of the exoplanets discovered in the habitable zone are either gas giants, or super-Earths, i.e., rocky planets that are more massive than Earth. All the habitable planets in are super-Earths, with masses less than 10 Earths, and they have greater ESI values than Mars. Extra-terrestrial life depends on more than Earth likeness naturally, such as stability, surface temperature variations, and chemical composition. Some may even turn out to be gaseous and have habitable moons. Also notable is the idea that astrobiology may be fundamentally different from ours, alleviating the need for similarity to Earth. However, for colonization purposes, a similar planet would be most convenient.

For our intelligent probe, we have chosen Tau Ceti and Gliese 667C as the target systems among the candidate star systems in , due to the close proximity of the former, and the high ESI values of the latter's three planets. Although the habitable super-Earths in Tau Ceti are yet unconfirmed, there is reasonable speculation in support. Tau Ceti e has a high ESI value, suggesting its atmosphere is similar to Earth. Although Tau Ceti f is said to be a cold planet, due to greenhouse effect, its surface temperature may vary, providing liquid water for complex life. Gliese 667C is naturally an attractive target as it is both close enough for a 21st century mission, and has three habitable planets. There is insufficient data about the habitability of these planets yet, however, there is ample time for future observations.

2.2 The Challenges Of Propulsion

It is common knowledge that chemical rockets do not have enough energy density to support interstellar travel within reasonable time frames, which suggests using nuclear and anti-matter rockets, and alternative propulsion concepts [24] . The first application of nuclear power to interstellar propulsion was the Orion project [8] , which used nuclear pulse propulsion by periodically detonating small nuclear explosives (fusion-enhanced fission reactions) against a pusher plate. Orion project was abandoned due to Partial Test Ban Treaty and issues of nuclear fallout.

Numerous credible design studies succeeded Orion, some of which replaced fission with smaller yield fusion reactions, as spacecraft design is limited by the size of smallest explosive package possible. The most comprehensive of such studies to date is the Daedalus project of the British Interplanetary Society which used D - He3 pellets for electron beam driven inertial confinement fusion, that directly transformed fusion products into thrust via a magnetic pusher plate [13] . Daedalus propulsion combines kinetic shock absorption with magnetic impulse from a superconductive shell. Each pellet of the Daedalus propulsion system is a miniature explosive package composed of a D - T trigger and D - He3 fuel encapsulated in a superconductive shell, which after magnetic injection into a hemispherical reaction chamber, burns into fusion and yields thrust, repeatedly detonated by the relativistic electron beam at 250 Hz.

The primary disadvantage of fusion pulse propulsion is the inordinate mass of the driver, cooling, conductance and plasma containment systems. The Daedalus mission weight for Barnard's Star was about 53000 tonnes which may present orbital construction challenges in the near-future. Project Icarus proposed replacing the electron beam driver with laser and decreasing the nuclear pulse to 150 Hz with smaller pellets [25]. The fusion-driven rocket partially solves the problem by using metal liners to both contain the plasma and conversion to thrust [34]. Light-sails work without any propellant, and laser-driven light-sails can reach up to 0.1c easily with around one-half GW power, making light-sails an ideal candidate for fly-by missions [21]. Antimatter ignited fusion pulse propulsion proposals solve the mass problem by substituting the lasers with antiprotons. Antiproton annihilation ignites a small fission reaction which then powers fusion in the pellets. Antimatter production and storage present research challenges of its own, however. Current research indicates that positron annihilation driven rockets is a feasible concept, as pursued by Positronics Research LLC. Simultaneously, groups like Positron Dynamics LLC have been reporting advances in positron storage. Likewise, small cylindrical inertial electrostatic confinement fusion devices pursued might turn out to be practical [28]. McGuire's follow-up work at Lockheed aims supporting 100 MW reactors in 2 metric cubes. Such a small fusion reactors can henceforth power efficient plasma rockets with high specific impulse, partially solving the dreaded mass problem with fusion rockets.

2.3 Artificial General Intelligence

Artificial General Intelligence (AGI) field seeks to build a human-level, general-purpose Artificial Intelligence (AI) system, which may be defined as a computer system that can solve any problem that humans can. The most fundamental feature of human intelligence is its apparent universal character, that it can in principle solve any problem. Furthermore, it has been observed that the problems of intelligence are essentially prediction problems, i.e., the most basic intelligence problem is that of extrapolating from data, which corresponds to inductive inference in scientific inquiry. That is to say, the task of formulating a general law from given observations forms the core of our intelligence. As such, Einstein's theory of general relativity is a fine accomplishment of induction, as well any scientific discovery. Ray Solomonoff's universal induction theory [37] addresses the universal inductive inference problem, based on a quite benign assumption: that the probability distribution of the universe is computable. This assumption apparently holds for the observable universe due to Bekenstein bound, since the observable universe has finite entropy, and thus has a computable probability distribution, even if quantum events are indeed random. When this assumption is satisfied, it has been proven that predictions have very small error dependent only on the universal computer chosen to represent information, and not the data. The predictions converge very rapidly (convergence theorem). Solomonoff's induction method is incomputable, however, it may be approximated arbitrarily, and many practical universal induction algorithms already exist. Solomonoff's theory has unveiled a beautiful concept, which is the probability of an object to be produced by a random program. The probability of bitstring x, which may be anything on a computer, is known as universal distribution and it is defined as:

$$P(x) = \sum_{U(\pi_i) = x*} 2^{-|\pi_i|}$$

(1)

where U is a universal computer (a computer that can interpret a programming language), x^* is x and any extension of x, and $|\pi_i|$ is the length of program π_i that generates x as a prefix. In application to prediction, it can solve arbitrary sequence, set, and operator induction problems [40]. Solomonoff's induction method fully formalizes Occam's razor, the distribution explicitly shows that probability of a program decreases exponentially with increasing program length, yet it allows multiple explanations at once (Epicurus's law of multiple explanations). The benefit of the universal distribution may be most clearly understood in the context of Bayesian inference. In Bayesian inference, if there is little data, the inference does not work well. There is also the problem of often not knowing the a priori probability distribution. The universal distribution acts as a universal prior for any application of Bayes theorem, alleviating these major problems. In our experiments, we have seen that universal induction works extremely well with small amounts of data.

Let us try to give a better sense of how an inductive inference engine works. Given a set $\{(x_1, y_1), (x_2, y_2), \dots\}$ of input, output pairs, operator induction can learn the generalized conditional pdf $P(Y \mid X)$, and it allows us to predict $arg\,max_Y P(Y \mid X)$. Operator induction solves any classical ML problem; x_i's may be faces and and y_i's names, and it is perfectly general. It has been argued in the literature that we can apply induction to solve any AI problem [16].

Some approximation methods exist for Solomonoff's universal inductive inference method, which are basically Levin's universal search [22] and evolutionary programming (which has also produced our intelligence). The major application of inductive inference is building a cognitive architecture that uses inductive inference module, an early example of which is the OpenCog system [11].

Some forthcoming challenges of AGI research are:
1. Choosing the right universal computer (variants of LISP, FORTH, machine language, MATLAB, etc.)
2. Designing an efficient approximation algorithm as the search space is exponential in the number of bits and parallelism is required.
3. Memory: designing a transfer learning method and making memory work with induction
4. Modularity and scalability: making a scalable cognitive architecture that can scale up to human-level complex problems, comprised of many kinds and instances of cognitive modules.

Examples of AGI systems we may recount here are
- Alpha [39]: assimilates narrow-AI and universal AI systems, it is modular, it has preprogrammed higher-order cognitive procedures that perform analysis and synthesis, and it can solve free-form time-limited optimization problems
- Gödel Machine [35]: Self-reflective AI agent design, which can use and improve any reaction policy
- AIXI [15]: extends universal sequence induction and it is an optimal reinforcement learning agent model which uses input, actions, rewards to make an optimal plan, and it can optimize expected future rewards.
- Teramachine [32]: a universal inductive inference engine that partially solves the memory and parallelism problems.

3. Semi-autonomous Agent for Intelligent Control
3.1 Rationale

Intelligent probes are required mainly due to communication latency with interstellar spacecraft, however, there are other factors which may be as significant in practice. There are multiple intelligence-requiring tasks on-board an interstellar spacecraft, the most immediate of which are:

Navigation: Neither is the interstellar environment void of hazards, nor do we know much about it. While future missions plan to map the heliopause, there will still be much that is unknown in the interstellar space, especially nearer the target system. In addition to this, the voyage shall take several years, which implies variability in system performance and operation, all of which point out that an intelligent navigation system would be most useful.

Scientific tasks: Without an adequate scientific payload and an array of informative scientific tasks, an interstellar expedition would merely be an engineering demonstration. Our lack of knowledge about the host system, however, implies much adaptivity in the execution of the scientific tasks, which casts doubt on pre-programmed scientific instruments. An AI system may also perform open-ended queries on a target system, employing as much creativity as a human, in finding answers to questions such as the presence of exobiology in the system.

Emergencies and fault-tolerance: Due to mission longevity requirements, we may expect many emergencies and faults during the mission. Intelligent recovery from such erroneous conditions will improve the robustness of the system. An AI system may also respond to such emergencies much quicker than any human can, and it may even be able to resolve emergencies which were not anticipated.

An AI control module thus affords several advantages that would be unwise to neglect. It first eliminates significant mass for the habitat module and extra shielding, while retaining every advantage of a human crew, a point which was also well taken by the Daedalus Project. It offers improved longevity, as AI may do well in conserving resources, and carrying out mission tasks as efficiently as possible. In contrast to a human crew, AI may have better rationality, as we may program it to be free of human emotions in its decision making. AI may have improved reaction times to all manners of hazards and faults during the voyage, and this might matter much, as for instance, one may imagine an unanticipated hazard in the fusion propulsion system which may be prevented with the right command within a matter of microseconds. A successful AI control system may also have superior error recovery abilities, as it may have command of every engineering method ever devised. For instance, whereas a human may start writing a MATLAB program, an AI may already have the answer from an obscure engineering journal and have solved an optimization problem prior to the accident in case any error of the variety might happen. Possibly, the most interesting point of an AI system however is increased intelligence, as the AI might be able to solve error recovery problems that would take a large community of human scientists to solve.

3.2 Agent Designs

An AI agent is an abstraction of an intelligent animal, which acts in an environment in an intelligent manner. Two common agent designs are relevant to interstellar probes: the goal-following agent, and the utility-maximizing agent. Both agent designs interpret sensor signals to infer the state of the world, and manage actuators intelligently so as to influence the environment. Both agents know how their actions will influence the world state. The goal-following agent chooses present (and future) actions in order to satisfy pre-determined goals. Likewise, the utility-maximizing agent chooses in actions that will maximize its (future, cumulative, or expected, or defined otherwise plausibly) utility. The latter kind of agent has received an unusually intense treatment in the Artificial General Intelligence community, the best known example of which is the AIXI reinforcement-learning agent which solves the problem in a universal setting [15] . A reinforcement-learning agent assigns positive or negative reward signals, much like an animal does, to solve the utility maximization problem. We shall show that both kinds of agent designs are fitting for the AI probe.

3.3 Agent Sensors And Actuators

Sensory input corresponds to spacecraft's sensor instruments and computer's instruments, such as its ability to read its RAM. The sensory input may be provided to AI in many ways. It may be provided as raw data to the AI, which then has to run appropriate perceptual processing algorithms to extract relevant information, which requires the highest level of intelligence and learning rate for the agent. It may be supplied in the form of calculations over raw data, such as location of pulsars from the X-ray telescope, or other relevant astrophysics calculations such as a power spectrum, which would accelerate perceptual processing. One may also run perceptual-specific narrow AI's and astrophysics calculations to directly supply the AI with such data structures like an astronomical map, much like the data structures autonomous driving programs work with.

Actuators are the outputs of the control system, and they correspond to every device which manipulates the environment and the spacecraft itself, such as the thrusters. Similar to sensors, there are many ways to deal with actuators; the AI can either drive the control signals of every subsystem directly, or it can issue high-level computer commands to actuator subsystems, for instance it can send the command "FUSION THRUSTER THROTTLE 40" to the propulsion subsystem. The distributed design seems more manageable and akin to large-scale project development.

3.4 Primary Mission Objectives

To better comprehend the problems that the agent will have to solve, let us enlist the most essential mission objectives in temporal order. Recall that for the AI to be specified in the right manner, they ought to be expressed in the most general manner of conceptualization to allow it freedom.

1. Navigate safely to the target star system: Travel to the host star system in the shortest time possible, using as few resources as possible, and incurring as little damage as possible, maintaining as many subsystems as fully operational.

2. Survey the planets: Chart the star system by determining the orbits and astronomical properties of all bodies with significant mass, then determine a short list of planets which may embody life, and then travel to the orbits of these planets and map the planets' topography and run the sensory instruments on the planets such that resources are not depleted for the mission duration.

3. Perform experiments: Carry out intelligent sub-plans corresponding to each scientific experiment in order of decreasing priority.

4. Establish communications: Determine the exact location of a FOCAL probe, deploy an inflatable RF antenna, and establish communication with the FOCAL probe such that bandwidth is maximized. Transmit as much relevant mission information as possible, in order of decreasing priority to the FO-CAL probe, such that energy is preserved during transmission.

Note that any/all of these objectives may be carried out concurrently.

3.5 Goal Specification For Goal-Following Agents

The goal-following agent may work with explicit statement of goal-states in a logical language. For instance, it may have a form such as:

$$DistanceLessThan(CurrentPos, TauCeti, 1\text{-}AU).$$

It may have natural language commands, as in OpenCog Bot [12] , which can answer natural language queries, and accept natural language commands. Thus, the above goal may be stated as "Travel to Tau Ceti system and stop around an orbit of 1 AU distance to Tau Ceti star", which the agent would first translate to an internal knowledge representation and carry out a plan which corresponds to the commands. The goals may also be expressed in a logical natural language such as LojBan [10] . Thus, a succession of goal-states may be either pre-programmed or transmitted to the spacecraft on-the-fly.

Another means to implement a goal-following agent would be to express the goal as a free-form optimization problem. For instance, the above goal may be expressed as an optimization problem of the following form.

$$min.d(\text{ current }, \text{ tauceti })-1\,AU \quad \text{¿}$$
$$s.t.\text{ spent-fuel }(t_{end})<\text{ total-fuel} \quad \text{¿}$$

In the context of AI probe, the free-form optimizer must be general enough to account for multiple objectives and multiple constraints, and must be adaptable to real-time operation, wherein the values of input variables may rapidly change.

3.6 Reinforcement Learning Agent

Discrete goals, such as the arrival to a star system of the preceding examples, may be expressed as 0/1 rewards to the reinforcement-learning (RL) agent. Numerical objectives may be mapped to utilities. For instance, a reward may consider the percentage of a planet's surface that has been mapped by the probe.

For reinforcement-learning agents, an important problem may be the question of how to combine the various rewards, as this may create unforeseen strange behaviors in bizarre, unanticipated circumstances. A simple method is a linear combination of rewards, however, coefficients must be then tried out in simulation to see if whether this results in stable behavior. Other more sophisticated approaches may use reward vectors, other possible reward structures (a tree may denote reward priorities) or statistical combination of various rewards. Yet more sophisticated approaches may have an optimizer that considers multiple rewards.

3.7 Autonomy

An important trade-off for the intelligent probe is specific vs. unspecific goals. A specific goal would contain numerically precise model states. For instance, as relevant to our goal example, it might be "Orbit around target star at 1.0 AU +/- 10 m". Such numerically precise goals run risk of failure, due to tight constraints. In some circumstances, it might be too difficult or costly to achieve them, leading the spacecraft to sub-optimal behavior. On the other hand, unspecific goals allow the probe the freedom to plan. For instance, we may instruct the probe to gather as much information as possible about the system. We call this kind of maximally general objective a "universal goal". Universal goals are likely more appropriate for generally intelligent agents, as they exploit the unbounded creativity of these agents.

Another relevant trade-off is fully autonomous vs. semi-autonomous intelligent agent. It is well known that fully autonomous agents may diverge and have drives of their own [30] , which may well be detrimental to (real) mission goals. We propose a simple solution to the problem of AI drives:

1. One must use physical constraints. There must be interpreted sensor inputs which account for basic physical measurements, such as location, velocity, energy spent, and so forth. Thereafter, the agent may be instructed to respect the physical constraints, such as a certain time-space bound is respected, and only a certain amount of energy is spent.

2. One must specify the goals generally, but at the same time sufficiently precisely. This is achieved by striking the right balance between specificity and unspecificity, as discussed before. The goal must be precise enough such that the agent knows what we wish it to achieve, and at the same time it must be imprecise enough such that the agent may conceive as many ways as possible to satisfy the goal.

3. One must avoid open-ended goals. Open-ended goal roughly means an optimization problem with an unbounded objective. For instance, maximizing the lifetime of the agent is such an objective. Plugging such objectives into the agent may interfere with other essential tasks. For instance, the survivalist agent given as an example would likely try to conserve resources and avoid making any scientific experiments eventually (as much the utility combination allows).

4. One may use priorities suitably. The use of weights/priorities corresponding to probe goals may be useful, in that, the agent knows which goal is the most important. For instance, arriving at the target system may be more important for a mission than achieving a stable orbit. In that case, the probe may decide to switch to a fly-by mission, since a propulsion component was damaged beyond repair.

4. Autonomous Agent Example

A quite unspecific agent may be expressed as an optimization problem of the following form.

4.1 Objective

The objective is to maximize amount of (true/verified) information discovered about the target system and transmitted back to Earth. The amount of information may be expressed as the expected cumulative information for the entire mission duration, thus it encompasses all future actions, resulting in an integrative plan. The amount of information may be calculated with respect to all questions that may be asked of the system, which may be formalized as improving the prediction accuracy for any induction problem that contains the system as a variable. The questions thus may be generated in order of increasing a priori probability of the question, assigning much more weight to simpler/shorter questions, and they may be weighed accordingly. Thus, it is more important for the probe to answer a question whether there are any rocky planets, than the number of mountains on a particular planet that have an elevation of more than 12000 meters. The list of these potential questions would be examined before mission, however, the importance of this approach is that as the probe increases its knowledge, the order of questions change, giving it an intelligent inquisitive character.

Note that an RL formulation is also possible. In this case, the idea is loosely equivalent to the Bayesian knowledge-seeking agent [31] , which can gather as much information about an unknown environment as possible.

4.2 Constraints

As the objective is general, so must the constraints.

1. Spacecraft resources are not depleted within maximum mission duration.
2. Spacecraft's critical subsystems remain operational for specified period.
3. Spacecraft remains within given space-time region and energy limits.
4. Generalized non-interference clause: spacecraft does not interfere with any intelligent agents encountered.

4.3 Advanced Formulation of AI Probe

An extremely advanced formulation of the optimizing/goal-following agents is possible due to Solomonoff's general-purpose AI system Alpha, stage 2 [39] which can solve time-limited free-form optimization problems. Alpha is of particular interest to us because it is the culmination of our research program, as teramachine was conceived as a candidate for Alpha, stage 1 [32] . Shortly, merely collecting as much information as possible is not enough. One must also optimize the rate of information extraction, which Solomonoff briefly explains in [39] . Also, real-time operation is of paramount importance for a spacecraft.

The advanced formulation optimizes the main objective function within a time-limit we call a planning quanta, which may be set as 1 millisecond. Thus, an action plan is continually updated. The plan optimizes the efficiency of knowledge extraction, in terms of bits/J•sec, that is, it optimizes the number of bits extracted per unit of energy spent within unit time. For this approach to work, Alpha must be made fully incremental, so that its batch processing approach can be converted to real-time. Another approach is to divide the plan into a top-level plan which is updated slowly and a reactive plan which is updated rapidly. Such hierarchy allows separation of reflective thinking and reactive thinking as in the Gödel Machine [35] , and as many levels as useful may be created for various temporal requirements.

4.4 Adding Specificity

We may modify the objective such that problems are restricted to astrophysics and astrobiology domains. This may be achieved by conditioning the problem generator on the corpuses that correspond to these domains.

We may also modify the objective such that prediction accuracy in answering given questions increase. Following are examples of such questions:

- Is there life in the host system?
- Is there intelligent life in the system?
- Are there technological artifacts in the system?
- What are the astronomical properties of bodies in the system?
- What are the chemical compositions of the bodies?
- What are the topographies of the bodies?

These are examples of questions we are truly curious about. It must not discourage the reader that these are most general questions. General approaches to solution of some of these questions are already known. For instance, in the absence of any evolution, we expect the proportions of chemicals in a planet to be much more uniform. Therefore, looking for any sort of skewed distribution of elements which may not be easily explained by usual geological interactions would be a general method to detect life. It is expected that the human-level AI knows and understands all such general methods sufficiently well, i.e., as well as any human scientist, therefore it should not be prohibitive to ask these questions in the simplest fashion possible. Furthermore, the set of pre-specified questions may be weighed, causing the probe to spend more energy on questions we are more wondrous about.

The unspecific agent in general may be much more flexible. Assume that the second question in the preceding text was answered positively, and an RF-capable civilization was detected on a planet. The AI could learn to communicate with the extra-terrestrial intelligence and directly ask them the questions it could not answer itself, translate them, and send us its findings. On the other hand, the specific agent of the sort outlined here may be more efficient due to the exploitation vs. exploration trade-off; note that there are many suitable proposals for information acquisition that may handle this trade-off automatically [41] . The correct application of curiosity in an AGI controlled interstellar probe seems, therefore, a matter of importance, and thus general theories of curiosity are relevant [36 ,42] . The probe must be curious, but must not be so curious as to diverge to random walks.

5. Training

The training is likely to start in 2030 using supercomputers, and should be regarded as the most expensive part of an AGI application. Since by 2030, we assume human-level energy efficiency will be achieved, training the AI should not take any more than training a human by that time, in fact, it should be much faster, since we will be using faster computers than human.

5.1 Modes Of Intelligence

Various modes of intelligence may be sought for the AI agent. Following are some scenarios from the simplest mode of intelligence to the most sophisticated.

- A high-level gating system that acts like an animal. Assume that there are several fixed programs that solve various subsystem functions in the probe. One way to visualize this is to consider all the sections in a Mission Control Room. Each section in mission control may be automated by a narrow AI system of its own, optimizing the behavior of given subsystem, using many fixed programs supplied to the probe, which perform the complex calculations required for orbit insertion and so forth. The various Mission Control AI's provide a narrow but useful degree of adaptivity to each command section. While, on the other hand, the general-purpose AI acts as a gating system, which knows enough to give the proper commands to the mission control AI's, but does not know in detail on its own how to perform them, i.e., it acts like a manager, or a mission directorate.

- A human-level AI that has expertise in related fields. The AI agent is trained, much like a university student, so that it is proficient enough to obtain a university degree in the relevant fields, for instance, astronautics, astrophysics, astrobiology, terrestrial sciences. The AI henceforth is a good scholar, and it can use applied knowledge it learned during its training to perform the required mission objectives.
- A self-reflective, self-improving trans-sapient agent (artificial star-fleet captain). This AI has accumulated a good portion of the knowledge generated by humans, and can process this information and invent new solutions at a much higher rate than human. It has demonstrated ability to learn new languages quickly and assimilate and apply new fields of inquiry as it has needed.

5.2 Background Knowledge And Testing
Standard material in any human-level AI encompasses:

- Training in pattern recognition problems (visual, audio, etc.).
- Extensive training in math, physics, English.
- Includes much of high-school/college curriculum.
- Capability to learn and apply human knowledge assessed (can pass SAT/GRE).

We estimate that the training of the standard human-level AI will take at most $100 M and 5 years once the algorithms are stabilized. Thus, if in 2025 we have the first human-level AI program, then in 2030 we may train it to a level where it can comprehend arbitrary text.

- Interstellar mission knowledge would be required.
- Expert-level training in physics, chemistry, astrophysics, astronomy, astrobiology .
- Spacecraft specific training for use and control of every subsystem.
- Mission training involving hand-crafted and random mission simulations.
- Mission readiness determined by an Interstellar Turing Test.

In 10 years, with an additional budget of $200 M, expert level training and realistic mission simulations may be achieved, in time for mission launch in 2040.

6. Human-Level AI Projection
We calculate a new upper bound for relevant human brain computational capacity to determine a worst-case estimation for when human-level AI will be feasible. To our knowledge, this figure was not achieved in this manner before. Number of neurons in the brain is about 10^{11}, and the number of synapses in the neocortex, the region which is thought to include higher-level cognition, is about 1.64×10^{14}, while total number of synapses is less than 5×10^{14}. Synaptic bandwidth is about 1500 bits/sec maximum [6] . Therefore, cortical speed is approximately 1.5 $\times 10^{17}$ *bits/sec*, which is about 3.8 petaflop/sec. Contrast with Moravec's estimate, which was 100 Teraflop/sec [29] ; a large gap which suggests that Moravec was optimistic.

Energy efficiency of cortical computation is thus 3.8 petaflop/sec at 20W, which is 192 Teraflop/sec•W. Note that tighter estimates are possible, but we are merely making a rough worst-case estimate. While it seems that Moore's law in its original form has been trumped, Koomey's law suggests that energy efficiency of computing doubles every 18 months, and it has been observed to be more stable than Moore's law. Our prior estimate using Moravec's optimistic estimate of human-level energy efficiency was 2026 [33] based on NVIDIA chips' energy efficiency. We now base our calculation on Adapteva's multi-core chips, which obtain 32 GigaFlops for $100 currently, at 72 GigaFlops/Watt energy efficiency for their 64-core CPU. When we extrapolate using Koomey's law for upper bound, we find that in 17 years human-level energy efficiency would be achieved, which sets our worst-case prediction as 2030. By then, we anticipate that human-level AI will already be available, and the interstellar probe will merely be an application.

6.1 Infinity Point

Infinity Point is a striking consequence of Solomonoff's mathematical analysis of social effects of AI [38] , and it is also known as singularity by authors who popularized this discovery consequent to Solomonoff. Solomonoff has observed that human-level AI accelerates Moore's law, as AI may run on hardware to which Moore's law is applicable, and it can accelerate computer hardware research, resulting in a positive feedback loop, improving the already exponential improvement of Moore's law. As such, it is a macro-economic hypothesis about proliferation of human-level AI technology.

Moore's law may be summarized as "number of transistors placed on a microprocessor at a fixed cost doubles every two years". Current doubling time is about three years, which means that Moore's law has already tapered off. However, let us first present the theory and show how it will be salvaged. According to the theory, we have two assumptions:

- Computer Science community size ~ rate of improvement.
- Computer Science community size ~ rate of logarithm of computing efficiency.

That is, the larger the community, the smaller the doubling time gets. Solomonoff's macro-economical theory suggests that if fixed amount of money is invested in AI every year, we thus obtain infinite improvement in finite time, which he describes as an impossible mathematical singularity.

In practice we have only finite improvement, we improve from 600 years from unaltered Moore's law to a few decades. However, Moore's law is already slowing down so it is inapplicable. We can replace Moore's law with Koomey's law and thus still predict an infinity point. By 2030, it will be a negligible amount of money to augment each computer with an equally efficient AI, which sets $R = 1$ in Solomonoff's theory, his calculations show the infinity point to arrive in less than five years with this rate of investment [38] . Therefore, infinity point is expected to occur by 2035 in the worst case, which turns out to be quite surprising. Note that this estimate rests on the assumptions stated above, and analysis of them is part of ongoing research.

6.2 Computer Technology by 2040

We extrapolate energy efficiency of computation by 2040, which is the launch date of our hypothetical mission. Without infinity point, we have 195 Petaflop/sec•W efficiency (101.5 x human); one brain simulation costs about 0.2 W. With infinity point, we assume human-level AI by 2035. At 20 W per brain simulation, we double CS community every year. This incurs a negligible cost with respect to global economy by then. Double-exponential improvement in energy efficiency occurs extremely rapidly, and infinity point then is reached in 4.62 years, which implies that computational resources will be abundant by 2040, and efficiency will be much closer to physical limits than present. For our design, however, we do not assume infinity point, and thus our projections may be interpreted as a worst-case scenario.

7. Brain Simulations for Virtual Crew

Brain scanning technology improves very rapidly. Human Brain Project will complete by 2025 and it aims to build the first complete brain simulation by then. By 2040, 20 W can simulate 100 virtual crew, and thus we can build a particular spaceship of the imagination that houses a virtual crew and take our best minds on a trip across the stars.

As Tipler and others have suggested brain simulations (sims) may interface with body images in VR and they can occupy a virtual bridge and a virtual city. Sims can carry a copy of the internet and all libraries with them and thus have access to vast knowledge resources.

Even more interestingly, we can build a trans-sapient artificial astro-physicist which will possess an extended neocortex in simulation, that will be able to directly perceive astrophysics modalities, and can invoke computer tools with no delay, allowing it to drive the ship's controls as it were its appendages.

Sims will be trained before voyage on virtual missions, allowing us to explore every mission variation and hazard. As with the AI, sims may use a sleep mode to conserve energy, and run at different speeds to accommodate various spaceship tasks. During the voyage, sims may continue collecting and interpreting data, and conduct scientific work, as well as preparing a rich log of the voyage for analyzing back at Earth. Sims may also engage in all manners of recreational and creative activities, as well as inventing and producing new technology. A major advantage of sims is that they have human experience and thus might more directly apprehend what we would prefer in case of unprecedented situations.

8. Subsystems

8.1 Command and control

By 2040, we will have ample speed to simulate 100 humans. If we allow for five times the resources required for virtual reality and auxiliary programs, or instead deploy 1 trans-sapient AGI agent (at 500x human speed), we require 19.5 exaflop/sec computing speed. We may also assume 10 exabyte storage. The entire power budget thus is about 100 W, and with three-way redundancy for the computer system, we require 300 W power, and only 1 kg payload (which fits into a 1U unit). The AI can scale down to 2 W on-route (which is 10x human speed), since not all tasks need to be given minute attention during a long voyage.

8.2 Communication

Two reasonable approaches are laser communication which requires only 20 W and a 3 meter telescope like Hubble, and gravitational-lensing amplification for RF (FOCAL mission) [27] . The FOCAL proposal exploits gravitational-lensing of Sun (and host system), and it requires a mission to 550 AU distance from Sun. We find that gravitational-lensing may be preferable since it might be lighter than optical communication, and since RF is not obstructed by interstellar medium. The analysis of radio communication using the FOCAL probe suggests that 40 W power would be enough and we may use only an inflatable RF antenna. We assume an inflatable 8m RF antenna shaped as a parabolic dish, that fits into a 3U unit with 5 kg mass, requiring 30 W. The material currently used is mylar, but we estimate that lighter materials will be available, and larger dishes can be constructed for the same mass.

8.3 Scientific Instrumentation

We assume a standard array of scientific instrumentation similar to those on interplanetary probes such as the New Horizons probe [9] . We propose a modular cubesat design and we have extrapolated approximate figures for various scientific instrumentation modules from current cubesat technology. The form, mass and power requirements of cubesat modules thus estimated are shown in Table 2 .

Name	Form	Mass	Power
Long-Range Imaging	3U	3kg	10W
Infrared Imaging Spectrometer	1U	1kg	10W
Imaging Spectrometer	1U	1kg	10W
Mass Spectrometer	3U	3kg	20W
LIDAR	1U	1kg	20W
Dust detector	1U	1kg	10W

Table 2: Scientific Instruments

8.4 Power

Power is vital in a long space mission. We think that the spacecraft must be supplied with various power systems so that during emergencies there is sufficient power to resume operation. We propose using the following power modules:

- Thermoelectric converter for main power: the converters will transform excess heat from the fusion chamber to electric power.
- We assume Quantum Well Film converters, which will provide 1.5 kW for 30 x 50 W modules, with 600 gr mass and a $\Delta T = 200$.
- We assume 1.5 kg coolant, which may fit in a 2U cubesat, with only 2 kg mass.
- Radioisotope Thermal Generator (RTG) for auxiliary power: we propose plutonium for the longer half-life required during the interstellar mission. The unit is supposed to provide at most 50 W for a 3U cubesat, with 3 kg mass.

- Solar panels for auxiliary power: these will be most useful at the target system, possibly giving the probe indefinite lifespan. We propose using a deployable cubesat solar panel, which will fit into a 2U, 2 kg unit, providing up to 50 W power.
- Battery (emergency power): useful when auxiliary power is not available and thruster has to be restarted, 2U, 2kg cubesat unit with 300 Wh capacity.

8.5 Propulsion

As described in Section 2.2 , fission, fusion, anti-matter and sail concepts are generally thought to be feasible, while a host of technological developments are necessary to realize them. Nuclear pulse propulsion seems too massive for small probes due to minimum pellet size limitation and massive containment. Laser/beam driver is massive as well, and requires auxiliary power and inter-dependent mission structure. Light-sail seems inappropriate for rendezvous missions. Pure antimatter rocket requires much antimatter which may not be available by 2040. We thus recall the anti-proton ignited nuclear pulse propulsion proposal (ICAN-II) [23], in which the basic idea is to employ antimatter annihilation to ignite micro-fission/fusion detonations, overcoming the massive overhead of usual nuclear pulse propulsion designs and taking a large payload to Mars. Likewise, reference [4] suggests combining antiproton induced fission and magnetically insulated inertial confinement fusion. Antiprotons to burn fusion pellets (Cassenti et al) A beam of anti-protons/positrons ignites fusion pellets which consist of a fissile core and fusion fuel encapsulated in a tungsten shell for containment, with an inner uranium shell.

On the other hand, AIMStar uses antiproton annihilation for burning fusion fuel droplets for a cubesat mission to the Oort cloud [19] . We have found that extrapolating the AIMStar mission is appropriate for our interstellar mission. AIM stands for Antimatter Initiated Micro-fusion; the crucial component is an antiproton cloud confined in a Penning trap. The trap is about 10 kg and has dimensions of *0.1 m x 0.1 m x 0.3 m* which is the size of a 3U cubesat. Fusion fuel is magnetically injected into the reaction chamber. Antimatter is supplied at the rate of 10^{11} anti-protons/sec. The fusion pulse is provided by a 42 ng *D - He3* droplet (5×10^{15} pairs), which is 45 nm in diameter. $5x\ 10^8$ antiprotons burn 2 molar mixture of fission fuel (e.g., U238) which fully ionizes the fusion fuel droplet, while the fission fragments are not radioactive. Thereafter, the droplet is magnetically compressed for a fusion ignition. A 50 Hz cycle is maintained yielding 0.75 MW continuous power in the form of protons and alpha particles. A chamber henceforth may transfer fusion power to hydrogen propellant, and an analysis of 100% efficiency is presented. We assume for sake of simplicity that such a chamber (not designed in AIMStar proposal) is possible and may be scaled down from the Daedalus chamber. We propose to maintain AIMStar's advantages, as micro-fusion is more cost-effective than Daedalus pellets, whereby propellant mass decreases by many orders of magnitude. If we assume a chamber made of molybdenum that is 1 inches thick and has a radius of 0.1m, then we estimate a 32kg chamber. Such a configuration would be feasible for interstellar probes, however note that additional components such as magnets would likely be required to harness the fusion products as thrust. In particular, one may wish to use the alpha particles as thrust and deflect the protons with a magnetic pusher plate.

Let us also note that Positronics Research LLC is currently developing a new positron rocket design that uses an attenuation matrix to transfer the energy of positron annihilation to propellant, while Positron Dynamics LLC is working on positron storage technology. We foresee another propulsion design for probes which annihilates positrons to ignite micro-fusion as we may expect sufficient amount of positrons to be storable by 2040, although it is not yet known if such a design is possible, either.

Another recent development is the quantum vacuum plasma thruster experiments developed by Eagleworks laboratory of NASA [44] . If the work in question bears fruit, it would instantly solve interstellar propulsion problems for it is a propulsion system that uses the quantum vacuum as propellant, requiring energy only for the generated fields.

8.6 Navigation

Four pulsars can be used to compute location [7], however for that a proper X-ray telescope is required. Traditional X-ray telescopes are too massive for a probe, while newly developed lobster eye optics improves efficiency up to 1000 times [14] . A mini lobster X-ray imaging module for picosatellites has been proposed by Hudec et. al and a 10 cm x 10 cm x 30 cm design is underway (3U cubesat). We estimate a 3 kg device with 10 W power.

We also require attitude control and auxiliary thrust for navigation. We assume 3x 3U Cubesat Ambipolar Thruster (CAT) plasma thruster modules, which spend 20 W, and have 5 kg mass each, with the performance of 2 mN continuous thrust for 10 W, and 20 mN thrust for pulsed 100 W, as recently proposed in a crowdfunding project by Benjamin Longmier [26]. Two modules shall have 4 x 2 small thrusters, 1 module shall have 3-axis 5 x 2 small thruster.

A sensor module provides navigation sensors, which we take to be accelerometers, gyros, and magnetometers for 3-axis. We also require an attitude-meter, a star-sensor and radiation monitor. The navigation sensors ought to fit into a 1U cubesat, with 1 kg mass, using 10 W power.

8.7 Shielding

Artificial mini-magnetosphere is an idea to shield spacecraft from charged particles by generating a magnetic field imitating earth's magnetosphere [2] . The laboratory experiment used a 0.5 T natural magnet, and in various publications Bamford recounts that 50 nT sufficient for space applications with a 100 *m* radius. We estimate 500 W, produced from fusion burn and a 1 kg additional weight for mini-shield. We also require a carbon nanotube EMI shield, which has been previously tested on cubesat. We have not yet considered neutron shields, although Project Daedalus has, and neutral particles must be considered in any interstellar voyage.

9. Mission Profile

Name	Mass (kg)	Power (kg)
Propulsion		
Reaction Trap	10	100
Chamber	32	
Power		
Thermoelectric	2	
RTG	3	
Solar Panel	2	
Battery	2	
Navigation		
Mini-Lobster	3	10
Sensors	1	10
Attitude Ctrl.	15	60
Name	Mass (kg)	Power (kg)
Science		
Long-Range	3	10
IR Imaging	2	10
Imaging Spectr.	2	10
Mass Spectr.	3	20
LIDAR	1	20
Dust Detector	1	10
Control		
AI	1	2-300
Shielding	1	0-500
Communication		
Inflatable RF	5	30
Spaceship Infr.	2	10
Total	91	302-1102

Table 3: Subsystems

Table 3 summarizes the subsystems in terms of mass and power requirements. Note that this is merely a preliminary design, which requires many additional components to be realistic. We attempted to show that a reaction mass on the order of 100 kg is realistic, although it may require many technological developments to achieve such mass efficiency. In particular, an antimatter ignited fusion propulsion system is likely going to be much bigger in practice, and also propulsion tanks are not accounted for in this calculation which is a major shortcoming. However, we still give a full mission profile in Table 4 assuming that all fusion energy is converted to thrust, because it corresponds to a best-case analysis for this propulsion technology. As it is quite likely that by 2040, technological progress will have been much accelerated compared to present rate.

	Tau Ceti	Gliese 667C
Distance	11.9 light-years	22 light-years
Cruise Speed	0.1c	–
Burnout time	9.183 years	–
Burnout distance	0.258 light-years	–
Antimatter required	0.97 milligrams	–
Fusion fuel required	36469 kg	–
Cruise Time	113.8 years	214.8 years
Total Voyage Time	132.2 years	233.2 years

Table 4: Mission Profile for AIM propulsion

	Tau Ceti	Gliese 667C
Distance	11.9 light years	22 light years
Mass	1561 kg	–
Cruise Speed	0.5c	–
Burnout time	18.5 years	–
Burnout distance	4.63 light years	–
Cruise Time	5.26 years	25.4 years
Total Voyage Time	42.3 years	62.5 years

Table 5: Mission Profile for Q-Thruster

Table 5 shows the mission profile assuming quantum vacuum plasma thruster technology. A SAFE-400 reactor with 512 kg mass and 400 kW thermal output, and 100 kW electrical output is assumed. We assume 4 N/kW thruster performance, and a thruster with 1000 kg mass. It is observed that the quantum thruster might achieve extraordinary performance.

10. Extended Roles for Intelligent Interstellar Probes

Intelligent interstellar probes may be supplemented with many technological tools for performing extended roles at the target system. Self-reproducing interstellar probes is a well-known concept, and valid extension of the Daedalus probe [17] . Likewise, our probe may be extended for this most intriguing extended role, however fashioned for high technology and the miniaturized design of our probe.

By 2040, we expect nano-assembly technology to be widely available. Such a machine is best characterized by the ability to construct nano-technological machinery by assembling atoms. If all the components in the above text are designed in this manner, a probe can assemble parts of itself for repairs and additional construction. An amount of material may be brought along, considering possible repairs, which is the most immediate application of a nano-tech assembler. However, if material can be mined at the host system, and designs only require materials that are easily mined, it may well be possible to 3d print the entire probe at the destination.

Refueling is almost as significant a role as reproduction and it is required for reproduction to be useful. It may be conceived that the probe may mine D and He3 from gas giants and water might be mined from carbonaceous asteroids, however, much additional hardware would have to be added to the probe for this role, defeating the point of miniaturization. To mine the gas giants, the probe may print balloon supported factories. Instead, we may try to design propulsion systems that use widely available fuel so that refueling task requires less effort.

Construction at the host system is an appealing role, and asteroid material might be sufficient for many products, given how versatile the carbon atom is. At the destination, it would be worthwhile to construct a station for enhanced solar (stellar) power, computation, and communication facilities. It may be possible to bootstrap essential parts of a technological civilization at the host system via this route. If mini-probes, robots, and landers may be printed, they can be used to extend the survey and increase the capabilities. For instance, if miner robots and more nano assemblers may be printed, miners can gather much more material, assemblers can produce required technologies, and an industrial base may thus be established.

Robotic bodies can be built for sims at the target system. Differences of sims can be communicated back to earth, so that sims at Sol may merge. Likewise, sims from Sol may be uploaded to the host system for visiting the facility

Acknowledgments

Thanks to participants of 100YSS symposium for making several suggestions which improved the paper. Thanks also to Centauri Dreams blog author Paul Gilster for keeping us up to date on interstellar research. Thanks to Zeynep Acuner for sending the reference on pulsar based navigation, and Gabriel Leuenberger for sharing his ideas on interstellar flight.

References

1. G. Anglada-Escudé, M. Tuomi, E. Gerlach, R. Barnes, R. Heller, J. S. Jenkins, S. Wende, S. S. Vogt, R. P. Butler, A. Reiners, and H. R. A. Jones. A dynamically-packed planetary system around GJ 667C with three super-Earths in its habitable zone. Astr. Ap., 556:A126, August 2013.

2. R Bamford, K J Gibson, A J Thornton, J Bradford, R Bingham, L Gargate, L O Silva, R A Fonseca, M Hapgood, C Norberg, T Todd, and R Stamper. The interaction of a flowing plasma with a dipole magnetic field: measurements and modelling of a diamagnetic cavity relevant to spacecraft protection. *Plasma Physics and Controlled Fusion*, 50(12):124025, 2008.

3. Justin R. Cantrell, Todd J. Henry, and Russel J. White. The solar neighborhood xxix: The habitable real estate of our nearest stellar neighbors. The Astronomical Journal, 146(4):99, 2013.

4. B. N. Cassenti, T. Kammash, and D. L. Galbraith. Antiproton catalyzed fusion propulsion for interplanetary missions. *Journal of Propulsion and Power*, 1997.

5. Schulze-Makuch D, Mndez A, Fairn AG, von Paris P, Turse C, Boyer G, Davila AF, Antnio MR, Catling D, and Irwin LN. A two-tiered approach to assessing the habitability of exoplanets. *Astrobiology*, 11(10), December 2011.

6. RR de Ruyter van Steveninck and SB Laughlin. The rate of information transfer at graded potential synapses. *Nature*, 379:642–645, 1996.

7. X. P. Deng, G. Hobbs, X. P. You, M. T. Li, M. J. Keith, R. M. Shannon, W. Coles, R. N. Manchester, J. H. Zheng, X. Z. Yu, D. Gao, X. Wu, and D. Chen. Interplanetary spacecraft navigation using pulsars. *Advances in Space Research*, 52:1602–1621, November 2013.

8. Ulam S.M. Everett, C.J. On a method of propulsion of projectiles by means of external nuclear explosions. Technical report, University of California, Los Alamos Scientific Laboratory, August 1955.

9. G. H. Fountain, D. Y. Kusnierkiewicz, C. B. Hersman, T. S. Herder, T. B. Coughlin, W. C. Gibson, D. A. Clancy, C. C. Deboy, T. A. Hill, J. D. Kinnison, D. S. Mehoke, G. K. Ottman, G. D. Rogers, S. A. Stern, J. M. Stratton, S. R. Vernon, and S. P. Williams. The New Horizons Spacecraft. Space Sci. Rev., 140:23–47, October 2008.

10. Ben Goertzel. Lojban++: An interlingua for communication between humans and agis. In AGI 2013, Beijing.

11. Ben Goertzel. Opencogprime: A cognitive synergy based architecture for artificial general intelligence. In George Baciu, Yingxu Wang, Yiyu Yao, Witold Kinsner, Keith Chan, and Lotfi A. Zadeh, editors, IEEE ICCI, pages 60–68. IEEE Computer Society, 2009.

12. Ben Goertzel, Hugo de Garis, Cassio Pennachin, Nil Geisweiller, Samir Araujo1, Joel Pitt1, Shuo Chen, Ruiting Lian, Min Jiang, Ye Yang, and Deheng Huang2. Opencog bot: Achieving generally intelligent virtual agent control and humanoid robotics via cognitive synergy. In *Proceeedings of ICAI 2010 Beijing*.

13. Project Daedalus Study Group. Project daedalus. the final report on the bis starship study. *Journal of the British Interplanetary Society*, 31, 1978.

14. R. Hudec, L. Pina, A. Inneman, and L. Sveda. Lobster - astrophysics with lobster eye telescopes. In AndreiP. Lobanov, J.Anton Zensus, Catherine Cesarsky, and PhillipJ. Diamond, editors, *Exploring the Cosmic Frontier*, ESO Astrophysics Symposia European Southern Observatory, pages 73–74. Springer Berlin Heidelberg, 2007.

15. Marcus Hutter. Towards a universal theory of artificial intelligence based on algorithmic probability and sequential decisions. *Proceedings of the 12th European Conference on Machine Learning* (ECML-2001), (IDSIA-14-00):226–238, September 2001.

16. Marcus Hutter. *Universal Artificial Intelligence: Sequential Decisions Based on Algorithmic Probability*. Springer, 2005.

17. Robert A. Freitas Jr. A self-reproducing interstellar probe. *Journal of the British Interplanetary Society*, 33, 1980.

18. R. K. Kopparapu. A Revised Estimate of the Occurrence Rate of Terrestrial Planets in the Habitable Zones around Kepler M-dwarfs. Ap. J. Letters, 767:L8, April 2013.

19. Kevin J. Kramer, Raymond A. Lewis, Kirby J. Meyer, Gerald A. Smith, and Steven D. Howe. Aimstar: Antimatter initiated microfusion for pre-cursor interstellar missions. AIP Conference Proceedings, 504(1):1412–1419, 2000.

20. Planetary Habitability Laboratory. Habitable exoplanets catalog. Retrieved from http://phl.upr.edu/projects/habitable-exoplanets-catalog, September 2013.

21. Geoffrey A. Landis. Advanced solar- and laser-pushed lightsail concepts. Technical report, Ohio Aerospace Institute, May 1999.

22. L. A. Levin. Universal sequential search problems. *Problems of Information Transmission*, 9(3):265–266, 1973.

23. R. A. Lewis, G. A. Smith, E. Cardiff, B. Dundore, J. Fulmer, B. J. Watson, and S. Chakrabarti. Antiproton-catalyzed microfission/fusion propulsion systems for exploration of the outer solar system and beyond. *AIP Conference Proceedings*, 387(1):1499–1504, 1997.

24. K. F. Long, R. K. Obousy, A. C. Tziolas, A. Mann, R. Osborne, A. Presby, and M. Fogg. Project icarus: Son of daedalus flying closer to another star. *In British Interplanetary Society Daedalus after 30 years symposium*, September 2009.

25. K.F. Long, R.K. Obousy, and A. Hein. Project icarus: Optimisation of nuclear fusion propulsion for interstellar missions. Acta Astronautica, 68(1112):1820 – 1829, 2011.

26. Benjamin W. Longmier, Leonard D. Cassady, Maxwell G. Ballenger, Mark D. Carter, Franklin R. Chang-Diaz, Tim W. Glover, Andrew V. Ilin, Greg E. McCaskill, Chris S. Olsen, Jared P. Squire, and Edgar A. Bering. Vx-200 magnetoplasma thruster performance results exceeding fifty-percent thruster efficiency. *Journal of Propulsion and Power*, 27(4), 2011.

27. Claudio Maccone. Focal mission to 1,000au as an interstellar precursor. In *Mathematical SETI*, Springer Praxis Books, pages 349–360. Springer Berlin Heidelberg, 2012.

28. Thomas J. McGuire. Improved Lifetimes and Synchronization Behavior in Multi-grid Inertial Electrostatic Confinement Fusion Devices. PhD thesis, *MIT Department of Aeronautics and Astronautics*, 2007.

29. Hans Moravec. When will computer hardware match the human brain. Journal of Transhumanism, 1, 1998.

30. Stephen M. Omohundro. The basic ai drives. In *Proceedings of the First AGI Conference*, 2008.

31. Laurent Orseau, Tor Lattimore, and Marcus Hutter. Universal knowledge-seeking agents for stochastic environments. In Sanjay Jain, Rmi Munos, Frank Stephan, and Thomas Zeugmann, editors, *Algorithmic Learning Theory*, volume 8139 of Lecture Notes in Computer Science, pages 158–172. Springer Berlin Heidelberg, 2013.

32. Eray Özkural. Towards heuristic algorithmic memory. In Jürgen Schmidhuber, Kristinn R. Thórisson, and Moshe Looks, editors, AGI, volume 6830 of *Lecture Notes in Computer Science*, pages 382–387. Springer, 2011.

33. Eray Özkural. Diverse consequences of algorithmic probability. In David L. Dowe, editor, *Algorithmic Probability and Friends. Bayesian Prediction and Artificial Intelligence*, volume 7070 of Lecture Notes in Computer Science, pages 285–298. Springer Berlin Heidelberg, 2013.

34. Anthony Pancotti, John Slough, David Kirtley, Michael Pfaff, Christopher Pihl, and George Votroubek. Mission design architecture for the fusion driven rocket. In *48th AIAA/ASME/SAE/ASEE Joint Propulsion Conference & Exhibit*. American Institute of Aeronautics and Astronautics, 2012.

35. J. Schmidhuber. Gödel machines: Fully self-referential optimal universal self-improvers. In B. Goertzel and C. Pennachin, editors, *Artificial General Intelligence*, pages 199–226. Springer Verlag, 2006. Variant available as arXiv:cs.LO/0309048.

36. Jrgen Schmidhuber. Powerplay: Training an increasingly general problem solver by continually searching for the simplest still unsolvable problem. *Frontiers in Psychology*, 4(313), 2013.

37. Ray J. Solomonoff. A formal theory of inductive inference, part i. *Information and Control*, 7(1):1–22, March 1964.

38. Ray J. Solomonoff. The time scale of artificial intelligence: Reflections on social effects. *Human Systems Management*, 5:149–153, 1985.

39. Ray J. Solomonoff. Progress in incremental machine learning. Technical Report IDSIA-16-03, IDSIA, Lugano, Switzerland, 2003.

40. Ray J. Solomonoff. Three kinds of probabilistic induction: Universal distributions and convergence theorems. *The Computer Journal*, 51(5):566–570, 2008. Christopher Stewart Wallace (1933-2004) memorial special issue.

41. J. Storck, S. Hochreiter, and J. Schmidhuber. Reinforcement driven information acquisition in non-deterministic environments. In *Proceedings of the International Conference on Artificial Neural Networks*, Paris, volume 2, pages 159–164. EC2 & Cie, 1995.

42. Yi Sun, Faustino Gomez, and Jrgen Schmidhuber. Planning to be surprised: Optimal bayesian exploration in dynamic environments. In Jrgen Schmidhuber, KristinnR. Thrisson, and Moshe Looks, editors, Artificial General Intelligence, volume 6830 of *Lecture Notes in Computer Science*, pages 41–51. Springer Berlin Heidelberg, 2011.

43. M. Tuomi, H. R. A. Jones, J. S. Jenkins, C. G. Tinney, R. P. Butler, S. S. Vogt, J. R. Banes, R. A. Wittenmyer, S. O'Toole, J. Horner, J. Bailey, B. D. Carter, D. J. Wright, G. S. Salter, and D. Pinfield. Signals embedded in the radial velocity noise. Periodic variations in the τ Ceti velocities. Astr. Ap., 551:A79, March 2013.

44. Dr. Harold 'Sonny' White, Paul March, Nehemiah Williams, and William ON. Eagleworks laboratories: Advanced propulsion physics research. Technical report, NASA, 2011.

45. Ivan Zolotukhin. The extrasolar planets encyclopaedia. Retrieved from exoplanet.eu, September 2013.

The Laser Starway: A Light Bridge To The Nearest Stars

Charles J. Quarra

7801 NW 37th St., Doral, FL 33166-6503

PTY #17572

harlls_quarra@yahoo.com.ar

Abstract

Beamed laser propulsion for interstellar flight is promising but it is severely limited by beam divergence over interstellar distances. In the current work, a system of power relays is proposed to deliver and route light power to accelerate and deccelerate ships flying in both directions between two stars, as well to keep the relays in their equilibrium positions. The system, once deployed, creates a natural radiation roadway where interstellar dust grains tend to evaporate, addressing the problem of relativistic impacts with high-speed ships.

Keywords

interstellar, laser, starway, propulsion,sail, beamed

1. Introduction

Fast Interstellar travel propulsion is fraught with technological difficulties, as well as hard limitations imposed by the laws of Physics. Rockets that carry their own fuel are subject to the limits imposed by Tsiolkovsky rocket equation. The only fuels that make the rocket approach workable for interstellar missions are those with the highest energy density per kilogram. Nuclear fission rockets have enough energy density for fast interplanetary missions inside the solar system, but usually top at velocities of $10^{-5}c$. Nuclear fusion rockets can get up to $0.2c$, but nuclear fusion power has been expected to be around the corner for the last 60 years. Besides, even if a breakeven reactor would be ready today, most confinement technologies are expected to be huge and heavy.

Antimatter-matter reactions could provide highly relativistic speeds of travel, but even if we ignore the fantastic costs of production of macroscopic quantities of fuel, safe storage of antimatter in large enough ratios of fuel mass to container mass is a physical problem that demands magnetic fields that far exceed the capabilities of even the most powerful superconductors known today. Another bold proposal that has come up in recent years is to leverage mini black holes as power sources of Hawking radiation, an approach proposed by Crane [5]. But, putting aside the problem of creating or capturing mini-black holes of 10^{-15} meters, there is the daunting problem of pushing back the tiny black hole together with the ship at macroscopic accelerations, as well as the problem of feeding the black hole and keeping it in a stable operating range.

On the other hand, there exist alternative proposals that do not involve carrying the ship fuel onboard. These kinds of propulsion concepts have their own kind of challenges: The emptiness of interstellar space makes almost impossible to replenish fuel along the way. The Bussard ramjet [3] is an attempt to work around this by scooping sparse interstellar hydrogen as nuclear fusion fuel, but its limitations are discussed at length elsewhere. The last method that can achieve fast interstellar travel without carrying the fuel is solar-powered laser propulsion, and will be the focus of the current work.

2. Solar-Powered Laser Propulsion Limitations

Robert Forward[6] proposed to leave the energy source at home instead of carrying it on with the ship, by using powerful lasers to drive a thin sail attached to a payload. Lasers will have a non-negligible spread over interstellar distances. The spread is limited by the laser wavelength and the laser beam width. Ideally, is desirable to keep the beam focused for long enough distances, in order to keep sails below a reasonable size, and still attain a final velocity that is a reasonable fraction of the speed of light. The beam divergence of a laser in the fundamental Gaussian mode of waist W_0 and wavelength λ is given by the expression [4]

$$\theta = \frac{1}{\pi} \frac{\lambda}{W_0} \qquad \qquad 1)$$

which is the divergence angle of the Gaussian mode of the beam. For a coherent, collimated beam, the total spot width at a distance D is given by

$$w(D) = W_0 \sqrt{1 + \left(\frac{\lambda D}{\pi W_0^2}\right)^2} \qquad \qquad 2)$$

where D is the distance between the beam source and the target spot. This total width is minimal when the following condition holds

$$\frac{1}{\pi} \frac{\lambda^2}{W^2} = \frac{\lambda}{D} \qquad \qquad 3)$$

when λ and D are fixed. In explicit form, the optimal beam width is

$$W = (\frac{\lambda D}{\pi})^{1/2} \qquad \qquad 4)$$

For $\lambda = 10^{-6} m$ (the average photon wavelength from sunlight) we have that sending a beam up to 10^{16} meters (roughly one light-year) gives an optimal beam-width of 100 kilometers, which implies that any sail smaller than $100\sqrt{2}$ kilometers will not receive the full power from the beam at one light-year of distance. This attenuation can be addressed by increasing the laser power output as the distance to the sail increases, but this power will need to increase quadratically with the distance to keep a constant acceleration on the probe.

Solar-powered laser sails are henceforth, limited by the size of the sail, which has some inherent weight, and most of that weight is not needed until the end of the acceleration phase.

There would be a number of open-ended problems in such interstellar mission, that are hard to address with light-sails. Among those is the amount of interstellar dust impacts the sail can take from interstellar dust before a severe structural damage collapses a significant portion of the sail. Also, the problem of deceleration at arrival, can only be partially solved by reusing the sail to brake using the solar radiation from the destination star.

Magnetic sails can also contribute somewhat to the braking force, but both approaches are inherently low-acceleration, so they place a natural bound on the maximum coasting velocity the ship can brake from. This problem can be ignored if one only intends a fly-by mission, but the amount of scientific information that can be gathered by such probes is limited.

3. Extending Solar Power Into Deep Space

Forward [6], again, proposed extending the range of laser systems by deploying thin, huge (500 km) Fresnel lenses between the laser and the sail, in order to refocus the light toward the accelerating sail. Landis [7] also discussed and analysed the performance obtained by launching multiple lenses in order to extend the reach of laser light to farther distances.

Is there a way to keep such vast structures in a stable position? All objects will follow some orbit that will drift them away of their angular position, unless the gravitational radial acceleration is countered exactly by an opposing force. Statites are such an example of an object in a stable position relative to the sun, being in equilibrium by the solar radiation pressure. In deep space, however, due to the quadratic attenuation of solar radiation with distance, we need to rely on laser power to keep a deep-space statite in a fixed position.

But there are other complications that arise at such huge distances. For instance, if either the sail or the lenses drift away from their expected position, the laser stations at home will not receive this information for days, months or even years. As the distances become larger, communication latencies becomes very large. Because of this, reliance on trajectory predictability becomes a dominant feasibility constraint.

The advantage of stabilizing a big Fresnel lens in space is that we can re-use the undoubtedly expensive device for launching multiple interstellar probes. Given enough economies of scale, the effective cost of building and deploying the lens becomes smaller.

If it could be stabilized in this way, the Fresnel lens acts as a reusable laser relay that delivers the laser light farther, at most a factor of 2. Once the first is deployed, can we use it to deploy and stabilize a new one in front of it, extending the laser distance by a factor of 3?

That possibility would be attractive for several reasons. If the distance between successive optical elements could be reduced, the problem of pointing the light output to the target, as well as tracking its movement would be significantly reduced. But at the same time, we would be able to extend the reach of the laser light to much larger distances, without necessarily increasing the width of the beam, or the span of the sails.

In the following section, we will analyze the power and material costs of creating and maintaining a laser relay system that would distribute laser power at all distances between any two stars, both for the acceleration and deceleration phases of an interstellar flight. We will defer the analysis of deployment schemes to a subsequent work.

4. A Road Made Of Light

It is common lore that the most important technological revolution in human transport was the wheel. It is amusing to notice that, in contrast, roads themselves have never been in any notable hall of fame of inventions. Even as it is obvious that wheels, by their nature, are pretty much useless without roads. Since the start of written civilization, roads had to be prepared before they could be used for payload transport. For long enough distances, horse stables had to become available, in order to provide shelter and food for the long road.

Can we extrapolate the above, arguably primitive technology, to bridge the interstellar voids? The main goal of this work is to perform an initial attempt to answer that question. Interstellar space is after all, extremely vast. Our terrestrial standards of distance and time fall too short to easily describe the scales involved. In earth, terrestrial roads are made of some material that took human workers some time to lie out. In space, a different approach and material is surely required.

An interstellar highway would simply consist of a geometrical path where laser beams are retransmitted along a relay chain. The relay chain is made of relay nodes that can keep their stable positions by computing adjustments and reflecting a portion of the incoming light to generate thrust. The rest of the light is transmitted to the next relay node. Unavoidably, a portion of the incoming energy is absorbed on each relay node, and as we will see, this thermal loss will be the dominant factor in the efficiency of the relay chain.

Let's assume that the positions for stars A and B are labeled as 0 and N+1, where N is the number of relay nodes in the chain, placed at regular intervals of distance D. Near each star, powerful lasers of width W deliver light of wavelength λ to the relay nodes R_1 and R_N, in opposing directions. Each relay node refocus the incoming light beam toward their neighbor nodes. A diagram of the starway is shown in Figure (1)}.

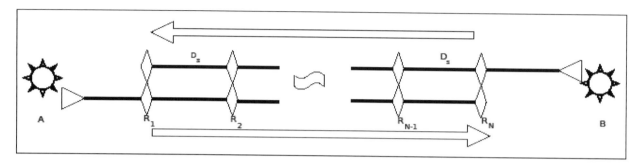

Figure 1: Schematic of a starway. Lasers near both stars transmit power to relay nodes that transmit over the chain, and manage it dynamically for ship propulsion, or just to keep the chain stable

We will simplify the current analysis by doing a number of assumptions: First, we don't specify what underlying optical element is used for the relays. We just assume a few generic properties that a relay will have, such as an effective width W, an effective surface density ρ_a, a transmission absorption coefficient f_n, and a drag factor η that accounts the contribution of the optical losses to the drift of the relay. The factor $1 - f_n$ will measure the ratio of light that is retransmitted to the next relay. Also, we assume that both stars send an equal amount of power

$$W_0 = W_{N+1} = W_L \qquad 5)$$

on their respective directions.

If we write down the k-th component of the total light momentum coming from the $q-1$-th node to the q-th one as $P^+_{k,q-1}$ and the total light momentum coming from the $q+1$-th node to the q-th one as $P^-_{k,q+1}$, conservation of momentum demands that

$$P^+_{k,q-1} + P^-_{k,q+1} = P^+_{k,q} + P^-_{k,q} + P^t_{k,q} + \Delta P^{n;+}_{k,q} + \Delta P^{n;-}_{k,q} \qquad 6)$$

Where $\Delta P^{n;+}_{k,q}$ and $\Delta P^{n;-}_{k,q}$ are momentum gained by the relay node due to absorption of incoming light from the right and left direction respectively, and $\Delta P^t_{k,q}$ is a (relatively tiny) portion of light that is reflected for thrusting the node back into its equilibrium position, which is lost. An ideal relay node that will not absorb any light, will have

$$P^t_{k,q} = \Delta P^{n;+}_{k,q} = \Delta P^{n;-}_{k,q} = 0$$

For realistic relay nodes, $P^t_{k,q}$ will be computed in such a way as to track and cancel position drift due to $\Delta P^n_{k,q} = \Delta P^{n;+}_{k,q} + \Delta P^{n;-}_{k,q}$. From now on, we will drop the vector index k and consider the longitudinal component only. Using the simplified assumption eq.(5), we can write general expressions for the available power and force at any relay node:

$$W_q = \left[e^{\beta^+_q} + e^{\beta^-_q} \right] W_L \qquad 7)$$

With

$$\beta_q^+ = \sum_{q'=1\cdots q-1} \ln(1 - f_n - \alpha_{q'}^+)$$

$$\beta_q^- = \sum_{q''=q+1\cdots N} \ln(1 - f_n - \alpha_{q''}^-)$$

where α_q^+ represents a fraction of available power consumed for thrust at node q coming from star A, while α_q^- represents the fraction of power consumed for thrust at q from star B.

Similar equations hold for the available light impulse at any relay node

$$F_q^+ = \frac{W_L}{c} e^{\beta_q^+} \qquad \qquad 8)$$

$$F_q^- = -\frac{W_L}{c} e^{\beta_q^-} \qquad \qquad 9)$$

we have that only at most $W_L(1 - f_n)^q$ power will reach the q-th relay node from the star A, where the convention is that positive force points in the direction from star A toward star B.

The dominant component of position drift in the nodes is caused by thermal absorption. Some of the light will be absorbed, and some of it will be scattered. The fraction f_n represents the net optical losses at each relay element, regardless of their physical origin. ηf_n represents the fraction of momentum that the light transfers to each optical element. η is an adimensional drag factor that estimates how the optical losses contribute to drift. In this work we will assume that all the losses are due to absorption, which is given by

$$\eta = 1 \qquad \qquad 10)$$

The net power available from both sides at q-th node will be

$$W_q = \left[(1 - f_n)^{q-1} + (1 - f_n)^{N-q}\right] W_L \qquad \qquad 11)$$

Or,

$$W_q = 2(1 - f_n)^{\frac{N-1}{2}} \cosh\left[(2q - N - 1)\ln(1 - f_n)\right] W_L \qquad \qquad 12)$$

The net power loss on this node is given by

$$W_q f_n \qquad \qquad 13)$$

and the net force by the absorbed light is

$$F_q^{drift} = \left[(1 - f_n)^{q-1} - (1 - f_n)^{N-q}\right] \frac{\eta f_n W_L}{c} \qquad \qquad 14)$$

$$F_q^{drift} = 2(1 - f_n)^{\frac{N-1}{2}} \sinh\left[(2q - N - 1)\ln(1 - f_n)\right] \frac{\eta f_n W_L}{c} \qquad \qquad 15)$$

367

Since this force cannot be switched off, even if no useful power is being consumed on the starway, we might need to cancel those forces by actively consuming some power from the distant star, but first we will analyze the gravitational influences experienced by the relay chain.

Conceivably, some of the absorption drift will be desired in order to keep the relay nodes as active statites against the gravitational attraction for the nearby stars. The gravitational attraction of relay node q from stars A and B is

$$-\frac{GM_A}{D^2 q^2} + \frac{GM_B}{D^2(N+1-q)^2} \qquad 16)$$

This gravitational acceleration needs to be countered with some laser pressure. By eq. 15, we have an absorption drift force that points away from both stars. We will, however, ignore the destination star gravitational attraction and consider only half of the starway. The absorbed force plus orbital correction force to keep the relay nodes as statites is

$$-\frac{GM_A}{D^2 q^2} + 2(1-f_n)^{\frac{N-1}{2}} \sinh\left[(2q-N-1)\ln(1-f_n)\right]\frac{f_n W_L}{c} \qquad 17)$$

The most significant observation that we need to derive from this expression is that gravitational attraction decreases quadratically by each successive step we move away from the star, while the absorption drift decreases only by a factor $1-f_n$. This means that if the absorption drift for the first node is equal to its gravitational attraction, nodes placed farther will drift away from the star, unable to propel back toward the sun. So gravitational pull can help to reduce the absorption drift only for relay nodes placed very close to the star (the first 10 nodes at most), the rest of the nodes need to be pushed actively toward their neighbor star by some other force.

This imposes a stringent constraint on the feasibility of a starway, because it requires that light power from the destination star B to be available to push back the nodes near star A into their equilibrium positions, and likewise on the other end. The argument above leave us free to ignore the corrections due to the gravitational forces from the nearby stars, sincethose represent small corrections to the stability forces. The stability constraint is expressed by the following equations

$$0 = F_k^{drift} + 2\alpha_k^- F_k^- \qquad 18)$$

$$= \left[\eta f_n(1-f_n)^{k-1} - (2\alpha_k^- + \eta f_n)(1-f_n)^{N-k}\right]\frac{W_L}{c} \qquad 19)$$

$$0 = F_{k-1}^{drift} + 2\alpha_{k-1}^- F_{k-1}^- \qquad 20)$$

$$= \left[\eta f_n(1-f_n)^{k-2} - (2\alpha_{k-1}^- + \eta f_n)(1-f_n-\alpha_k^-)(1-f_n)^{N-k}\right]\frac{W_L}{c} \qquad 21)$$

$$0 = F_1^{drift} + 2\alpha_1^- F_1^- \qquad 22)$$

$$= \left[\eta f_n - (2\alpha_1^- + \eta f_n)(1-f_n)^{N-k}\prod_{i=2}^{k}(1-f_n-\alpha_i^-)\right]\frac{W_L}{c} \qquad 23)$$

Similar equations can be demanded on the α+. The factor of 2 on the adjustment thrust is justified on the account that it is generated by reflecting a portion of the incoming light. This system can be resolved recursively for the α coefficients. It can be shown that the maximum value of f_n that will have consistent solutions is given by

$$N = 2\frac{\ln\left[\dfrac{\eta}{2}\right] - \ln\left[2 + (\dfrac{\eta}{2} - 1)f_n\right]}{\ln\left[1 - f_n\right] + \ln\left[1 + (\dfrac{\eta}{2} - 1)f_n\right]} \qquad 24)$$

The solution and the derivation of this equation is detailed in the appendix A. This equation establishes a relationship between the minimum transmissive efficiency and the number of nodes in a starway stabilized against absorption drift. If we use the thermal optical absorption assumption eq. (10) we can simplify further and obtain

$$N = 2\frac{\ln\left[\dfrac{1}{2}\right] - \ln\left[2 - \dfrac{1}{2}f_n\right]}{\ln\left[1 - f_n\right] + \ln\left[1 - \dfrac{1}{2}f_n\right]} \qquad 25)$$

The starway must receive laser light from both directions, which means that optical elements need to be arranged in such a way that drift forces on the individual elements does not cause unwanted net torque on the node. A way to avoid this would be to arrange four or more optical elements in a ring-shaped structure such that the average net torque is zero. In any case, multiple optical elements is a requirement to guarantee minimal redundancy of power in case of partial outages or failures in some of the nodes.

A ring-shaped structure for a relay leads naturally to a concept where the flight traffic would be compartmentalized in regions near the axial line joining the rings. The laser relays must implement some method to deviate a portion of the light in another direction for stabilization thrust, and that same mechanism will be used to provide beamed propulsion to passing spacecrafts.

Since relays are placed one in front of the other in the line-of-sight to the star, safety measures and flight traffic protocols must be developed to ensure that all ships move within their transport lanes tolerances. Depending on the velocity of an incoming ship and the distance to the next relay, maneuvering countermeasures might be difficult or altogether impossible.

5. Available Propulsion Thrust

The figure of merit of performance of a given starway design is the maximum thrust force available in a given direction, since it gives a measure of how much payload can be transported from one star to the other, and at what accelerations. By using eq. A15 from the appendix we are able to estimate the maximum distributed propulsion thrust fraction to be

$$T \leq T_m = \frac{(4 - f_n)(1 - f_n)^{\frac{N}{2}} - (1 - \dfrac{f_n}{2})^{-\frac{N}{2}}}{(1 - f_n)^{\frac{N}{2} - 1}(3 - f_n)} \qquad 26)$$

Given Eq. (26), we can compute the laser power required to provide a given acceleration a_S for shuttles of a given mass as

$$W_L = \frac{a_S n_S M_S c}{2T_m} \qquad 27)$$

where n_S is the maximum number of simultaneous allowed shuttles of a given size and payload accelerating on the starway. The term $n_S M_S$ can be called ***traffic mass*** to emphasize the fact that is the total mass being accelerated on a direction lane of the starway. $\dfrac{a_S M_S c}{2}$ is the amount of power that a shuttle must receive in order to accelerate at a_S (assuming perfect reflection, it will be lower than that in practice).

If we altered some of the flight parameters (mass of the vehicles, radiation pressure-induced acceleration), we can increase or decrease the number of vehicles supported. Another straightforward method is by adjusting the laser power at the sources, but this needs to happen over timescales comparable to the time it takes light to travel from one endpoint to the other, to allow enough time for the starway to self-adjust to new equilibrium forces.

5.1 Laser-Driven Thermal Management

Some brief remarks about general thermal limitations in laser-driven sails are in order. Laser-pushed ships do not need to carry any propellant on board, all they need is an efficient sail or mirror. However, laser-pushed ships are still limited by their thermal capacity to dispose heat. Assuming a total mass $\sum_i M_i$ and a maximum waste heat disposal rate of $\sigma \sum 2\varepsilon_i A_i T_i^4$, we have the following bound on the ship parameters:

$$\sum_i M_i \le \frac{4\sigma}{\alpha a_S c} \sum \varepsilon_i A_i T_i^4 \qquad 28)$$

where α is the absorption coefficient of the sail. If we ignore all the other terms and keep only the payload mass, sail mass and sail heat terms explicit, and assuming the payload is cold enough to ignore its waste heat, we are left with the following:

$$M_P \le A_S \left(\frac{4\sigma}{\alpha a_S c} \varepsilon_S T_S^4 - \rho_S \right) \qquad 29)$$

where ρ_S is sail area density and M_P is the payload mass. Since this is a direct bound on the payload mass, people have been trying to optimize the right hand side since Robert Forward proposed laser-pushed sails for interstellar missions. The latest improvement to this are microwave-pushed carbon sails[2], with area densities of 5×10^{-3} kilograms, absorptivity of $\approx 10\%$ and operating temperatures above 3000 K.

Such a sail accelerated at one G would have a thermally-bounded payload of $m_p \le 4.5 A_s \times 10^{-2}$ kg. So it would take a sail of 3.1×10^5 square meters (radius a little above 300 meter) to accelerate a payload of ten tons without evaporating the sail. If we relax acceleration to 0.1 g we have $m_p \le 6.1 A_s \times 10^{-1}$ kg. Hence, with the same sail size we are able to increase the payload to nearly 200 tons.

Existing concepts for interstellar carbon laser-pushed sails (with a laser at home and no optical refocusing) would require sails of tens or hundreds of kilometers wide. At these accelerations, such sails would be far from being thermally limited, given their large area. However, we still have a limited distance to accelerate before the beam spreads beyond the size of the sail. Thus, high accelerations are required to achieve relativistic velocities. On the other hand, if we can keep the laser light focused on a narrow area (which is precisely the case for a starway), the mass and thermal optimization analysis might change: For instance, a light enough material with good thermal conductivity, may be able to balance its additional mass by increasing the net radiator area, As long as it is less dense than the sail itself. An example of this kind of approach would be to have a sail with extremely low absorptivity $\le 10^{-5}$ operating at relatively cooler temperatures (≈ 800 K), and dump most of the heat to thin graphene sheets covering a large area. Cooler temperatures means a much larger total radiator area, but also a wider array of material and design options for the sail.

Given the fantastic heat conductivity and small weight of graphene ($\approx 10^{-6}$ kilograms per square meter), we could expect in the near future, efficient and realistic graphene-based radiator designs, able to dump most of the heat at a tiny fraction of the mass of both the sail and the payload. In such a scenario, accelerating big payloads in the starway at one G or higher would be limited only by the available laser power at the source.

6. Materials Cost analysis

A simple analysis of material costs can be made by assuming that the optical elements in the relay nodes have a uniform surface density ρ_n. Since there are N relay nodes covering the distance D_s between the two stars, separated uniformly by a distance of D_n, and by the optimal beam width relation (Eq. 4), the total mass for all relay nodes optical elements in the starway is

$$N\frac{\pi}{2}W^2\rho_n = N\lambda D_n\rho_n = \lambda D_s\rho_n \qquad 30)$$

which as we see, does not depend on how many relay nodes are there on the starway because it only depends on the wavelength, the overall distance between the endpoints and the surface density. This of course, assumes that the relay node mass depends linearly on the beam area. As long as this assumption holds, the number of relay nodes will not affect the overall mass of the structure, which means that we can choose smaller relay nodes placed at smaller intervals, or bigger ones placed at larger distances. However, heat disposal will still favor bigger nodes, and the amount of heat that needs to be disposed depends on the relay efficiency f_n.

The thermal waste characteristics of the q-th relay node, from eq. (12) and (13), demand a total radiator area of

$$A_R = \frac{f_n W_q}{\sigma\varepsilon T^4} = 2(1-f_n)^{\frac{N-1}{2}}\cosh\left[(2q-N-1)\ln(1-f_n)\right]\frac{W_L}{\sigma\varepsilon T^4} \qquad 31)$$

This thermal energy needs to be disposed by radiators, since we are in the vacuum of space. Assuming a heat dissipation of 1000 W/m^2 at somewhat below 400K for keeping the optical elements of the relay node relatively cool. Further, we assume a surface density of 0.1 kg/m^2 for liquid droplet radiators [9], which gives us a radiator mass of

$$M_R = 0.1 A_R = 10^{-4} f_n W_q \qquad 32)$$

$$= 2\times 10^{-4} f_n(1-f_n)^{\frac{N-1}{2}}\cosh\left[(2q-N-1)\ln(1-f_n)\right]W_L \qquad 33)$$

The total radiator mass M_{TR} for the entire starway becomes

$$M_{TR} = 2\times 10^{-4} f_n(1-f_n)^{\frac{N-1}{2}} W_L \sum_{q=1}^{N}\cosh\left[(2q-N-1)\ln(1-f_n)\right] \qquad 34)$$

7. Modeling the Sol-Alpha Centauri starway

For our toy model of the Sol-Alpha Centauri starway, we will assume a lightway with a wavelength of $\lambda = 10^{-7}$ meters (region between soft UV and visible light). Further assumptions will include a relay absorption of $f_n = 10^{-4}$, and a relay node surface density of $\rho_n = 10$ kilogram per square meter. For covering 4×10^{16} meters we will assume 4000 relay nodes, each separated by a distance of 10^{13} meters. From eq.(24) we can numerically compute a critical transmissive efficiency of $1-4.62\times 10^{-4}$.

Our model of the starway is conceived assuming an efficiency of $1-10^{-4}$. This number, besides being slightly larger than the critical value, is otherwise arbitrary, and it is assumed in order to carry on with estimations on the other relevant quantities. This kind of optical efficiency might be tricky to reach with current diffractive optics, even with fused quartz optics and advanced anti-reflection coatings, in the proposed wavelengths[8, p. 195]. But reflective optical alternatives could be devised for the relay nodes. Reference [10] experimented with mirror surfaces fine-tuned with pixelated capacitive elements. Also, dielectric mirrors[1] can attain reflectivity coefficients of $1-10^{-5}$ over a narrow optical bandwidth, so we are definitely not talking about material requirements far from our current technical capabilities.

By using eq.(26) we are able to estimate the maximum distributed propulsion thrust fraction to be

$$T_m \leq 0.883 \qquad\qquad 35)$$

Since our model will be just a proof of concept, we will aim for a traffic mass capacity of 3.0×10^5 kilograms at 1-G (half the mass of the ISS). Given the above and eq.(27), this requires a laser power of $W_L = 10^{15}$ watts down each side of the starway.

From our assumed absorption coefficient, this implies that each node receives $10^{15}(1-f_n)^{q-1}$ watts on a given direction, and absorbs $\approx 10^{11}$ watts. A heat dissipation of $1000\frac{W}{m^2}$, at somewhat below 400 K is assumed. This gives a required radiator area of

$$10^8 (1-f_n)^{\frac{N-1}{2}} \cosh\left[(2q-N-1)\ln(1-f_n)\right]$$

square meters. Assuming 0.1 $\frac{kg}{m^2}$ for liquid droplet radiators [9], we are left with a mass for radiators of

$$10^7 (1-f_n)^{\frac{N-1}{2}} \cosh\left[(2q-N-1)\ln(1-f_n)\right]$$

kilograms per relay node. This radiator mass depends mostly on the absorption coefficient and total laser power. Also, as discussed in sec. 4-1 even if graphene radiators will allow game changing opportunities regarding heat management for solar and laser-pushed sails, the present exercise will still be enlightening as a high bound on material costs.

Given the internode distance of $D_n = 10^{13}$ meters, eq.(4) implies an optimal beam width $W_b = 800$ meters. From eq. (30) we can derive a total optical element mass for the whole starway of $2 \times 10^9 \rho_n = 10^{10}$ kg. From eq. (34), and evaluating the sum, gives a total radiator mass of $M_{TR} = 6.7 \times 10^{10} kg$ so we have roughly that about 77% of the relay node mass is just for heat management. From the above thermal estimates, the radiator of the closest node to the Sun has about 1.77×10^{-8} kilograms of mass for each watt of laser power W_L, in our case that amounts to 1.77×10^7 kilograms. Gravitational acceleration from the Sun at D_n will be 1.3×10^{-6} meters per square second. That implies that countering gravitational force with laser light will require $3.9 \times 10^2 M_n$ watts, where M_n is the relay node mass, and follows that 7.0×10^{10} watts would be required to balance gravitational drift.

Since that node already absorbs 10^{11} watts from the laser, this gives further credence to our original statement that gravitational drift is not a determinant factor in the stability and energy efficiency of a starway. Contrary to what intuition would otherwise suggest, building a physically realistic starway to Alpha Centauri would take no more mass than that of a small asteroid. If we allow a redundancy factor of 10, that is, 10 beams travelling parallel between relay nodes, we are in the ballpark of 10^{12} kg, still suggesting that we can build a starway by consuming a medium-sized asteroid.

By simple relativistic kinematics, assuming constant acceleration of 1-g until half-way trip and constant deceleration on the second half, a starway-accelerated vehicle at 1-g would take about 1000 days to travel

2×10^{16} meters (about 2 light years, which is half the full distance to Alpha-Centauri). The proper time experienced on ship would be about 700 days, which is a little less than 2 years.

For the purpose of reference, some of the parameters for similar laser starways are shown below. The targets are two interesting stellar systems in our neighborhood that have one or more confirmed exoplanets: Tau Ceti and Gliese-581. These parameters assume the same internode distance of 10^{13} meters and the same laser wavelength.

7.1 Tau Ceti Starway

- Distance: 11.9 light years (approximated as 1.2×10^{17} meters for simplicity)
- Radial velocity: -16.4 km/sec
- Tangential velocity: 32.3 km/sec
- number of possible nodes: 1.2×10^4
- critical transmissive efficiency: $1 - 1.54 \times 10^{-4}$
- optical mass estimation with $\times 6$ redundancy: 7.2×10^{10} kg
- time to destination at 1-g (home frame): 5070 days
- time to destination at 1-g (ship frame): 1864 days

7.2 Gliese-581 Starway

- Distance: 20.2 light years (approximated as 2.0×10^{17} meters for simplicity)
- Radial velocity: -10 km/sec
- Tangential velocity: 35 km/sec
- number of possible nodes: 2.0×10^4
- critical transmissive efficiency: $1 - 9.2 \times 10^{-5}$
- optical mass estimation with $\times 6$ redundancy: 1.2×10^{11} kg
- time to destination at 1-g (home frame): 8010 days
- time to destination at 1-g (ship frame): 2180 days

8. The Problem Of Interstellar Dust

The vacuum of interstellar space is not entirely empty. According to Matloff [8,p. 156], dust grain densities and sizes in interstellar space could be enough to require a significant amount of shielding over any kind of velocity above 0.1c.

But assuming a starway like one proposed here is deployed: Parallel light beams of a 10^{15} watts of a couple of kilometers in width, would represent energy fluxes of the order of $10^9 \ watt/m^2$. Grains inside this beam would tend either to evaporate due to absorption, or to accelerate. In any case, the beam of radiation around the starway would create a thermal gradient around itself that would tend to eliminate or reduce the amount of interstellar dust, which would reduce the risks for vessels travelling the starway at relativistic speeds. The author is not aware of a precise estimation of how much interstellar dust would be evaporated or removed automatically by this effect. This might be an interesting area of research for a future work.

9. Conclusions

We have drawn inspiration from Robert Forward's proposal to use Fresnel lenses with the purpose of increasing the reach of laser power into deep space to propel photon sails. Starting from that idea, we are proposing a system of stabilized, equally spaced optical relay elements between two stars. This architecture will enable a bidirectional, relativistic, safe and economical interstellar flight corridor.

Among the notable benefits of such an approach, there are a few that deserve special mention:

- Sustained power availability for the whole duration of the spaceflight, including deceleration phases, enabling true relativistic travel
- Long-term reusability and flexibity, opening a two-way corridor between two neighboring solar systems
- Smaller distances between neighboring power transmission nodes, which imply softer uncertainty requirements in trajectory prediction, as the time between position observations is smaller and constant.
- Decrease in the expected amounts and size of interstellar dust grains present along the starway due to thermal evaporation.

We have analyzed a simplified, symmetric model of the starway, and considered the stability of the optical nodes against drift due to light thermal absorption. This puts some constraints on the absorption coefficient f_n and the number of nodes N. Less transmissive efficiency implies less nodes in the chain, demanding bigger lenses and bigger lasers at the source stars.

There is however much work still to be done. In this regard, the most notable absence in this work is the problem of deployment. Presumably, two conceivable deployment schemes might be studied in the future: The first possibility is launching multiple lenses together with the sail, which was already suggested by Landis[7]. The other possibility requires reaching the destination star with some other method, and build a minimal amount of self-assemblying infrastructure at destination. After that infrastructure exists, it will proceed to create the solar-powered lasers and relay nodes that will be pushed toward a similar train of nodes travelling from the sun, and eventually braking as both ends approach and meet, half-way between the two stars.

The architecture of the relay nodes is left intentionally vague, as we have required only a few high-level features from them, like the ability to reflect a desired portion of light in order to generate thrust, some maximum thermal disposal capacity, some transmissive efficiency given by $1 - f_n$. We established a relationship between the minimum transmissive efficiency and the number of nodes in a starway stabilized against absorption drift, which we think is the most important result in this report. For our model of the sol-Alpha Centauri starway, 4000 nodes demands an absolute minimum transmissive efficiency of 4.61×10^{-4}. This number might be tricky to reach, even with fused quartz optics, in the proposed wavelengths. But alternatives to diffractive optics using catadioptric elements and dielectric mirrors could be devised for the relay nodes that are not far from our current technical capabilities.

As discussed in section 4-1, laser-pushed sails are limited by their rate of excess heat removal. This is a key subject as payload masses per ship depend strongly on this. Developments in single-layer graphene manufacturing will be essential to remove or reduce thermal limitations on laser shuttles.

We have assumed a $1000 W/m^2$ power dissipation at 400K to keeping the optical elements of the relay nodes cool. This implies that optical elements in the relay nodes need to operate in a somewhat higher temperature. Recirculating index-matching liquids as currently used in some high-power laser applications, are an interesting possibility to pursue. Further research in material science will be required to find optimal materials that combine the required low absorption rate and refraction index at high operating temperatures. Within current material technology, liquid droplet radiators could be used to increase the power dissipation per radiator mass to $10^4 \frac{watt}{kg}$. Future improvements in technologies like graphene could make extremely light-weight heat sinks, so we could still see a reduction of several orders of magnitude in the radiator mass. We could also argue that the temperature estimate of 400 K is rather conservative. But the point that the present work aims to remark, is that even with a worst-case scenario of modest technology developments in the key technologies to develop laser starways, they are absolutely realistic engineering undertakings.

Some redundancy is absolutely required, since relay nodes will need downtime for maintenance or emergency repairs. Each energy transmission loss due to failures will propagate down and uplink. Without redundancy, those losses will combine and produce long outages, or catastrophic instability.

The size of fluctuations in the energy flow due to unscheduled thrust corrections along the chain needs to be quantified in order to completely assess structural stability. Given that information about correction requests travel at the speed of light, an algorithm that can forecast and minimize such fluctuations will be needed to route and grant request priorities for power and take decisions in a distributed way.

As we analyzed the material costs in terms of mass, it became clear that the solar system has more than plenty mining resources in order to build at least a couple of starways to the closest stars. The energy bill of 10^{15} watts might seem high by current standards, but it represents a microscopic fraction of the energy budget that generates our sun and goes to waste in the vacuum of space. Energy costs cannot be simply extrapolated from present earth economy, because we already know that beamed solar power could, if implemented, provide for all the energy demand of our global economies. That means in particular, that given the right infrastructure, the cost of delivered power can be brought as low as infrastructure maintenance costs permit.

The focus of the current analysis is on propellant-less radiation-pressure propulsion. Conceivably, further efficiencies in the laser energy usage could be obtained with laser-heated propellant drives, at least for the early acceleration stage. Needless to mention, the starway architecture is completely unaffected by specific shuttle architectures and concepts: as long as the ship adheres to the safe transit protocols that will have to be enforced to avoid catastrophic accidents at relativistic speeds, each ship is free to use the energy it receives from the nodes in the way that better suits its purposes.

Even so, large laser powers will be required. In order to generate such large-scale laser beams, possibly many hundreds or thousands of laser beams will need to be combined in order to produce a single coherent beam. FEL (Free electron lasers) have a number of characteristics that could make them a suitable choice: acceptable energy efficiency, relatively low thermal generation and the absence of a gain medium, which will reduce the maintenance costs.

Given the amount of heat that will be disposed on each relay node, is unavoidable to think that life, and possibly civilization will thrive in the vicinity of these. Populations will be capable to drift outside the star road over the generations and live from the rejected heat, in a similar way that our ancestors did when they decided to leave Africa. The starway will have not only enough redundancy of power lines, but it will have to support multiple lanes, both for acceleration and deceleration of ships coming from both directions. Special lanes could be designed in for emergency braking.

With enough power, and self-repairing capabilities, a starway can work for centuries, possibly even more. As both star endpoints slowly move in their orbits around the galaxy, and their relative motion changes, the starway has plenty of time to dynamically adjust, insert or remove relay nodes as required. In this way, an advanced civilization can create a metropolitan stellar network of light bridges that communicate neighboring stars to each other.

Acknowledgments

The author wishes to thank Adam Crowl of Icarus Interstellar for helpful discussions on the subject of solar sails and laser beamed propulsion.

Appendix

A: Recursive Thrust Equations

If we extend equations 18 thru 22 to allow for the expenditure of propulsion power T_i^- on s nodes in the far half of the starway, as well as drift correction power α_i^- on the nodes of the near half, a recursive solution is given in the following form:

$$\alpha_k^- = \frac{\eta}{2} \frac{\left[f_n (1 - f_n)^{2k - N + s - 1} - \Pi_T \right]}{\Pi_T} \qquad A1)$$

$$\alpha_{k-1}^- = \frac{\eta}{2} \frac{\left[f_n(1-f_n)^{2k-N+s-2} - (1-f_n-\alpha_k^-)\Pi_T \right]}{(1-f_n-\alpha_k^-)\Pi_T} \qquad A2)$$

$$\alpha_1^- = \frac{\eta}{2} \frac{\left[f_n(1-f_n)^{k-N+s} - \Pi_T \prod_{i=2}^{k}(1-f_n-\alpha_i^-) \right]}{\Pi_T \prod_{i=2}^{k}(1-f_n-\alpha_i^-)} \qquad A3)$$

Where $\Pi_T = \prod_{i=i_1}^{i_s}(1-f_n-T_i^-)$ is the combined node transmission over the s nodes that are spending laser power

for propulsion of ships.

For a given configuration of the relay chain of N nodes, the critical configuration happens when all the remaining power from the remote star is consumed to push back the relay R_1. If there are higher losses than this, the starway will collapse.

We translate the above insight as the following condition:

$$1-f_n-\alpha_1^- = 0 \qquad A4)$$

which is equivalent to ask that there is no light power left from the distant star, after adjusting for absorption drift at R_1. The first step is to find a sequence that expresses succinctly the recursive product. Assume that

$$1-f_n-\alpha_{j+1}^- = \frac{H_j}{H_{j+1}} \qquad A5)$$

For a suitable sequence H_j. This implies that the product of the sequences will cancel in tandem, giving the result

$$\prod_{i=j+1}^{k}(1-f_n-\alpha_i^-) = \frac{H_j}{H_k} \qquad A6)$$

From this, we can compute inductively the value of $1-f_n-\alpha_j^-$ to be

$$1-f_n-\alpha_j^- = \frac{M\Pi_T H_j - \frac{\eta}{2}f_n H_k(1-f_n)^{k+j+s-N-1}}{\Pi_T H_j} \qquad A7)$$

where $M \equiv 1+(\frac{\eta}{2}-1)f_n$ for convenience. This expression will conform to the sequence expressed in eq. (A5) only if $H_k \propto \Pi_T$. More so, if we use eq. (A1) in order to obtain the initial value of the sequence for $j = k$,we arrive at the expression

$$1-f_n-\alpha_k^- = \frac{M\Pi_T - \frac{\eta}{2}f_n H_k(1-f_n)^{2k+s-N-1}}{\Pi_T} = \frac{H_{k-1}}{H_k}$$

Which gives the first term of the sequence $H_k = \Pi_T$. This simplifies relation eq.(A7) for H_{j-1} as:

$$H_{j-1} = MH_j - \frac{\eta}{2} f_n (1 - f_n)^{k+j+s-N-1} \qquad A8)$$

or, in nonrecursive form:

$$H_j = M^{k-j} \Pi_T - \frac{\eta}{2} f_n (1 - f_n)^{k+j+s-N} \left[\frac{(1 - f_n)^{k-j} M^{k-j} - 1}{(1 - f_n) M - 1} \right] \qquad A9)$$

11.1.1 A1: Critical Transmissive Efficiency Relation

First, we consider the case where all the power is being used to keep the starway stable, and there is no leftover power for anything else. This is the case when $s = 0$ and $\Pi_T = 1$. By using the critical constraint eq. (A4), eq. (A5), and taking $2k = N$ as the point where the drift correction thrust begins (half of the starway), we arrive after a few algebraic manipulations at the desired relationship between critical transmissive efficiency and the number of relay nodes:

$$N = 2 \frac{\ln\left[\dfrac{\eta}{2}\right] - \ln\left[2 + (\dfrac{\eta}{2} - 1) f_n\right]}{\ln\left[1 - f_n\right] + \ln\left[1 + (\dfrac{\eta}{2} - 1) f_n\right]} \qquad A10)$$

Fixing N, this can be solved iteratively for f_n. The table A1 shows several computed values for different sizes of the relay chain.

N	f_n
200	9.19×10^{-3}
2000	9.23×10^{-4}
4000	4.61×10^{-4}
1.2×10^4	1.54×10^{-4}
2.0×10^4	9.24×10^{-5}
4.0×10^4	4.62×10^{-5}

11.1.2 A2: Available Propulsion Thrust

In order to have any power left to thrust interstellar vehicles, we want to consider the region

$$1 - f_n - \alpha_1^- = \frac{H_0}{H_1} > 0 \qquad A11)$$

It is easy to check that $H_j \geq 0$ holds for $0 \leq j \leq k$ if eq.(A4) holds. In particular, $H_1 > 0$. So eq. (A11) is equivalent to

$$H_0 = M^{\frac{N}{2}}\Pi_T - \frac{\eta}{2}f_n(1-f_n)^{s-\frac{N}{2}}\left[\frac{(1-f_n)^{\frac{N}{2}}M^{\frac{N}{2}}-1}{(1-f_n)M-1}\right] > 0 \quad A12)$$

which can be rewritten as

$$\frac{\prod_{i=i_1}^{i_s}(1-f_n-T_i^-)}{(1-f_n)^s} > \frac{\eta}{2}\frac{f_n}{(1-f_n)^{\frac{N}{2}}}\left[\frac{(1-f_n)^{\frac{N}{2}}-M^{-\frac{N}{2}}}{(1-f_n)M-1}\right] \quad A13)$$

In the case where a single ship is being accelerated in a given direction ($s = 1$) the formula of the available thrust fraction becomes

$$T_i^- < \frac{\left[2+(\frac{\eta}{2}-1)f_n\right](1-f_n)^{\frac{N}{2}}-\frac{\eta}{2}M^{-\frac{N}{2}}}{(1-f_n)^{\frac{N}{2}-1}\left[2-\frac{\eta}{2}+(\frac{\eta}{2}-1)f_n\right]} \quad A14)$$

if $\eta = 1$, this simplifies further to

$$T \le T_m = \frac{(4-f_n)(1-f_n)^{\frac{N}{2}}-(1-\frac{f_n}{2})^{-\frac{N}{2}}}{(1-f_n)^{\frac{N}{2}-1}(3-f_n)} \quad A15)$$

References

1. J. H. Apfel. "Phase retardance of periodic multilayer mirrors." *Applied Optics*, 21:733–738, 1982.

2. James Benford. "Starship sails propelled by cost-optimized directed energy", 2011.

3. Robert Bussard. "Galactic matter and interstellar flight." *Acta Astronautica*, 6:179–94, 1960.

4. William Chang. "Principles of lasers and optics." Cambridge University Press, Cambridge, UK New York, 2005.

5. Louis Crane and Shawn Westmoreland. "Are black hole starships possible", 2009.

6. Robert L. Forward. "Roundtrip interstellar travel using laser-pushed lightsails." *J. Spacecraft*, 21:187–195, 1984.

7. Geoffrey A. Landis. "Optics and materials considerations for a laser-propelled lightsail." paper IAA-89-664, 1989.

8. Gregory L. Matloff. *Deep Space Probes*. Springer, 2000.

9. T. Mattick and A. Hertzberg. "Liquid droplet radiators for heat rejection in space". In Energy to the 21st century; Proceedings of the Fifteenth Intersociety Energy Conversion Engineering Conference, pages 143–150, 1980.

10. T. S. Taylor, L. W. Brantley, Anding R. C., and D. Halford. *Membrane Optic Research Program Internal Documentation.* Teledyne Brown Engineering and The National Space Science and Technology Center, Huntsville, AL, 2002.

100 YEAR STARSHIP™

Interstellar Aspiration—Commercial Perspiration:
The Next 30 Years of Space Start-ups and
Commercialization

Interstellar Aspiration—Commercial Perspiration

Chaired by Amy Millman

NASA/NIAC Fellow

Track Description

The Internet. Global Positioning Systems (GPS). Autonomous Systems. Cordless Tools. None would exist if it were not for government funding, but it is through the private sector that these technologies reach our everyday life. This session will include current and potential commercial applications for space technology and exploration in the next 30 years. Papers should illustrate business and technology innovations spanning several years, strategies for crossing valleys of [funding] death, and creating market with revenues and profits from application in space and on earth.

Track Chair Biography

Amy Millman

CEO, Springboard Enterprises

Amy Millman is a passionate advocate for women entrepreneurs building Big Businesses Starting Small. In 2000, she co-founded Springboard Enterprises, a non-profit venture catalyst which sources, coaches, showcases and supports women-led companies seeking equity capital for product development and expansion. Springboard has assisted hundreds of women entrepreneurs in raising billions in investments and connecting with thousands of expert resources. The successes of Springboard entrepreneurs include 10 IPOs, legions of high value M&As and a community of accomplished serial entrepreneurs. During her career in Washington, DC, she served as a representative for several industry groups and was appointed as Executive Director of the National Women's Business Council during the Clinton Administration. She served on the boards of many organizations including her current service with JumpStart Inc. and Enterprising Women Magazine.

Reducing Operation Risk for Deep Space Mission through Predictive Modeling

Timothy D. Meehan, PhD, and Jason Held, PhD

Saber Astronautics LLC

10300 Jollyville Rd. Austin TX 78759 USA

timmeehan@saberastro.com

Abstract

The great distances traveled during deep space missions will result in significant communication delays with commensurate challenges to Earth based support. New methods of space operations are therefore needed to diagnose spacecraft faults and control complex systems in a reduced risk/reduced cost fashion without relying solely on terrestrial control centers. Saber Astronautics' predictive modeling software (PIGI) reduces operations risk by utilizing "Big Data" analytics approaches. Although designed with ground operations in mind, PIGI is equally capable of residing on manned spacecraft for crew managed operations. PIGI is widely applicable to a range of operational areas from accurately predicting mission consumables, to estimating the effects of space weather events on spacecraft performance. PIGI can augment in-flight control with real-time "how" and "why" diagnostics essential to accurately and quickly recovering from defects. Rather than the traditional one-to-one, information-to-operator interface provided by conventional space flight control, PIGI applies the latest advances in diagnostics intelligence with accelerated, 3D graphical user interface for a system that is ergonomic, intuitive and responsive to mission needs. The real world utility of PIGI has been demonstrated by the performance analysis of the NASA Advanced Composition Explorer (ACE) satellite. Experiments showed greater than 95% accuracy in estimating faults and in validating cause-and effect chains in the ACE satellite. Models formed using ACE data from the 2003 solar storm were accurate years later during both nominal and hazardous conditions in 2008.

Keywords

Bayesian, predictive, diagnostics, model, ACE Satellite, space weather

1. Introduction

The current state of operations for the command, control and diagnostics of space craft remains, as it has since the dawn of the space age, a human centered and ground based endeavor. The decisions made by ground operations are frequently be made within tight time constraints, and carry serious and potentially expensive implications for the mission. Due to the current requirement of highly skilled personnel for ground operations, training often takes 18 months in order to achieve flight readiness. Because of the human centric nature of operations, the safety of the craft and crew, and ultimately mission success, relies upon efficient and rapid communication among ground staff, and on manned missions, between individuals on the ground and among the crew. [1] These extensive training requirements and the high level of expertise of the personnel contribute to the cost of a mission. In fact, it is not uncommon for one third of mission costs to be consumed by operations.

1.1 Challenges of Conventional FDIR

It is common for a satellite to present ground operations personnel with thousands of telemetry items which need to be monitored. As spacecraft technology progresses, and Moore's law enables a reduction in the size and mass of instrumentation, the complexity of space craft will undoubtedly increase with a commensurate increase in the number of telemetry items. [2] The conventional method for displaying the health and welfare diagnostic information of a space craft to the crew, and or the ground operators, is through text on a screen and spread sheet print outs. By monitoring the text display of telemetry data, operators are expected to detect and then correct for an anomalous reading. To aid the human eyes on the telemetry, a number of automation approaches have been employed which can be generally referred to as Fault Detection Identification and Recovery (FDIR). [3] In practice, the output of FDIR is typically text-based where operators' attention is draw to what the system determines to be anomalous readings by the words turning red.

This text based user interface nonetheless has significant drawbacks in that it requires a high degree of human oversight which is inherently time consuming and subject to human error. Erroneous warning messages can distract the crew and operators and the root cause of a legitimate anomaly can be difficult to identify. All of which leads to eye strain, cognitive overload, the reliance on operator intuition and an increased risk for operator errors. [4]

Perhaps the best data to support the assertion that text based output of diagnostic telemetry can be found by looking at the results of tests given to commercial airline pilots. Commercial aircraft diagnostic information output systems are similar to those used in the space industry having obvious common heritage and functions. In a recent study, 25% of seasoned pilots given simulator assessments failed to notice warning messages. [1] One might expect highly stressed, overworked and under rested crew or ground operators working through emergency scenarios with limit situational awareness and communication delays might perform even more poorly.

1.2 Machine Centered Diagnostics Needed for the Future

While the benefits in a transition away from human-centered and ground-based operations are apparent, future missions which travel farther from the Earth will necessitate such a paradigm shift. Increasingly complex, future spacecraft systems will result in a commensurate increase in the volume of diagnostic information. The prohibitive time delays imposed by the time required for signals to reach an Earth based ground station from a deep space mission will make reliance on ground operations support for real-time tactical and strategy mission decisions impossible. The consequences of this situation are the needs for self-reliance of the crew and/or spacecraft on onboard FDIR, and more intuitive and responsive diagnostics.

Reliance on onboard systems will consequently require increased onboard situational awareness by the craft and crew. Where manned deep space missions are concerned, the need for a small crew to mitigate cognitive overload will be key in enabling them to successfully make time-constrained operational decisions under potentially physically and psychologically stressful circumstances. Nuisance, erroneous warning messages will need to be avoided, actionable failure information must be provided and accurate detection and identification of root cause failure chains will be essential in future diagnostics.

2. Traditional FDIR

Recognition of the need for increased autonomy of crew and craft from ground support operational constraints is nothing new. Indeed, great strides have been made in autonomous anomaly detection and diagnosis. Past efforts at autonomous FDIR can broadly be categorized by the following labels which proceed chronologically to the present time: limit checking, expert systems and model reasoning / computational simulation.

2.1 Limit Checking

Limit checking assigns nominal values for each metric, with warning signals initiated when the value is outside the range which is determined to be safe. It is similar in principle to historic pressure or temperature gauges having green, yellow and red regions indicated on a dial corresponding to safe, caution and dangerous operating modes. Limit checking is straightforward and often effective at detecting predictable anomalies in simple systems, but it does not provide any information regarding the cause of the failure. [5]

2.2 Expert Systems

Expert systems, as the name implies, utilize in depth, expert knowledge of the system in a more sophisticated iteration of the limit checking heritage systems. Many FDIR of expert systems can also control simple systems from an operation stand point. The high degree of domain knowledge necessary makes it impossible to account for unexpected or unknown unknowns however. Expert systems can accommodate some changes in the states of a system, as long as these changes are accounted for a priori, however expert systems often fail if unpredictable or rapidly dynamic states of systems occur. [6]

2.3 Computational Models

Model based reasoning, also known as computational modeling, has shown great promise in its ability to permit rapid reconfiguration of systems. Perhaps the most noteworthy example of model reasoning is the Livingstone software developed by NASA Ames. [4] Using Livingstone, a model of a system is developed in order to predict behavior. During operation, Livingstone continuously compares this computational model with the actual sensor values in real time. If sensor values diverge from the predictions of the model, a diagnosis is made to isolate the cause of the discrepancy. [7]

3. Challenges of Traditional FDIR

While all of these FDIR configurations have great utility, they share some fundamental weakness which can be traced to the top down logic which has thus far been applied to FDIR. The deductive reasoning which is the basis of these methods works well for simple systems and has the benefits of being linear, and therefore gratifying in being comprehensible in terms of the if-then logical progression of failure events.

To establish all of the rules for a complex system such as a spacecraft however requires a high level of domain knowledge as every new scenario needs a new rule. Without such expert domain knowledge, it is difficult to accurately assign nominal values to system metrics in advance, discern what faults are possible during the mission and predict what the downstream system consequences (fault chains) will be. [8]

Under (unattainable) ideal circumstances, system experts predict all possible problems that can occur with a space craft or mission, all of the possible consequences of these root faults, all the consequences of these first consequences, ad infinitum – an unlikely scenario. Practically speaking, the determination of as many possible fault scenarios as reasonable requires a large amount of time expended by a large team of highly skilled (i.e. highly paid) system experts. Of course, as anyone spaceflight enthusiast is aware, unexpected problems do occur nonetheless, sometimes with catastrophic consequences.

The deductive, rules based logic of model based reasoning works very well, as long as all of the rules are known and nothing that can change the rules varies after the rules have been set in stone. As missions may evolve based on new discoveries, or unpredicted external factors such as space weather, the rules of the model based FDIR may need to be adjusted to compensate for new conditions or priorities. This requires re-training the model which can be expensive, time consuming and risky once the mission has begun. For this reason, a time-invariant FDIR system which respond autonomously to dynamic environments, and therefore does not require re-training, has become somewhat of a holy grail for many system engineers.

4. Saber's Novel Approach to Predictive Modeling

To address the current and future need for responsive spacecraft diagnostics, Saber Astronautics has developed the next generation of health and operations diagnostics applying a dynamic Bayesian network statistics to the big data challenge of spacecraft telemetry. This software package, currently referred to as the Predictive Interactive Ground station Interface (PIGI), applies state of the art probabilistic algorithms on the back end. The front end presents information to the operator using accelerated, 3D graphics for intuitive operation and superb situational awareness.

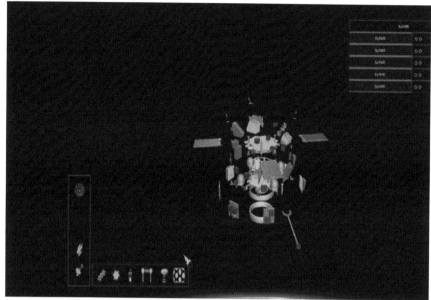

Figure 1: Exploded engineering schematic view of spacecraft components as display to an operator using PIGI.

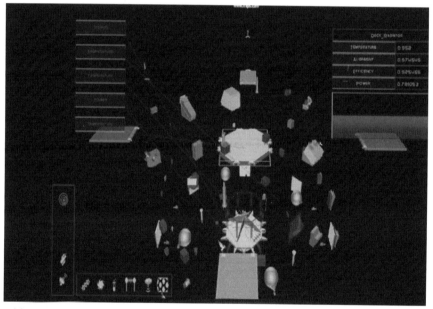

Figure 2: Graphic representation of failure chain at component level as displayed to operator using PIGI.

Red components are malfunctioning; blue components have malfunctioned but have recovered and do not require immediate attention.

PIGI estimates faults, predicts performance and identifies the root cause of failure chains. Our statistical approach mitigates the reliance on if-then rule sets and is therefore not constrained by the need for expert domain knowledge as many previous systems have been. PIGI is able to semi-autonomously acquire data for the construction of the system model from telemetry, not human experts. As such, PIGI does not require complete expert knowledge a priori. [9]

PIGI diagnoses performance at the system level and allows drill down to components. By employing a global systems model, Saber is able to track cause and affect chains of any event which degrades performance. For example, if a space weather event occurs PIGI is able to instantly quantify the effect the event has on satellite subsystems. Most importantly, PIGI's algorithms are resilient to dynamic state changes and have demonstrated degrees of time-invariance obviating the need for continuously retraining the models.

4.1 How Saber Develops Models

Saber develops the model of a system in PIGI from the telemetry of the spacecraft by first abstracting the health and welfare information into performance metrics. The working definition for metric used in this paper is a data driven equation which is based upon telemetry. A system of systems analysis approach is used starting from the high level, mission statement logically drilling down to the systems. Interactions between performance metrics are identified and a System of Systems (SoS) map is developed.

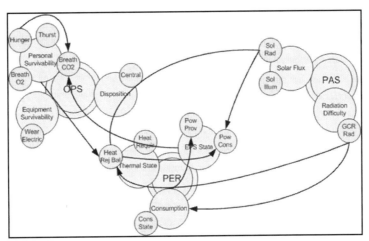

Figure 3: Example of a System of System (SoS) map. Arrows indicate interactions between metrics.

From the SoS map, we are able to drill down to the component level. This process provides an understanding of the cause and event chains enabling the ability to trace back up the failure chain to identify the root cause of malfunctions. While much of this process utilizes a degree of automation, to speed the development iterations, a degree of skill and expertise is required on the human development side as related to the selection of the appropriate performance metrics.

5. Saber Demonstration on ACE Satellite

To illustrate the process of developing a predictive model, we will look at the example of Saber's demonstration for NASA's Advanced Composition Explorer (ACE) satellite. The ACE satellite sits at Lagrangian point 1 between the sun and the Earth where it monitors space weather events. In November of 2003, the largest solar flare measured in modern times occurred. Two weeks of data, consisting of 1200 metrics, collected from ACE during this solar flare event was kindly provided to Saber by NASA for the demonstration. Of these 1200 metrics, 22 telemetry and 3 space weather metrics were selected by Saber from which to develop the model.

Although the data obtained for ACE was collected during an extreme weather event, the model which was developed from this data, if it was an accurate general solution, should have predicted future performance of the satellite during nominal conditions as well. In addition, the model would ideally be time invariant, remaining accurate over time during normal conditions and when space weather gets rough. This level of time invariance has been elusive for the developers of many of the previous expert systems and means that previous models required frequent retraining, being valid only under a limited set of circumstances.

Saber's demonstration for the ACE satellite was highly successful in many respects. The diagnostics identified faults and nominal performance with greater than 97% accuracy. The single event upsets, referred to as Black Swan events, were predictable with an unexpectedly high accuracy of 50-70%.

Perhaps the most profound example of the accuracy of the model however is shown be the time invariance of the model years after it was initially formed. As described earlier, data from the predictive model for the ACE satellite was collected during the space weather event of 2003. In 2008, another large space weather event occurred. The Space Weather Prediction Center in Boulder Colorado recorded the solar flare as shown here:

389

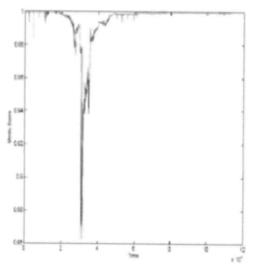

Figure 4: 2008 solar event as recorded by the Space Weather Prediction Center.

If Saber's predictive model based on data from 2003 was in fact an accurate, general solution with time invariance, the model should be expected to be able to predict the performance of ACE during the 2008 storm. To test this, Saber took data obtained from ACE during the 2008 solar flare and input this performance telemetry into the model which was developed from 2003 data. The output from the model is shown here:

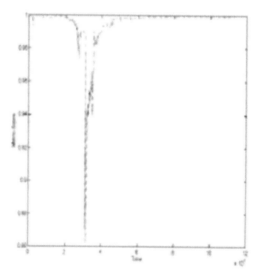

Figure 5: Prediction output from Saber's model for the 2008 space weather event which resulted in the data from ACE which was input into the model developed using 2003 data.

As can be seen, there is a high degree of similarity between the actual solar flare data as recorded by the Boulder Weather Center. The demonstration that the model was able to accurately predict the radiative flux of the solar flare that caused the 2008 telemetry which was input into the model dramatically shows the accuracy and time invariance of the model.

6. Conclusion

Where every minute of satellite downtime can result in millions of dollars of lost revenue, Saber's viability in the present space market is clear. Our statistical approach has benefits over previous expert systems by reducing the time and cost for creating the model. Our models are highly accurate and do not require long time scales and in depth, expert system knowledge. Additionally, the streamlined monitoring and diagnosing provided by PIGI serves to reduce personnel costs and operator training times.

While Saber's technology has obvious application to future deep space missions, where the reliance upon ground control is not realistic, it also provides huge cost and capability benefits to government and commercial space missions right now. Rapid, or even real time, diagnostics and an intuitive, intelligently designed graphic user interfaces such as Saber has developed will reduce the cognitive load for operators, increase the efficiency of day to day operations and can vastly improve mission success. Saber's method of presenting only relevant diagnostic information to the operator reduces workload. In fact, the graphic nature of the interface enables a single operator to monitor and control multiple independent space craft or entire constellations. Innovative solutions developed by small New Space companies like Saber to the problems of today will become the enabling technologies which will tomorrow take us to the stars.

References

1. Garcia-Galan, C., "Advanced Technologies for Future Spacecraft Cockpits and Space-based Control Centers," Internat. Aerospace Conference (2006).

2. Swartwout, M., "Engineering Data Summaries for Space Missions," Aerospace Conference, IEEE 2, 391-401 (1998).

3. Spirkovska, L., "Anomaly Detection for Next-Generation Space Launch Ground Operations," Proceedings AIAA SpaceOps 2010 Conference (2010).

4. McCann, R.S., "Automating Vehicle Operations in Next-Generation Spacecraft: Human Factors Issues," Space (2005).

5. Takehisa Y., "Telemetry-Mining: A Machine Learning Approach to Anomaly Detection and Fault Diagnosis for Space Systems," 2nd IEEE International Conference on Space Mission Challenges for Information Technology (2006).

6. Kawahara Y., "Diagnosis method for spacecraft using dynamic Bayesian networks," Proc. of 8th International symposium on Artificial Intelligence, Robotics and Automation in Space (2005).

7. Hayden S., "Linvingstone Model-Based Diagnosis of Earth Observing One," Proc. AIAA Intelligent Systems (2004).

8. Kurien, J. "Intrinsic Hurdles in Applying Automated Diagnosis and Recovery to Spacecraft Systems," Man and Cybernetics, Part A: Systems and Humans, IEEE Transactions 40(5) 945-58 (2010).

9. Held, J. "Supply requirement prediction during long duration space missions using Bayesian estimation," Internat. J. Logistics Res. Apps. 10(4) 351-66 (2007).

Economies in a Stellar Civilization: Carrying a Bit of Earth to the Stars

Zubin Ray

MBA, Indian Institute of Management Calcutta

zubinr2012@email.iimcal.ac.in

Abstract

Concepts of value, property and trade have defined the nature of economic activity on Earth since pre-history; however a space-based civilization has no precedent to transplant as a system, and requires a unique approach for unique problems. These include very long time spans, exploitation focussed gains, and an umbilical cord tying spacefarers with Earth. The desire to involve private entrepreneurship and investment into space exploration further complicates this equation, requiring time bound value generation and necessary socio-legal structures to encourage capital flow. In this paper, I consider the possible evolution of stellar economies, their relationship with the home planet and progressing towards a self-sustaining stellar society. A brief examination of economic development through history is considered, with focus on theories of value and emergence of modern monetary and capital systems. Hypothetical visions of human life in space are presented, including ideas on mineral exploitation, planetary colonization, self-sufficiency, trade relations and political sovereignty. Then, we evaluate need provision, want satisfaction and reward systems which could be successfully applied to space investors and space explorers. These are sorted into 3 categories: Environment Dependant, Ability Dependant and Investment Dependant, and the essential requirements to generate each of these are laid out from the background discussed. Potential near-term solutions are exhibited, drawing inspiration from public and private initiatives to solve analogous problems through human history. Social aspects of achieving this are discussed, including prestige, expectations and communication as tools to achieving collective buy-in. The paper is closed with a pragmatic evaluation of the necessary combination of circumstances for a real push to space exploration and the possible negative outcomes of a space gold rush.

1. Introduction

Historically, economic expansion through the transformation of society from nomadic to agrarian, and the development for feudal through industrial economies, have seen growth in the quantity of output, the value of output and the diversity of output. Changes in political economy and social structure have also gone hand in hand with technological change (whether progress or regress). As we look towards expanding humanity into space, a new stellar economy needs to take the place of those that have gone before. Just as technological innovation utterly changed the pre-industrial economy, a push into space just as a spatial change will necessitate an economy without precedent, goods which are unknown or niche markets may become commonplace items in a space-faring civilization. Services so far unknown may need to be provided.

Whether this stellar economy precedes or follows social transformation that might accompany such an economy is limited to conjecture. However, to achieve such an eventual result, we would need to utilize the economics available to us currently, including the same conceptions of value, property, returns and expectations that provide the infrastructure for exchange and growth.

To consider changes in attitude from this angle, we may first consider space exploration as it is now: a public enterprise with private offshoots. Public investment (particularly defence and related R&D) have played the major role in humankind's stretch to the stars. Yet public expenditure and application depend on public opinions perhaps not the most predictable or reliable source of support and backing[2]. During the space race, fear of the US lagging behind the Soviets was a strong impetus to the public and to President Kennedy, which led to one of the most resounding triumphs of human initiative, and a true example of human potential. But this was not sustainable, a war that is over no longer requires resources to fight[3][4]. Economic troubles such as the crisis of 2008 also exacerbate this impact, making people less well-disposed to what appears to be a non-essential exercise, as noble as it might be.

The impact of this type of development is wide ranging, the space industry as it exists today is not an industry, but a vast non-profit generating technological advancement without direct returns4. To clarify here, by direct returns I do not mean that society has not benefited from such programs, but these programs are not seen as the source of benefit, excepting those who are interested in the subject. The space industry is perceived as a wellspring of ideas and achievement, but also as a surplus activity, to be sustained when there is enough bandwidth to expend extra resources on further research and exploration[5].

In recent time, there has been a drive towards greater involvement of the private sector in space travel. Much of this has been centred on commercial investment which can generate direct returns – firms charging to ferry tourists to space, or carrying cargo for government enterprises6. All of these businesses are expected to offer a competitive commercial proposition related to space, and earn their spurs (and more importantly, their bottom lines) through the strength of their offerings. However, much of the promising commercial enterprise remains centred on providing either to public entities (shipping to the ISS paid for by the government) or leveraging public perception and the novelty factor.

The future of space travel and the question of humanity transcending Earth therefore becomes one dependant on mundane concerns. Some views are not optimistic at all on the possibility of deliberate or graduated change, indeed the school of revolutionary change in history believes that without crisis of some sort any true transformation is impossible7. However, unless we are to wait for an existential crisis to strike humanity (a depressing outcome to wait for) to spur public initiative towards space, some connection must be made between space as is and humanity as it is now, and will be in the near future.

2. Observing the Past for Cues

As setting out a plain statement of needs, it would be appropriate to discuss the goal at hand. What would constitute a functioning stellar economy? And how would we get there?

Looking at science fiction from the standpoint of social science, one assumption is that life in the technologically advanced future is recognizably similar to life today. Most works of science fiction have some demarcated gender differentiation, existence of social classes, differentiation between work and leisure and of course enough human emotion to make a story. Complex systems make it difficult to assess the impact of a radically changed environment, and may not be relevant for the near future. Though there are as many ideas on what space life would be like as there are possibilities, I submit a basic framework laid out below, for discussing this paper. Since we are concerned with the economics of stellar civilizations, the framework is focussed on these aspects rather than technological setups and achievement.

To decide what this framework should be, I looked at the historical record of socio-economic systems to see what aspects of humanity are most persistent through time despite technological and social changes8. This of course leaves out many more recent issues (say, would astronauts need access to the internet on a daily basis to update themselves and keep up with a changing society on earth?) but gives a probable indicator of likely retentions in economic activity. The essentials are:

1. Property – An ancient human invention, it remains a well entrenched system of economic allocation amongst agents in the system

2. Employment – division into owning and earning groups remains as the prominent method of economic organization; we should note that the continuation of this style of organization does not translate into retaining the associated class structures per se, but rather assumes the continued utility of a role division along these lines

3. Money – As the essential unit of abstracting value, we can reasonably expect that money value and it's residual and perceptual components will continue to play an important part in economic activity

4. The State – government (of whatever kind) has been the standout feature of human civilization, some (or many) regulating authority-bearing version of current national and global conglomerations will probably be around in the future too

5. Private Enterprise – private business and trade have been around equally as long, from traditional manufactures and markets to modern corporate entities; they may or may not be encouraged depending on the state, but they are certainly present

6. Savings & Investment cycle – the newest one on this list, the practice of investing savings (as opposed to hoarding as the classical concept of saving) is not as antiquated as the others mentioned above, but has evolved into the crucial liquidity and growth infrastructure of modern economies, especially as a lifeline of high-risk activities like space travel

Generally speaking, if there is to be a stellar civilization established in the near future, it would seem likely to bear out the key characteristics seen today. Further along, there may be radical differences but in a timeframe exceeding our lifetimes and reducing the scope for action.

The second question is how we would collectively attain this stellar civilization. At the moment, economic activity remains centred around Earth. The pale blue dot is still the lifeboat of humanity through the universe. Total change is unlikely in the near future as it would require at least one more habitable planet with a biosphere compatible with us, which we can then reach and utilize. These imply some necessary constraints to an evolving scenario: chief amongst these is the dependence on Earth for food, even though there may be water and oxygen found on accessible extra-terrestrial sources. Above life sustenance, there would be some need to provide explorers with the ability to live a semblance of a normal life, possibly with family and children, social activities and relationships, all the way up to possible psychological complications arising from affinity with nature and the absence of it in space.

It seems reasonable to say therefore, that any space civilization will be bound to Earth for a prolonged period in its nascence. This necessity of continuously returning, trading and maintaining an economic relationship will be the bond tying any space civilization to its Earth roots for a prolonged time. Whatever system pioneers wish to use for their life in the cosmos will always be moderated in this sense by retaining elements sufficiently in common with Earth to sustain a dependant relationship, as foreseen in many works of science fiction. In this sense, space farers will always be carrying a bit of earth with them to the stars, which will affect how they live, work and relate to each other.

Building a self-sustaining structure in space thus depends upon satiating the needs and wants of an earthbound support system that has to provide the goods and services to build this, and desires to be compensated or rewarded for the same. It becomes necessary to use a method by which property can be identified, useful employment provided, value generated, rules and norms upheld, individuals allowed to participate and returns on investment to be realized.

3. Framing the Problem

Building on this train of thought, the development of several economic systems with changing technological and social environments is of particular interest to us. By carefully observing the innovations and disruptions encountered in the past, we may make some shrewd guesses as to the challenges we can face in the future.

The transition of economies can be seen in many different ways. In some schools of political economy, viewing changes in labour or class relationships is seen as the major transition systems, slave economy to feudal economy to industrial economy and so on. Technological viewpoints are defined in terms of capabilities possessed in distinct periods, civilizational timespans as eras of the wheel, iron, irrigation; and onwards to steam, the atom and information9. Taxonomy is not a concern for us, nor are the debates over what and which system is the right one. Instead, our perspective depends upon the key elements serving as the foundation of the modern system as it is exists, and which need to be harnessed in order to achieve our goal of expanding into space.

The key issue is clearly modern capitalism, the system which either rode on the back of the industrial revolution or caused it depending on your view, to become the globally dominant method of doing things. This system has features that are both driving the impetus for growth and expansion and simultaneously creating many of the roadblocks towards space conquest.

Some of the advantages are the huge advances made in technological capacity, which bear a strong correlation to the competitive drive so strong in this system [10]. While not all discoveries are for pure profit, the intensity with which the search is pursued for beneficial technology has a major role to play in the addition of knowledge and capabilities of humanity as a whole, though perhaps more in accelerating the rate of knowledge accrual compared to actually acquiring it [11]. Similarly, the rising economic surplus makes possible ever more additional investment and expansion, though the application of these has a lot to do with competing influences in the public mindspace. Distributing and redistributing surplus is one of the most pressing questions in the modern economy, and will have a major political role in the future path of our collective civilization.

Disadvantages are more subtle, yet have long ranging effects. For instance, an expectation of more rapid rewards (returns on investment) substantially shortens the available time to a business or an upcoming industry to be able to satisfy the prevailing market sentiment. Consider the contrast between traditional family businesses (such as in India) and the modern entrepreneurial capitalism in the US and other countries. Indian family businesses are hereditary, they are socially entrenched, community focussed, have strong resistance against competition (including caste and gender biases) [12] and otherwise possessing many feudal characteristics. However, the necessity of inheritance and high barriers between the family and outsiders creates tremendous scope for long term planning. Indian business interests often invest with an eye to inter-generational gains over decades. This phenomenon is not just limited to the business families, but pervades India, and may be a major factor behind a national investment preference for land and gold, both of which are seen as timeless assets which can be transferred to the next generation. Even a lack of tangible returns is not deterrence to their allure, particularly gold.

Current concepts of entrepreneurship are however based on shorter and shorter time spans. Towards an extreme end in the tech sector, small firms are able to grow at astronomical rates with VC and PE funding. However, such funding necessitates exit within a matter of a few years through an IPO or locating some other buyer for the stake held. The trade-off in this case appears to be that in exchange for much greater liquidity and expansion opportunities, the horizon for expected returns is shortened considerably[13], which can be simply shown as:

Say X and Y are two competitors for investment, eventually providing a return of r after T_x and T_y years respectively, with a probability of P(X) and P(Y) respectively. Assuming an individual discounts each year's delayed returns by d, her expectation E can be

$$E(X) = X.r.P(X) * \left(\frac{1}{dTx}\right)$$

$$E(Y) = Y.r.P(Y) * \left(\frac{1}{dTy}\right)$$

For the same principal invested $E(X) = E(Y)$ *iff* $\frac{P(X)}{P(Y)} = \frac{Tx}{Ty}$

For a case where X is the terrestrial investment, while Y is the extra-terrestrial, one can reasonably assume lower P(Y) and higher TY , leaving the equations in disequilibrium, and the only hope of competing with X as to offer a much larger "r". How much can actually be offered given the current possibilities is an open question.

In addition to being the theme in vogue, a preference for this system and the glamour and speed associated with it can allow short term investment opportunities to crowd out longer term competitors for capital, in much the same rationale that government borrowing (preferred low risk alternative) can crowd out private borrowing, except time is an added variable to risk.

What emerges from this, is that while modern capitalism has seen an expansion of markets and securitization based on all sorts of value propositions, some types of markets are either neglected or possibly even actively discouraged. In a society like India, families hold savings as a portfolio diversified across time (shares and deposits vs land and gold) as well as risk and return. On the surface, there does not appear to be investor demand for such a product, certainly there is no organized market that is able to leverage different preferences on time without adding it into a risk component, though there is no reason why this should not be technically possible.

This is a key problem for attracting investment into space based activity. Difficulties in transport and return on a space venture make the T problem significant in a way it is not necessarily on earthbound investment opportunities. Add to that the risk is substantially higher, and one can consider that the return then required is probably too complex and uncertain to estimate. Competing with regular forms of investment is perhaps so difficult, that it should be no surprise that historically expectations for space investment are either premised on some disaster making it a necessity or at best some miracle technology changing the reward matrix like the mineral "Unobtanium" from the film Avatar.

4. Science Fiction to Science Fact

Given all these difficulties, it would be relevant at this time to consider some proposed solutions to the stellar economic model postulated through fiction, so often inspiring reality in this field. Science fiction has visualized a variety of possibilities in this regard, growing scenarios, collapsing scenarios, vibrant economic life, stagnant economic decay, and all sorts of genetic, mental, class and other variations of a star society.

Some of the nearer term options explored are mining the solar system for resources to trade with Earth. This has the advantage of meeting a tangible and existing demand on Earth, being reasonably possible with involvement on the Moon, and allowing for the creation of an actual business model with which to appeal to investment. Sending a spaceship to the destination would be the lion's share of the cost, which could be brought down to $2000 per kg of spaceship to the moon [14]. All this appears to make technology and investment the primary barrier to actualizing the business, though some have taken initial steps toward this.

However there are many pitfalls, at its core, the science fiction argument for this industry rested on resource exhaustion and this is economically sound too. As of today, it is hard to think of any mineral paucities on earth that market price rise is not able to correct by opening up additional supply routes on Earth itself. One of the key resource demand centres, carbon energy sources like oil and gas, are not so easily accessible (though they are visibly present on Titan). Often, the fictional environment was post-industrial, where resource allocation was scarce and rationed according to planned outlays [15]. Compared to these, competing with industries already on Earth makes the proposition more difficult, though not impossible.

Moreover, the trite example of helicopters dropping printed money works equally well when the effective assets of gold or platinum or lithium is 2 or 3 planets worth what it was but demand is the same or growing at the same pace. The success of a program to tap celestial resources might become its own worst enemy. To condition everyone into adaptation requires demand disruption and control of the supply, perhaps like the diamond industry16, which would cause huge terrestrial disruption and decimate the comparative advantage of trade that is a hope for many poor but resource rich countries.

In more expansive tones, there are issues with controlling and exercising the rights that emerge from stellar business. Many of these build on colonial history of clashes between the home country and the colonies over autonomy, rights, or taxation and economic policies or social ideas. Few have dealt with persisting national or territorial affiliations from Earth being carrier over to space. However, it appears to be highly likely that they will, and political attitudes on earth might play a large role in the evolution of humanity into space. Issues arising representation, distribution of the gains, and the effect on the markets of having a sudden increase in the accessible supply would be ever present. Geopolitical realities on Earth are a true complicating factor of any space based ventures. Driving into space for profit might be acceptable, but there would almost certainly be both the option of using a technological advantage for strategic purposes, and the suspicion of others doing the same. It should be no surprise that most fiction writers envision post-apocalyptic scenarios as being the best setting for such a venture.

Alternatively, as the global economy changes, there may be much greater scope for space-sourcing many minerals and materials, especially rare ones not easily found on earth. A possible tactic in this might be a space enterprise which spread its wings across Earth, or at least those parts which might object to its activities. Sharing the profit with distributed supply and demand centres might be a safe, equitable and practicable method within the near future.

5. Identifying Key Agents

This brings us to the difficult task of sorting out what can be done within a visible time frame to further the hope of building a permanent and growing human presence in space (hopefully it will not be enough just to build robots, though that may end up as the only possible outcome). In the perspective that is being followed here, any space based civilization must be able to fulfil many requirements at the same time. In reality, probably the first who are able to do something about it will set the template for everyone else, and once it's done anything and anyone which was left out or negatively affected will either lump it or fight back until a winner is decided or peace is declared.

As a paper exercise, it is possible to plan for many eventualities, though only a few of them may emerge in reality. Pessimistic visions aside, we can carry out a thought experiment on what it is that can be done if we were to plan out a strategy to make a sustainable foothold in space and how to build upon it for the longer term. Since the approach in this paper is drawing analogies from history, the first step in this would be to classify the needs and wants of the different parties involved.

First, let us consider some of the grouped interests in this. One might be the highly involved, those dedicated to the vision, inspired by the literature or passionate about the science. This would be a primary group, a highly motivated set involved in many aspects of planning and probably most of the actual work involved. A secondary group would be potentially involved people, including investors, various industries which might see a complementary or a competitive interest, and related sciences and research interests. The tertiary group would be those at more than an arm's length, such as the media, other interest groups, and the general public across the globe.

The Primary group might be small, closely knit. We can assume their first priority would be to fulfil the goal of setting up lasting space industries, subject to maybe some larger purpose of space exploration. They would need funding, cooperation from government entities, and sufficient support from the larger community. Perhaps there is no limit to what they can do in the field apart from how much support they get, hence they would want more of what they have.

The Secondary group has more interests to take care of. An investor would consider many alternative factors, and there would probably be large differences between sub-groups who have differing levels of interest or confidence in the field. The secondary group needs results in their own language (whether it is profit or cost or product or any other proxy of value) and wants the primary group to ensure or at least support the interests of the secondary.

The Tertiary group is distanced from the actual events taking place. As the largest and most inertial group, it is both non-essential as a day to day player but is potentially a key variable in deciding the outcome of the primary-secondary relationship.

Second, I propose that each requirement for this goal can be broken down into a few categories. The categories I have in mind are Environment, Ability and Investment. In fact they may all be connected, maybe more investment leads to more abilities, or a different environment leads to more investment and so on, but separating the requirement for each simplifies an exercise looking for immediate causality towards the final goal. This might look like:

Environment	Ability	Investment
<ul><li>Public and state support for expansion of capabilities</li><li>Competing industries for limited pie of attention/investment</li><li>Economic climate and social priorities</li><li>International agreement over expansion into space</li></ul>	<ul><li>Long term human habitation in space</li><li>Range of activities (research, mining, manufacturing or even agriculture off-Earth)</li><li>Returning space products to Earth</li><li>Travel beyond Earth neighbourhood</li></ul>	<ul><li>Magnitude of development (experimental vs expansive)</li><li>Rate of development</li><li>Involvement outside small primary pool</li><li>2-way economic relationship or 1 way funding</li></ul>

These are far from an exhaustive list of the myriad requirements and complexities of setting up a space civilization, however my interest is in the segregation and causality. This is simply because identifying the key causal relation to each requirement is revealing of the degree of control we can exercise over that climate.

Of course an environment where the Earth was threatened with imminent destruction by an asteroid would be highly conducive to attracting investment and building infrastructure for a big jump in our spacefaring capabilities, but dea ex machina aside, this really exhibits the lack of control over an environmentally derived input to the goal.

The mapping between the groups also becomes clearer; Primary interests have a strong say over the Ability related, while Secondary parties have a large but not absolute say over the investment section. Tertiary groups are the environment in a certain sense, but are also exposed to other external stimuli.

6. Four Proposed Approaches

These groups and dependant activities need some form of synergy and symbiotic action amongst themselves if all their expectations are to be realized. It could be argued that the primary actors in space exploration till date have been mostly tertiary connected, rising to dizzy highs when the environment was favourable (such as during the Space race) and falling to lows when the environment declined (perhaps such as the current economic crisis).

It might be that the Secondary and Primary interaction is seen as a clash of opposing groups, especially on the point of deciding and planning abilities on where the conglomeration should go. However, given the long odds on tertiary interest swinging back in favour, or some miraculous change in the environment, partnership between Primary and Secondary groups is a necessity of rapid and continuous expansion in space, though possibly with mutual caution on both sides.

There are many problems in this alliance, some of which have been covered in this paper. Yet there are some parallels from previous experience which can assist with the task.

Since we are dealing with resolving Primary and Secondary groups, we can speak in terms of targeting 1 or more variables in the basic equation:

$$E(X) = X.r.P(X) * \left(\frac{1}{dTx}\right)$$

Where X = principal, r = rate of return, P(X) = probability of realizing r, d = discount on value of return, Tx = time to achieve returns on X

6.1 Barriers and Monopoly Rents

Despite the focus on competitiveness as the driver of market economics and the instrument of change and dynamism, many new businesses in history were equally supported by Monopoly powers and strong barriers to expansion [17]. One business which ended up having a huge impact on history, the spice trade, rested on both a reaction to Arab-Ottoman monopoly, and the profit basis also rested upon the formation of new monopolies, generally through use of military force, eventually leading to the creation of the colonial empires. First the Portugese, then the Dutch and the English formed large cartels or megalithic companies which were able to absorb and redistribute the profit base.

This is analogous to r_{xt} argeting in our equation, where the preferential treatment of investors into the company might outdo the relative advantage a competitor with lower T(X) or higher P(X).

$$E(X) = X.r_x.P(X) * \left(\frac{1}{dTx}\right)$$

This is the case when searching for gains ex ante the realization of the opportunity. Ex post, a much more potent monopolization can be created by targeting P(X) and rx simultaneously. Patent rights can also be considered a variation on offering a monopoly incentive.

Offering monopoly rents through creating artificial barriers has mixed acceptability as a method of competition in the current global economy; however there is scope for recreating aspects of the same agreement within a cooperative framework of Secondary and Primary parties. In the ex ante phase, when secondary commitments to the strategy are speculative, offering a larger incentive by guaranteeing the absence of competition at least for some part of the time frame post realization can sweeten the deal considerably. With the pace of change in a digital world, offering barriers (which would not be difficult to create given the difficulty of building the technology) would be a meaningful advantage for secondary agents.

The Secondary sector, combined with an investment dependant environment (where investors can choose avenues instead of avenues choosing investors) is most benefited by this system of returns. Not only does it mitigate many risk concerns, but increases the appeal of space investment compared to existing high-competition low-barrier industries on Earth. Ability expansion is also likely to be rapid. The primary group will be initially boosted, but possibly long-term constrained.

The role of the state and the tertiary are important here in deciding the extent of returns. In the aforementioned example of colonialism, national governments played key roles in supporting and building the institutions of profit. In one extreme example, the British government guaranteed returns to many of the private firms building railways in India, which allowed them to mint money of course but also led to a nationwide railway system from practically nothing. While the source of profit would not be as easy in space as it was with a wealthy country under the yoke, offering a powerful incentive with a whiff of permanence is a classical way of promoting involvement.

6.2 Arbitrage on Time

The cultural phenomenon shortening the available time horizon of gauging profit has had, and will almost certainly continue to have, a detrimental impact on long term approaches to return. To service this, most of the forecasting accuracy Secondary players depend upon is short term in nature. To think of stellar economies in the approach of capitalism is to paraphrase Keynes, we will all be dead before that spaceship comes back.

However, there are still areas where the intergenerational aspect is still strong, and shows signs of remaining so. India, the Middle East and many other parts of Asia and the world gradually growing wealthier show distinct signs of maintaining the family-community tie of wealth, and in fact seem to have adapted the model to smoothly fit the market economy.

This is analogous to d targeting in our equation, where the different perceptions of time discount for certain assets among different populations can be used as source of arbitrage.

$$E(X) = X.r_x.P(X) * \left(\frac{1}{dTx}\right)$$

The tendency of some Secondary groups to think in much longer terms for return imply there can be a market to appeal for a return which reaches fruition outside of the initiators lifetime.

Another aspect to this is legacy investments, which also have a powerful, modern and western lineage. The wealthy of the gilded age have created a reputation for philanthropy by ensuring their name lives on with various worthwhile and socially beneficial initiatives permanently associated with them. Universities, foundations, museums and many other institutions reward the investments into them by carrying fame of a long gone person far into the future. The desire to compete and be ranked high socially as well as economically, could play a key role in attracting capital to high profile ventures which have a strong altruistic component and public impact.

Using this as a model has some inherent problems, differences in value over time can have as much to do with the nature of the asset under discussion as with the preferences of the decision makers. Unknown long shot benefits from space exploration are unlikely to attract this kind of investment, providing the converse incentive to the one desired. However there can be a genuine argument that providing a source of return with a reasonably high P(X) on a timeframe which exceeds other alternatives can be an advantage. A major possibility is infrastructure related to space industry. Some possibilities can be options near earth with high possibilities of retaining value and having multiple uses, maybe permanent lunar settlement or orbital factories.

Of the options available, this is most friendly to the Primary group, since it might include significant no-conditions support, with the lustre of a name or history being the only reward. It is also less dependant on the secondary environment, and nullifies investment dependency. The downside is that it could be ability dependant, if ability should already exist to attract such investment, then it's utility might be reduced.

6.3 Securitization and Fannie Mae

This might be a highly suspicious option given the recent events of the housing collapse, however it is worthwhile remembering that the creation of government sponsored enterprises in the property market in the US played a key role in overcoming a major barrier18. The major opposition to many being able to buy a house once was the lack of credit with a suitably long repayment cycle for borrowers with modest means, which was in turn due to matching and forecasting problems. Creating a intermediate structure between Primary (would be buyers who want steady rates and long enough terms) and Secondary (lenders who want predictable outcomes and don't want exposure over long time frames) and a securitization of the loans over time allowed for a market that didn't exist before to come into existence.

This is analogous to P(X) targeting in our equation. Risk mitigation through external agency is a task which has been done before, disconnected with limited liability and equity provisions.

$$E(X) = X.r_x.P(X) * \left(\frac{1}{dTx}\right)$$

The essential question when trying to add such a system is what is the underlying that would be securitized that can allow for market forces to function within the limited framework? Moreover, doesn't the inherent lower risk in real estate justify this market?

In some senses, this may only be possible once there is already some good to which access is difficult due to capital raising purposes. However, in fact there is a key synergy between Primary and Secondary players here that can be utilized. While primary agents require committed resources over the long term at acceptable rates of return, secondary parties are faced with a quandary of methods of financing even if they may have sufficient incentive to engage in the process. Long term projects extract a liquidity cost, sucking cash out of the system and "trapping" it in an investment. This adds complexity to investment, particularly post the financial crisis holding liquidity as a form of security has been a high priority for almost all financial institutions.

As opposed to creating an aggregation designed to lower risk (as with the housing market) a hypothetical Space GSE could fragment investment over time instead. Splitting the total credit requirement by fracturing demand into equal short term credit bundles for sale in the market, akin to time based bond issuances by governments, could approximate the aggregate demand effect. Splitting by period would allow each time interval to be valued independently, somewhat like the yield curve for government debts over different time intervals. However, the sensitive and problematic part is that an intermediary would have to provide cash to the industry, while supplying the market with liquidity. The major question remaining is where would such an organization come from, and for now, the only option appears to be the state.

6.4 Bubble Creation: Riding the Wave

A last possibility presented here is based on an additional criteria of irrationality in investing, which may be more common than is often supposed.

Since irrationality is difficult to mathematically represent, we conveniently add an addition criteria, Chemical X, to the mix, assuming it will induce the overwhelming bias in favour of E(X) vs any E(Y) regardless of any other variables.

$$E(X) = X.r_x.P(X) * \left(\frac{1}{dTx}\right) * (ChemicalX)$$

Chemical X is an overriding emotion which induces investment into the space sector regardless of any other qualities.

Inducing this type of inflow is rare, and the result is usually a bubble, an inflating industry where the balance of investment dependency changes in favour of the receiver's rather than the givers. Bubbles, like the housing bubble or the dotcom bubble, can be economic hot potatoes. Encouraging them can be a powerful method to spur wide, broad based growth. For instance, the housing created wealth expansion across income levels and regions in the US and UK. The UK government is trying to stimulate the housing market again (post crisis) in order to spread employment and benefits to larger population.

Of course, when bubbles burst, there is wide economic disruption. This is strong enough reason to not actively pursue bubble creation, more so because information asymmetry and communicative distortions can play a major role in the creation of bubbles. However, a bubble could take place due to a variety of reasons. These include an excess of liquid cash but no viable seeming alternatives (not unlike the current global scenario), or a rise in public sentiment and interest in the subject (usually due to media coverage, movies, wide headlines).

In part, the communicative aspect of generating interest and curiosity has a strong investment role as well, especially when it comes to new industries. Possibly, the last few decades have created an environment where secondary parties are actively looking for the next big thing which further amplifies the communicative aspect of selling investment ideas.[19]

In effect, this method uses the tertiary group to break down the barrier between primary and secondary. An upswing in tertiary due to the lack of options, the necessity of maintaining the savings-investment cycles, and communication inspiring interest in the subject could create a rush of money into the field. It is possible to ride such a bubble for some lasting benefits, for example the creation of long term infrastructure for construction or launch of space materials, a large cadre of experienced workforce, attracting new talent into the field, and even providing accurate information to the market enabling systemic investment calculation from then on.

7. Some Notes of Caution

Whatever possibilities there are for bridging the current gap between the Primary and Secondary groups, much of it will rely on the difficult to predict and hard to control Tertiary. Sufficient changes in this group can overwhelm many barriers, or create new ones that make the task almost impossible.

However, one element in this grouping is important, and that is the state. The role of the state in fostering and directing interests and resources is substantial, even in areas where it may choose to exercise a limited influence. The scale of action is so significant, the not taking any interest has as large implications as an in-depth involvement. In fact, as states in the past have played key roles in directing the success of their affiliates through domestic and foreign support, the modern state is likely to have the last say in directing a move deeper into space.

Should the state have such a role? Realistically, there are few ways of doing anything without the support of the state. The question of obtaining state support is also a question of obtaining popular support, making a key part of the tertiary grouping. This is hardly the end of it, since there are multiple states, and all of them have the high ground when it comes to Ability dependency at the current point in time. Some will be more encouraging of non-state involvement, others uninterested, or actively discouraging. Regardless the likelihood of getting by without a state presents more problems than it does opportunities.

The importance of this can be seen by examining further historical examples of what occurs in the general absence of a regulating entity. At worst, such a scenario could lead to anarchic chaos, however assuming that earth-bound institutions are strong enough to prevent the extreme scenario, what else could occur?

One possibility is a space gold rush, where due to the abundance of resources suddenly available with the opening up of new asteroids, moons et al, combined with shrinking economic and employment opportunities on Earth leads to surge of people seeking to make their fortune in space. This kind of disruptive activity has been seen before, such as the California or Yukon gold rushes. Communicative disruption is a key part of the creation of such a rush, implying the need of an entity to ensure information adequacy and accuracy. A body with sufficient credibility is often only the state, and non-state alternatives (market set such as Libor or agency credit ratings) are perhaps not sufficient alternatives at the current time.

8. Conclusion

To conclude, the approach in this paper has relied upon various trends, patterns and events that have occurred in the past. These have been extrapolated to consider potential applications in the future. The obvious shortcoming is the absence of genuinely new or transformational aspects, since the approach necessarily excludes that which has not been seen before.

There may be any number of possible methods not explored here to ensure humanity's progression into space, and ensure that the transition is speedy, humane, inclusive and transformational. However, from a limited perspective, my own perception and analysis is that we have collectively been unable to make a clean break with the past especially when it comes to the socio-economic world we live in. Though its continuance may dampen some of the hopes that go with space travel, we can still be optimistic that it can foster our collective expansion into space for some time to come.

References

1. Do People Want Something for Nothing: Public Opinion on Taxes and Government Spending., Citrin, Jack, National Tax Journal, v32 n2 p113s-29s Jun 1979

2. Radio's Impact on Public Spending*, David Strömberg, The Quarterly Journal of Economics (2004) 119 (1): 189-221

3. Averting a Sino-US space race , Author(s): Martel, WC (Martel, WC); Yoshihara, T (Yoshihara, T), WASHINGTON QUARTERLY Volume: 26   Issue: 4   Pages: 19-35   DOI: 10.1162/016366003322387082 Published: FAL 2003

4. Public opinion polls and perceptions of US human spaceflight, Roger D. Launius, Space Policy 19 (2003) 163–175

5. The Myth of America's Love Affair with the Moon, Jeremy Hsu, http://www.space.com/10601-apollo-moon-program-public-support-myth.html

6. Entrepreneurs to play big role in space, Marc Kaufman, Washington Post, Sunday, October 5, 2008

7. Race, Class and Power: Some Comments on Revolutionary Change, Leo Kuper, Comparative Studies in Society and History / Volume 14 / Issue 04 / September 1972, pp 400-421

8. Endogenous Preferences: The Cultural Consequences of Markets and Other Economic Institutions, Samuel Bowles, Journal of Economic Literature Vol. 36, No. 1 (Mar., 1998), pp. 75-111

9. Does Technology Drive History?: The Dilemma of Technological Determinism, edited by Merritt Roe Smith, Leo Marx, MIT Press 1994

10. Periodizing capitalism, Technology, institutions, and relations of production, Gerard DUMENIL and Dominique LEVY, Phases of Capitalist Development, edited by Robert Albritto

11. Technology, its Innovation and Diffusion as the Motor of Capitalism, Peter J. Hugill, Comparative Technology Transfer and Society Volume 1, Number 1, April 2003 pp. 89-113

12. Successor Attributes in Indian and Canadian Family Firms: A Comparative Study, Pramodita Sharma & A. Srinivas Rao, Family Business Review December 2000 vol. 13 no. 4 313-330

13. Time-Varying Return and Risk in the Corporate Bond Market, Eric C. Chang and Roger D. Huang, Journal of Financial and Quantitative Analysis / Volume 25 / Issue 03 / September 1990, pp 323-340

14. A lunar vision at $2,000/kg, Sam Dinkin, http://www.thespacereview.com/article/284/1

15. Utopia and Science Fiction, Raymond Williams, Science Fiction Studies Vol. 5, No. 3 (Nov., 1978), pp. 203-214

16. Markets: Continuity and Change in the International Diamond Market, Spar, Debora L., The Journal of Economic Perspectives, Volume 20, Number 3, Summer 2006 , pp. 195-208

17. Schumpeter on Monopoly and the Large Firm, Edward S. Mason, The Review of Economics and Statistics Vol. 33, No. 2 (May, 1951), pp. 139-144

18. The Limits of the Housing Finance System, Susan M. Wachter, Journal of Housing Research Volume 1, Issue 1 163-175

19. On the ingredients for bubble formation: Informed traders and communication , Jörg Oechsslera, Carsten Schmidtb, Wendelin Schnedlerc, Journal of Economic Dynamics and Control Volume 35, Issue 11, November 2011, Pages 1831–1851

100 YEAR STARSHIP™

Life Sciences in Interstellar

Chaired by Ronke Olabisi, PhD

Assistant Professor, Biomedical Engineering Department, Rutgers University

Track Description

The life sciences in space exploration today make assumptions about the type of crew members, their tasks and even the requirements for life to be carbon based elsewhere. What strategies, techniques, basic science, uses of space as an experimental platform, and philosophies about life must be addressed to transition to human interstellar space exploration?

Track Summary

The Life Sciences in Interstellar track addressed the challenges of sending humans and other biological matter into space. At present, microgravity has profound effects on every system in the body, and radiation is a danger once we leave the Earth's protective atmosphere. This track discussed the present challenges, postulated new unforeseen challenges, and explored various ideas how to overcome them. The difficulties of using diagnostic equipment in microgravity was discussed, and a prototype blood sampling device for use in microgravity was described. Training missions to the space station or Mars were suggested, and the notion that countermeasures to prevent adaptations to microgravity might be unnecessary on a generation ship for all but the generation that would actually arrive at the interstellar destination. Proposed was the use of a cyanobacterial carbon dioxide scrubber, the prototype of which produces oxygen in exchange without producing toxic waste, just biowaste that could potentially be recycled. Two presenters discussed a reexamination of astronaut selection criteria. One focused on a reduction in average astronaut size while the other discussed the complex microbiome every human carries and that selection criteria should include a consideration of the "microcosmonauts," the microbiome each astronaut carries, since some microorganisms become more virulent in space. Finally, reliable lifeboat technologies were discussed, and what criterion must be considered in order to recover everyone safely should there be a need to escape a ship. The talks provoked much discussion and were a very engaging reminder that solving the problems for longterm space travel would solve problems on Earth.

Track Chair Biography

Ronke Olabisi, PhD

Assistant Professor, Biomedical Engineering Department, Rutgers University

Dr. Ronke Olabisi is an Assistant Professor in the Biomedical Engineering Department at Rutgers University and a member of the 100YSSTM Research team (the Life Sciences focus). Dr. Olabisi conducts tissue engineering and regenerative medicine research, particularly in the area of orthopedic and dermal tissues. She is a recipient of the 2013 Charles and Johanna Busch Biomedical Memorial Fund Grant and has received fellowships from the Gordon Research Conference, the National Space Biomedical Research Institute, and the National Science Foundation. Her collaborative research while at Rice University is currently being considered for a patent. She has presented her work in peer-reviewed journal articles, book chapters and conferences in 3 countries and her published work has been highlighted in Science and The Spine Journal. Dr. Olabisi is a member of the Orthopaedic Research Society, the Society for Biomaterials, the Biomedical Engineering Society, the American Society for Bone and Mineral Research, and the American Society of Biomechanics.

Dr. Olabisi received her bachelor's degree in Mechanical Engineering from MIT, masters' degrees in Mechanical Engineering and Aeronautical Engineering from the University of Michigan, her doctorate degree in Biomedical Engineering from the University of Wisconsin, and postdoctoral training at Rice University and City of Hope hospital. Dr. Olabisi received one of four nationally awarded Postdoctoral Fellowships from the National Space Biomedical Research Institute and as a graduate student was the recipient of the National Science Foundation's GSK-12 award.

Dr. Olabisi can be contacted at ronke.olabisi@100YSS.org

Every Body is an Ark:
How the Microorganisms We Carry will Impact an Interstellar Mission

Caitlin A. Contag

University of Southern California

contag@usc.edu

Abstract

The human microbiome is essential to our health and deserves special consideration in the closed environments of space travel. The dynamics of host-microbe interactions change when normal immune functions are altered, and space travel is associated with significant immune abnormalities. Opportunistic pathogens common in the human microbiome, including those in the genera Candida, Aspergillus, and Staphylococcus, could spread among crew-members and put them at risk of serious disease. Conversely, isolating a subset of the human population during space travel could exclude organisms that confer a significant health advantage. Not only will the microbiome be important to the maintenance of crew health, it will be critical if a new human population is established from the small group of founders. This imposed bottleneck on human evolution and the associated microbial communities offers incredible opportunities to eliminate common pathogens and promote symbiotic and commensal organisms. The characterization of the human microbiome is a relatively recent area of investigation, and the full functionality of the vast microbiota living in and on the human body is not yet well understood. Data suggest microbial involvement in diverse areas of human health and further studies will likely yield novel strategies to maximize the benefits of individuals' microbial communities in a particular environment. Developing a more complete understanding of the benefits and harms conferred by the fungi, viruses, archaea, and bacteria that exist in and on our bodies will guide our determination of what non-human organisms can and should be included in a long-term space mission.

Keywords
microbiome, microbiota, pathogens, immune function, space travel, space epidemiology

1. Introduction
The spread of disease will occur very differently in an entirely enclosed spacecraft on a long-term mission, and effective prevention of disease requires thoughtful and evidence-based strategies. No traveler will board a spacecraft alone; each human carries with them innumerable microorganisms that can both aid and injure the host. The human microbiome will be of great significance and deserves special consideration during this type of mission. Nuanced and specific preventive health strategies need to be developed to respond to anticipated health challenges

that will accompany interstellar travel. A more complete understanding of the benefit and risk posed by the fungi, viruses, archaea, and bacteria that colonize the human body and can transferred among personnel and determining what non-human organisms are desirable on the mission is essential for success and cannot be overlooked.

2. Human and Microbial Physiology in Space

2.1. Mammalian immune function in space

Immune function during space travel has been studied using animal models and human subjects in both simulated and real microgravity experiments. It is clear that space travel, whether through the associated stress, radiation exposure, or something peculiar to space itself, alters the function and distribution of immune cells in mammals [1][2][3]. Space travel is associated with decreased circulating lymphocyte numbers and lymphoblastogenic capability, decreased monocyte control, and decreased eosinophil percent [4]. Key immune organs, including the spleen, liver, and thymus, lose mass during space travel, and the expression of genes that control oxidative stress is decreased [5]. The space-associated alterations in immune cell proliferation and distribution, the atrophy of immune organs, and changes in gene expression results in immunosuppression. These reductions in immune capability could result in increased risk of infection for space travelers, even from what might be considered on earth as nonpathogenic species.

2.2. Microgravity alters microbial physiology

In addition to risk of infection due to immunosuppression, certain physiological changes occur in microorganisms during exposure to microgravity conditions that increase pathogenicity and virulence. Pathogenic E. coli has been found to increase production of enterotoxins [6], and form more copious and stress-resistant biofilms [7]. Incubation of Salmonella enterica serovar typhimurium in a high-aspect-ratio vessel, a bioreactor that simulates microgravity conditions, significantly lowers the lethal dose for 50 percent of mice (LD50) when compared to control organisms incubated under normal gravitational conditions in an oral challenge [8]. The mechanisms of the changes in microorganisms' pathogenicity and virulence in microgravity are still unknown. Additionally, deletion mutations occur two to three-fold faster in a model organism during a forty-day space flight than in an earth-bound control [9]. Increased mutation rates could result in rapid emergence of novel pathogenic capabilities in space. The full extent and mechanisms of physiological changes that occur in microorganisms during space travel remain to be investigated, but the current data suggest that space travel will present unique infectious challenges to maintaining a healthy complement of microorganisms and controlling infections.

2.3. Space epidemiology

Some epidemiological studies have evaluated the transfer of moderate-risk pathogens commonly present in the human microbiome during space travel, but use older methods of culture-based identification and DNA amplification rather than 16S RNA-based assays, which are the current standard. In 1995 and 1996, data was published regarding the transfer of *Staphylococcus aureus* and *Candida albicans* between crewmembers during Space Shuttle flights [10][11]. Microbiome-associated infections were not reported have a significant impact on Space Shuttle missions of the 1990s, and no significant changes in crew microbiota were detected, though it was noted that surface contamination with human-associated microorganisms increased as mission length increased [12]. These results differ from those of the Apollo missions. A NASA report published in 1975 shows significant transfer of pathogenic microflora between crewmembers on several Apollo missions (notably Apollo 7, 12, 13, and 17), including *S. aureus, Pseudomonas aeruginosa, C. albicans, beta-hemolytic streptococci*, and *Trichophyton* [13]. The authors conclude the chapter by expressing the need for improved preventive care and diagnostics to protect against infection. These case studies highlight the problems faced by space travelers, including autoinoculation that can cause serious illness, and transmission of harmful species among crewmembers. Epidemiological studies with larger sample sizes and increased duration are necessary to provide data more directly relevant to an interstellar mission. While advances have been made to preventing infection during space travel, it is clear that pathogenic species in the human microbiome and the potential for emerging pathogens may pose a threat to personnel health during an interstellar mission.

3. Harms and Benefits of Microbiota

3.1. Risk posed by organisms in the microbiome

Interstellar travelers are arks for billions of microorganisms: fungi, viruses, archaea, and bacteria that differentially colonize most of the human body. These stowaways represent countless species and subspecies that are capable of aiding in digesting food and vitamin synthesis, and protecting their hosts from pathogens. However, some of these organisms can cause life-threatening opportunistic infections with long-term sequelae. Candida and Aspergillus fungi are common members of the oral microbiome in healthy humans, but some species can cause serious infections when present at other anatomic sites, and infection risk increases with immunosuppression [14]. Systemic Candida infection is especially threatening to low birth weight infants, and can cause significant neurodevelopmental defects if there is nervous system involvement [15]. *S. aureus*, a causative agent of skin infections on the Apollo mission and infamous nosocomial pathogen, is commonly isolated from the anterior nares of healthy humans [16]. The hospital environment has many similarities to that of a spacecraft – immunosuppressed individuals interacting in close quarters. It is therefore not surprising that infections caused by members of the human microbiota and associated with inpatient care were problematic during the Apollo missions.

More alarmingly, diseases previously considered "non-infectious" have been linked to the transfer of microbial strains between individuals. Housing healthy and cancer-prone mice together can induce susceptibility to colorectal cancer; the transfer of gut microflora from cancer-prone individuals to healthy individuals appears to cause the increased susceptibility in healthy mice [18].

The above examples are a small sample of the diseases associated with organisms present in the human microbiome; many other organisms in the human microbiome pose similar threats to human health. An outbreak of disease caused by any of the high and moderate-risk pathogens found in the human microbiome could put the health of space travelers at significant risk. Isolation and limited medical resources increase the potential for infection and cause high morbidity and mortality during space travel.

3.2. Certain microbiota promote human health

Despite the wide range of opportunistic pathogens in the human microbiome, humans also are home to a variety of commensal and symbiotic organisms that promote human health. The gut, having a high density of microorganisms, is a primary target in microbiome studies. Recent data suggests a strong link between a variety of metabolic and digestive diseases and individuals' microbial profile. Researchers have correlated the presence of certain gut microbes with increased and decreased risk of metabolic syndrome [18], obesity [19][20], and diabetes [21] [22]. The constellation of inflammatory bowel disorders (IBD) is closely related to the diversity of the gut microbiome [23][24][25]. The symptoms of IBD can be ameliorated by introducing beneficial organisms: for example, inoculating mice with a certain strain of *Lactobacillus acidophilus* increases tolerance to pain caused by intestinal stretch by changing the density of opiate and cannabinoid receptors [26].

The skin is another densely populated organ where a thriving microbial population can confer significant health benefits. Germ-free (GF) mice have a significantly decreased immune response to cutaneous pathogens. The immune response of GF mice to cutaneous pathogens can be induced by inoculating the skin with Staphylococcus epidermidis, which activates interleukin-1 and MyD88 signaling in T cells [27]. The close connection between skin immune function and skin microflora is further illustrated by the role of skin microbial diversity in Atopic Dermatitis (AD). AD, also know as eczema, often results in secondary infections due to skin cracking associated with the disease. Lowered skin microbial diversity is correlated with increased severity and frequency of AD flares, and disease course is closely tracked by fluctuations in skin microflora diversity [28]. Clearly, maintenance of the skin microbiome is vital to ensuring protection against skin pathogens, autoimmune inflammation, and cutaneous infection.

These examples only briefly summarize of the full range of bodily functions associated with the microbiome. The omnipresence of microorganisms in the human body is an indication of their importance. Better characterization of the microbiome is necessary to create meaningful recommendations for long-term space travel. However, the current data suggest several opportunities in microbial preparation for an interstellar mission.

4. Opportunities

4.1. Exclusion of moderate-risk pathogens

Preventing infection during interstellar travel would require careful selection of participants who do not carry potentially harmful microorganisms. Colonization with particular organisms, such as *S. enterica serovar typhimurium* or *Mycobacterium tuberculosis*, would necessitate exclusion from close-contact travel due to the inherent threat of infection. Beyond obvious high-risk pathogens, isolating a very small subsection of the human population in long-term travel presents an interesting opportunity to eliminate moderate and low-risk pathogens from the community. For example, by excluding carriers of herpes simplex virus 1 and 2, Trichophyton, and Streptococcus mutans, the satellite population will be free from herpetic lesions, athlete's foot, and dental caries. The exclusion of these pathogens could result in significantly reduced health costs and disease burden of crewmembers.

4.2. Development of probiotic therapies for use on earth

Microbiome research in preparation for an interstellar mission provides significant opportunities to develop effective probiotic therapies. Despite the prevalence of probiotic dietary supplements on the market ("Proprietary strain promotes immunity!" and "Over 100 million good bacteria!" are ubiquitous claims in the yogurt aisle), there is limited support for the efficacy of these commercial products and concern for the honesty of labeling [29]. While there is some evidence to support the use of probiotic or microbial replacement therapy, there are not yet products approved in the United States by the Food and Drug Administration for the treatment of any disease [30]. Developing effective therapies to prevent overgrowth of harmful microorganisms or treating emerging conditions in space would benefit astronauts as well as earth-bound patients.

A challenge posed by the development of probiotics for space travelers on earth is that an effective microbial profile on earth might not be effective in a highly controlled and human-designed spacecraft environment. Any probiotic designed for interstellar travelers must be tested in the spacecraft environment and with the spacecraft diet. By developing an ideal microbial community alongside an ideal spacecraft, benefits can be maximized.

4.3. Microbial library

Additionally, the maintenance of an extensive microbial library will aid interstellar travelers by providing an extended ability to re-seed microbiomes if warranted. Spacecraft are designed to be relatively sterile environments, inoculated only by their human passengers, and crewmembers might suffer without the constant exposure to novel organisms through the environment. Monoculture and overgrowth of undesirable organisms is a significant concern on a starship mission, and a microbial library would allow for the reintroduction of desirable organisms.

However, an attempt to shape the microbiome of future generations might exclude helpful organisms and result in unintentional consequences. An indispensable component of preventive health care in an interstellar mission will be determining the role of particular organisms in human health and determining the microbiome that will confer the most benefits in the interstellar traveling environment. Through studies of the human microbiome on earth, truly beneficial and potentially harmful organisms can be identified.

5. Challenges in Current Research

5.1. Limitations of assays

One of the major limitations of the analysis of the Apollo missions in 1975 was the lack of high-throughput genetic assays and the reliance on culture-based methods. The sensitivity of culture-based identification methods is much less than the sensitivity of current RNA and DNA analyses. Advances in nucleic-acid based assays have expanded the opportunities for characterizing microbial communities, but there are still limitations in these techniques. Different procedures for extracting genetic material from samples result in different output, and sampling limitations prevent obtaining a complete picture of the dynamics of these populations. Results from DNA analysis of saliva samples using enzymatic and mechanical lysis procedures yielded results that differed depending on the extraction method that was used [31]. Each genera differs in their cell wall composition and the ability to maintain the integrity of their nucleic acid after removal from the body, and presents challenges for comprehensive analyses.

Moreover, shotgun sequencing of 16S RNA does not address the genetic changes that can occur through mutation or horizontal gene transfer, nor does it identify novel organisms that do not match with a sample from the existing databases. Plasmids and phage can significantly change the function of an organism, but are not necessarily reflected in the 16S RNA frequently amplified from subject samples. Moreover, novel organisms are frequently isolated from highly colonized regions of the human body, and without the routine use of culture-based methods, it will be difficult to identify and characterize these organisms. In order to make a recommendation for the composition of interstellar travelers' microbiomes, more sensitive and specific assays must be developed.

5.2. Geographic, cultural, and socioeconomic microbiome diversity

In selecting an "ideal" set of organisms to be included for a space mission, a comprehensive understanding of the true diversity of the human microbiome must be established. Culture and diet determine the abundance and type of organisms present in the human body [32]. Current data is limited in the diversity of subjects; there is much information available about the microbiomes of populations surrounding academic medical centers, but information about other populations' microbiome is just beginning to emerge. Important questions remain unanswered about the true extent of human microbial diversity.

5.3. Bioethics

Finally, the ethics of the investigation of the human microbiome must be addressed. Like genetic information, there is a certain level of privacy that must be afforded the collection of organisms found on and in an individual's body due to the propensity for prejudicial behavior, perhaps outweighing that of genetic prejudice due to the human aversion to infectious diseases. While there are certain organisms for which an indisputable argument can be made for exclusion from the interstellar travel population, there are many more organisms that occupy a gray area of pathogenicity. Should the isolation of S. aureus from your anterior nares prevent you from joining the brave new world?

In order to fully sculpt the microbiome of interstellar travelers, they may need to be born and raised in a controlled environment that only includes desirable organisms, not unlike gnotobiotic laboratory animals. This type of isolation is not an option, as it would prevent the members of an interstellar mission from ever living in normal human society. The narrowness of their exposure to humanity would limit their ability to be ambassadors of humankind to the next nearest star. Preferably, rigorous therapeutic and re-colonizing regiments would be investigated to eliminate undesirable organisms from participants, and the potential tremendous benefits for people on earth currently suffering as a result of undesireable microbiota. Those individuals suffering from Clostridium difficile infections, for example, would benefit greatly from improved methods of controlling this infection by modulating their microbiome.

6. Conclusion

The human microbiome can be both an asset and a risk to interstellar travelers, and there is not enough known about the organisms carried within and on the human body to make concrete recommendations about the most desirable microbiome of starship crewmembers. Research on earth will dramatically impact the manner in which we address common diseases, especially those of the gut and the skin, and will aid in the development of novel tools to promote health. Over forty years ago, Apollo mission doctors and researchers recognized the need for extensive microbial monitoring of astronauts, and advances in genetic analyses will allow for broader and deeper understanding of the microorganisms we will bring on the journey.

References

1. Sonnenfeld G, Mandel AD, Konstantinova IV, Taylor GR, Berry WD, et al. Effects of spaceflight on levels and activity of immune cells. Aviat. Space Environ. Med. 61(7):648-53. (1990)

2. Sonnenfeld G, Mandel AD, Konstantinova IV, Berry WD, Taylor GR, et al. Spaceflight alters immune cell function and distribution. J. Appl. Physiol. 73(2 Suppl):191S-195S. (1992)

3. Sonnenfeld G. Space flight, microgravity, stress, and immune responses. Advances in Space Research. 23(12):1945-1953. (1999)

4. Taylor GR. Immunologic analyses of U.S. Space Shuttle crewmembers. Aviat. Space Environ. Med. 57(3):213-217. (1986)

5. Bagai FP, Gridley DS, Slater JM, Luo-Owen X, Stodieck LS, et al. Effects of spaceflight on innate immune function and antioxidant gene expression. J Appl. Physiol. 106(6):1935-1942. (2009)

6. Chopra V, Fadl AA, Sha J, Chopra S, Galindo CL, et al. Alteration in the virulence potential of enteric pathogens and bacterial-host cell interactions under simulated microgravity conditions. J Toxicol. Environ. Health A. 69(14):1345-70. (2006)

7. Lynch SV, Mukundakrishnan K, Benoit MR, Ayyaswamy PS, Matin A. Escherichia coli biofilms formed under low-shear modeled microgravity in a ground-based system. Appl Environ Microbiol. 72(12):7701-7710. (2006)

8. Nickerson CA, Ott CM, Mister SJ, Morrow BJ, Burns-Keliher L, et al. Microgravity as a novel environmental signal affecting *Salmonella enterica* serovar Typhimurium virulence. Infect Immun. 68(6):3147-3152. (2000)

9. Fukuda T, Fukuda K, Takahashi A, Ohnishi T, Nakano T, et al. Analysis of deletion mutations of the rpsL gene in the yeast *Saccharomyces cerevisiae* detected after long-term flight on the Russian space station Mir. Mutation Research 470(2):125-132. (2000)

10. Pierson DL, Chidambaram M, Heath JD, Mallary L, Mishra SK, et al. Epidemiology of *Staphylococcus aureus* during space flight. FEMS Immunol. Med. Microbiol. 16(3-4):273-281. (1996)

11. Pierson DL, Mehta SK, Magee BB, Mishra SK. Person-to-person transfer of C. albicans in the spacecraft environment. J. Med. Vet. Mycol. 33(3):145-150. (1995)

12. Pierson DL. Microbial contamination of spacecraft. Gravity and Space Biology Bulletin. 14(2). (2001)

13. Ferguson JK, Taylor GR, Mieszkuc BJ. "Chapter 2: Microbial Investigations." Biomedical Results of Apollo. Ed. Johnston RS, Dietlein LF, Berry CA. NASA. (1975)

14. Ghannoum MA, Jurevic RJ, Mukherjee PK, Cui F, Sikaroodi M, Naqvi A, Gillevet PM. Characterization of the Oral Fungal Microbiome in Healthy Individuals. PLoS Pathogens. 6(1): e1000713. (2010)

15. Friedman S, Richardson SE, Jacobs SE, O'Brien K. Systemic Candida infection in extremely low birth weight infants: short term morbidity and long term neurodevelopmental outcome. Pediatric Infectious Disease Journal. 19(6): 499-505. (2000)

16. Grice EA, Kong HH, Conlan S, Clayton DB, Davis J, Young AC, Bouffard GG, Blakesley RW, Murray PR, Green ED, Turner ML, Segre JA. Topographical and Temporal Diversity of the Human Skin Microbiome. Science. 324(5932): 1190-1192. (2009)

17. Zupancic ML, Cantarel BL, Liu Z, Drabek EF, Ryan KA, et al. Analysis of the Gut Microbiota in the Old Order Amish and Its Relation to the Metabolic Syndrome. PLoS ONE 7(8): e43052. (2012)

18. Hu B, Elinav E, Huber S, Strowig T, Hao L, Hafemann A, Jin C, Wunderlich C, Wunderlich T, Eisenbarth SC, Flavell RA. Microbiota-induced activation of epithelial IL-6 signaling links inflammasome-driven inflammation with transmissible cancer. Proc Natl Acad Sci USA. 110(24):9862-7. (2013)

19. Ley RE. Obesity and the human microbiome. Curr. Opin. Gastreenterol. 26(1):5-11. (2010)

20. Ley RE, Backhed F, Turnbaugh P, Lozupone CA, Knight RD, et al. Obesity alters gut microbial ecology. Proc. Natl. Acad. Sci. USA. 102:11070-11075. (2005)

21. Caricilli AM, Picardi PK, de Abreu LL, Ueno M, Prada PO, et al. Gut Microbiota Is a Key Modulator of Insulin Resistance in TLR 2 Knockout Mice. PLoS Biol 9(12): e1001212. (2011)

22. Carvalho BM, Guadagnini D, Tsukumo DML, Schenka AA, et al. Modulation of gut microbiota by antibiotics improves insulin signaling in high-fat fed mice. Diabetologia. 55:2823-2834. (2012)

23. Manichanh C, Rigottier-Gois L, Bonnaud E, Gloux K, Pelletier E, et al. Reduced Diversity of faecal microbiota in Crohn's disease revealed by a metagenomic approach. Gut. 55:205-2011. (2006)

24. Ott SJ, Schreiber S. Reduced microbial diversity in inflammatory bowel diseases. Gut. 55:1207. (2006)

25. Qin J, Li R, Raes J, Arumugam M, Burgdorf KS, et al. A human gut microbial gene catalogue established by metagenomic sequencing. Nature. 464: 59-65. 2010.

26. Rousseaux C, Thuru X, Gelot A, Barnich N, Neut C, et al. Lactobacillus acidophilus modulates intestinal pain and induces opiod and cannabinoid receptors. Nature Medicine. 13:35-37. 2006.

27. Naik S, Bouladoux N, Wilhelm C, Molloy MJ, Salcedo R, et al. Compartmentalized control of skin immunity by resident commensals. Science. 337(6098):1115-1119. 2012.

28. Kong HH, Oh J, Deming C, Conlan S, Grice EA, et al. Temporal Shifts in the skin microbiome associated with disease flares and treatment in children with atopic dermatitis. Genome Res. 22: 850-859. 2012.

29. Slashinski MJ, McCurdy SA, Acenbaum LS, Whitney SN, McGuire AL."Snake oil," "quack medicine," and "industrially cultured organisms:" biovalue and the commercialization of human microbiome research. BMC Med Ethics. 13(28). 2012.

30. NIH National Center for Complementary and Alternative Medicine. Oral Probiotics: An Introduction. Accessed 17 Sept 2013. Updated Dec 2012. http://nccam.nih.gov/health/probiotics/introduction.htm

31. Lazarevic L, Gaia N, Girard M, Francois P, Schrenzel K. Comparison of DNA Extraction Methods in Analysis of Salivary Bacterial Communities. PLoS One. 8(7): e67699. 2013.

32. Nasidze I, Li J, Quinque D, Tang K, Stoneking M. Global diversity in the human salivary microbiome. Genome Research. 19(4): 636-643. 2009.

Redefining Astronaut Corps for Deep Space

Paul Frenger M.D.

A Working Hypothesis Inc, 814 Silvergate Drive, Houston, TX 77079

pfrenger@alumni.rice.edu

Abstract

Voyaging into deep space will be dangerous. A NASA document lists many of these hazards. These missions will become one-way trips, the longest flights necessitating multigenerational spacecraft. Precious supplies must be conserved and regenerated en route. We must send Astronauts to the stars to prevent the "single point of failure" of the cataclysmic loss of Earth's biosphere from destroying our human potential. Conventional Astronauts will be needed for near space missions, but deep space crews will be different. As we send people further from Earth with only their spaceship and its initial cargo of fuel and supplies, smaller and lighter crewmembers may have important survival advantages. This reflects the author's experience with robot design, where smaller is better. Small Astronauts with an average height below 100 cm (39.4 in) will beneficially impact spacecraft and launch vehicle design for voyages throughout the solar system. Beyond that, longer missions may favor cybernetic-amplified crew who could live for centuries, or non-biological avatars to reach galaxies more than 25,000 light years beyond the Milky Way. Reproductive issues will challenge traditional ethics and mores on multigenerational missions. Genetic manipulation research needed for deep space missions will benefit those who remain on Earth. Reducing bodily sensitivity to radiation, curing cancer, promoting faster healing, making metabolic adjustments, improving cognition and sensori-motor functions will produce a "space dividend" for Earthlings as our Astronauts head inevitably toward the stars.

Keywords

avatar, cybernetics, dwarf, genetics, intergalactic, interstellar

1. Introduction to Deep Space Travel

Manned interstellar space travel represents the most complex, dangerous objective ever undertaken by mankind [1]. A gantlet of hazards await the dedicated Astronauts: tissue damage from radiation, microgravity effects on muscle and bone, hypoxia, hypercapnea, decompression, hypothermia, inadvertent poisoning, starvation, dehydration, depression, fatigue, boredom, panic, claustrophobia, agoraphobia, blood loss, loss of body functions, accidents, impacts with micrometeorites and space debris, EVAs gone wrong, planetary landing misfortunes, running out of fuel or other vital supplies and just getting lost. Why therefore should we make these expensive, perilous journeys to other star systems in the flesh? There are many potential reasons, explored in detail elsewhere, but to this author the compelling one is to preserve the human race and its culture in the event of the destruction of the Earth's biosphere. These heroic missions will challenge our creativity, our determination, our mores and our ethics as we attempt to leave Sol and Earth behind.

This paper describes considerations for deep space missions which will affect Astronaut selection, training, bodily modifications, and their working environment in space.

2. Circumventing Spacecraft Limitations

In another presentation at the 100 Year Starship™ 2013 Public Symposium, the author described how mission duration and purpose would affect Astronaut support systems [2]. This might be depicted by drawing a familiar concentric ringed "bull's-eye target" around the Earth (for missions up to Moon-distance) or the Sun (for missions to any of the planets or beyond). In the former case, the existing corps performs well. However, with increasing distances in the latter case, adjustments to Astronaut selection must be considered.

2.1 Small Astronauts

Interior space per Astronaut is one of the most crucial parameters to consider. NASA Publication "Human Integration Design Handbook" (HIDH) shows a graph which indicates that the longer the duration of a manned mission in space, the more pressurized volume is required [3]. Whereas the single-Astronaut two day Mercury capsules only provided about 3 cubic meters for their one occupant, the six-month ISS mission afforded about 100 meters per crewmember for an approximately six man team. Equation 1 describes this relationship (HIDH, pg.563):

$$\text{habitable volume per crewmember (m}^2) = 6.67 \text{ x (duration in days)} - 7.79 \tag{1}$$

Making spacecraft bigger after launch is a very costly proposition; Mir and the ISS were constructed in sections or modules, each of which had to be lifted into orbit by expensive rocket launches over months or years.

One way of dealing with spacecraft for longer deep space missions with an increased crew complement would be to put some crewmembers in a kind of suspended animation in "stasis pods" or chambers. In this condition they are immobilized, so they don't require room to move around to perform duties, eat, entertainment themselves or take care of hygiene. These pods monitor their health while unconscious and tend to their bodily needs. This is discussed in detail in the author's other 100 Year Starship™ 2013 paper mentioned above.

Another way of reducing the interior space needs for crew would be to utilize smaller human Astronauts.

The author's experience with robot design is that reducing their size and weight allows a decrease in servo power, battery capacity, mass and other important attributes. Consider that the average NASA Astronaut today is 148.6 - 194.6 cm (58.5 - 76.6 in) tall. Going back to the ringed bulls-eye metaphor, the first ring would extend from Earth to the Moon and be the realm of conventional crew. The second ring would utilize Small Astronauts (abbreviated SA's), those persons up to 100 cm (39.4 in) height or about one-half the height of current near-Earth crewmembers, and extend to the limits of the solar system. This includes achondroplastic and pituitary dwarfs, lower extremity amputees and persons with certain birth defects which reduce their height such as phocomelia [4-7]. Figure 1 below shows the famous actor Herve Villachaize, who had achondroplasia, in a television publicity photograph with his normal sized costar.

On Earth, these persons seem ungainly in their movements; in weightless space, they are graceful. To overcome issues of strength and mobility in SAs, in his other presentation the author described using motorized exoskeletons, i.e.: those suggested by Berkeley, EKSO and Sagawa Electronics [8-10]. This is an extension of existing computerized prostheses offered to limb amputees such as Claudia Mitchell, former USMC, whose amputated left arm was replaced by a very realistic thought-controlled mechanical limb [11].

An advantage of achondroplastic dwarfs (and some others) is that their genes can produce normal-height offspring at the end of one-way and multi-generational missions for colonization. SAs require less food, water, oxygen, living space, radiation shielding and equipment mass. Their compact, lighter craft can be launched by smaller, safer, more maneuverable rockets. For SAs, their short leg length leads to less significant lower extremity muscle mass loss and bone decalcification. Their reduced cross sectional area makes them smaller targets for radiation damage. Their exercise programs in space should be simpler as well; for example, a Nitinol-powered exoskeleton could provide passive range of motion exercises while the SA is resting. Non-Astronaut dwarf counterparts will be essential for building their smaller spacecraft and equipment on Earth prior to launch. SAs should be suitable for any destination within the solar system. There are known problems to overcome with some SAs (such as achondroplastic dwarf atlanto-occipital instability and the wide variability of limbs / digits with phocomelia) but these should be remedied with appropriate Astronaut medical research, which will ultimately benefit all members of these groups on Earth.

Figure 1: Herve Villachaize and Ricardo Montalban, 1977.
(Photo courtesy of Commons.wikimedia.org)

The author believes that the penguin should be the official mascot for the Small Astronaut. On land, penguins are clumsy and appear ungainly. However, these birds "fly" through water in a most graceful, beautiful, energetic way, like eagles soaring in air over the plains.

2.2 Genetic Manipulation

Once Earthlings travel beyond the heliopause and enter the region of the bow shock, the third ring of our bulls-eye, the influence of our solar system will be left behind. Astronauts who reach this point eventually will be continuing on to an interstellar or intergalactic destination rather than returning to Earth. What kind of Astronauts will weather these voyages? We may initially accept the premise that SAs will be given the task of these continuing missions, if stasis pods are available. Other options, more heroic and controversial, may be chosen.

Genetic manipulation may be used to improve or replace various body functions in space, per genomic pioneer J. Craig Venter [12]. One can do much more than inserting a fluorescent gene in primates to create monkeys that glow green in ultraviolet light [13]. For example, ionizing radiation, always a consideration beyond Earth's protective influence, must be mastered by reducing the body's sensitivity to it (as with some insects such as cockroaches), repairing the genetic damage caused by it (as with bacteria such as Deinococcus radiodurans) or combinations of both. Control of telomerase, an enzyme notably present in embryonic stem cells, which prevents aging of cells when they divide, would confer virtual immortality of cell function and would have application in curing cancer and promoting faster wound healing [14]. Complete regeneration of amputated limbs is present in many higher animals such as the salamander; learning how to promote this process would be extremely useful to Astronauts. In humans, regeneration of fingers and toes has been documented; the author's great-grandfather was observed to re-grow several toes lost to diabetic gangrene at the age of 80 years.

Using genetics derived from arthropods to give humans a chitin exoskeleton could eliminate the need for full-body pressure suits in the vacuum of space; only a simple face mask would seem to be required.

Chitin body armor would also protect our easily-injured skin to mitigate most accidental lacerations, penetrating injuries and burns [15]. Also, giving humans chlorophyll-containing intracellular organelles (chloroplasts, from plants) would allow them to produce their own carbohydrates for energy when exposed to light and bypass much of the mission planner's anxiety associated with growing fruits and vegetables in space [16].

Melanin is known to promote conversion of light to electrical energy; it is used by radiotrophic fungi to harmlessly create useful energy from gamma rays [17, 18]. Either of these capabilities would be an outstanding addition to any Astronauts expressed genome.

Medicinal or genetic means to make metabolic adjustments (such as producing a moderate hypothyroid condition) will reduce an Astronaut's oxygen and food demands. This would be even more helpful if certain tissues could be protected from the effect, such as neural cells, selectively improving cognition and sensori-motor functions relative to the person as a whole. Other beneficial metabolic manipulations are possible.

2.3 Cybernetic Augmentation

Advancing far beyond the Claudia Mitchell limb prostheses mentioned above, extensively cybernetic-modified crewmembers (somewhat organic, mostly machine) would be able to live and work in space under drastically different conditions than non-modified humans [19]. Reminiscent of the Officer Murphy character in the "Robocop" movie series, these Astronauts would have the most essential organs (brain, gonads) secured within a pressure container, with replaceable synthetic support organs such as liver, lungs, heart, hormonal, hematologic and immune systems attached. Extensive computer augmentation of their nervous systems would be included. The final suit design might be very esthetic and externally natural-appearing. These cyborgs would have built-in life support, radiation shielding, power sources and enhanced sensory-motor functions able to communicate directly with shipboard computer systems. Under these conditions, without the worry of an irreplaceable organ failure or injury, cybernetic crewmembers might survive for hundreds of years and voyages of hundreds or thousands of light years. The author described the cybernetic option at a NASA conference seven years ago [20].

In 2006 the author designed an interface circuit for the Texas Instruments MSP430FG439 mixed-signal CMOS microcontroller which could create and react to biologically-identical nerve action potentials [21]. This capability or something similar could help connect computer signals to an Astronaut's brain. More recently the author demonstrated how to create organic field-effect transistors (OFETs) and circuits using biologically-safe natural materials; the semiconductor material was melanin from squid ink. The circuits were so safe that they could be eaten [22]. Melanin can be easily recovered from plant and animal sources. The OFETs could be safely attached to nerve tissue using a carbon nanotube interface to achieve the neural augmentation.

Parenthetically, in his other presentation at the 100 Year Starship™ 2013 Public Symposium, the author proposed adding robot crewmembers to deep space voyages to assist the human Astronauts. He called this synthetic crewmember "GRANNIE", an acronym for General Robotic Assistant with Neural Network, Intellect and Emotions [23]. GRANNIE, derived from his previous anthropomorphic research, was given a human-like synthetic personality, intellectual and emotional traits, and autonomous actions via artificial intelligence (A.I.). The robotic component included artificial vision, complex hands, speech input/output and facial expressivity. The GRANNIE android would perform a variety of tasks, from serving meals or playing games, to assisting with mission-critical functions and medical emergencies.

Now back to Astronauts in deep space. At NASA in 2011 the author described how he placed much of his own knowledge, emotional reactions and personality in a blank GRANNIE A.I. program (without robot body) to create his Doppelgänger or cognitive mirror: in effect, a synthetic intelligence which thought it was a person [24]. This technique could serve to monitor and prompt each Astronaut in the event that he or she began to experience a mild to moderate loss of cognitive function in space (a form of dementia, like Alzheimer's disease). This approach could increase the safety margin for deep space missions [25]. Figure 2 above shows the author's GRANNIE hardware-software layered modular architecture used for the cognitive mirror, discussed in more detail in his other presentation at the 100 Year Starship™ 2013 Public Symposium.

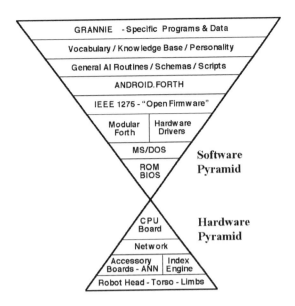

Figure 2: Author's GRANNIE A.I. and Robot architecture suitable for Cognitive Mirror / Doppelgänger use.

2.4 Avatar Astronauts

Using a more highly developed process than that described above, virtual crewmembers ("avatars") could be created having no living tissue whatsoever. These Astronauts would possess a human donor's neural patterns, knowledge base, preferences and emotions stored in an electronic or other recoverable format. They would have a form of consciousness indistinguishable objectively and subjectively from that of their original organic donors. Their DNA and synaptic patterns would be preserved for eventual synthetic reconstitution of their human bodies and minds at their final destination in space. These avatar Astronauts would be in effect immortal since they could be rebuilt ad infinitum, surviving ages past the demise of their original selves back on Earth. Such crewmembers could in theory travel outside of the Milky Way for the first intergalactic voyages which might take many millennia to accomplish. Actor Arnold Schwarzenegger's cloning in the 2000 movie "The 6th Day" suggests one way the end-of-voyage effect would be produced. This reconstitution would be an extension of proof-of-concept research done by Doctor Eckard Wimmer at the University of NY, in which he synthesized an RNA poliovirus using a gene description file which he obtained from the Internet. When the virus was injected into mice it paralyzed and killed them, demonstrating that the newly-synthesized virus was "alive" [26, 27].

Once one speculates about the possibility of reconstituting human beings from genetic code and neural pattern data streams, space travel becomes much more interesting. Star Trek-like "beaming" of personnel at the speed of light simplifies the entire deep space voyage. The only glitch in this hypothesis is the necessity for a receiver to reconstitute the Astronaut at the termination end. Still, there are some considerations that might mitigate this difficulty. First, receivers may already be present throughout the Galaxy (and the Universe), having been placed there previously by a much older race of beings for their own use. If so, we would only have to discover the data formats and frequencies they use, something like what actress Jodie Foster employed in the 1997 "Contact" movie, or like the mass relays in the "Mass Effect" video games. Another consideration would be that an advanced sentient race might be monitoring our manned space program, so that when they discover our initial attempts to send men to other planets / solar systems they will reveal themselves and help us (like the Vulcan scouts in the 1996 movie "Star Trek First Contact" when the first human warp-capable ship was encountered). Admittedly, neither of these possibilities is very likely, but not known to be impossible.

What if we master a "beaming process" which uses a different technology, perhaps related to quantum entanglement? According to Prof. Juan Yin at the University of Science and Technology of China at Shanghai, the lower limit to the speeds attainable via entanglement is more than 10,000 times faster than the speed of light [28]. That speed would make interstellar flight practical: Alpha Centauri (4 light years away) could be reached in under 3.5 hours, the Canis Major Dwarf Galaxy (25,000 light years distant) would take less than 2.5 years, and Andromeda (2.5 million light years away) would take 250 years … or not, if the effective speeds are much faster.

On the off chance that any of this might be usable for a manned space program, the subject deserves further serious investigation.

3. Population Issues and Ethics

Multigenerational ships leaving Earth orbit will necessarily contain relatively few Astronauts, possibly no more than two dozen [29]. Some of them likely will be in stasis pods initially to conserve supplies. While awake they will be expected to perform the mission, breed and train the next generation(s) of crewmembers. Besides their bacterial, fungal and viral loads, Astronauts will have their genomes scrutinized carefully pre-launch to weed-out known deleterious genes and assure beneficial ones which inevitable inbreeding would accentuate. Still, this size herd is probably insufficient to provide the genetic diversity needed for a viable population (no one really knows the required number), so genetic redesign and manipulation to create artificial diversity will be have to be employed en-route using techniques not yet developed here on Earth.

Ethics and mores will have to be adapted to accept new sexuality and breeding practices [30]. Astronauts in space might not expect to be as restricted in their sexual encounters as on Earth, but their breeding partnerships will have to be controlled for the good of the herd. Same-sex relationships would not be problematic unless they interfered with the reproductive contributions of each partner to the group. Polygamy and polyandry might be required at times, with the female-to-male sex ratio being emphasized for reproductive reasons, and women breeding with multiple men to increase genetic mixing. Some offspring might be placed in stasis soon after birth to utilize their special traits at a different point in the mission. Of course, in vitro fertilization techniques would impact all physical mating practices.

4. Conclusion

Venturing into deep space is not optional if we are to attempt to preserve humanity beyond the limited lifespan of our fragile alma mater, Earth. To assure human survival, dozens to hundreds of such flights should be undertaken. Physical limitations on these flights will be imposed by the kinds of crewmembers we select to perform them. The conventional Astronaut corps will tend near-Earth space. Small Astronauts will enable missions up to the very edge of the solar system, and with stasis techniques, well beyond. Cybernetic-augmented Astronauts, with their artificially prolonged life spans, would facilitate voyages throughout the Milky Way Galaxy. Non-organic avatar Astronauts could survive for millennia to enable conquering the vast distances between galaxies. Beaming digital representations of human Astronauts into space at or beyond light speed would further enable stellar, galactic and intergalactic travel. We humans may seed the stars with our offspring, creating interesting new races of intelligent hominids in our wake. This may be our destiny.

Research initially required to prepare Astronauts for deep space will benefit those who remain on Earth. This will reduce our radiation sensitivity, help to prevent or cure most cancers, wipe out heart and organ diseases, improve the healing process including limb regeneration, fine-tune biochemical aspects of metabolism, improve cognition to alleviate dementia, and sharpen sensory and motor functions. Our Astronauts departing for the stars will confer a "space dividend" for their Earth-bound families and friends as long as we can receive their transmissions from space.

Acknowledgments

The following entertainment resources were referenced in the text of this paper.
- "Contact" movie, Warner Brothers (1997)
- "Robocop" movie, Orion Pictures (1987)
- "Star Trek" TV series, Paramount Pictures (1966)
- "Star Trek First Contact" movie, Paramount Pictures (1996)
- "The 6th Day" movie, Phoenix Pictures (2000)
- "Mass Effect" game, Bioware, Canada (2007)

References

1. NASA Human Research Program Architecture, 2010. Available: http://humanresearchroadmap.nasa.gov/architecture.

2. Frenger, P., "Redefining Astronaut Support for Deep Space", 100 Year Starship™ 2013 Public Symposium, 19-22 Sept 2013.

3. Human Integration Design Handbook (HIDH), NASA/SP-2010-3407, 27 Jan 2010, Figure 8.2-2, pg.562. Available: http://ston.jsc.nasa.gov/collections/trs/_techrep/SP-2010-3407.pdf.

4. National Institutes of Health Genetics Home Reference: Achondroplasia. Available: http://ghr.nlm.nih.gov/condition/achondroplasia.

5. National Institutes of Health Genetics Home Reference: Isolated growth hormone deficiency. Available: http://ghr.nlm.nih.gov/condition/isolated-growth-hormone-deficiency.

6. Kegel, B., Carpenter, M.L., Burgess, E.M., "Functional capabilities of lower extremity amputees", Arch Physical Medicine Rehabil, Mar 1978; 59(3): pg.109-120.

7. National Institutes of Health Genetics Home Reference: Phocomelia. Available: http://ghr.nlm.nih.gov/glossary=phocomelia.

8. Berkeley Lower Extremity Exoskeleton (BLEEX). Available: http://bleex.me.berkeley.edu/research/exoskeleton/bleex.

9. EKSO Bionic Suit. Available: http://www.eksobionics.com/ekso.

10. Powered Jacket Sagawa Electronics MK3 Exoskeleton Suit. Available: http://www.techngadgets.com/tag/exoskeleton.

11. Brown, D., "For 1st Woman With Bionic Arm, a New Life Is Within Reach", Washington Post, 14 Sept 2006. Available: http://www.washingtonpost.com/wp-dyn/content/article/2006/09/13/AR2006091302271.html.

12. Wall, M., "Biologist: Space Travelers can Benefit from Genetic Engineering", Space.com, 1 Nov 2010. Available: http://www.space.com/9439-biologist-space-travelers-benefit-genetic-engineering.html.

13. Chan, A.W.S., Chong, K.Y., Martinovich, C., Simerly, C., Schatten, G., "Transgenic Monkeys Produced by Retroviral Gene Transfer into Mature Oocytes", Science, 291(5502), 12 Jan 2001, pg. 309- 312.

14. University of Copenhagen, "'Fountain of youth' telomerase: Scientists successfully map enzyme that has rejuvenating effect on cells", ScienceDaily, 5 Nov 2013. Available: http://www.sciencedaily.com/releases/2013/03/130327133341.htm.

15. Chitin. Wikipedia. Available: http://en.wikipedia.org/wiki/Chitin.

16. Chlorophyll. Wikipedia. Available: http://en.wikipedia.org/wiki/Chlorophyll.

17. Melanin. Wikipedia. Available: http://en.wikipedia.org/wiki/Melanin.

18. Radiotrophic fungus. Wikipedia. Available: http://en.wikipedia.org/wiki/Radiotrophic_fungus.

19. Dubrovsky, D., "Cybernetic immortality. Fantasy or scientific problem?", 2045 Strategic Social Initiative. Available: http://2045.com/articles/30810.html.

20. Frenger, P., "Convergence between Robots and Humans via Cybernetics", CLCTS INNOVATION, 2006, NASA / JSC, pg.6.

21. Frenger, P., "Creating a Perfect Artificial Neuron", Can Medical Biological Engineering Conf, 2006, Vancouver, Canada, Proceedings Section SC-8.6, pg.1-3.

22. Frenger, P., "Edible Organic Semiconductors", IEEE Green Technologies Conference, 19-20 April 2012, Tulsa, OK, pg.199.

23. Frenger, P., "GRANNIE 4: Helping Astronauts in Deep Space", AIAA Symposium, 17 May 2013, NASA / JSC, pg.29.

24. Frenger, P., "The Doppelgänger Project: The Robot Who Thinks He's Me", Workshop on Automation and Robotics, 2011, NASA / JSC Houston, pg.7.

25. Frenger, P., "The Dementia Coprocessor: Reducing the Tragedy of Alzheimer's Disease", Workshop on Automation and Robotics, 2012, NASA / JSC Houston, pg.6.

26. Wimmer, E., "The test-tube synthesis of poliovirus: The simple synthesis of a virus has far reaching societal implications", EMBO Reports, 2006 (7): S3–S9.

27. Pollack, A., "Traces of Terror: Scientists Create A Live Polio Virus", The New York Times, 12 July 2002. Available: http://www.nytimes.com/2002/07/12/us/traces-of-terror-the-science-scientists-create-a-live-polio-virus.html.

28. Dodson, B., "Quantum 'spooky action at a distance' travels at least 10,000 times faster than light", Gizmag, 10 March 2013. Available: http://www.gizmag.com/quantum-entanglement-speed-10000-faster-light/26587.

29. Generation ship. Wikipedia. Available: http://en.wikipedia.org/wiki/Generation_ship.

30. Moskowitz, C., "Sex in Space and Other Interstellar Travel Challenges Revealed", Space.com, 1 Oct 2011. Available: http://www.space.com/13149-space-sex-interstellar-travel-challenges.html.

Therapeutical Method for Repair of Bone Fracture Using Ca+ Resulting from Artificial Gravity

Angelo Karavolos

NTB Technologies and Associates, Inc.

Abstract

There are many applications and needs for bone fracture repair. Among them are bone damage due to automobile or flight accidents. Others applications are arthritic bone repair.

Purpose

The objective of this paper is to develop a technique which leverages the use of micro gravity in order to move molecules such as ionized water, porous collagen- calcium sulfate (PCCS) and oxygen into bone material by increasing the available surface area of the bone.

Methodology

A coating of collagen – calcium sulfate nano material was applied to a set of calcium deficient bovine bone samples. The material was aerosolized by applying an electric current to a substrate coated with a layer of the collagen-calcium sulfate. The bovine samples were placed at the base of an evaporation chamber and allowed to collect the collagen-calcium sulfate by advection and adsorption. The samples were then coated with a layer of gold and observed and observed under a JEOL scanning microscope at 10,750 magnification, and compared to healthy bovine bone samples.

Results and Discussion

Based upon EDX analysis of the bovine samples, approximately 15-37% of the bone mass was increased by treating the bone material with the collagen-calcium sulfate nano material.

Conclusions

The preliminary data demonstrates that it is possible to increase bone mass using a collagen-calcium sulfate coating technique.

1. Introduction

An important issue in the health of a long duration crew is the condition of bone material. Bone loses its mass after a period of time after it does not experience some sort of load, and this is evident when sections of bone are removed from specimens and viewed under microscope. However, bone which is used, i.e., experiences periodic load, retains its mass, and does not lose internal structure.

Examples of this effect can be see seen in Figure 1a and Figure 1b.

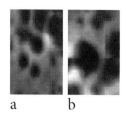

a   b

Figure 1a and 1b. Illustration of bone exposed to load and bone exposed to no load.

Notice the large pores in the sample. This is lost bone mass which is a result of calcium and collagen which is removed from the material. Research activities by numerous authors have demonstrated that bone which is not under load begins to deteriorate (Vico et. al., 2001, Rubin et.al., 2001, Goodship et. al.,1998).

2. Purpose

The purpose of this investigation is to demonstrate that samples which have deteriorated bone mass (i.e. calcium and collagen) can be replaced with collagen-calcium sulfate nano material.

3. Methodology

Sample bone samples were acquired from Sigma Aldrich Chemical Company and the University of Texas El Paso School of Medical Sciences. Samples were obtained from hosts which were healthy and hosts which were suffering from bone loss due to lack of use of the limbs. These subjects were animals which had lost the use of their legs because of birth defect or paralysis.

A set of bone samples from normal bone were prepared for observation under a microscope. A JEOL scanning electron microscope was used to view each of the samples. The magnification was set at 10750X.

Another set of samples were viewed which were from hosts which did not have the use of their legs. These were also observed under the optical microscope at 10750X.

The samples which were from hosts which did not have use of their legs were washed with distilled water for treatment with collagen-calcium sulfate. Next, these samples were placed in an evaporation chamber with a small 5 cubic mm sample of collagen-calcium sulfate.

The collagen-calcium sulfate sample was prepared by combining 50 grams of powdered collagen, reagent grade, 50 micron diameter, and 50 grams of 50 micron diameter powdered calcium sulfate, reagent grade in a GE blender and mixed thoroughly at 1500 rpm for 30 seconds.

This material was then placed in the evaporation chamber for deposition upon the bone sample. The sample was allowed to adsorb the collagen-calcium sulfate for 30 seconds and then placed under the microscope for observation at 10750x magnification.

Another preparation involved the approach of fabricating a gelatin material of collagen-calcium sulfate and water. The sample was allowed to soak in a gelatin of 0.2 M collagen-calcium sulfate and water, mixed as a paste. The bone sample was placed on a glass slide and the gel was deposited over the bone sample.

The gelatin was placed in a clean dry environment with low relative humidity (<10%) and room temperature. The gelatin slowly diffuses into the pores of the bone and solidifies after 24 hours.

4. Results and Discussion

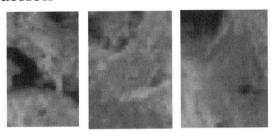

Figure 2. Micrographs of rat femur bone that has not been introduced to collagen-calcium sulfate nano particle material.

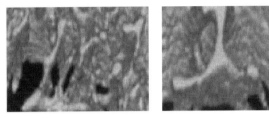

Figure 3. Micrographs of rat femur bone that has been introduced to collagen-calcium sulfate nano particle material.

Based on a density study of micrographs in Figures 2 and 3, the collagen-calcium sulfate gel filtered through the porous bone material. In addition, the pore volume of the bone was reduced by 94.3 percent. The sample in this particular case was prepared by mixing the collagen-calcium sulfate gel and placing it in the evaporation chamber.

A second density study under the microscope did not produce a reduction of pore volume as significant as the approach above, but there was less visible damage to the bone material. Using this approach, only 53.4 percent of the original pore space (97%) was occupied by the collagen-calcium sulfate nanoparticle gel.

Further investigations using this approach would provide evidence that this collagen-calcium sulfate nano material could be useful in repairing bone material. An added advantage of this material is that it uses material that is not foreign to biological tissue. Another issue to resolve with the use of this material is how to deliver the material to the bone non invasively or at least minimally invasively. This will be the focus of the next study.

References

1. Goodship, A.E., Cunningham, J.L., Oganov, V., Darling, J., Miles, A.W., and Owen, Gwen. "Bone Loss During Long Term Space Flight is Prevented by the Application of a Short Term Impulsive Mechanical Stimulus." Acta Astronautica . 43(1998): 65-75

2. Rubin, Clinton, Xu, Gang, and Judex, Stephan. "The Anabolic Activity of Bone Tissue, Suppressed by Disuse, is Normalized by Brief Exposure to Extremely Low- Magnitude Mechanical Stimuli." The FASEB Journal. 15(2001): 2225-2229

3. Vico, Laurence, Collet, Philippe, Guignandon, Alain, Lafarge-Proust, Marie-Helene, Thomas, Thierry, Rehailia, Mohamed, Alexandre, Christian. "Effects of Long-Term Microgravity Exposure on Cancellous and Cortical Weight-Bearing Bones of Cosmonauts." The Lancet . 355(2000): 1607-1611.

Design of Sustainable CO$_2$ Absorbing-O$_2$ Materials for Extreme Environments

Angelo Karavolos

Graduate Student, UTEP

Civil Engineering Department

Abstract

There are many applications for recycled carbon dioxide, and even more for a method of recycling carbon dioxide waste into consumables such as oxygen and carbon molecules. This is similar to the process that plants undertake during photosynthesis. The objective of this investigation describes the properties of a new material which captures carbon dioxide, and releases oxygen. It also accumulates carbon rich molecules within the chamber itself. A container of dry ice was allowed to sublimate through a tube to a filter containing a sol gel –cyanobacteria mixture. The conditions were set for 24 hour periods at 20 C, 1 Atm pressure and lighting between 440 to 680 nm. Quantities of Carbon Dioxide, Oxygen and Carbon material were measured using an Ultra Mettler Balance. The dielectric constant was measured with a digital multimeter. The results of the experimentation showed that carbon dioxide reduction was inversely proportional to oxygen production. In addition, carbon material residue also increased within the Dielectric Chamber at a linearly proportional rate. The dielectric constant of the material increased proportionately with the rate of consumption of carbon dioxide in the chamber. Conclusions drawn from this experiment are that the rate of carbon dioxide consumption is proportional with the accumulation of oxygen within the chamber

1. Introduction

Oxygen is vital to the sustainability of life. Without oxygen, ecosystems would not be able to sustain a balanced interconnection between producers and consumers. Nature has for millions of years developed processes that produce consumables for animal life from carbon dioxide from the air. These organisms, bacteria (cyanobacteria), plants, fungi and algae, even some primitive single celled animals, have all used this process to sustain themselves.

Removal of carbon dioxide waste gas and production of consumables such as oxygen and carbon film are of great importance in several aspects of sustainable industrial processes, maintaining sustainable ecological environments, and conserving valuable habitat resources.

One particular application for the usefulness of the material is to produce oxygen for isolated crews and remove carbon dioxide before its levels become toxic. Specifically, canisters of the material can be constructed which can passively remove carbon dioxide gas from breathing air. An added benefit from conventional carbon dioxide filters is to utilize the carbon dioxide to produce oxygen and carbon molecules, with the assistance of water and sunlight.

2. Purpose

The paper discusses the properties of a newly developed dielectric material designed to produce voltages proportional to the amount of trapped oxygen and carbon dioxide gas within it. The dielectric material consists of a mixture of tetraethyl orthosilicate (TEOS) sol gel, high valence Ta_2O_5, methyl cellulose and carbon dioxide consuming- oxygen producing cyano bacteria.

The relationship between the consumption of carbon dioxide and production of oxygen, as well as the production of carbon material residue will be quantitatively evaluated and measured by calculating the change in the dielectric constant of the dielectric material between the charge conductive plates between the plastic grids (Figure 3a).

The purpose of this investigation is to characterize the properties of a dielectric material designed for sensitivity to carbon dioxide gas bubbles (or HCO_3) within it. The dielectric material, defined in this report, is a mixture of TEOS, methyl cellulose, (both of which act as water containing polymers), tantalum oxide, which acts as a binding agent for the cyanobacterial material, which acts as the carbon dioxide fixing component.

The cyanobacterial component is responsible for removing the carbon dioxide gas moving within the dielectric, and producing oxygen gas bubbles within the material. In addition, due to the metabolism of the carbon dioxide, the dielectric material increases in weight due to the increase in carbon based metabolites produced.

3. Previous Research

There are several areas of research that are relevant to the development of the carbon dioxide removal. These are biomimetic gas processing designs, carbon dioxide removal systems and physical processes, using microbial activity. Brief selections of these techniques are discussed briefly below.

The tasks which the material must address are first to capture the gas in a suspended form for microbial metabolism. This can be accomplished by creating a material such as a sol gel, which contains soluble water, and a porous material such as methyl cellulose that can adsorb carbon dioxide. The other components of the mixture, tantalum pentoxide, are a non corrosive metal that can serve as a binding agent, or substrate, for the cyanobacteria.

Organisms such as cyanobacteria can survive in environmental conditions of high temperature, high pressure, chemical toxicity, acidic pH and absence of photosynthesis.(Bridger and Sundaram (1976), Nakagawa and Takai, (2006), and Narayan et al. (2009) have studied organisms that have developed efficient metabolic pathways for assimilation of inorganic CO_2 from the external environment. These resistant exotherms provide excellent possible candidates for materials that can be used in extreme environments for carbon dioxide capture.

Many groups have looked to nature for the solution to the complex problems facing the life support community. Magalon et al. (2009) has done work on carbon dioxide fixing enzymes in various species of fish, parasites, particularly Hystorothylacium aduncum.

The work outlines the metabolism associated with the gas fixing enzymes. As Magalon et al. (2009) points out, enzymes cannot be used in materials without accompanying buffers and other molecules such as water that are important in maintaining the enzymes' functionality and structural stability. Thus, using isolated enzymes in the approach discussed in this investigation would be complicated to build and difficult to maintain.

Work done by El-Zahab et al, (2008) showed that molecules such as glutamate dehydrogenase which can be co-immobilized with carbon monoxide dehydrogenase. Reactions were performed by dissolving CO_2 in an aqueous suspension. Productivities of 0.02 μ mol methanol/h/g-enzyme were achieved. This value was lower than (but comparable to) the 0.04 μ mol methanol/h/g-enzyme observed for free enzymes and cofactor at the same reaction conditions. The authors found that 80% of their original product was retained after 11 sequential transformations, with a yield based on the amount of cofactor yield. The cyanobacteria utilized in this investigation produce glutamate dehydrogenase and carbon monoxide dehydrogenase, which provide some insight as to how carbon dioxide is metabolized and carbon converted into molecules such as sugars.

Another approach by Xu et al. (2006) developed an alginate-silica (ALG-SiO2) hybrid gel, which used calcium silicate material to provide the caging agent, once the mixture was trapped in the cementatious material by hardening; it was exposed to an external magnetic field for interrogation and orientation. Another approach by Desimone et al., (2009) developed a method where intact microbial cells were imbedded and immobilized within sol gel material.

While many of these biomimetic approaches are indeed valuable, very little work has been conducted on these materials in the harsh environment experienced in space. Karavolos (Patent 10-901895, 2004, 2009) attempted to accommodate many of the issues associated with carbon dioxide removal and oxygen accumulation. Other issues such as radiation mitigation and impact resistance were addressed in a later investigation. This investigation described a unique TEOS sol gel cellulose-cyano bacteria mixture that captures carbon dioxide and metabolically produces oxygen gas and carbon sugars.

Perry et al. (2006) developed a carbon dioxide removal system consisting of a set of pumps and filters. The filter material used was polyphenylene benzobioxazole (PBZO). The system also offered some protection against thermal and radiative heat losses. The unit in Figure 1 is the carbon dioxide scrubbing unit used on the space station and is responsible for scrubbing out carbon dioxide, but has no capability to refurnish oxygen. The unit uses Lithium hydroxide canisters or amine canisters to capture (scrub) and retain carbon dioxide. The unit is effective, but as with all electronic units, is susceptible to breakdown.

Figure 1. Current carbon dioxide removal system on the International Space Station (courtesy of NASA)

There has been much research in enhancing this type of system for both space exploration and terrestrial applications. Memier et al. (2010) completed work on various techniques for carbon dioxide fixation.

Similar systems that use lithium canisters to scrub carbon dioxide are commonly used on board submarines (Ryder et al. 1998). These chemical/physical systems use amine derivatives that have been demonstrated as being effective in capturing carbon dioxide (DaSilva and Svedsen 2010, Dang and Rochelle, 2001, Monteiro et al. 2010) Luther and Hall, 2010, Ruess et al. 2006). The advantages of using these types of systems are that they are simple, but they also use toxic materials that require additional system control.

Each of the efforts by previous researchers mentioned above, while addressing important issues concerning either organic or inorganic processing of carbon dioxide, fall short in an important detail. This detail involves the integration of carbon dioxide removal and consumables replenishment (oxygen and carbon film). The techniques also fail to satisfactorily produce a system where waste is not accumulated.

4. Methodology

Silicate sol gel provides a liquid medium with which to grow bacteria. Methylated cellulose provides food for bacteria and traps liquid water within it. This material can be obtained from Chemical Company. Tantalum oxide provides a binding substrate for cyanobacteria. (American Tissue Culture Consortium, 2013).

The process whereby carbon dioxide gas adsorption, oxygen production and carbon residue build up within the chambers is summarized below: three samples of dry ice were acquired from Sigma Aldrich Chemical Company. The sample is placed in a clear acrylic container 25 cm, by 25 cm, by 25 cm, with a 1 cm diameter port and 1 meter long clear plastic tube which transfers the sublimated gas, kept at 1 Atm, 20 C to a test tube containing the dielectric material. The air flow for this system can be illustrated in the following steps: the air enters the port located at the top of Figure 3b. Air then moves into miniature canister (Figure 3b). Air moves through concentric cylinders inside Figure 3a.

Air moves out of concentric ports with carbon dioxide capture dielectric material and into top four ports. (Figure 3b). Air moves from four ports located at top of Figure 3b, and into port located in Figure 3a at top right. Air moves into consecutive grids 5, 4, 3, and 2 (numbered left to right) via plastic grid material coated with cyanobacteria coated dielectric material. Air moves from port 7 and into exit port (Figure 3a).

This material consists of a 50 %, amount by weight of TEOS sol gel, 40 % by weight Methyl Cellulose and 10 % by weight cyano bacterial culture. The total weight of the mixture (500 grams) was placed between two plastic grids with 1 mm diameter openings. (Figure 3a). This screen grid serves as a conduit for air passage and contact with carbon dioxide by the dielectric material containing carbon dioxide capturing bacteria- cyanobacteria ssp. The grid itself is also coated with the dielectric material, and a thin electroactive polymer (Polyaniline) is placed over this screen grid.

A control sample where no carbon dioxide is introduced into the sol gel- cyanobacteria sample, and another control where carbon dioxide was introduced but no cyanobacteria was included in the mixture, were prepared and background oxygen levels and dielectric constants were measured using a Digital Multimeter and PINPOINT II dissolved oxygen meter.

The process involved for carbon dioxide waste removal, and oxygen consumable production can be summarized in ten steps. Carbon dioxide gas flows into chamber 1. Gas flows into cylindrical canister within chamber (Figure 2). Carbon dioxide is adsorbed onto cylinder surfaces that contain carbon dioxide fixing bacteria (Figure 2).

Bacteria begin to digest carbon dioxide and release oxygen gas. Outgased oxygen and remaining carbon dioxide are transferred to chambers 2-7, repeating the process. Carbon residues accrue on cylinder surfaces. Cylinder surface contains two gas permeable membranes, one for carbon dioxide and the other for oxygen. Material sandwiched between the membranes contains a dielectric type material composed of TEOS sol gel and methyl cellulose, needed for water detainment and a food source for bacteria. The gas flows into filter material. Carbon dioxide can then be adsorbed by bacteria. Metabolic processes by the bacteria release oxygen (a consumable) and carbon metabolites. Oxygen gas is harvested by applying a mild vacuum to the chamber.

5. Results and Discussion

Two issues involved in this approach are that the bacteria capture carbon dioxide faster than they release oxygen. This can be compensated for by creating a reservoir with high gas contact surface area, and a large gas residence time. A second issue is that a film of carbon accumulates on the two membrane surfaces, partially blocking the pathway of oxygen to the other side of the membrane. The cartridges in the chamber are cleaned after 13 days of continual operation (Karavolos, unpublished data, 2010).

Below (figure 2) is a schematic representation of the device and description of the materials and functions of the components within it.

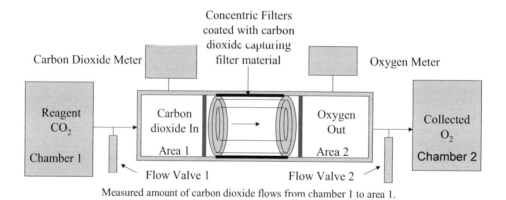

Measured amount of carbon dioxide flows from chamber 1 to area 1. Mass of gas measured at area 1.

Carbon Dioxide moves into concentric filter chamber via semi permeable membrane. Carbon Dioxide captured and metabolized by cyanobacteria within two semi permeable membranes containing carbon dioxide capture material (dielectric). Oxygen moves through semi permeable membrane out of chamber.

Oxygen moves out of concentric filter chamber via semi permeable membrane into area 2 and measured. Oxygen collected in chamber 2.

Figure 2. Canister that will be used for inflow gas carbon dioxide adsorption and oxygen production. The dielectric is illustrated in the dotted pattern of the device. The top and bottom portion of each of these patterns are connected to an RC circuit. The voltage and capacitance of the arrangement will be measured by connecting leads from a voltmeter to each end of the resistor in the circuit.

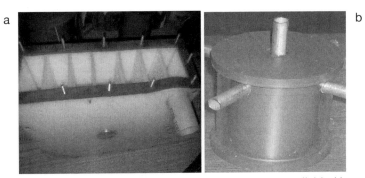

Figure 3a. This device is a square design whose compartments, divided by permeable screens that are coated with nano bio sol gel material containing cyano bacteria. This material is the active material which captures carbon dioxide, collects carbon film, and releases oxygen. The figure to the right (Figure 3b) is a representation of the cylinder that is placed within each chamber in the square compartments, once the compartments are enlarged.

Table 1. Relationship between concentration of carbon dioxide, dielectric constant, and the material capacitance during the mass balance experiment.

Test Number	Mass of Exiting O₂ (grams/l)	Mass of Introduced CO₂ (grams/l)	Mass of Carbon Material (grams)	Change in Dielectric Constant of Material
1	0.999	2.5	0.003	From 0.35
2	0.999	2.5	0.0035	From 0.35
3	0.999	2.5	0.004	From 0.34
4	0.999	2.5	0.0043	From 0.33

The data in the table above shows that the dielectric constant of the sol gel material is proportional to the concentration of carbon dioxide in the sample. Both the dielectric constant and capacitance of the material increase with increasing amounts of introduced carbon dioxide gas. In addition, the data indicates that the material removes carbon dioxide at a proportional rate to the introduction of oxygen into the air from the material.

Table 2. Sample Controls for measurement of sample dielectric constant.

Test Number	Mass of Exiting Oxygen (grams/l)	Mass of Introduced Carbon Dioxide (grams/l)	Mass of Carbon Material (grams)	Change in Dielectric Constant of Material
1	0.27	1.0	0.93	From 2.51 to 2.59
2	0.27	2.0	0.92	From 2.49 to 2.56
3	0.27	3.0	0.93	From 2.51 to 2.59
4	0.27	4.0	0.93	From 2.51 to 2.59

Data in Table 2 suggest that an increasing amount of carbon dioxide introduced into the system, produced a steady amount of oxygen and carbon material is produced. This corresponds to a consistent increase in dielectric constant for each experiment.

Table 3. Control values for four experiments, characterizing the mass of carbon dioxide and oxygen while cyanobacteria fix the carbon dioxide and release oxygen.

Test Number	Mass of Exiting Oxygen (grams/l)	Mass of Introduced Carbon Dioxide (grams/l)	Mass of Carbon Material (grams)	Change in Dielectric Constant of Material
1	0.284	1.0	0.90	From 1.60 to 1.73
2	0.288	1.0	0.92	From 1.62 to 1.74
3	0.284	1.0	0.92	From 1.62 to 1.74
4	0.283	1.0	0.92	From 1.62 to 1.74

The data in the control experiments above indicate that the amount of oxygen produced by the cyanobacteria with no introduction of carbon dioxide was small, owing to the small amount of carbon dioxide present in the ambient air.

The data in Tables 1, 2 and 3 were taken for dielectric material that contained cyanobacteria ssp. It was observed that the inclusion of growing cyanobacteria ssp. provided a large source of carbon dioxide fixing material, and at the same time, oxygen producing material. Virtually no statistically significant amount of oxygen is produced without the cyanobacteria (Table 4). The amount of carbon material present in the filter material remained relatively constant for both control experiments.

Table 4 Set of controls for each dependent variable (mass oxygen, mass carbon dioxide, mass carbon) and the independent variable (dielectric constant) for the experimental procedure. Each dependent variable was set at its baseline (minimum) to verify that the dielectric constant did not drift.

Control Test	Mass of Exiting Oxygen (grams/l)	Mass of Introduced Carbon Dioxide (grams/l)	Mass of Carbon	Dielectric Constant Change
1	0.001	0.0	0.002	0.001
2	0.046	1.0	0.099	0.003
3	0.046	1.0	0.100	0.003
4	0.046	1.0	0.100	0.003

What Table 4 indicates is that for a given baseline of oxygen production (2, 3, and 4) and a constant introduction of carbon dioxide during the initial stage of the gas exchange, little carbon mass had accumulated with no change in dielectric constant. Furthermore, when no carbon dioxide was introduced into the system, (1), very little carbon mass and oxygen production was observed.

Other experiments were completed to ensure that neither the sol gel nor the methyl cellulose contributed to the production of oxygen in the mass balance experiment. They may have contributed to the small increase in carbon in the filter material. This possibility must be addressed by further experimentation.

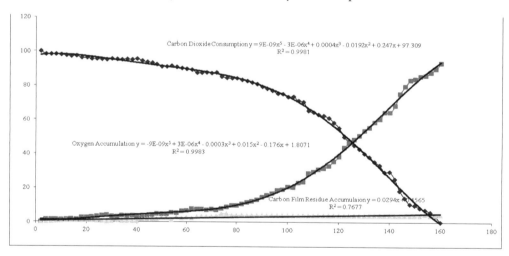

Figure 4 Relationship between the amount of carbon dioxide lost and the amount of oxygen gained in mass balance experiment vs. time.

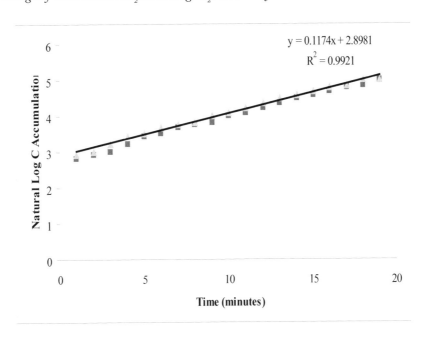

Figure 5. Amount of carbon accumulation with respect to time for mass balance experiment.

The data in Figures 4 and 5 illustrate two important aspects of the mass balance experiment. One, carbon materials accumulate at a proportional rate with respect to time and the continuation of carbon dioxide consumption by the cyano bacteria. In addition, the second illustration is that the amount of oxygen production in the mass balance system is also proportional to the amount of carbon dioxide reduction, and carbon material accumulation.

The control data for the mass balance experiment illustrated in Table 2 indicates that there was neither accumulation of oxygen gas nor reduction of carbon dioxide for the TEOS, methyl cellulose and polypropylene material used in the experiment.

In addition, based on the calculation of the slope of the carbon dioxide consumption and oxygen accumulation slopes, the rate of consumption/accumulation of each gas appears to be linearly proportional to each other. The difference in the slope and the reciprocal slope of the carbon dioxide consumption and oxygen accumulation lines, respectively, is likely due to the accumulation of carbon material within the dielectric material between the electroactive polymers.

Thus, the following conclusions may be drawn from this experiment:

1. The amount and rate of carbon dioxide consumption is proportional to the amount and rate of oxygen production by the cyanobacteria.
2. The amount of carbon residue that accumulates in the filter material is proportional to the amount of carbon dioxide removed and the amount of oxygen produced.
3. The dielectric constant of the sol gel material is proportional to the rate of carbon dioxide consumption during the mass balance experiment.
4. The methyl cellulose and sol gel TEOS do not impact the production of oxygen.
5. Based on a statistical analysis of the data, a significant amount of carbon dioxide can be removed from the newly developed filter assembly, and a significant amount of oxygen is produced as well.

References

1. Bridger, G., Sundaram, T., Occurance of Phosphenolpyruvate Carboxylase in the Extremely Thermophilic Bacterium Thermus Aquaticus. Journal of Bacteriology. Vol 125 No. 3. pp 1211-1213. (1976).

2. Dang, H., Rochelle, G., CO2 Absorption Rate and Solubility in Monoethanolamine/Piperazine/Water. First National Conference on Carbon Sequestration. (2001).

3. DaSilva, E., Svendsen, H., The Chemistry of CO2- Adsorption in Amine Solutions Studied by Computational Chemistry. Norwegian University of Science and Technology (2010).

4. Desimone, M., Alvarez, G., Foglia M., Diaz, L., Development of Sol-Gel Hybrid Materials for Whole Cell Immobilization. Recent Patents on Biotechnology 3, 55-60. (2009).

5. El- Zahab, B., Dunnelley, D., Ping, W., Particle-tethered NADH for production of methanol from CO_2 catalyzed by coimmobilized enzymes Biotechnology and Bioengineering. Vol. 99 Issue 3. pp 508-514 (2008).

6. Karavolos, Patent Application 03062002 Non Invasive Hydrated Detection Methods for Environmental Agents (2002).

7. Karavolos, A. Patent Application 06062004 Chemical Detection Methods Using Hydrated Materials (2004).

8. Luther, M., Hall, T. Exergy Applied to Lunar Base Design, 40th International Conference on Environmental Systems. 2010.

9. Magalon, D., Benitez, R., Valero, A., Adroher, F., CO_2-fixing enzymes and phosphoenolpyruvate metabolism in the fish parasite Hysterothylacium aduncum (Ascaridoidea, Anisakidae).Dis Aquat Organ. 23; 85(3):217-23 (2009).

10. Meunier, C., Rooke, J., Leonard, A., Xie, H., Su, B., Living hybrid materials capable of energy conversion and CO2 assimilation. Royal Society of Chemistry. Chem. Communications. Vol. 46 pages 3843-3859 (2010).

11. Monteiro, J., Pinto, D., Hartono, A., Svendsen, F., Reactive Absorption of CO_2 into Aqueaous Solutions of N, N Dielthylethanolamine (DEEA). The Norwegian University of Science and Technology. (2010).

12. Nakagawa, S.; Takai, K. Methods for the isolation of thermophiles from deep-sea hydrothermal environments. *Methods Microbiol.* 35, 55–91 (2006).

13. Oceaneering Space Systems, Communication CooRs Research Meeting (2009)

14. Perry M., Bodiford, K., Burks, M., Cooper, M., Fiske M., Lunar In Situ Materials-Based Habitat Technology Development. Marshal Space Flight Center Internal Paper (2006).

15. Perry M., Bodiford, K., Burks, M., Cooper, M., Fiske M., Lunar In Situ Materials-Based Habitat Technology Development. Marshal Space Flight Center Internal Paper (2006).

16. Ruess, F., Schaenzlin, J., Benaroya, H., Structural Design of a Lunar Habitat. Journal of Aerospace Engineering (2006).

17. Ryder, J., Francis, R., Wray, D., Lithium Hydroxide- Is it Hazardous when Used in Manpowered CO_2 Scrubbing Systems. UHMS Meeting Abstracts, Submarine Technology (1998).

18. Xu, S. , Yang, L., Li, Y., Jiang, Z., Wu, H. Efficient Conversion of CO_2 to Methanol Catalyzed by Three Dehydrogenases Co-encapsulated in an Alginate–Silica (ALG–SiO_2) Hybrid Gel. *Ind. Eng. Chem. Res.*, 45 (13), pp 4567–4573 (2006).

100 YEAR STARSHIP™

Destinations: Hidden Obstacles

Chaired by Joe Ritter, PhD

Open Source Starship Alliance

Track Description

Papers in this track are invited to offer strategies, techniques, processes and solutions will help us continue to explore and understand what is really going on in space.

Track Summary

The 2013 Destinations and Hidden Obstacles session was renamed from the 2012 100YSS Destinations and Habitats session. With multiple cross-disciplinary submissions, nine abstracts were approved by 100YSS Track chair committee. There were five speakers who were able to attend, so the track chair Ritter added two additional lectures of his own to round out the session. The talks are described below in order of presentation:

"Dark Earths: Initial Goals for Interstellar Exploration" by Thomas Marshall Eubanks Asteroid Initiatives, LLC started off our day. This was a fascinating talk based on credible calculations describing potential exploration options suggesting a reasonable near-term goal of exploration should be to find dark nomadic planets within ~1 light year of the Earth. Marshall's science case was compelling and the idea resonated with everyone present.

"Novel Advances for Remote Sensing of Exoplanets" was next, by Joe Ritter from Neoteric Physics, Open Source Starship Alliance (Starshipalliance.org), Icarus, and 100YSS.org. This talk discussed novel instrumentation for exoplanet investigation including high dynamic range telescope designs, physics of inducing polarized signals in exo-atmospheres, spectropolarimetry for increasing signal to noise ratios, and methods of building large apertures with actuated solids as well as an update on the original DARPA 2011 100YSS conference application of NASA NIAC OCCAMS photonic muscle membranes to future starships for propulsion, power generation, power distribution, narrow beam communication as well as advanced imaging instrumentation.

"Astrobiological Matrix" by Michael Paul Ziolo, University of Liverpool, was one of Ziolo's unusually visually stunning presentations dynamically relating Lineweaver studies on the Galactic Habitable Zone (GHZ) and the possible concentration of civilizations in the Milky Way and the likely range of biologies implied by Kauffman's analysis of autocatalytic sets and the universality classes comprising CHONPS-based lifeforms. The information density was as dazzling as the graphics.

"Nano-arcsecond Exoplanet Imaging With Spacecraft Constellations: Extreme Ultra Baseline Temporal Correlation Intensity Interferometry", was a fill-in last minute talk by Joe Ritter from Neoteric Physics and University of Hawaii Institute for Astronomy Advanced Technology Research Center on Maui. Described were potentially radical advances over the pioneering Hanbury Brown Twiss work of estimating an object by measuring magnitudes of Fourier components. Included were updates of using phase closure techniques to reconstruct images using a correlation function retaining an estimate of the derivative of the phase function of the object in the Fourier domain. Consider this scale to understand the image enhancement scale implied here: the Hubble can resolve a football at 600km. Nanoarcsecond imaging scales to (theoretically) resolve a DNA strand at that distance. Stunning if possible someday.

"Empirical Evidence Suggest a Need For a Different Gravitational Theory" was a talk given by Benjamin Solomon ISETI, LLC. This talk reviewed a controversial idea that force is expressed as a Non Inertia Field and not by the exchange of virtual particles. Solomon claimed inconsistencies in contemporary physical theories, and suggested the potential to manipulate subspace rather than spacetime to 'translocate' starships across vast distances. This was a controversial talk that expressed alternative views on gravitational physics.

"Is Our Closest Neighbor a Potential Threat?" was a talk by Christopher Odetunde and Emmerson Edwards, AATO Technical Opinions, Texas Southern University. The idea was that an asteroid impacting the Earth may be mankind's least concern and that instead, consideration should be given to Moon fragments as a higher probability of hazard to Earth. No models substantiating this were discussed but claims were that lunar impact debris fields are a hazard to Earth.

Finally we had a lively "General Discussion Panel and Questions Session." During this, the speakers and many audience participants ate chocolate macadami nuts from Hawaii and discussed the science behind each presentation and the relative merits of various ideas in the session. The presentations ranged from visionary to unsubstantiated, but all of them out of the ordinary. In the true spirit of exploration both mental and physical, and within the excellent and always intense exploratory goals of the 100YSS community we all learned something and had fun. Progress was made toward our mutual goal of developing science toward generating the capability of "building a starship within 100 years."

Track Chair Biography

Joe Ritter, PhD

NASA/NIAC Fellow

Joe Ritter, a NASA/NIAC fellow, has worked in government and private sectors and held faculty appointments in diverse areas from Space Systems Engineering to Astronomy to Animal science. He is working on a number of cutting-edge projects that sound like something out of a science fiction movie, but in fact are real: Current projects include developing laser powered meta-material nano-actuators optical systems with the goal of launching 100 meter giant ultra-lightweight space telescopes, working on optical systems for Earth based analysis of exoplanet atmospheres and through a new advance radically reducing light pollution that affects astronomy, humans, sea turtles and other endangered species (www.EcoScienceLighting.com). He is on the advisory board of the Open Source Starship Alliance (www.StarshipAlliance.org) and CEO of Neoteric Physics. Joe believes that having the big picture (an interdisciplinary view) is critical to scientific advancement. His previous research and consulting covered many fields, including Artificial Intelligence, Teratology, Genetics, Satellite Oceanography, Solar Power, Space Plasma Physics, Radiative Transfer, Active Structures, Adaptive Optics and many other fields.

Is Our Closest Neighbor a Potential Threat?

Christopher Odetunde, Ph.D.

Professor and Chair, Aeronautics and Astronautics Engineering,

Kwara State University (KWASU) and Texas Southern University

Emmerson Edwards

Owner and President, AATO Technical Opinions,

Minority and Veteran Owned Company, Houston, Texas

Abstract

The international scientific community is focused on asteroids hitting the Earth. Therefore, asteroid research is directed towards their identification and methods for interpreting available data to deflect their flight path. The authors believe that an asteroid impacting the Earth may be mankind's least concern. Instead, consideration should be given to objects originating from our closest neighbor, the moon. Moon fragments could be the source of future hazards to Earth. This premise is based on an underlining theme. The need for intergalactic space travels, because one day mankind may be required to abandon planet Earth. This blind theory is related to the probability of an object impacting, or destabilizing the moon and setting in motion an inevitable collision with the Earth. New research tools and processes can be used to identify specific deep space threats that have the potential of pushing the moon into a collision trajectory. If the hypothesis that an event such as this will occur is correct, the greatest threat to Earth is not only an asteroid, but objects that impact the moon first. Astronomers have provided data related to the moon's orbit, which includes data related to the periods of time when the moon is closest to Earth. Some of this data can be used to develop a trajectory model that can predict the probable angle and points of impact on the moon. A fully developed trajectory model can predict the origin of a threat, the point of impact on the moon and the inevitable intercept on Earth.

The ability to identify and track a possible source of a predetermined cataclysmic event in space is the science of the future. Archeological evidence and data of past impacts on the moon and Earth will be utilized to support the development of a new model. Our paper will focus on identifying the objects capable of delivering a fatal blow to the moon. The discovery of an object that can result in such a strike will contradict the current scientific perception that the moon protects the Earth from space debris. The new theory will prove that the moon will become a factor in the destruction of Earth. This proposed theory may be viewed by many as a "blind theory". However, there is visible evidence of impacts craters on the surface of the moon. Researchers who concentrate scientific efforts towards objects on a trajectory towards Earth and ignoring trajectories towards our moon could contribute to a disaster. Therefore, alternative approaches to research, that look beyond the obvious, could be responsible for saving mankind in the future. Since the probability of a collision between the moon and Earth is considered highly improbable, there is currently minimal research being conducted in this area. The premise that the moon will always remain in its current orbit or configuration ignores the concept that "nothing remains the same". We have the technology and workforce capable of starting the deep space journey to solve this challenge. There is a difference between researching the acceptable, obvious and unknown.

Keywords
asteroid, interstellar, space, moon, collision, meteorites, craters, cataclysmic

1. Introduction
Humanity's passion for space exploration has changed directions many times. New limits and boundaries are set and reset in the search for commercial success or the survival of the planet. This paper expand on the idea that humanity has been riding on a fragile ship, a temporary way station on an evolving planet of which humanity has limited control and recourse for survival due to the natural forces of nature. Considering the many perils that can beset humanity the thought that one day our moon, in its wide arching elliptical orbit could actually be a pendulum announcing the end of life on the planet is one of the points raised by this paper. The other point that is being made centers on current national programs that are clearly focused on planetary research, moon missions, mars missions, star missions, asteroid studies, robotic technology, efforts beyond the solar system and the commercialization of space activities. This mind set is an Earth centered approach to space. There is clearly an absence of research efforts in deep space trajectories threatening the moon. Once a moon threat concept is accepted a totally new area of focus will be born. The new studies would be directed towards Moon to Earth areas of impact. Including the probability of Moon to Earth Strikes (MES) or Moon to Earth Debris Deflections (MEDD) which are real areas of concern.

Satellite and lunar probe imagery changed the mindset of scientists about previous thoughts of volcanic activity on the moon. These images and the work of geologist Grove Karl Gilbert and Eugene Shoemaker in the 1960's confirmed that the craters on the moon were formed by impacts. NASA sent probes to the moon to survey the best possible places to land the lunar astronaut missions. This precaution was performed to avoid the rough terrain and existing impact areas that had been identified by NASA. That is why the decision was made to select the Sea of Tranquility as the first lunar landing site during the Apollo program. [1] The choice was made after years of researching the surface of the moon.

This paper implores the scientific community to take a new look at the moon. Instead of performing research to land on the moon, build a moon habitat and investigate ways to mine the minerals, the authors see an opportunity to look at future strategies to avoid the destruction of our civilization. This new area of focus will require in depth studies of impact trajectories that occurred on the moon billions of years ago. These impact studies are important because of the possibility that a High Velocity Huge Mass (HVHM) impact on the moon, even if it's not a direct hit, that becomes a glancing blow can ultimately be deflected towards the Earth. This deflection could scrape the Earth's upper atmosphere or worse become a glancing blow that reshapes the Earth's surface.

2. Motivation
2.1 Humanity's Survival
Researchers can't disregard predicable occurrences that we all know will happen at some point in time. We have examples and theories of possible near Earth passes of huge asteroids. The approach of Apophis in 2035 is certainly a predictable occurrence. We can even look back in ancient times and use past events as present day road maps that address new phenomena. Fragments of asteroids are now being tracked today. Some nations have joined together and formed annual events to share information regarding deep space phenomena. Today's technology allows us to look deeper into space for future threats. There are organizations using technology to track and monitor objects and their projected paths.

NASA has an ongoing program that currently releases information related to deep space objects. This data is provided in the form of the objects trajectories, speed and size. NASA's program addresses near misses (to the Earth) based on calculations in the thousands of miles range. This paper puts forth the idea that we should analyze and evaluate the data in a manner that allows us to decide whether an object's collision trajectory is towards the moon. This finding would make the object a candidate for review to determine if a deflection could alter its path towards Earth.

2.2 Trajectory Models

There are existing math models that could be used to single out predictable trajectories. These trajectories would be focused on identifying moon to Earth; deep space - moon – to Earth and asteroid - moon to Earth types of destructive paths. Simulations can be developed and tweaked with increases in mass and velocity based on a variety of variances of objects that could be on a collision course with our planet.

There are at least four possible directions that deflected moon or moon fragments can go in when hit by a massive object. These points of deflection are numbered from one through four. The first strike could cause the moon to be deflected into a trajectory towards the sun. A second possibility would involve a strike that would result in the moon heading towards other planets. The third type of deflection would alter the orbit of the moon; thereby affecting the balance of nature with the Earth. The fourth and most probable, is a strike that results in a deflection of the moon terminating with a collision with Earth.

Taking into consideration all four possible angles of deflection, the two most threatening angles would be the deflection to the upper portion of the Earth. They would be identified as angles three and four which would be the most cataclysmic. Angle three would result in a counter clockwise relative direction of the moon's well established orbital path over specious 6 billion years. The ripple affect of something like this occurring is unimaginable, primarily because it is a circumstance that has never been considered. When you combine the angle of deflection with a possible angel of impact a clearer picture of a known catastrophic event becomes more focused. Figure 1 provides a generalized sample of deflection profiles.

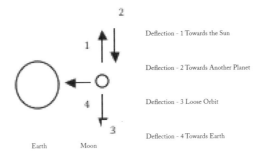

Figure 1. Possible Deflection Profiles

2.3 Predictable Timetables

The opportunity for a cataclysmic event becomes plausible when a review of the current known list of timetable occurrences is analyzed. When considering the link between the Earths's atmosphere and the moons, the realization that any gradual degradation of the atmosphere on Earth can be a significant indicator of issues with the moons orbit. All of the occurrences below are precursors that set the stage for a moon or Earth strike.

Attempts to predict any of these types of an occurrence can be divided into three primary areas of research. One is obviously an object striking the moon. The second would be the moon breaking apart and part of the moon striking Earth. The final blow would be a deep space object either first hitting the moon or striking the Earth directly.

Table 1. Earth/Moon Predictable Occurrences

	Predictable Occurrence	Possible Impact	Timetable
1	Carbon atmosphere	Irreversible	2040 -2050
2	Ozone Layer depletion	Atmospheric Window Damage	Unknown
3	Asteroid Encounter	"Apophis" close encounter	2029 - 2036
4	Absence of Fresh Water	Irreversible?	2080

As highly unlikely as it may seem, a review of named asteroids can provide a tight cluster of possible asteroid strike points. A review of some of the numerous craters on the moon (and the probable trajectories that caused

443

them) can provide a cluster of impact data that can be used to validate future hits or misses. Some of the major strikes on the surface of the moon include a violent impact that occurred in the [2] Ibrium Basin on the moon's surface four billion years ago. This strike hit with such a force it went deep enough to excavate the moon's crust. Another impact followed the Ibrium Basin landing in the Aristarchus surface of the moon only a half a billion years ago. The list of massive strikes on the surface of the moon includes Copernicus the biggest moon crater which is 60 miles in diameter and 2 miles deep. The moons youngest crater "Tyco" is 53 miles across and 3 miles deep. When considering the list of strikes on the Earth, a review or research of strikes from deep space reveals ocean and land craters. One strike is attributed to causing the dinosaurs to become extinct. Therefore the Earth can also be a source of data on perspective catastrophes.

Figure 2 attempts to illustrate the most vulnerable quadrant for a moon to Earth strike. The illustration provides a view of Quadrants I and IV with the Earth exposed to deep space and the orbit of the moon.

If an errant object is traveling through space and enters into these quadrants there is a strong possibility that the Earth and (or) moon will be struck. The real challenge is to understand the impact challenges created by the orbit profiles. This understanding will lead to a further understanding of the deterioration of orbit profiles and the part that it will play on the deflection variables. What can't be illustrated is that the moon is not always the same distance from the Earth. The moon has a noticeable affect on the Earth in the form of tides. It also affects the motion and orbit of the Earth. Keep in mind the moon does not orbit around the center of the Earth; they both revolve around their masses. Therefore, when attempting to perform a trajectory analysis, identifying a threat profile, modeling/analyzing a strike versus a threat profile, or doing modeling/proximity predictions and intercepts of a possible strike, the challenge is to make sure that regardless of the location of the errant object in quadrants I and IV, that the orbit of the moon is known. Remember the angle and the velocity of the mass striking the moon will determine if the strike will result in a collision with Earth. That is why new studies have to begin to develop data that can be analyzed to answer the questions of deflection and trajectory. Without precise data backed by research, the ability to resolve the deep space threats becomes very challenging. Our most pressing research concern is that the future of Earth will befall either to a scrapping of our atmosphere, a collision with a deep space object or our closet neighbor being pushed into our planet causing a major change to our planet forever.

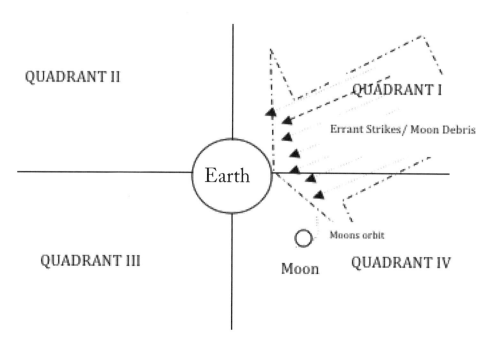

Figure 2. Collisions Versus Destabilization

3. Schedule

The timetable we recommend for this project would require six years to develop the infrastructure necessary to perform and deliver project data in a timely fashion. This would mean that all of the developmental, verification requirements, processes, studies and the research formulas would be in place.

The succeeding years would be devoted to perfecting modeling analysis and reporting processes. A brief high level draft of the *Is Our Closet Neighbor A Potential Threat?* is provided below:

Draft Schedule: Is Our Closet Neighbor A Potential Threat?

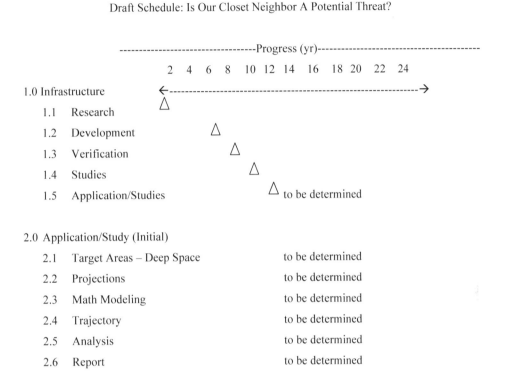

4. Concern

There has never been a study involved with a possible collision between the moon and Earth and if not the moon, a fragment of the moon, the best comparison of mans approach to the problem is the ocean. We research the affect s over time. We find tranquility in the fact that the major catastrophes are a small part to pay to live on the planet. While not paying attention to fate. Just as small pains over time become unmanageable and eventually lead to death. Our inability to translate the small occurrences our planet has on its relationship with one nearest neighbor could be a precursor to the demise of the planet brought about by a chain reaction collision that starts in deep space, strikes the moon and alters our way of life on Earth forever.

If we make a list of all the current space programs and projects. The list would be impressive until you realize that you can group them into five definitive groups. Our list would look like:

* Missions to the moon, Mars, stars – these are all efforts being made to support in this area
* Asteroids studies – there are plans to land and lasso on an asteroid
* Robotic technologies – robotic technology is one of the key ingredients to deep space
* Deep Space Exploration – there are more countries that are involved in this effort
* Commercialization of space – Low orbit commercialization continues at a rapid pace

5. Conclusion

Please keep our closet neighbor on your mind after you complete reading this paper. As you can see from the list above, the one research area that is noticeably absent is the study of our closet neighbor. One can conclude that it has been studies enough; therefore there is no need to look again. Included in this thought process is that having been there, the only new work should be devoted to habitability. Our paper clearly proposes another look. This time we challenge the fact that we have accomplished a landing on the moon and even have returned to the surface occasionally to perform studies, mappings etc. These are human directed considerations that are tied to sustaining human life on the moon. Our approach is to look at the environment of activity in and around the moon that would make it a potential threat to our planet's existence.

When the science issues we have taken for granted become the focus of our survival. The energy expended on exploration will be refocused on deep space, as the impetus for our survival.

Acknowledgements

Dr Odetune: I would like to extend a thank you to Dr Odetune for his assistance in this project. It was very important to have a mentor who understands the concepts and believes in the value of Space Exploration. There are a hand full of professors who have the vision of the impact that Science, Technology, Engineering and Mathematics can do for Deep Space Exploration and the survival of mankind.

Margaret: I always have to thank my wife for being so patient and putting up with the pursuit of my passion for Deep Space Exploration. I hope my grandchildren will one day benefit from the efforts of everyone involved in Space Exploration.

References

1. Kennedy, George P. "World Explorers: Apollo to the Moon." Chelsea House Publications USA 1962

2. W. David Woods" How Apollo Flew to the Moon." Editor - Apollo Flight Journal 2008 Glasgow, UK; Praxis Publishing, Chilchester, UK reprint 2009 and 2012

3. Cortright, Edgar M. "Apollo Expeditions to the Moon." The Nasa History, Dover Publications, Minneola NY 2009

Empirical Evidence Suggest A Need For A Different Gravitational Theory

Benjamin T. Solomon

iSETI LLC, Denver, USA

benjamin.t.solomon@iseti.us

1. Abstract

Two significant findings compel a rethink of physical theories. First, using a 7-billion year old gamma-ray burst, Nemiroff [2012] showed that quantum foam could not exists. And second, Solomon [2011] showed that gravitational acceleration is not associated with the gravitating mass, that gravitational acceleration g is determined solely by τ the change in time dilation over a specific height multiplied by c^2 or $g=\tau c^2$. Seeking consistency with Special Theory of Relativity, as means to initiate this rethink, this paper examines 12 inconsistencies in physical theories that manifest from empirical data. The purpose of this examination is to identify how gravitational theories need to change or be explored, to eliminate these 12 inconsistencies. It is then proposed that spacetime is much more sophisticated than just a 4-dimensional continuum. And, that the Universe consists of at least two layers or "kenos" (Greek for vacuous), the 4-dimensional kenos, spacetime (x, y, z, t) and the 3-dimensional kenos, subspace (x, y, z) that are joined at the space coordinates (x, y, z). This explains why electromagnetic waves are transverse, and how probabilities are implemented in Nature. This paper concludes by proposing two new instruments and one test, to facilitate research into gravitational fields, the new torsion-, tension- and stress-free near field gravity probe, the gravity wave telescope, and a non-locality test.

Keywords

Relativity, Special Theory of Relativity, General Theory of Relativity, Entanglement, Baking Bread, Transverse Wave, Electromagnetism, Separation Vectors, Gamma Ray Burst, Quarks, Gravity Modification, Exotic Matter, Photons, Strings, Shielding, Cloaking, Invisibility, Near Field Gravity Probe, Wave Function, Gaussian.

1. Introduction

1.1 Is There a Need?

Do we need a new theory on gravity? If so, why? Nemiroff [1] used photon arrivals from a 7-billion year old gamma-ray burst to show that quantum foam cannot exist. If corroborated this would require significant revisions to quantum theory. A new theoretical approach would then be required. But why wait?

1.2 Can A New Theory Provide New Insights?

Solomon [2] proposed a different formalism, schemas, for analyzing gravitational fields. A schema is an outline of a model of a complex reality to assist in explaining this reality. The work of various researchers [2] in the gravity field can be presented by the conceptual formalism referred to as source-field-effect schema. The source-field-effect schema corresponds to the mass-gravity-acceleration phenomenon, respectively. With this approach one can take out the source or mass and just consider the field-effect or gravitational-field-gravitational-acceleration.

One could rewrite [2] & [3] General Relativity's separation vectors as a function of Ω, as follows,

$$g = j\left(\frac{d^2\xi^z}{dt^2}\right) \tag{1}$$

$$\frac{d^2\xi^z}{dt^2} = 2\frac{Gm}{c^2 r^3}\xi^z \tag{2}$$

$$\Omega = 2\frac{Gm}{c^2 r^3} \tag{3}$$

$$\frac{d^2\xi^z}{dt^2} = \Omega\xi^z \tag{4}$$

or,

$$\frac{d^2\xi^z}{dt^2} = k\left(\xi^z\right) \tag{5}$$

Equation (1) expresses gravitational acceleration g as a function j of the separation vectors. Equation (2) presents the standard z-direction separation vector as a function of gravitational mass m, and gravitational constant G at a distance r from the source. The mass source of the gravitational field can be replaced with an Ω function as defined by equation (3). Therefore, equation (2) can be rewritten as a function of Ω as equation (4) or simply as a function k as in equation (5). Solomon's schema can be described as three parts, first the mass source or equation (3), second the field or equation (5), and third the field effect or acceleration, equation (1).

Rewriting, equation (1) gives equation (6) that gravitational acceleration is primarily a field effect, and one does not really need to know what precisely is Ω as long as it is a function of matter.

$$g = j\left(\Omega\xi^z\right) \tag{6}$$

One could ask the question, what part of matter causes the gravitational field? Contemporary theories use mass as a measure of that matter. Matter, however, consists of at least two parts, mass and quarks. These are impossible to distinguish empirically with current technology. So if mass is a proxy for matter, could it be that the real source of a gravitational field is quark interaction, and not mass? We don't know, and thus the need for a better theory for gravitational source to probe such questions. This separation vector approach support the premise that one could develop a field-effect relationship for gravitational acceleration per (1) that does not require a prior knowledge of the mass of the gravitating source.

1.1 New Inferences From Empirical Results?

Using the source-field-effect schema, and with extensive numerical modeling Solomon [2] & [4] discovered a new, elegantly simple formula for gravitational acceleration g that does not require one to have a prior knowledge of the mass of the gravitating source,

$$g = \tau.c^2 \tag{7}$$

Where gravitational acceleration g is defined by the velocity of light squared c^2 multiplied by τ the change in time dilation divided by the height across this change in time dilation or a purely field effect. Note there is no mass source in this equation (7). This is akin to knowing the frequency of a photon without having to know the properties of the photon source.

Equation (7) provide three inferences, first that gravitational acceleration is a 4-dimensional (x, y, z & t) problem. No further dimensions are required. The second, that the source-field-effect schema is correct as it is now possible to investigate the field-effect schema without taking into consideration the source component of the full source-field-effect schema. Similarly, one should be able to investigate the source-field schema without taking into consideration the effect component. And, third [2] & [4], that the gravitational effect on an elementary particle is independent of the internal structure of that particle. This independence suggests that any particle-based theory could in principle explain gravitational acceleration. That is, it need not be quantum- or string-based particles. It could be something else, say, quantized compressive structures that contract with energy as opposed to string theory's quantized tensile structures that expand with energy.

With three major gravitational theories (relativity, quantum & string) why would one need a fourth? Equation (7) provides an answer. All contemporary theories require mass in their calculations, while equation (7) does not. One now has a means to evaluate gravitational acceleration without know the gravitating mass. This therefore, hints of new theoretical and technological approaches to modifying gravity without using mass.

1.2 Wasn't Gravity Modification Disproved?

With respect to gravity modification, the literature reviews [2] point to inconclusive theoretical explorations and experimental results. The pertinent research is the work of Podkletnov [5] & [6], Solomon [7], Woods[1], Cooke, Helme & Caldwell [8] and Hathaway, Cleveland & Bao [9]. Podkletnov [5] & [6] observed both gravity shielding or attenuation and amplification. Solomon [7] showed that any hypothesis on superconducting gravity shielding should eventually explain four observations, the stationary disc weight loss, spinning disc weight loss, weight loss increases along a radial distance and a weight increase. Woods, Cooke, Helme & Caldwell [8] attempted to reproduce Podkletnov's [5] & [6] work without much success as (quoting the authors) "the tests have not fulfilled the specified conditions for a gravity effect". Their primary focus was to reproduce Podkletnov's ceramic disc. In the nomenclature of the source-field-effect schema, they focused on the source component, and had not reached the field-effect components of this schema. Therefore, their results were inconclusive.

Solomon [7] using the field-effect schema, proposed that two vital components of Podkletnov's experiments were missing from the Woods, Cooke, Helme & Caldwell [8] investigation. First, the bilayer disc, top-side superconducting and bottom-side non-superconducting, may not have been built correctly. Second, the electric field was missing from Woods, Cooke, Helme & Caldwell experimental investigation. The field-effect schema, therefore, advocates a need for a new theory on gravity that will facilitate the investigation into gravity modification. The photo in the Woods, Cooke, Helme & Caldwell paper shows a sample disc with the crack in the middle. The disc was not able to withstand the rotational forces that Podkletnov's disc could.

Hathaway, Cleveland & Bao [9] paper suggests that they too had similar difficulties. They [9] report a rotational speed of between 400–800 rpm, very substantially less than Podkletnov's 5,000 rpm. This suggests that there were other problems in their disc not reported in their paper. With 400–800 rpm, if they were to observe a significant weight change it would have been less than the repeatable experimental sensitivity of 0.5mg.

Quoting Hathaway, Cleveland & Bao's original paper "As a result of these tests it was decided that either the coil designs were inefficient at producing …", "the rapid induction heating at room temperature cracked the non-superconducting disk into two pieces within 3 s", "Further tests are needed to determine the proper test set-up required to detect the reverse Josephson junction effect in multi-grain bulk YBCO superconductors".

It is obvious that neither teams were able to faithfully reproduce Podkletnov's work. It is no wonder that at least

---

[1] Three teams set out to investigate Podkletnov's claims. The first was led by RC Woods. The second led by Hathaway. These are discussed in this paper. Ning Li led the third team comprised of members from NASA and University of Huntsville, AL. It was revealed in conversations with a former team member that Ning Li's team was disbanded before they could build the superconducting discs required to investigate Podkletnov's claims.

Woods *et al* team stated "the tests have not fulfilled the specified conditions for a gravity effect". This statement definitely applies to Hathaway, Cleveland & Bao's research.

2. Insights from Empirical Inconsistencies in Contemporary Theories

Physics is always changing, improving, and getting closer to the true description of Nature, all the time. This is achieved by exploring all avenues, even if some of those avenues initially sound ridiculous. By a process of back tracking the physics community eliminates those branches of the tree of empirical & theoretical exploration, that turn out to be dead ends. Sometimes this may take a single journal paper and sometimes many decades.

So is there a method to speeding up this branch and bound exploration process? Operations research search procedures known as mathematical programming techniques would suggest a judicial use of boundary conditions that one would not want to cross. This reduces the scope of mathematical programming search by reducing the size of the feasible region to search, thereby arriving at a solution sooner rather than later.

Is there an equivalent to mathematical programming boundary conditions in physics? This author proposes that inconsistencies with the empirical data are the equivalent of boundary conditions. These boundary condition inconsistencies, raise a flag signaling to the community of physicists that something is not quite right here and that there is a very high probability that Nature does not operate in this manner. Many times new solutions will lead to new boundary condition inconsistencies. Like physics, boundary condition inconsistencies are always changing, improving, and getting us closer to the true description of Nature, all the time.

In this section, 12 inconsistencies between the empirical evidence and accepted theories are documented and explored. They are as follows:

2.1 Exotic Matter Cannot Exist in Nature

Bondi [10] proposed that negative mass was consistent within General Relativity and negative mass or exotic matter would gravitationally repel while positive mass or normal matter would gravitationally attract and if the "... motion is confined to the line of centers, then one would expect the pair to move off with uniform acceleration ..."

There are two problems with this. The first is perpetual motion physics. Attach two thin capsules to two radial spokes. The other end of these spokes are attached to the axis of an electric generator. The spokes are fixed a small angle apart so that the capsules are close to each other. The capsules are very, very thin so as to remove any significant complications with the normal matter of the thin capsule material. In one capsule insert exotic matter, and in the other insert normal matter. Release the spokes. What does one observe? Per Bondi's "one would expect the pair to move off with uniform acceleration" one observers that the attraction-repulsion caused by the exotic-normal matter interaction would turn the electric generator to produce electrical energy. One concludes that exotic matter results in perpetual motion, a sacrilege in physics. Therefore, since Nature abhors perpetual motion, one infers that exotic matter cannot exist in Nature.

The second problem, however, is more subtle. The esteemed Bondi [10] was able to authenticate exotic matter using General Relativity or rephrasing, General Relativity was able to endorse perpetual motion physics. Therefore, any physical theory that uses exotic matter is now doubtful. The lesson here is that one has to be careful not to modify or develop a theory that leads to perpetual motion physics.

2.2 The Baking Bread Model is Incorrect

The baking bread model has problems. To quote from the NASA[2] page,

"The expanding raisin bread model at left illustrates why this proportion law is important. If every portion of the bread expands by the same amount in a given interval of time, then the raisins would recede from each other with exactly a Hubble type expansion law. In a given time interval, a nearby raisin would move relatively little, but a distant raisin would move relatively farther – and the same behavior would be seen from any raisin in the loaf. In other words, the Hubble law is just what one would expect for a homogeneous expanding universe, as predicted by the Big Bang theory. Moreover no raisin, or galaxy, occupies a special place in this universe – unless you get too close to the edge of the loaf where the analogy breaks down."

---

[2] http://map.gsfc.nasa.gov/universe/bb_tests_exp.html

Notice the two qualifications. The obvious one is "unless you get too close to the edge of the loaf where the analogy breaks down". The other is that this description is only correct from the perspective of velocity. But there is a problem with this.

On some nights one can see the band of stars called the Milky Way[3]. Notice that the Earth is not at the edge of the Milky Way. The Earth is half way inside the Milky Way. So since we are halfway inside, "unless you get too close to the edge of the loaf where the analogy breaks down" should not happen. Right?

Wrong. The Earth is only halfway in and one observes the Milky Way severely constrained to a narrow band of stars. That is, if the baking bread model is to be correct one has to be far from the center of the Milky Way to observe this narrow band. Halfway definitely cannot be considered "*too close* to the edge".

The Universe is on the order of 10^3 to 10^6 times larger. Using our Milky Way as an example the Universe should look like a large smudge on one side and a small smudge on the other side if the Earth is even half way out from the "center" of this baking bread model. One should be surrounded by an even distribution of galaxies, in any direction, if the Earth is at the center of the Universe. And if the Earth was off center, the center-facing side of the Universe should have more galaxies than the edge-facing side of the Universe. More importantly by the distribution of the galaxies on each side one could calculate our position with respect to the center of the Universe. But the Hubble pictures show that this is not the case. One does not see directional nonrandom distribution of galaxies, but a random and even distribution of galaxies across the sky in any direction one looks.

Another problem with the baking bread model is that the early Universe should only be visible at a specific region in the sky where the 'center' was/is supposed to be. Hubble shows that this is not the case. Therefore the baking bread model is an incorrect model of the Universe and necessarily any theoretical model that is dependent on the baking bread structure of the Universe is incorrect. One "knows" that the Earth is not at the center of the Universe. The Universe is not geocentric. Neither is it heliocentric. The Universe is such that anywhere, where one is in the Universe the distribution of galaxies across the sky must be the same.

Einstein[4] once described an infinite Universe being the surface of a finite sphere. If the Universe was a 4-dimensional surface of a 4-dimensional sphere, then from any perspective or from any position on this surface, all the galaxies would be moving away from each other due to the expansion of this 4-dimensional Universe sphere. More importantly, unlike the baking bread model one could not have a 'center' reference point on this surface. That is the Universe would be (to coin a term) 'isoacentric' and both the velocity property and the center property would hold simultaneously.

This raises another question. Given that the Universe is most likely to be the surface of a 4-dimensional sphere, how would contemporary physical theories define a flat and non-flat Universe? Therefore, it is advisable that one should develop cosmological models of the Universe in the context of a well-defined physical shape of the Universe. One could add that the baking bread model is symptomatic of the lack of research into the shape of the Universe. Such research could eliminate some of the theoretical cosmological models.

2.3 Only Compressive Particles Exist in Nature

For the sake of discussion, when particles increase in energy they can elongate (are tensile), contract (are compressive) or experience no change (are inelastic). Therefore, from the perspective of energy increase there are three types of particles, tensile, compressive and inelastic.

To arrive at equation (7), Solomon [2] & [4] model compressive particles that deformed under the space, time and mass deformations $\Gamma(a)$ in a gravitational field.

$$\Gamma(a) = 1 / \sqrt{(1 - 2GM / rc^2)} = x_0 / x_a = t_a / t_0 = m_a / m_0 \qquad (8)$$

Where and x, t & m are space, time and mass at infinity (with subscript 0) and at gravitational acceleration a (with subscript a) at a distance r from the gravitational source of mass M. The gravitational acceleration on any elementary particle is the internal effect of the deformation of the shape of the particle due to non-inertia transformations $\Gamma(a)$ present in the local region of the gravitational field such that the spacetime transfor-

---

[3] Google Dan Duriscoe's *Milky Way from Death Valley, California*, to see an excellent picture of our Milky Way.

[4] TV series *Cosmic Journey*, Episode 11, "Is the Universe Infinite?"

mations $\Gamma_{s(x,y,z,t)}$ are concurrently reflected as particle transformations $\Gamma_{p(x,y,z,t)}$ or,

$$\Gamma_{p(x,y,z,t)} = \Gamma_{s(x,y,z,t)} \tag{9}$$

String theories require particles be tensile because in string theories "particles" elongate when their energy is increased. The empirical evidence suggests the opposite. Consider a photon's wavelength. It decreases with increases in energy. Consider Lorentz-FitzGerald transformations $\Gamma(v)$ for space x, time t and mass m, at velocity v, equation (10). Length contracts with increased velocity or energy. Therefore, Lorentz-FitzGerald transformations require particles be compressive.

$$\Gamma(v) = 1\Big/\sqrt{\left(1 - v^2/c^2\right)} = x_0/x_v = t_v/t_0 = m_v/m_0 \tag{10}$$

One could presume that tidal gravity was the main influence in string theories' axiom that particles elongate with increased energy. Macro bodies elongate[5] as the body falls into a gravitational field, and one presumes that this elongation is the paradigm for this axiom. However, let's reexamine this tidal behavior with the additional requirement that this tidal gravity property be consistent with Lorentz-FitzGerald transformations or Special Theory of Relativity.

To be consistent with Lorentz-FitzGerald transformations, the atoms and elementary particles would contract in the direction of the fall. However, to be consistent with tidal gravity's elongation, the distances between atoms in the macro body has to increase at a rate consistent with the acceleration and velocities experienced by the various parts of the macro body. That is, as the atoms get flatter, the distances apart get longer. One suspects that this axiom's inconsistency with the empirical evidence has led to an explosion of string theories, each trying to explain Nature with no joy.

Nature favors compressive properties. Therefore tensile particles cannot exist is Nature. And by similar deduction inelastic particles per theories in quantum gravity cannot exist in Nature, too. If one is to pursue a particle-based theory of gravity, these particles need to have compressive properties. But the really important observation here is equation (9), that whatever deformation is locally present in spacetime, must be also observed by a particle in that same local region of spacetime.

2.4 Spacetime is More Sophisticated than a Continuum

Solomon [11] had proposed the 5-particle Box Paradox to show that spacetime could take on any length contraction and time dilation simultaneously, and concurrently. See Figure 1. The four particles, A, B, C and D form a square of length s under a specific set of conditions. A, B, C, and D, are at rest relative to each other. Their relative velocities are zero, and, therefore, no relativistic effects are present with respect to each other. From the perspective of particle D which has no relativistic effects, the distances of CD, S_{CD} and AD, S_{AD} are given by the respective equation (11),

$$S_{CD} = s \tag{11}$$

and by the hypotenuse of the right angled triangle, ACD, equation (12),

$$S_{AD} = s\sqrt{2} \tag{12}$$

Add a fifth particle, particle E. Particle E is moving at a velocity v along CD on a collision course with D. To eliminate any possibility of relative simultaneity we require particle E to collide with D. At the moment of collision, the distance between D and E, S_{DE} is zero.

$$S_{DE} = 0 \tag{13}$$

At this moment, E is aligned with D such that it, too, forms a four-sided shape with A, B and C, or ABCE. At this moment, since E is moving perpendicularly to B, the relative velocity between B and E, v_{BE} is zero.

$$v_{BE} = 0 \tag{14}$$

---

[5] This was attributed to Roger Penrose who, in the 1950s, proved this, however, this author could not find the reference in time for this paper.

However, from the perspective of particle E within the four-sided shape ABCE, E has relativistic effects along the x-axis CE and along the diagonal AE. The Lorentz-FitzGerald contraction dictates that particle E's measurement of CE, S_{CE} and AE, S_{AE} are determined by the respective relative velocities v_{CE} and v_{AE},

$$S_{CE} = s\sqrt{\left(1 - v_{CE}^{2}/c^{2}\right)} \tag{15}$$

and

$$S_{AE} = \left(s\sqrt{2}\right)\sqrt{\left(1 - v_{AE}^{2}/c^{2}\right)} \tag{16}$$

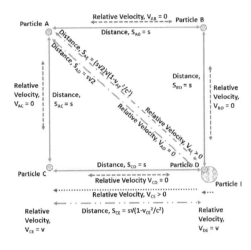

Note that particles A and C are one and the same for both particles D and E; and D and E are both at the same location. Therefore, the space between particles in this particle arrangement is the same.

The only logical resolution to the differences in distances is that the measurement of distance with respect to particles D and E are different due to their different relative velocities. That is, different relative velocities transform measurement of distances differently, per Lorentz-FitzGerald transformations.

The necessary inferences are that many different measurements, and therefore rulers, can co-exist in the same spacetime region. Further, spacetime as a continuum is a simplification of its true nature, and obviously spacetime is more sophisticated a structure than General Relativity requires.

Therefore, new theories on gravitational fields need to be able to account for different measurements in space for the same 'amount' of space.

2.5 Mass is a Proxy for Matter

As discussed in the Introduction, mass is a measure of the quantity of matter. However, digging deeper the question still remains, which part of matter causes the gravitational field?

One could divide matter into several components, electron shell, nuclei and quarks. Mass as a measure of quantity cannot distinguish between any of these three when matter is in its atomic state.

Therefore for discussion's sake, one could propose three possibilities. First, that gravity is caused by the electron-proton interaction between the electron shell and the nuclei. Second, the proton-neutron interaction within the nuclei is the cause of gravity. And third, that it is quark interaction within the protons and neutrons that cause the gravitational field.

Which is which? Contemporary theories on gravity generally focus of the field structure (of the source-field-effect schema). There isn't a theory or hypothesis that attempts to investigate the gravitational source that is not dependent upon mass as a proxy for the quantity of matter.

If there were, one could attempt to device experimental tests to falsify such hypotheses.

2.6 The Wave Function is Inconsistent

All particles, with and without mass, have wave functions that spread out into the region of space surrounding the particle. As a result, single and double slit experiments exhibit wave interference irrespective of whether particles are mass-based or not.

This would suggest that both photons and mass-based particles have similar, if not identical mechanisms for the wave function that is not originated from the mass of the particle.

However, photons travel at the velocity of light ($v_p=c$) and mass-based particles travel at less than that ($v_p<c$). To be consistent with Lorentz-FitzGerald and Special Theory of Relativity, anything traveling at the velocity of light must have zero thickness and cannot spread out like the wave function does in the direction of propagation.

The logical resolution is that the wave function has zero velocity $v_{wf}=0$, that it does not travel. The wave function is not moving. It is independent of v_p. A zero velocity $v_{wf}=0$ wave function is consistent with both types of particle velocities $v_p<c$ and $v_p=c$. How could Nature implement such a property?

Here is an analogy. Take a garden rake, turn it upside down and place it under a carpet. Move it. What does one observe?

The carpet exhibits a wave function like envelope bulge that appears to be moving in the direction the garden rake is moving.

But the bulge is not moving. It shows up wherever the garden rake is. The rake is moving but not the bulge. The bulge is simply a displacement of the carpet caused by the rake.

The wave function, like the carpet bulge is a displacement disturbance in spacetime caused by the presence of the particle. Therefore, the wave function is not moving and therefore it spreads across the spacetime where the photon or particle is.

This zero-velocity bulge-like wave function is consistent with Einstein's Special Theory of Relativity and with the empirical Lorentz-FitzGerald transformations.

The Standard Model is successful because, just as the shape of the carpet bulge is unique to the shape of the garden rake, so are the wave function displacement disturbances of spacetime unique to the properties of the respective particles.

That is, the Standard Model correctly describes a particle's signature displacement disturbance in spacetime, but not the particle itself.

Therefore, any new theory on gravitational fields or particles, will have to account for particle displacement disturbance of spacetime.

2.7 Particle Probability is not Gaussian

Extensive numerical analysis [14] & [15] of the Airy disc, involving comparing the intensity dispersion with known and new statistical distributions confirms that photon localization on the Airy disc at some distance from the pin hole, is governed by a single probability field described as the 'spatial probability field'. This probability field is described by a *variable* Gamma distribution along the radius, orthogonal to photon propagation. It is thus named the Var-Gamma distribution.

The Gamma distribution is determined by the shape and scale parameters $\alpha>0$ and $\beta>0$, respectively in equation (17),

$$f(r) = \frac{1}{\beta\Gamma(\alpha)}\left(\frac{r}{\beta}\right)^{\alpha-1}e^{-r/\beta} \qquad (17)$$

In the Var-Gamma distribution, the shape and scale parameters are not constants, but functions of the orthogonal radius r, as follows,

$$\alpha = r \qquad (18)$$

$$\beta = r/\sqrt{u} \qquad (19)$$

$$u = \pi/\lambda D_A \sin(\theta) \qquad (20)$$

where the intensity of the photons passing through a pinhole, and hitting the visual plane screen is described by I the transmitted intensity of light on the visual plane as a function of the angle θ, the angle between the perpendicular from pinhole and screen, to the hypotenuse from the pinhole, λ is wavelength of light photon, DA is aperture diameter of the pinhole and r is radius of the Airy pattern concentric circle on the visual plane screen.

That is, if the standard hypothesis is that the photon probability is Gaussian, there now is an alternative hypothesis, it is not. It is a Var-Gamma distribution. The power of the Var-Gamma distribution is that it lends itself to the unification of shielding, transmission, and

Shielding Effectiveness

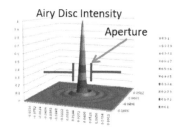

Shielding Effectiveness, SE_p, is defined as the ability to stop photon propagation through holes of radius r in the material. Or ratio of probability outside the hole to the total.

$$SE_p = 10\log_{10}\left[\frac{P_\infty}{P_{\leq r}}\right] = 10\log_{10}\left[\frac{1}{P_{\leq r}}\right]$$

Figure 2(a). Photon shielding.

invisibility as a single phenomenon, with the further clarification that cloaking and resolution are variations of the transmission phenomenon. See Figures 2(a),(b) &(c).

And squeezing the Var-Gamma distribution leads to a new definition of invisibility that is similar to neutrino behavior; that squeezing the spatial probability field results in a smaller spatial probability field and lowers the probability that the photon will interact with its surrounding environment.

The observation here is that there exists a single volume spatial probability field in spacetime that governs photon localization in space. Therefore, a new theory on gravitational fields will need to account for spatial probability fields as a consistent property of spacetime.

2.8 Spectrum Independent Photon Analytics

Radio antennas [12] exhibit a skin effect that the electromagnetic energy inside the antenna goes to zero. Where else in the nanowire [13] no skin effect is present. Using the new Var-Gamma distribution, Solomon [14] & [15] showed that it is possible to get similar nanowire behavior as Oulton, Sorger, Genov, Pile, & Zhang [13] if the nanowire is treated as a radio antenna. That the light photon in a nanowire behaves in the same manner as a radio wave in a radio antenna.

This suggests that photon interaction with matter is related to the ratio λ/d of the photon wavelength λ to orthogonal distance d to the surrounding region. Therefore, radio wave properties can be translated to microwave, optical and higher frequencies, by taking into account this λ/d ratio. Further, research is necessary, but it is quite clear [11] that a spectrum independent photon analytics will soon be a reality.

The inconsistency here is that unlike our physical theories, the photon does not "know" it is a radio wave, microwave, infrared, light, ultraviolet, x-ray or gamma ray. The photon as a single type of particle is responding to the physical structure of its environment in a manner that is consistent across the electromagnetic spectrum. Therefore, our physical theories need to comprehend photon analytics in an all-encompassing manner, too.

2.9 Consistency Between Γ(v) and Γ(a)

A body falling in a gravitational field from infinity (where t_∞ is time dilation at infinity) has both acceleration a and velocity v. Solomon [2] & [4] showed that the gravitational time dilation derived from the non-inertia transformation $\Gamma(a)$ produces the correct instantaneous free fall velocity when plugged into the inertia transformation $\Gamma(v)$. That these transformations are consistent in some manner or that the time dilations as a function of acceleration $t(a)$ and time dilation as a function of velocity $t(v)$ are equal or $t(a) = t(v)$. To state it differently, the Lorentz-FitzGerald transformations of flat spacetime is observable in non-flat gravitational fields and this could be considered evidence that local space is Lorentzian.

However, Misner, Thorne, & Wheeler [4] point to elementary particle experiments that demonstrate time measured by atomic clocks depend only on velocity and not on acceleration; but by the principle of equivalence that all effects of a uniform gravitational field are identical to the effects of a uniform acceleration of the coordinate system, one could propose that the time dilation $t(a)$ derived from $\Gamma(a)$ and the time dilation $t(v)$ derived by $\Gamma(v)$ should not be correlated or $t(a) \neq t(v)$ should in general be true. This is contrary to the empirical evidence [2] & [4].

Transmission(Cloaking) Effectiveness

Cloaking Effectiveness, CE_p, is defined as the ratio of the distribution that is present outside the obstruction of radius r to the total, i.e. the probability distribution that 'escapes' around the disc or obstruction.

$$CE_p = 10\log_{10}\left[\frac{P_\infty}{P_{\geq r}}\right] = 10\log_{10}\left[\frac{1}{P_{\geq r}}\right]$$

Figure 2(b). Photon transmission.

Therefore, the derivation of time dilation from the non-inertia $\Gamma(a)$ demonstrates that in addition to the principle of equivalence, in free fall Nature requires inertia $\Gamma(v)$ relationships to be consistent with non-inertia $\Gamma(a)$ relationships;   that these two transformations are not separate from or independent of each other. This consistency holds even when inertia motion is not a degenerated special case of non-inertia motion because it is verifiable for any acceleration a and velocity v ($|v| \ll c$).

One infers firstly, that the nature of transformations govern time dilation, length contraction, mass increase, velocity, and acceleration. Second, that $\Gamma(v)$ and $\Gamma(a)$ co-exist in a manner that is consistent with each other and possibly imply that other (as yet unknown) transformations may exist consistently with these two. Third, for there to be consistency, the inertia $\Gamma(v)$ and non-inertia $\Gamma(a)$ transformations are specific properties of something more general, the Non-Inertia Ni field, a spatial gradient of time dilations and thus a spatial gradient of velocities. And therefore fourth, that $\Gamma(v)$ and $\Gamma(a)$ are different representations of this Ni field. Therefore, this $\Gamma(a)$ & $\Gamma(v)$ consistency could be used to test for real versus theoretical gravitational fields. Therefore, any new theory of gravitational fields must account for these Ni field consistencies.

2.10 Forces are Not Transmitted by Virtual Particles

Solomon [2] & [4] constructed extensive numerical models of an elementary particle in gravitational field that obeyed the gravitational transformation $\Gamma(a)$ equation (8). Equation (8) necessarily requires that particles are compressive and this extensive numerical modeling led to the discovery of equation (7) $g=\tau c^2$.

Briefly, τ the change in time dilation divided by the height across this change is described as a Non Inertia Ni field, a spatial gradient of time dilations and thus a spatial gradient of velocities. Solomon [2] & [4] showed that equation (7) correctly evaluated gravitational, electromagnetic and mechanical accelerations, which neither quantum or string theories have been able to achieve to date. This shows that macro forces are not transmitted by exchange of particles, but are present where Ni fields are. Therefore, any new theory of gravitational fields will be similar to General Relativity but will evolve from Ni field considerations.

2.11 Photon Structure should be Consistent with Special Theory

In §2.6 above, an alternative wave function concept was proposed that would be consistent with Special Theory of Relativity. One can apply the same logic [11] to the electromagnetic transverse wave. Since the transverse wave is travelling at the velocity of light c by Lorentz-FitzGerald transformation, its thickness must be zero in the direction of propagation but this is not the case with the transverse wave.

Both the electric and magnetic field components are zero thickness vectors whose magnitudes oscillates sinusoidally between -100% and +100% of field strength in phase with each other. The Lorentz-FitzGerald zero thickness requirement combined with the in phase property necessarily implies that the total energy oscillates between 0% and 100% of the transverse wave energy. But total energy cannot be created or destroyed. Therefore, logic requires that this energy is transformed in such a manner that it is conserved but not observable with our contemporary theories.

To solve this apparent destruction/creation problem Solomon [11] proposed that the Universe consists of at least two kenos (Greek for vacuous), or overlapping layers or regions. The first kenos is the familiar spacetime continuum K(x, y, z, t), the second is subspace K'(x, y, z) a type of spacetime that does not have the time dimension.

Spacetime and subspace, under specific conditions (see §2.12), are joined at the common (x, y, z) coordinates. That is, the intersection of spacetime and subspace is not an empty set, and both (x, y, z) positions map one-to-one. The subspace kenos concept then allows for the conservation of energy by requiring the electric and magnetic vectors to rotate from spacetime through subspace, and back into spacetime per rotation. Necessarily these vectors are 90^0 out of phase between spacetime and subspace. The projection of this rotation in spacetime is then observed as electromagnetic transverse waves.

This model of the photon is now consistent with both Lorentz-FitzGerald transformations and conservation of mass-energy, right down to the minute vector components. Therefore, contemporary electromagnetic

Invisibility Effectiveness

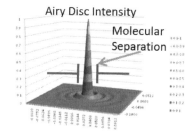

Invisibility Effectiveness, IE_p, is defined as the ability to pass through the spaces between atoms and molecules of radius r without interacting with the material. The ratio of the distribution that pass through the molecular separation to the total.

$$IE_p = 10\log_{10}\left[\frac{P_{\leq r}}{P_\infty}\right] = 10\log_{10}\left[P_{\leq r}\right]$$

Figure 2(c). Photon invisibility

transverse wave photon models are inconsistent with Special Theory of Relativity and the Lorentz FitzGerald transformations. Addressing this inconsistency has led to the proposal of two new properties of the Universe that of kenos and of subspace. Therefore, any new theory of gravitational fields will need to incorporate the concept of kenos.

2.12 How are Probabilities Implemented in Nature?

Neither quantum theory nor string theories have addressed this question. The basic approach in contemporary theories has been, that there is this Gaussian formula that dictates how probabilities behave. This is not the same as asking the question, how are probabilities implemented in Nature? This paper proposes that the photon's spatial probability field exists as a joined spacetime and subspace structure. That spacetime by itself is not probabilistic, and probabilities are only observable in that region where subspace is joined to spacetime.

From the perspective of the photon's structure, one possible inference is that photons can modify spacetime. The numerical modeling [14] suggests that the photon's spatial probability field is of a large volume, 32m in radius and approximately 100,000 km long. This probability field changes direction with the direction of the photon propagation and suggests that the photon is able to modify spacetime around itself to maintain this probability field. That is, just as mass is able to modify spacetime to deformed it gravitationally, photons and other particles are able to modify spacetime by joining subspace to spacetime, in the region of the spatial probability field.

Since, in the plane orthogonal to motion, the probability of photon localization $P(L)$ along any orthogonal radius is governed by the Var-Gamma probability distribution, one can propose that in this orthogonal plane, localization is necessarily independent of time. That is, the photon does not move to that point where it localizes. It can localize anywhere simultaneously and instantaneously within the spatial probability field.

Therefore, one infers that the probability field is absent of the time dimension, and that the large volume spatial probability field comes about by the photon modifying that specific volume of space such as to remove any effects of time to itself within this volume. Equation (21) illustrates this probability of localization $P(L)$ as a function ρ of spatial coordinates x, y, $\&$ z.

$$P(L) = \rho(x, y, z) \qquad (21)$$

That is, the probability of localization is the property of the subspace kenos $K'(x, y, z)$ as the time dimension is missing. Given that localization is simultaneously & instantaneously realizable, would suggest two more properties for this probability field. First, that any information I (Greek letter iota) within this probability field is simultaneously & instantaneously present everywhere in this field. That is, given any two random points within this large volume probability field, the information $I(x_A, y_A, z_A)$ at point A must be identical to the information $I(x_B, y_B, z_B)$ at point B.

$$I(x_A, y_A, z_A) = I(x_B, y_B, z_B) \qquad (22)$$

The photon is able to modify or apply a transformation Φ to spacetime $S(x,y,z,t)$ such that spacetime is converted into a large volume spatial probability field $\rho(x,y,z)$.

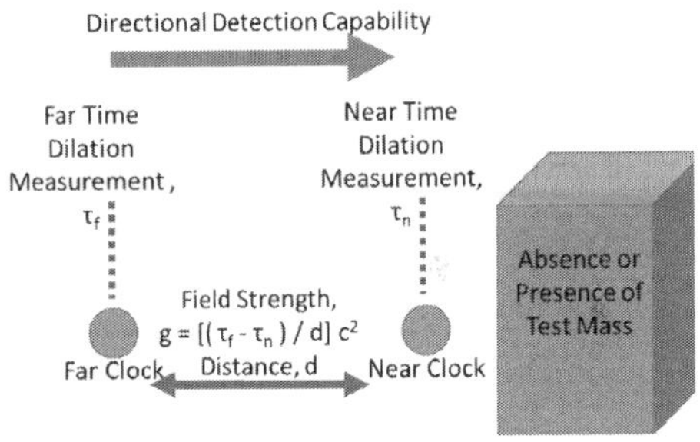

Directional Detection Capability

Far Time Dilation Measurement, τ_f

Near Time Dilation Measurement, τ_n

Field Strength, $g = [(\tau_f - \tau_n) / d] c^2$

Far Clock Distance, d Near Clock

Absence or Presence of Test Mass

Figure 3. Near Field Gravity Probe.

$$P(L) = \Phi S(x, y, z, t) = \rho(x, y, z) \qquad (23)$$

In effect making the subspace kenos accessible from the spacetime kenos. But equation (21) is not a sufficient condition for the probability field because by the Var-Gamma distribution, probability of localization $P(L_{r1})$ is less, at a radial distance r_1 further away from the axis of motion than the probability of localization $P(L_{r2})$ where it is nearer r_2 such that,

$$P(L_{r1}) < P(L_{r2}) \quad \text{for } r_1 > r_2 \qquad (24)$$

That there is a deformation present in subspace that alters the probabilistic behavior but not the x, y $\&$ z dimensions or the information content $I(x,y,z)$. Suggesting that space has more properties than just spatial x, y $\&$ z. Without time t, subspace has the ability to deform in such a manner as to exhibit a probability field. And without time it also has the ability to exhibit information $I(x,y,z)$ simultaneously & instantaneously across a region that has been transformed into a probability field.

That is, spacetime is a very much more sophisticated structure than just a 4-dimensional continuum, and is capable of multiple measurements, multiple kenoses, and probability fields. There is also, a much closer relationship between spacetime and particle structure, and any new theory on gravity needs to account for these.

3. New Instruments & New Experiments

Any new hypothesis needs to be falsifiable. Therefore, one method of testing a new hypothesis is to propose new experiments or instruments. This paper proposes three tests, the near field gravity probe, the gravity wave telescope, and the non-locality test.

3.1 The Near Field Gravity Probe

Recent attempts to measure [16], [17], [18], [19], [20], the gravitational constant G has not led to a single value. Unlike direct measurements of force using torsion balance, laser interferometer, pendulums, torsion pendulums, this paper proposes a new method using time dilations. This is possible as equation (7) provides for measuring gravitational acceleration directly by measuring the change in time dilation. See Figure 3.

The experimental set up consists of two clocks, near and far, to measure the effect of time dilation in the presence of the test mass. In the absence of test mass both clocks should have the same time dilations. Approximately, the total noise N_T in the time dilations can be attributed to three parts, equipment noise N_E, local environmental noise N_L and stellar & galactic noise N_G, per equation (25)

$$N_T = N_E + N_L + N_G \tag{25}$$

If the clocks are identical and close together the equipment noise N_E and local environmental noise N_L are essentially identical, and can be reduced to a combine noise N_C. The galactic noise measured by the near and far clocks can be denote as N_{Gn} and N_{Gf}. The local time dilation without the test mass is denoted by τ_0. Or the measurements of near τ_n and far τ_f time dilations are

$$\tau_n = \tau_0 + N_C + N_{Gn} \tag{26}$$

$$\tau_f = \tau_0 + N_C + N_{Gf} \tag{27}$$

Therefore, the equation (7) requires the difference in time dilations τ_n-τ_f divided by the separation d of the two clocks, giving,

$$g = \left(N_{Gn} - N_{Gf}\right)c^2 \Big/ d \tag{28}$$

That is, the error attributed to this measurement is due to galactic noise. When the test mass is present and alters the near and far time dilations by δ_n and δ_f gives

$$g = \left[\left(\delta_n - \delta_f\right) + \left(N_{Gn} - N_{Gf}\right)\right]c^2 \Big/ d \tag{29}$$

This method eliminates the equipment and local noise while recognizing that galactic noise can alter measurement results. G can then be calculated since one knows the new horizontal acceleration g. By observing N_{Gn}-N_{Gf} over a period of a year, one can determine the minimum mass required of the test mass to arrive at a stable repeatable G.

3.2 Gravity Wave Telescope

The proposed gravity wave telescope, Figure 4, inverts the proposed near field gravity probe into a telescope as one is needs to measure the galactic noise, N_G or τ_G.

Assuming that the clocks are fairly close, the signal τ_G one is interested is the galactic noise, N_G. Since the clocks are some distance d apart, the far clock receives the same signal τ_{Gf} delayed by d/c. To process the signal of interest requires a 2-pass method. First to minus out the equipment and local noise from both signals. These signals will have no delays. Second to match far signal τ_{Gf} to the near signal τ_{Gn} by introducing the d/c delay into the near signal. This gives an amplified signal τ_{Ga},

$$\tau_{Ga} = \left(\tau_{Gn} + \tau_{Gf}\right) \tag{30}$$

458

This method allows for directional searches as the separation between the two clocks provides a means to filtering out all other galactic signals. If the clocks are much further apart such that the local environmental noise N_L is no longer the same, one can eliminate this noise by removing any signals that don't appear on the other clock, or remove any signals having delays that are greater than d/c removed.

3.3 Non-Locality Test

The Airy disc is proof that the spatial probability field exists. What is of interest to test is the spatial behavior, equation (24) to the information hypothesis, equation (22). Locality [21] demands the conservation of causality, meaning that information cannot be exchanged between two space-like separated parties or actions. Quantum entanglement [22] can be described as non-local interactions or the idea that distant particles do interact without the hidden variables. The information hypothesis, equation (22) suggest that non-locality is a property of the subspace kenos, just as causality is a property of the spacetime kenos.

By equation (24), the strength of the spatial probability field decreases with the radius that is orthogonal to propagation. Then the ability to maintain information (22) should reduce with the orthogonal radius as the strength of the spatial probability field reduces (24). If non-locality is due to the information hypothesis (22) one could use quantum entanglement to test for this information hypothesis. That is, information between point A and point B is preserved when localization occurs or,

$$\text{I}(x_A, y_A, z_A) = \text{I}(x_B, y_B, z_B)\big|_{P(L)=1} \quad (31)$$

And information is not preserved when localization cannot occur, as the strength of the spatial probability field has been significantly reduced or,

$$\text{I}(x_A, y_A, z_A) \neq \text{I}(x_B, y_B, z_B)\big|_{P(L)=0} \quad (32)$$

Therefore, if quantum entanglement is due to the spatial probability field, one should be able to observe a degradation in observable quantum entanglement as the orthogonal distance between two entangled photons are increased.

Assuming that entangle photons have a joint probability distribution, using extensive numerical modeling Solomon [14] showed that this joint distribution reduces as the two entangled photons are separated orthogonally. See Figure 5(a), (b) & (c). The average joint probability within the orthogonal cross section areas (16m^2, 16m^2 & 64m^2) shown is 8.3%, 8.2% & 1.6% for 0.1m, 0.4m & 2.6m separations, respectively. The joint probabilities approximately 0.0% when the separations is greater than 12m for red light wavelength $\lambda = 700$nm per the Airy disc parameters $\lambda/D_A = 2$, $D_P = 100$mm.

Figure 4. Gravity Wave Telescope.

Directional Detection Capability

Far Time Dilation Measurement   Near Time Dilation Measurement

Far Clock   Near Clock

Incoming Gravity Wave

Distance d

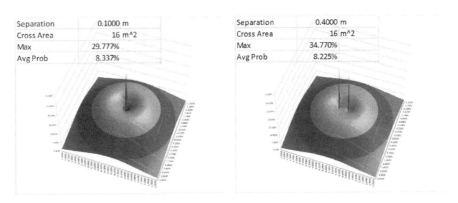

Separation	0.1000 m
Cross Area	16 m^2
Max	29.777%
Avg Prob	8.337%

Separation	0.4000 m
Cross Area	16 m^2
Max	34.770%
Avg Prob	8.225%

Figure 5(a). Joint Probability at 0.1m Separation.

Figure 5(b). Joint Probability at 0.4m Separation.

The work of other experimenters, [22], [23], [24], [25], [26] were reviewed for physical layout. Except for Howell [22] very little information of the physical layout of these experiments are provided. Howell's experimental set up was ≤0.5m across and one infers that Aspect's [23] and Yao's [24] experiments were on the order of 6m and 1m, respectively. The exception to these experiments is Tittel *et al.* [27] 10km experiment in Geneva, which appears to confirm quantum entanglement at 10km except that in this experiment returning photons are required and therefore overlapping probability fields were present. To exclude the effects of the spatial probability field, some restrictions on physical layout of entanglement experiments, are necessary. (1) Entangled photons travelling in parallel must be >32m apart. (2) Entanglement testing cannot be done when photons are coming together head on as their probability fields overlap. (3) Photons are only allowed to be reflected away from each other as reflection of the probability field is not fully understood at this time. (4) There can be no other reflections other than returning the photons to parallel paths. And, (5) No returning photons as their probability fields would interfere with the test.

A weak confirmation requires, entanglement substantially ceases to exist when two entangled photons are orthogonally separated by a distance of 32m, this would prove that the spatial probability field and the subspace kenos are the mechanisms for non-locality. A stronger confirmation requires that the degradation in observable entanglement should be governed by the joint distribution per Figure 5(a), (b) & (c), and would prove the existence of the joint distribution.

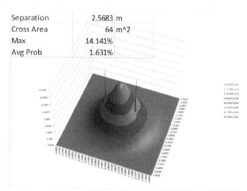

Separation	2.5683	m
Cross Area	64	m^2
Max	14.141%	
Avg Prob	1.631%	

Figure 5(c). Joint Probability at 2.6m Separation.

4. Conclusion

Twelve inconsistencies have been documented and where possible alternative solutions have been proposed. As a result it is possible to propose two new instruments, and a test for non-locality. The first instrument, the near field gravity probe, provides a means of measuring G, without moving parts, stress, tension or torsion and a means to define the minimum mass required of the test mass to determine repeatable measurements of G. The second instrument, the gravity wave telescope, has the ability to directionally seek gravity waves as two clocks are used in a sequential manner. Finally, this paper has proposed a non-locality test that could substantiate the existence of the subspace kenos, and the mechanism for particle probabilities.

Previous Publication Note

This paper was first published in Special Issue on Gravitation, Astrophysics and Cosmology, Journal of Modern Physics, Volume 4, Number 8A, August 2013, and presented at the 2013 100 Year Starship Symposium. http://www.scirp.org/journal/PaperDownload.aspx?paperID=36276

References

1. R. Nemiroff, "Bounds on Spectral Dispersion from Fermi-detected Gamma Ray Bursts", Phys. Rev. Lett. 108, 231103 (2012) http://dx.doi.org/10.1103/PhysRevLett.108.231103

2. B.T. Solomon, "Gravitational Acceleration Without Mass And Noninertia Fields", Physics Essays, Vol. 24, 327, 2011. http://dx.doi.org/10.4006/1.3595113

3. C.W. Misner, K.S. Thorne, J.A. Wheeler, "Gravitation" (W.H. Freeman and Company, New York, NY, 1973).

4. B.T. Solomon, "An Approach to Gravity Modification as a Propulsion Technology," in the proceedings of the Space, Propulsion & Energy Sciences International Forum (SPESIF-09), Edited by Glen A Robertson, AIP Conference Proceedings 1103, Melville, New York, (2009). http://scitation.aip.org/proceedings/confproceed/1103.jsp

5. E. Podkletnov, "Weak gravitational shielding properties of composite bulk YBa2Cu3O7-x superconductor below 70K under e.m. field," lanl.gov, (1997).

6. E. Podkletnov, R. Nieminen, "A Possibility of Gravitational Force Shielding by Bulk YBa2Cu3O7-x Su-

perconductor" Physica C, 203, (1992), pp. 441-444. http://dx.doi.org/10.1016/0921-4534(92)90055-H

7. B.T. Solomon, "Reverse Engineering Podkletnov's Experiments," in the proceedings of the Space, Propulsion & Energy Sciences International Forum (SPESIF-11), Edited by Glen A Robertson, Physics Procedia, Elsevier Science. http://www.sciencedirect.com/science/journal/18753892/20

8. R.C. Woods, S.G. Cooke, J. Helme, C.H. Caldwell, "Gravity Modification by High-Temperature Superconductors", in the proceedings of the 37th AIAA/ASME/SAE/ASSEE Joint Propulsion Conference & Exhibit, 8-11 July, 2001, Salt Lake City, Utah.

9. G. Hathaway, B. Cleveland and Y. Bao., "Gravity Modification Experiments Using a Rotating Superconducting Disk and Radio Frequency Fields", Physica C, Volume 385, Issue 4, p. 488-500.

10. H. Bondi, "Negative Mass in General Relativity", Reviews of Modern Physics, Vol. 29, No. 3, July 1957. http://dx.doi.org/10.1103/RevModPhys.29.423

11. B.T. Solomon, An Introduction to Gravity Modification: A guide to using Laithwaite's and Podkletnov's experiments and the physics of forces for empirical results. Universal Publishers, Boca Raton, 2012. http://www.universal-publishers.com/book.php?method=ISBN&book=1612330894

12. W. C. Elmore, and M.A. Heald, Physics of Waves, Dover Publications, New York, (1985), p. 241.

13. R.F. Oulton, V.J. Sorger, D.A. Genov, D.F.P. Pile, and X. Zhang, "A hybrid plasmonic waveguide for subwavelength confinement and long-range propogation," Nature Photonics, 2, August 2008

14. B.T. Solomon, "Non-Gaussian Photon Probability Distributions," in the proceedings of the Space, Propulsion & Energy Sciences International Forum (SPESIF-10), Edited by Glen A Robertson, AIP Conference Proceedings 1208, Melville, New York, (2010). http://scitation.aip.org/proceedings/confproceed/1208.jsp

15. B.T. Solomon, "Non-Gaussian Radiation Shielding," in the proceedings of the 100 Year Starship Study Public Symposium (100YSS), 2011.

16. E.S. Reich, "G-whizzes disagree over gravity", Nature 466, 1030 (2010) http://dx.doi.org/10.1038/4661030a

17. J. H. Gundlach, and S. M. Merkowitz, "Measurement of Newton's Constant Using a Torsion Balance with Angular Acceleration Feedback" Phys. Rev. Lett. 85, 2869 (2000). http://dx.doi.org/10.1103/PhysRevLett.85.2869

18. H. V. Parks and J. E. Faller, "A Simple Pendulum Determination of the Gravitational Constant" Phys. Rev. Lett. http://xxx.lanl.gov/abs/1008.3203 (2010).

19. Jun Luo, Qi Liu, Liang-Cheng Tu, Cheng-Gang Shao, Lin-Xia Liu, Shan-Qing Yang, Qing Li, and Ya-Ting Zhang, "Determination of the Newtonian Gravitational Constant G with Time-of-Swing Method" Phys. Rev. Lett. 102, 240801 (2009). http://dx.doi.org/10.1103/PhysRevLett.102.240801

20. St. Schlamminger, E. Holzschuh, W. Kündig, F. Nolting, R. E. Pixley, J. Schurr, and U. Straumann. "Measurement of Newton's gravitational constant", Phys. Rev. D 74, 082001 (2006). http://dx.doi.org/10.1103/PhysRevD.74.082001

21. M.D. Eisaman, E.A. Goldschmidt, J. Chen, J. Fan, and A. Migdall, "Experimental test of nonlocal realism using a fiber-based source of polarization-entangled photon pairs," Phys. Rev. A, 77, (2008), p. 032339. http://dx.doi.org/10.1103/PhysRevA.77.032339

22. J.C. Howell, R.S. Bennink, S.J. Bentley, and R.W. Boyd, "Realization of the Einstein-Podolsky-Rosen Paradox Using Momentum and Position-Entangled Photons from Spontaneous Parametric Down Conversion," Phys. Rev. Lett., 92(21), (2004), pp. 210403-1-4. http://dx.doi.org/10.1103/PhysRevLett.92.210403

    A. Aspect, J. Dalibard, and G. Roger, "Experimental Test of Bell's Inequalities Using Time-Varying Analyzer," Phys. Rev. Lett., 49(25), (1982), pp. 1804 – 1807. http://dx.doi.org/10.1103/PhysRevLett.49.1804

23. E. Yao, S. Franke-Arnold, J. Courtial, and M.J. Padgett, "Observation od quantum entanglement using spatial light modulators," Optics Express, 14(26), (2006). http://dx.doi.org/10.1364/OE.14.013089

24. T. Yarnall, A.F. Abouraddy, B.E.A. Saleh, and M.C. Teich, "Experimental Violation of Bell's Inequality in Spatial-Parity Space," Phys Rev. Lett., 99, (2007), p. 170408. http://dx.doi.org/10.1103/PhysRevLett.99.170408

25. J. Leach, B. Jack, J. Romero, M. Rirsch-Marte, R.W. Boyd, A.K. Jha, S.M. Barnett, S. Franke-Arnold, and M.J. Padgett, "Violation of a Bell inequality in two-dimensional orbital angular momentum stat-spaces," Optics Express, 17(10), (2009). http://dx.doi.org/10.1364/OE.17.008287

26. W. Tittel, J. Brendel, B. Gisin, T. Herzog, H. Zbinden, and N. Gisin, "Experimental demonstration of quantum-correlations over more than 10 kilometers," Phys. Rev. A, 57, (1998), p. 3229. http://dx.doi.org/10.1103/PhysRevA.57.3229

The Astrobiological Matrix: Minimizing the Trauma of First Contact

Paul Ziolo, PhD

Senior Research Fellow, University of Liverpool

m.p.f.ziolo@gmail.com

Abstract

"Any future encounter between humanity and an extraterrestrial civilisation will likely end in a fiasco"
(Stanisław Lem)

As the human species spreads into outer space, the likelihood of detecting evidence of, or of eventual contact with, an advanced technological civilisation (ATC) of extraterrestrial origin will exponentially increase, though it is doubtful whether we will either detect or make contact with a civilisation of this type while we remain a planet-bound species, nor whether we are as yet sufficiently mature as a species to survive the challenge of such an encounter, should it occur. Nevertheless, Lem's pessimistic prognosis could be avoided if future interstellar pioneers were adequately prepared for this eventuality. A better understanding of "alien" psychology would be enhanced by relinquishing the "species-narcissism" from which much human thinking is prone, and by adopting an ideational outlook that emphasises the mutability and contextuality of "Being" as implied by the astrobiological matrix. Such an outlook may challenge some very fundamental "humanistic" assumptions. This paper will show how the "Drake Equation" may continue to function as an evolving Bayesian heuristic that will incorporate knowledge as further advances are made in exoplanet discovery and in the evolutionary and biological sciences. The implications of the Lineweaver studies on the Galactic Habitable Zone (GHZ) and the possible concentration of ATC's in the Milky Way will be addressed, as well as the likely range of biologies implied by Kauffman's analysis of autocatalytic sets and the universality classes comprising CHONPS-based lifeforms. Consideration of hypothetical evolutionary trajectories of advanced chordate (arthropodic) intelligence may serve as an example.

1. What Does It Mean to Be "Human"?

Fig. 1. The Mir Space Station

According to reports of the Shuttle-Mir mission STS-63, when the American shuttle crew first had sight of the Mir space station (Fig. 1 above), their first impression was that "it had come from another universe" (Dumoulin 2001). Evidently, the Russian solutions to space station technology seemed completely alien to the Americans – even if this technology "worked". Of course, Russian ad American space programs originate from different research traditions – Von Braun vs. Tsiolkovsky, yet if two human groups have difficulty understanding one another's" technologies, what would happen were we to meet a totally alien, extraterrestrial technology – one that in all probability would be far more advanced? Many well-known SF stories explore the less than felicitous consequences of such a scenario including Roadside Picnic (Пикник на обочине), written by the Strugatsky brothers and published in 1971, numerous stores and novels by Stanisław Lem (*Solaris* (1961), *His Master's Voice* (1968), *Fiasco* (1987) etc.) as well as Carl Sagan's *Contact* (1985) and Iain Banks' *Excession* (1996).

As a species still in the course of emerging from its primal evolutionary matrix, humanity has a sell-image problem – one of extreme narcissism. While this trait proved useful for humanity's emergence on the Environment of Evolutionary Adaptiveness (EEA), it may decidedly prove less than useful in our exploration of the Cosmos beyond Earth.

Fig. 2. Earth as seen from Mars
(composite image from the Mars Exploration Rover Spirit, 63rd day of the mission,)

Fig. 2 above, the only authenticated NASA image of Earth from our nearest true planetary neighbour, Mars, may convey some impression of our visual "impact" on the Solar System. It is by no means obvious at this distance that there is any evidence of "intelligent life" on Earth.

Nevertheless, the likelihood of detecting evidence of, or of eventual contact with, an advanced technological civilisation (ATC) of extraterrestrial origin will exponentially increase as we expand into space, though it is doubtful whether we will ever detect or make contact with a civilisation of this type while we remain a planet-bound species, nor whether we are as yet sufficiently mature as a species to survive the challenge of such an encounter, should it occur. If the word "human" is taken to mean "that which is grown from earth" (>Lat. "humus" → "humanus'), i.e. the chreod (see below) or species variant that finally emerged from its home world', then when such an encounter does finally occur, we should not be surprised to find that the "alien" in question will consider itself to be "human", in the sense of "we who have finally emerged from our original biological matrix". The species will consider itself to embody all "truly human" values, no matter how many tentacles of multi-facetted eyes its original form may possess.

2. The Continuity Thesis.

The "continuity thesis" has been advanced by a number of scientists and philosophers (see for instance: Fry 1995; Gardner 2004; Ćirković 2012), and holds that 1) there is no discontinuity between so-called "inanimate" and "living" matter, 2) there is no discontinuity between the simplest sensorimotor reaction of the mist primitive unicellular organisms and the most "profound" or "advanced" manifestations of "intelligent thought and 3) the evolution of consciousness (or "sentience" itself) proceeds without radical discontinuities (Fig. 3 below). Furthermore, biological life itself may simply be one of many transitional stages between "inert" and "fully sentient" matter. We find ourselves now approaching a critical point in the evolution of the "machinic phylum" (Deleuze & Guattari 1987; Johnston 2008) where levels of human and machine intelligence seem to be approaching convergence. "The Machine will not dominate the Human: Human and Machine will become One" (Sandberg 2013), but what form this synthesis may take is still unclear.

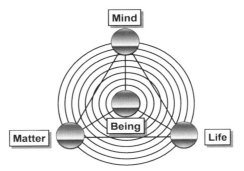

Fig. 3. The Continuity Thesis

3. The Encyclopedia Galactica: Perspectives on Humanity.

Fig. 4 below shows the Hertzsprung-Russell Diagram of stellar evolution with the approximate position of Sol (our Sun) as an average G2-spectral class star on the "main sequence".

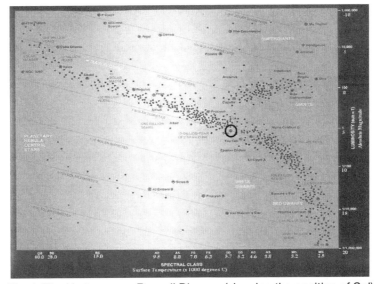

Fig. 4. The Hertzsprung-Russell Diagram(showing the position of Sol)

Main sequence stars with spectral classes ranging from F0 → K9 have lifetimes guaranteed long enough to permit the genesis & evolution of biospheres – and eventually, ATC's. This is not to say that biospheres cannot evolve outside this range – just that biospheres within this range are optimal in terms of our current knowledge of biology and astrobiology. Nucleosynthesis in stellar interiors involves the conversion of helium to carbon according to the sequence $3He4 \rightarrow C12 + 2\gamma$, an essential step in the creation of organic, carbon-based life. But this step would normally proceed far too slowly for carbon to be synthesised at a rate consistent with its demonstrated abundance in the Universe. Burbidge et al. (1957) showed however, that this reaction in fact proceeds with the aid of a beryllium catalyst (Be8) as follows:

$$2He^4 + (99 \pm 6)KeV \rightarrow Be^8$$
$$Be^8 + He^4 \rightarrow C^{12} + 2\gamma$$

Eq. 1.

The energy level of C12 (7.6549 MeV) lies just above that of Be8 + H4 (7.3667 MeV) permitting a reaction to take place within the resonance level 7.656 ± 0.008 MeV. Furthermore, the O16 nucleus has an energy level of 7.1187 MeV lying just below that of C12 + He4 (7.1616 MeV) thus stabilising this reaction by inhibiting the rapid depletion of all carbon to oxygen through alpha capture via C12 + He4 → O16. Such "fine tuning" of resonance levels provides further evidence of how "auspicious" the "laws" of physics would seem to be in relation to the emergence of organic life.

Photons emitted at the fusion core of a star reach the surface by traversing a "random walk" produced by collisions and deflections by other particles (electrons and charged ions). The Thomson cross-section (σT) for the effect of electron-induced scattering is $\sigma T \sim \alpha 2me-2$ with the mean free path (i. e. λ - the average distance) travelled by photons between collisions) being $\lambda \sim (\sigma Tne)-1$ with an electron number density ne $\sim$ NR-3. Under these conditions, the time taken to traverse a random path from the fusion core to the boundary is:

$$t_{ex} \sim \left(\frac{R}{\lambda}\right) \times R$$

Eq. 2,

The luminosity of the star L is obtained by dividing the available radiation energy by the escape time from the core, hence:

$$L \sim \frac{T.^4 R^3}{R^2 / \lambda} \sim f\left(\frac{\alpha}{m_e^2}\right)^{-1} \left(\frac{N}{N.}\right)^3 \alpha_G^{-\frac{1}{2}}$$

Eq. 3,

where f is the dimensionless factor governing deviations from the Thomson scattering which might result in low density or high temperature. This gives an estimate of:

$$L \sim 5 \times 10^{34} \left(\frac{M}{M.}\right)^3 \text{ erg } s^{-1}$$

Eq. 4,

a value independent of the stellar radius and temperature. With respect to H2-burning stars, setting $\varepsilon \sim 0.007$ as the fusion efficiency factor and dividing the resultant energy by L, we obtain:

$$t_0 \sim \frac{E_f}{L} \sim \frac{\varepsilon \alpha \alpha_G^{-1}}{m_e} \left(\frac{M.}{M}\right)^2 \sim 10^{10} \left(\frac{M.}{M}\right)^2 \text{ yr}$$

Eq. 5,

with the time-dependent mass factor calculated as:

$$t_{ms} \sim \left(\frac{hc}{Gm_N^2}\right)\left(\frac{h}{m_N c^2}\right) \cong 10^{10} \text{ yr}$$

Eq. 6.

Yet against the background of the Universe's probable age, the time-span for the emergence of an ATC may be comparatively brief. As Lem writes: "The Universe is a continual explosion extending over a time of perhaps 1011 years that appears as a majestic solidification only to the eyes of a transient being like man" (*Microworlds*, 1986). Against this background, Carl Sagan offers a hypothetical analysis of the dominant species on Sol as it might appear in some future Encyclopedia Galactica:

World 806.4616.0110
Civilisation type: 1.0 J. Society code: 4G4 "Humanity".
Star G2V, r = 9.844 kpc, θ = 00°95'24", ϕ = 206°28'49"
Planet: third. a = 1.5 x 10^{13} cm. R = 6.4 x 10^8 cm. p = 8.6 x 10^4 s. P = 3.2 x 10^7 s.
Extraplanetary colonies: none. Planet age: 1.4 x 10^{17} s.
First locally initiated contact: 1.21 x 10^9 s. ago. Receipt first galactic nested code:
Application pending.
Biology: C, N, O, S, H, O, PO_4 deoxyribonucleic acid. ***No genetic prosthesis.***
Mobile heterotrophic symbionts with photosynthetic autotrophs.
Surface dwellers, monospecific, polychromatic O_2 breathers,
Fe-chelated tetrapyroles in circulatory fluid. ***Sexual mammals.***
m = 7 x 10^4 g. t = 2 x 10^9 g. Genome: 4 x 10^9.
Technology : ***exponentiating/fossil fuels/nuclear weapons/***
organised warfare/environmental pollution
Culture: ≈ 200 nation states, ≈ 6 global powers:
cultural & technological homogeneity imminent.
Prepartum/postpartum: 0.21 [18],
individual/communal: 0.31 [17], artistic/technological; 0.14 [11].
Probability of survival (per 100 yr): <1%.

Fig. 5. "Encyclopedia Galactica" report on the Human Race
(adapted from Carl Sagan's COSMOS (1978-9))

The comments in bold type – reflecting the present author's emphasis – describe those traits that, in the opinion of the present author, are likely to account for the estimated survival rate of c. 1%. The very traits that conferred adaptive strength on the EEA may prove to be the evolutionary nemesis of the species.

Throughout the Universe, even within the single range of carbon chemistry (CHONP-based life-forms), the range of evolutionary variance is likely to be extremely wide. There are good enough grounds for assuming carbon chemistry to be the optimal "main sequence" for complex biological evolution within our present Universe (given its laws and fundamental constraints) without postulating other more exotic, hypothetical biochemistries. (Barrow & Tipler 1986: ch. 8). Kauffman (1986, 1993) identifies of a wide range of "universality classes" even within the range of CHONPS-based (Carbon – Hydrogen – Oxygen – Nitrogen – Phosphorus - Sulphur) life. (Fig. 6 below).

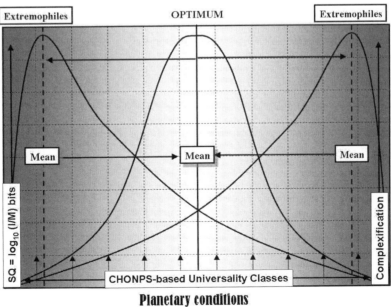

Fig. 6. Different planetary conditions generate different evolutionary optima for the emergence of sentience

In this chart, we assume the conditions we experience on Earth to be the "Goldilocks zone" for "intelligent" life (the central mean), but given a wide range of variance in planetary conditions that still remain favourable to

CHONPS-based life, certain "earthlike" worlds may evolve conditions in which what we might classify as "extremophile" life forms become, on that world, the mean. This would further imply that on a cosmic scale, multiple orders of life subsuming a wide variety of universality classes may be scattered prolifically across the Universe, creating the statistical likelihood that sentience will emerge in sufficient strength to meet the challenge of the final "singularity" whatever its nature (Fig. 7 below). Although teleological issues remain far beyond the scope of this paper, we choose to assume that the ultimate destiny of sentient life is somehow bound up with that of the Universe we inhabit. This view of the co-evolution of matter and form (which is also the basis of Tibetan Buddhist traditions such as the rDzogs-chen: the "Great Perfection" or Matrix of Mystery (Guenther 1984, 1989)), is termed hylomorphism (> Gk. ὑλο- hylo-, "wood, matter" + μορφή, morphē, "form") and/or hylopathism (the thesis that sentience is the dominant evolutionary vector in the Universe). The Western roots of this philosophy, which also forms the basic premise of the continuity thesis, are found in the works of Aristotle (Physics 194b: 9; 195a: 16; 1949b: 9, 23 – 24; Metaphysics 1045a: 26 – 29; Nichomachean Ethics 1098a: 1 - 5, 7 – 8, 16 – 18; On the Soul 412a: 9).

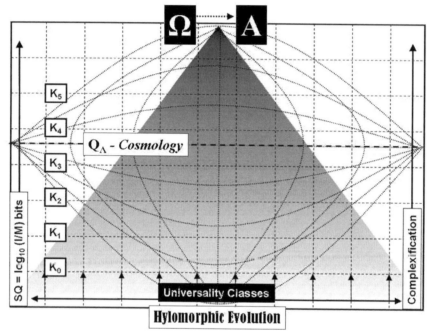

Fig. 7. Is the ultimate "fate" of sentient life bound up with that of the Universe?

4. Defining a Apecies in Terms of Morph-dependent Computation.

"Morph-dependent computation" is the expression of the foundational concepts of embodied cognition (Lakoff & Johnson 1999) and the Quine-Duhcm thesis (Gillies 1998) in terms of "machinic" philosophy. We might define "sentience" in terms of "computational power" provided that we do not limit the terms "computation" or "machine" to anything within our current range of experience. Allowing for this, in The Calculi of Emergence: Computation, Dynamics and Induction (1994) James Crutchfield defines "species" (pl.) as "metastable, invariant languages – ... temporary (hyperbolic) fixed points in the evolutionary dynamic" (p. 49). In other words, evolutionary advance is defined in terms of increasing computational power, and radical advances in computational power imply radical physical re-structuring. Innovation necessarily defines speciation – the essence of the posthuman challenge.

In Crutchfield's Calculus, "agents", redefined as "species", may be considered as autonomous, goal-seeking programs evolving on two adaptive levels: 1) within a particular domain and 2) as independent agents within the general context of cosmic evolution (compare the perspective described in Devising the Prime Radiant – this volume). "Species" are therefore stochastic dynamical systems (SDS's) co-evolving with their own biospheres and, upon emergence from these biospheres, within a deterministic dynamical system (DS) – the known Universe (Fig. 8 below). All CHONPS-based life forms, despite radical genomic divergence, share a similar embodied substrate – physical, chemical, macromolecular or metabolic. What differentiates them are the classes of model each agent creates in order to make sense of its environment and to interact with other agents in a manner that best serves its own interests.

468

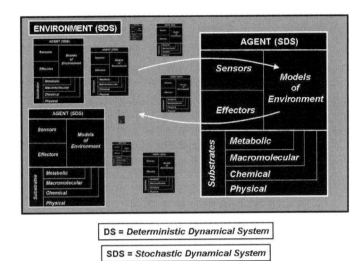

Fig. 8. The co-evolution of agents within a deterministic Universe
(After Crutchfield (1994))

The evolution of a particular species may therefore be characterised in terms of the "metastable, invariant language" used by that species to classify the environment in which it finds itself at a given point in time. "Evolutionary advance" (for that species) would mean an advance in the range and power of the computational language employed to deal with that environment. Fig. 9 below shows a "hierarchy" of machine languages (as we currently understand them). This chart is intended only as a conceptual heuristic, not as an actual means of encoding "real" alien languages. What is most important here is to observe that this "hierarchy" broadens out over an increasingly wide domain base as well as advancing "upwards" in terms of complexity.

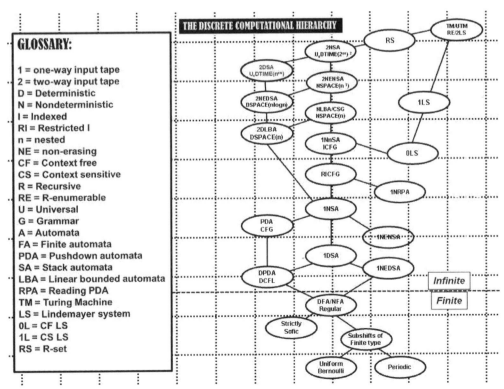

Fig. 9. The Hierarchy of Machine Languages
(After Crutchfield (1994))

Advances through this language hierarchy are effected by what Crutchfield calls "ε-machine reconstruction" ("epsilon-machine reconstruction') where ε represents the level of accuracy of measurement in a given model, i.e. the degree of discrete quantization utilized in that model (see Devising the Prime Radiant (this volume) – Fig. 15). Computational "style" reflects a species" structure and structure is a product of adaptation. Epsilon-machine reconstruction may radically alter the perspective from which an environment is viewed and therefore radically alter a species evolutionary trajectory. We have seen (Fig. 6 above) how species structure determines how "optimum" conditions necessary for adaptation to a particular environment are evaluated. Agreement as to what this "optimum" consists of will determine the model of what members of a particular species collectively define as "intelligent" behaviour at any given point in time and for each species, this "optimum" will be the point of maximum statistical complexity in terms of its collectively-determined model. The efficacy of a model is determined solely by the accuracy of its predictive capacity in terms of the environment in which it arose. Different trajectories may converge onto identical futures, a slight difference in the initial conditions of two near-identical trajectories may cause their futures to diverge radically, hence "morph equivalence induces conditionally-independent states" (Crutchfield, op. cit. p.18).

5. Statistical complexity

"Complexity" is not the same thing as "randomness". The Kolmogorov-Chaitin complexity of a structure (x) is defined as the smallest number of bits necessary for a minimal representation of x on a Universal Turing Machine or UTM (Shannon & Weaver 1962; Solomonoff 1964; Kolmogorov 1965; Chaitin 1966). If x is considered as a string s_L of L discrete symbols, produced by an information source such as a Markov chain with Shannon entropy rate h_μ , then the growth rate of the Kolmogorov complexity of x will be:

$$\frac{K(s^L)}{L} \xrightarrow[L \to \infty]{} h_\mu \qquad \text{Eq. 7,}$$

and for a chaotic system (with continuous state variables):

$$K(s^L) \underset{\substack{L \to \infty \\ \varepsilon \to 0}}{\propto} h_\mu L \qquad \text{Eq. 8,}$$

where ε is the "discretization" factor (i.e. how coarse- or fine-grained the measurement of x is) and is

$$s_\varepsilon \in \{0, 1, 2, \ldots, \varepsilon^{-d} - 1\}$$

with d = the state space dimension. K (x) is a measure of randomness – but a measure that obscures the underlying structure of x since all bits – including the "random" bits – are included in K(x) and by implication, in the process that produced x. On the other hand, statistical complexity $C_\mu(x)$ discounts the computational effort a UTM must expend in simulating random bits in x, so that as $K \to \infty$, $C_\mu(x) = 0$ while for simple processes such as x = 0.0000000, ..., 0, $C_\mu(x) = 0$ (Fig. 10). The relation between both complexity measures is:

$$K(sL) \approx C_\mu(sL) + h_\mu L \qquad \text{Eq. 9.}$$

Statistical complexity $C_\mu(x)$ is a measure, not only of "randomness", but also of the deep structure underlying this "randomness", It is therefore reasonable to ask whether there is any such thing as "randomness" or if "random" simply means "we don't know" (at our current level of development. $C_\mu(x)$ approximates what Kauffman (1993) means by "the liquid region at the edge of chaos" (as a single optimum), but indicates that this "liquid region" is not absolute but relative – contingent both on the system and process being measured and by the structure of whatever or whoever is measuring it. Taking into account a probabilistic measuring system such as a Bernoulli-Turing machine (BTM), we contrast K(x) and $C_\mu(x)$ as follows:

$$K(x) = \| M_{min}(x|UTM) \| \qquad \text{Eq. 10}$$

and

$$C_\mu(x) = \| M_{min}(x|BTM) \| \qquad \text{Eq. 11.}$$

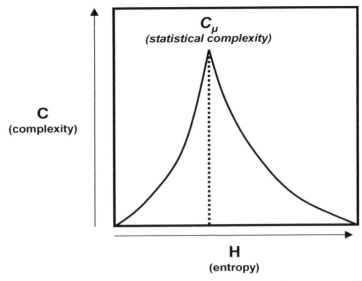

Fig. 10. Morph-dependent computation: measuring statistical complexity (Cμ): at either extreme of H, "complexity" is minimal in terms of Cμ(x).

As we have seen from Fig. 9, advances in modelling complexity do not simply follow a vertical hierarchy, but also spread out to cover different classes of complexity that reflect more faithfully the range of universality classes encompassed by the space of CHONPS-based life-forms. Fig. 11 simulates this space in 3D, showing ranges across three branchings of machine language hierarchies in metamodel space: from periodic to chaotic, from stochastic to deterministic and from stationary to multistationary.

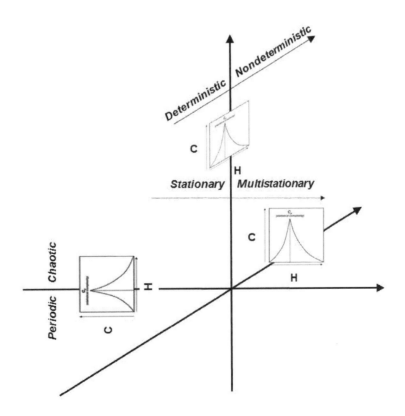

Fig. 11. Meta-models in 3D (I)
(After Crutchfield (1994))

Especially important for us at the present time as we create ever more ambitious plans for future human evolution, is the fact that computational optima will evolve and change as the information-processing architecture of a species becomes subject to radical modification as various subspecies emerge through speciation (Fig. 12). As we evolve therefore, our perspective on the Universe we inhabit may change beyond all recognition. The most subtle and refines arguments relating to astrobiological possibilities or human evolution will also mutate beyond all recognition. These mutations are indicated in Fig. 12 by the rotation of the complexity/entropy diagrams around the vertical axis. For any emergent sentient species, both its evolutionary drive and the limiting factors to speciation are always determined by the resource base at any given level – hence the Kardashev scaling.

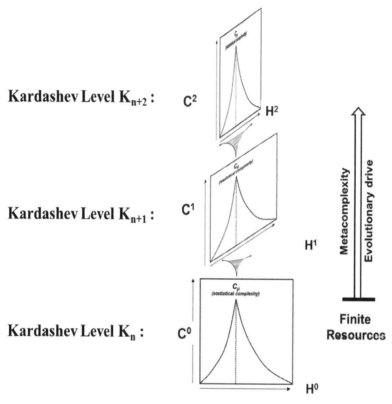

Fig. 12. Meta-models in 3D (II)
(After Crutchfield (1994))

6. The Chreod

A useful conceptual and analytic tool for approaching the study of complex, self-organising entities is the chreod. René Thom (1972) conceived of a given form as the representation of a structurally-stable attractor in the space of internal variables. The creation or disappearance of this form is therefore the result of the disappearance and replacement of this attractor – i.e. the result of transformations undergone by it – and a topological catastrophe is a map of these transformations in the space of external variables. The set of catastrophes that unfold during the lifetime of a given form comprise the chreod ("kray-ode') of the form, and the significance of a chreod is therefore determined by this set. The term is not synonymous with "organism", "species" or "phylum".

The word "chreod" originated with C. H. Waddington (1957) in connection with morphogenetic fields, and was used to describe an overall system of homeorhesis (maintaining the stability of basic structure) as opposed to homeostasis (maintaining the stability of a given state). The term is now most frequently encountered in connection with the deep structures underlying language (Thom 1989; Ziolo 2004) and is here extended as chreodic analysis - the central methodology in a hylomorphic approach to evolution where we consider only "matter" (in its most general sense) as it changes and transforms, either evolving into configurations of increasing complexity or decomposing to more fragmented, rudimentary states, In so doing we do not necessarily distinguish between the organic and the non-organic since according to the continuity thesis, both form a smooth, differentiable continuum from the level of ultrastructure to that of macrostructure. From this perspective, the chreod is ideally suited as a "unit of study" in that although it is essentially qualitative in conception, it is a topologically precise tool whose parameters are measurable within certain limits. Since it is also central to Thom's key studies in structural stability and morphogenesis, the following topological definition is given, based on that of Thom (1989):

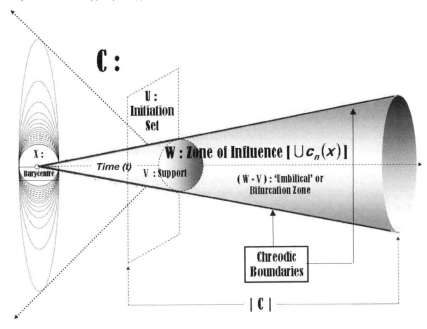

Fig. 13. The Chreod: basic structure

In Fig. 13, a chreod C in space-time R3 × R consists of an open set U (the initiation set) in the hyperplane t = 0 and a zone of influence W. This zone of influence (the "cone" in Fig. 13 above) in turn consists of the union of all "light-cones" $\bigcup c_n(x)$ emanating from a barycentre X (the "germ" or point from which the chreod unfolds – lit. "centre of gravity")1. From a hylomorphic perspective, a chreod metabolises (organically or non-organically) and therefore requires material as a metabolic source or "food set".. There is therefore an open set V contained in W and containing U in its boundary. This is the "support" |C| of C and contains a morphogenetic field, defined up to isomorphism on V. The set (W – V) is the "umbilical" or bifurcation zone of C.

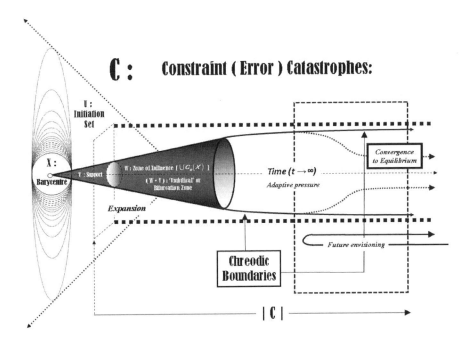

Fig. 14. A bounded (asymptotic) chreod

The "chreodic boundaries" in Fig. 13 are the limits of W (by analogy, any events beyond the limits of a relativistic light cone are inaccessible to the source-point of that cone). These boundaries may begin to flatten out in what Thom calls an asymptotic chreod (Fig. 14 above) and in the case of living systems (i.e. species), turn back "inwards" towards the vertex of C (the line = time beginning from x above) – as happens when a species proves unable to adapt and becomes extinct. The limiting factors in such cases are the Constraint and Error Catastrophe theorems identified by Kauffman (1993).

A chreod C may contain subchreods Jn within its zone of influence provided that the initiation sets and supports of Jn are found in the support zone |C| of C, Conversely, C may in turn be a subchreod of a superchreod C++ under the same conditions. A subchreod may detach itself completely from its parent chreod once the intersection of its zone of influence with that of the parent diminishes to zero. Bearing in mind that a chreod is defined strictly as the set of all catastrophes that govern the unfolding of a given form, where, in the case of a species (considered as the expression of a biological chreod), would the initiation set be found? The superchreod of all biological life on Earth is the biosphere itself, with its barycentre X being located in pre-space - the domain of Schrödinger evolution (Penrose 2005). Every species expresses a subchreod within its own genus, and that in turn of the particular phylum according to the Linnaeus classification system, all the way up to the "terrestrial" superchreod, which is itself a subchreod of the "ultimate" biological superchreod: sentient life in the Cosmos. The initiation set of each species' chreod (like that of the genus and phylum) may be defined as the point of genomic closure, i.e. when a given group ceases to be able to breed with other groups and becomes its own closed "gene pool". Whereas the details of species classification may at times be somewhat "murky", the genetic definition remains fairly robust. Under these criteria, humanity is the expression of a single biological chreod – there being no human ethnic group that cannot interbreed with another. From any non-biological perspective however (e.g. social, political, linguistic etc.) other subchreods may be identified according to the analytical criteria employed (as is the case with the "Thom-Pomian Historical Chreod" as studied by Petitot (1978)).

All chreods consist of open sets that operate on embodied entities in a biological aggregate. In the latter case, the aggregate is formed through modes of nucleation from smaller to greater, with each mode forming a nucleate in its own right according to the self-organising principles determined by the chreod. The nucleate therefore refers to structure while the chreod refers to the dynamics (catastrophe sets) expressed by the interactions between nucleates and their evolution over time. The nucleate determines the initiation set and conditions that in turn fix the mode of nucleation at the next, "higher" level. Within humanity, there exist many nucleates such as families, groups, societies, nations etc. The catastrophe sets expressed by their social and cultural dynamics may be considered as individual "chreods" if we are looking at their separate origins, growth and evolution in time, or as "subchreods" if we are considering how the sum of their interactions create a "higher level" structure. Each and every species may have its own modes of nucleation, and each nucleate may therefore be studied on its own terms for a specific purpose.

7. General Characteristics of a Chreod

A chreod is founded on an "initiation set" – in a "cultural or disciplinary chreod, a philosophical presupposition" or "prime symbol" that functions as a focus or source of all value systems in that chreod and guarantees logical consistency between them.

1) A chreod constitutes a "meaningful-causal unity".

2) All chreods, superchreods and subchreods have the following generic properties:

(i)   Reality - emergent properties that differ from those of its components.

(ii) Individuality (uniqueness).

(iii) Interdependence of components

(iv) The emergent properties of the whole remain stable despite changes in components - i.e. a chreod possesses structural stability.

(v) "Change in togetherness" regarding components - see (iii)

(vi) Changes to the whole are self-directing (immanent) and self-determining, so that global transformation does not result in a fundamentally different entity.

(vii) A chreod is selective as regards external influences.

(viii). There is therefore limited variability within each chreod.

8. The Drake Equation as an Evolving Bayesian Heuristic

The Drake Equation has long served as an "iconic" tool in the estimation of the number of possible civilisations in the Galaxy. As our acquisition of exoplanet data increases, the Drake Equation becomes increasingly subject to refinement, evolving from a "chainsaw" heuristic to a "laser-scalpel" heuristic. In other words, as exoplanet data improves, the ε-factor (section 5 above) in our modelling capacity increases. The standard form of the Drake Equation and the meaning of its various terms is shown in Fig. 15 below.

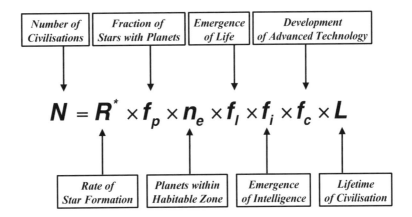

$$N = R^* \times f_p \times n_e \times f_l \times f_i \times f_c \times L$$

Fig. 15. The Drake Equation

On this basis it is possible to construct a matrix with which to collate exoplanet data (Table 1) to the extent of measurement scale accuracy (i.e. the ε (epsilon) precision factor).

DRAKE MATRIX (1961): $N = R^* \times f_p \times n_e \times f_l \times f_i \times f_c \times L$

Object type	Location	Metals / MATTER	Organics	H_2O	Molecular Stability	Energy Sources	Time Stability
Interstellar dust	Grain surfaces	Low	Variable	No	Variable	UV/cosmic rays	Variable
Asteroids	Subsurface	High	High	Early	Rel. good	UV/cosmic rays/impacts	Short, early
Comets	Subsurface	Moderately high	Moderately high	Early	Rel. good	UV/cosmic rays/impacts	Short
Ice moons	Subsurface/ surface	Moderately high	Moderately high	Early – tidal	Good in outer zones	Differentiation Radioactive/ tidal	Short
Silicate planets	Subsurface/ surface	High	Moderately high	Variable Surf/subs	Good near surface	Differentiation-radioactive	Long - decreasing
Giant planets	Atmosphere	Mid-range	Low	Atmos. vapour	Good in atmos.	Contraction	Decreasing
Brown dwarfs	Atmosphere	Low	Low	Atmos. vapour	Good in upper atmos.	Contraction	Late - decreasing

Table 1. An astrobiological matrix based on the Drake Equation

To date (25/11/2013), 1048 exoplanets in 794 star systems have been discovered, including 175 in multiple planetary systems (Schneider 2011). Based on data relating to red dwarfs, Sara Seager (Seager 2012) of MIT has refined part of the Drake Equation as shown below in Fig. 16.

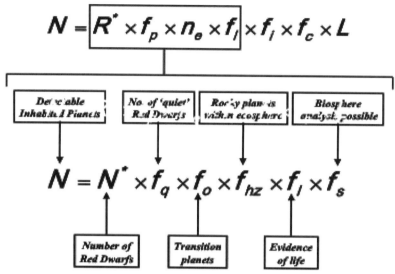

Fig. 16. Seager's (2012) expansion based on red dwarf estimates

9. The Lineweaver Studies: Quantifying Metallicity as a Selection Parameter.

Lineweaver (2001) has made an estimate of the hospitality range and number of earthlike planets and their rate of formation based on a study of metallicity as a selection parameter. For a given exoplanet, the H2 mass fraction (X) is :

$$X = \frac{m_H}{M} \text{ , (Solar Value: Xsun = 0.70)} \qquad \text{Eq. 12,}$$

where M is the estimated mass of the system and mH the estimated H2 mass. Similarly, the He mass fraction is given by:

$$Y = \frac{m_{He}}{M} \text{ , (Solar Value: Ysun = 0.28)} \qquad \text{Eq. 13.}$$

The remaining mass fraction of elements heavier than He (Z) is calculated by:

$$Z = \sum_{i > He} \frac{m_i}{M} = 1 - X - Y \qquad \text{(Solar Value: Zsun = 0.02)} \qquad \text{Eq. 14.}$$

Most recent solar estimates for Eqs. 12 – 14 above and the metrics below are found in Chaplin et al. (2007). The general metric for the estimation of a system's metallicity is:

$$[Fe/H] = log_{10}\left(\frac{N_{Fe}}{N_H}\right)_{star} - log_{10}\left(\frac{N_{Fe}}{N_H}\right)_{sun} \qquad \text{Eq. 15,}$$

General metric for specific element: where NFe and NH are the number of iron and hydrogen atoms per unit of volume respectively. A metric for specific elements has the following form:

$$[O/Fe] = log_{10}\left(\frac{N_O}{N_{Fe}}\right)_{star} - log_{10}\left(\frac{N_O}{N_{Fe}}\right)_{sun}$$

Eq. 16,

$$= \left[log_{10}\left(\frac{N_O}{N_H}\right)_{star} - log_{10}\left(\frac{N_O}{N_H}\right)_{sun}\right] - \left[log_{10}\left(\frac{N_{Fe}}{N_H}\right)_{star} - log_{10}\left(\frac{N_{Fe}}{N_H}\right)_{sun}\right]$$

where [O/Fe] represents the difference in the logarithm of a given star's O2 and Fe abundances compared to those of the Sun. From this data it has been possible to refine existing models of the Galactic Habitable Zone (GHZ). There are high rates of star formation and high rates of metallicity near the Galactic core, but in this zone, high radiation levels and supernova rates preclude the formation of long-lasting earthlike planets. In addition, the formation of "hot Jupiters" (a number of which have been found in other star systems) also act as constraints on the lifetimes of high-metallicity planets within the solar ecosphere. Levels of metallicity also decrease towards the Galactic Rim. Given these considerations, Lineweaver et al. (2004) have developed a "Goldilocks" model for the formation of earthlike planets within the GHZ. Fig. 16 shoes a "top-down" image of the GHZ, while Fig. 17 shows a "lateral" view.

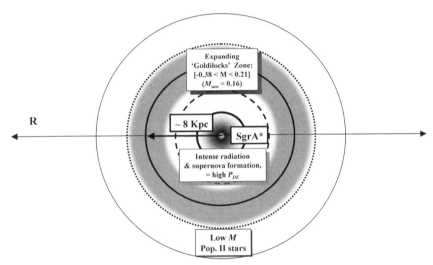

Fig. 16. The Galactic Habitable Zone (GHZ)

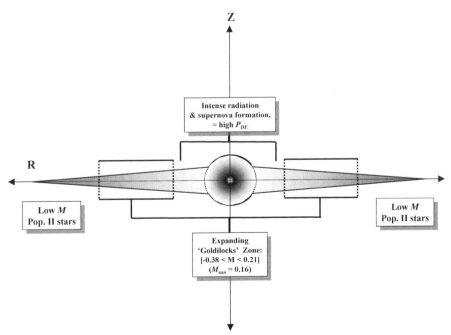

Fig. 17. The Galactic Habitable Zone: "lateral" view

10. Lineweaver et al.'s (2004) Refinement of the Drake Equation

According to this model, how many earthlike life-bearing planets may have emerged within the Milky Way since its formation? What is the probable age range of these planets? From the Lineweaver studies, the population of planets in the GHZ is given by:

$$P_{GHZ} = SFR \times P_{metals} \times P_{evol} \times P_{SN}$$

Eq. 17,

where SFR is the Galactic star formation rate, Pmetals is the overall probability of harbouring earthlike planets, Pevol(t) is a cumulative integral for estimating the time taken for the emergence of complex life with a normal distribution of 4 Gy and a spread of 1 Gy (i.e. based on terrestrial data) and PSN is the probability that complex life survives supernova events. the probability of destruction by supernovae is given by:

$$P_{DE}(M) = \frac{N_H(M)}{N(M)}$$

Eq. 18,

where M is defined as in Eqs; 12 - 14 above, and N as in Eqs. 15 – 16. The probability of harbouring earthlike worlds (PHE) is therefore given by:

$$P_{HE}(M) = P_{PE}(M) \times [1 - P_{DE}(M)]$$

Eq. 19,

where PPE is the probability of producing earthlike worlds. Given the overall planet formation rate:

$$PFR(t) = A \times SFR(t) \times f(t)$$

Eq. 20,

where the age determinant A = 0.05 (5% of star-forming matter creates sunlike stars) and

$$f(t) = \int P(M, \overline{M}(t)) \, P_{HE}(M) \, dM$$

Eq. 21,

where M = local metallicity = (Fe/H)/Fe/H) $\odot$, $\overline{M}$ the metallicity of the Universe and P(M, $\overline{M}$ (t)) the Gaussian distribution given by:

$$P(M, \overline{M}(t)) = \frac{1}{\sigma\sqrt{2\pi}} exp \left[\frac{(M - \overline{M}(t))^2}{2\sigma^2} \right]$$

Eq. 22,

fp in the Drake Equation would be given by:

$$\left. \begin{array}{l} PFR \propto SFR \\ \frac{dM}{dt}(t) \propto SFR(t) \end{array} \right] - \int_0^t SFR(t')dt' \sim \overline{M}(t)$$

Eq. 23.

Figs. 18 – 19 below show this data in graphic form:

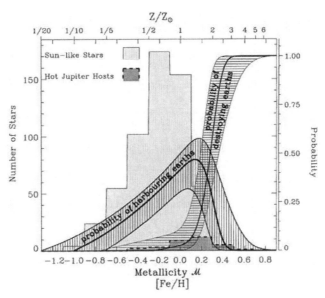

Fig. 18. Evolution of metallicity in the Galaxy (after Lineweaver (2008))

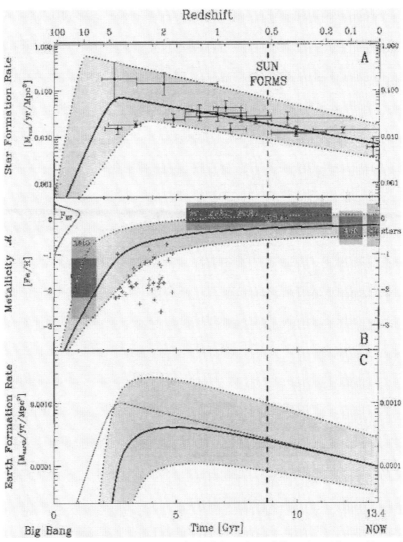

Fig. 19. Star formation rate (top), metallicity (middle) and earthlike planet formation rate (bottom)
(after Lineweaver (2001))

479

The most significant outcomes of Lineweaver et al.'s estimates are:

1. that there are at least ~ 10 million earthlike planets in the Galaxy (this being the most conservative estimate),
2. that their average age is 6.9 ± .9 × 109 years,
3. that complex life on these world will therefore be ~ 1.8 ± .9 × 109 years older than that on the Earth,
4. that any ATC's that have evolved on these worlds is likely to be around 2 billion years in advance of us.

This, if true, is very sobering data which puts terrestrial "civilisation" more thoroughly in perspective. What was happening on Earth 2 billion years ago? We are not likely (unless we are celebrities on acid) to talk to or form a relationship with, bacteria or unicellular organisms. We are more likely to experiment with them or utilise them in specific projects. This may also throw further light on the so-called "Fermi Paradox".

11. Different Phyletic Emergences: the Case for Arthropodic (Insect) Intelligence.

In many ways the rise of the mammals to dominance on this planet may be an anomaly. Certainly in the case of humans, the very traits that appeared to confer adaptive strength on the EEA now threaten to become the evolutionary nemesis of the species. It may be very likely that some ATC's at least may be of arthropod (insect) origin. This of course does not mean "giant ants" in the manner of THEM! but much more subtle forms of evolved intelligence (see for instance George M. M. Martin's story Sandkings (1979)). The structure and functional organisation of the social insects (Wilson 2008) suggest that the evolution of supoerorganic forms of sentience may prove highly adaptive – more so than mammalian sentience since after all, human advance and dominance are largely due to the hive-like or superorganic traits adopted by human societies and there is little question that future post-human evolution will tend more and more towards the "borganic" (Sandberg op. cit.). Minor variants in planetary conditions (see Fig. 5) are likely to favour the emergence of such phyla. It is ironic that insect intelligence and borganic-type societies are so often the subject of SF horrors - see for instance the film documentary *The Hellstrom Chronicle* (1972) and of course, the Star Trek Borg. Two studies that go far in dispelling anthropomorphic or anthropocentric illusions about swarm or borganic intelligence are E. O. Wilson's *The Superorganism: The Beauty, Elegance and Strangeness of Insect Societies* (1978) and Anders Sandberg's *We, Borg* at www.aleph.se/Trans/Global/Posthumaniyu/WeBorg.html.

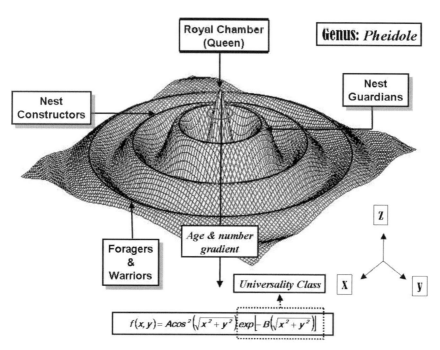

Fig. 20. Arthropod (insect) hive structure

Fig. 20 shows the main structural and functional features of the advanced social insect hive (in this case, that of the ant genus Pheidole).Hive structures of this type can be represented as a type of function known as a "sombrero" (for obvious reasons). Universality classes are linked by the relationship between the exponents of generative functions (see Fig. 6 and associated text). It is this type of highly flexible and efficient structure that may prove to be a favoured adaptation channel in the space of cosmic life-forms.

12. 12-tone Serial Technique: A Clue for the Decoding of Alien Transmissions?

A fruitful avenue of research from the SETI standpoint might be a search for "totally parametrised" languages structured serially or in parallel that lie concealed beneath seemingly chaotic data. Combinatorially-based algorithms exist for such an approach – based on the 12-tone serialist quest for 12-tone sets of specific type and order (Hook 2009). The 12-tone serial world was an unusual flowering of music-theoretic research at a time (the 70's and 80's) known for its "liberalisation" tendencies – but which also included advances in many directions that have since been abandoned as global society returned to a far more conservative frame of mind. "12-tone music" proved far too complex and "alien" for the embodied human intelligence – probably as was to be expected. Nevertheless, the "alien" quality of this musical style and thought – which still emerged spontaneously from a sentient species (humanity) – may well provide an important clue for the understanding of a truly "alien" intelligence and the decoding of its transmissions. Multi-parametric serialised languages of the serial type can be adapted to all forms, scalings and ranges of the electromagnetic spectrum, including the quantum realm. The scaling of computational languages of this type will relect the scaling of sentient systems in the Universe (Perez-Mercador 2002). Assimilation of the quantum domain is crucial. It is this domain – that of Schrödinger evolution – that may prove to be a more "popular" playground for ATC's than the 21 cm. H2 band. Human scepticism over the quantum realm is simply a consequence of our limited morph-dependent computational powers. As S. R. Haddon says in the film version of Carl Sagan's *Contact* (1995) "An alien intelligence has got to be more advanced. That means efficiency functioning on multiple levels and ... in multiple dimensions."

13. Epilogue

Future research may reveal that life is abundant in the cosmos – but that many advanced technological civilisations (ATC's) may be far in advance of us, i.e. that we are "new kids on the block". ATC's that are ~ 2 × 109 years in advance of us are unlikely to communicate with us, or respond to any efforts at communication from our side although the much sought-after "evidence" for their existence may be abundant – right "under our noses" in fact – but due to the model constraints of morph-dependent computation discussed in sections 4 and 5 above, this evidence is not perceived. To us at our current level, ATC technologies are probably indistinguishable from "natural law" as we currently understand it. Ants walking on the wall of a corporate high—rise in Manhattan probably imagine they are walking on some kind of smooth stone.

Unmodified "natural" humans are unlikely ever to travel into deep space. If they ever do so, it will be with the support of infrastructures created and maintained by posthuman pioneers and their successors. As regards future human evolution, speciation will accelerate in proportion to our advance along the Kn axis. Only at K2 and beyond will we have developed sufficiently to experience (and competently handle) some form of contact with an ATC.

"Many are called but few are chosen" (Matt. 22:14). The Biblical proverb may apply not only to "selection criteria" for arcology citizens or interstellar crews,, but to the emergence of ATC's in general – Darwinian selection may be operative throughout the Cosmos with "eligibility for convergence at the Final Singularity" serving as the "fitness value". For participants at this humbler level of transition from K0 → K2 the traditional "right stuff" selection criteria – "normal", "well-balanced" (even if biologically-fit) humans - may be less than ideally suitable for a one-way trip into the Void. Motivation is everything, and Antarctic-based studies have shown that those most able to endure high-stress, high-risk environments with the ideal combination of telic and paratelic behaviours tend to be "highly-motivated civilians" rather than the meticulously-trained "right stuff" (Harriison et al. 1990).

"A species only reaches maturity when the nature of Mind is fully understood" (Amoroso & Martin 1995). We have a long way to go in this direction, although we have certainly taken some initial steps. For our K3-level successors, the word "human" might come to mean "that which is grown from earth" (>Lat. "humus" → "humanus"), i.e. "the chreod or species variant that finally emerged from its home world". They will come to understand biological life as simply an early transitional form between "inert" and fully "sentient" matter. A readiness to encounter the truly alien would require that they regard "humanity" not as a single family, but as a "speciation crucible" of which they are but one of the possible emergent branches. In possessing a boundless, empathic appreciation of the infinite potentialities of Being, they will have come to accept the potentially infinite mutability of form and nature and will have renounced their unique human identities on order to transcend the collective limits of that identity. Whether they will weep or exult in this transcendence will be their own affair.

References

1. Amoroso, R. L. & Martin, B. E. (1995). "Modelling the Heisenberg Matrix: Quantum Coherence and Thought at the Holoscape Manifold and Deeper Complementarity". Scale in Conscious Experience: Is the Brain Too Important To Be Left to Specialists to Study? Proceedings of the Third Appalachian Conference on Behavioural Neurodynamics, pp.351-77. Lawrence Erlbaum Associates Inc., Mahwah, NJ.

2. Barrow, J. D. & Tipler, F. J. (1986). The Anthropic Cosmological Principle. Oxford University Press, Oxford & New York.

3. Burbidge, E. M., Burbidge, G. R., Fowler, W. A., & Hoyle, F. (1957). "Synthesis of the Elements in Stars". Revs. Mod. Physics vol. 29, pp. 547 – 650.

4. Chaitin, G. (1966). "On the length of programs for computing finite binary sequences". J. ACM vol. 13: 145.

5. Chaplin, W. J., Serenelli, A. M., Basu, S., Elsworth, Y., New, R. & Verner, G. A. (2007). "Solar Heavy Element Abundance: Constraints from Frequency Separation Ratios of Low-Degree p-Modes". The Astrophysical Journal, vol. 670: 1, pp. 872-84.

6. Ćirković, M. (2012). The Astrobiological Landscape: Philosophical Foundations of the Study of Cosmic Life. Cambridge University Press.

7. Crutchfield, J. (1994). "The Calculi of Emergence". Physica D. Proceedings of the Oji International Seminar: Complex Systems – from Complex Dynamics to Artificial Reality.

8. Deleuze & Guattari, F. (1987). A Thousand Plateaus. University of Minnesota Press.

9. Fry, I. (2000). The Emergence of Life on Earth: A Historical and Scientific Overview. Rutgers University Press, New Brunswick, NJ.

10. Gardner, J. (2007). The Intelligent Universe: AI, ET and the Emerging Mind of the Cosmos. New Page Books, NJ.

11. Gillies, D. (1998). "The Duhem Thesis and the Quine Thesis". In Philosophy of Science: The Central Issues, (Curd, M. & Cover, J. A. eds.) Norton, New York, pp. 302-19.

12. Guenther, H. (1984). The Matrix of Mystery. Shambala, Boulder & London.

13. (1989). From Reductionism to Creativity: rDzogs-chen and the New Sciences of Mind. Shambala, Boston/Shaftsbury

14. Harrison, A. A., Clearwater Y.A. &McKay, C.P. (1990). From Antarctica to Outer Space: Life in Isolation and Confinement. Springer-Verlag, New York & London.

15. Hook, J. (2007). "Why are there 29 Tetrachords? A Tutorial on Combinatorics and Enumeration in Music Theory". Music Theory Online, vol. 14: 4 http://www.mtosmt.org/issues/mto.07.13.4/mto.07.13.4.hook.html

16. Johnston, J. (2008). The Allure of Artificial Life: Cybernetics, Artificial Life and the New AI. MIT Press, Cambridge, Mass., London.

17. Kauffman, S. (1986). "Boolean systems, adaptive automata, evolution". Disordered Systems and Biological Organization (Bienenstock, E., Fogelman-Soulie, F. & Weisbuch, G. (eds.)), Series F: Computer and Systems Sciences 20. Springer, New York.

18. (1993). The Origins of Order: Self-Organization and Selection in Evolution. Oxford University Press, New York & Oxford.

19. Kolmogorov, A. N. (1965). "Three approaches to the concept of the "amount of information"". Prob. Info. Trans, vol I: 1.

20. Lakoff, G. & Johnson, M. (1999). Philosophy in the Flesh: the Embodied Mind and its Challenge to Western Thought. Basic Books, New York.

21. Lem, S. (1986). Microworlds. Mariner Books, New York.

22. Lineweaver, C. H. (2001). "An Estimate of the Age Distribution of Terrestrial Planets in the Universe: Quantifying Metallicity as a Selection Effect". Icarus 151, pp. 307-13, arXiv:astro-ph/0012399.

23. (2004) & Fenner, Y. & Gibson, B. K. "The Galactic Habitable Zone and the Age Distribution of Complex Life in the Milky Way". Science 302 (5654), pp. 59-62, arXiv:astro-ph/0401024.

24. Perez-Mercader, J. (2002). Scaling Phenomena and the Emergence of Complexity in Astrobiology. Springer, Berlin.

25. Schneider, J. (2001). Interactive Extrasolar Planets Catalog: http://exoplanet.eu/catalog/ accessed 28/11/2013 : 1800 GMT.

26. - - -

27. Seager, S. (2012). "An Equation to Estimate the Probability of Identifying an Inhabited World Within the Next Decade". http://seagerexoplanets.mit.edu/ accessed 28/11/2013: 19.4 GMT.

28. Shannon, C. E. & Weaver, W. (1962). The Mathematical Theory of Communication. Univ. of Illinois Press, Champaign-Urbana, Ill.

29. Solomonoff, R. J. (1964). "A formal theory of inductive control". Info. Control vol. 7: 224.

30. Thom, R. (1989). Structural Stability and Morphogenesis. Addison-Wesley Advanced Book Program, Reading, MA.

31. Wilson, E. O. (2009). The Superorganism: The Beauty, Elegance and Strangeness of Insect Societies. W. W.Norton & Co. New York/.

32. Ziolo, M. P. (2004). "Trauma and Transcendence: Psychosocial Impacts of Cybernetics and Nanotechnology". Proceedings of the PISTA 2003 International Conference on Informatics and Systemics (AAAS) - also available on the World Systems Analysis Archive :: http://wsarch.ucr.edu/archive/papers.htm

100 YEAR STARSHIP™

Student Track:
The Next Generation

Chaired by David Alexander, PhD

Professor, Rice University, Physics and Astronomy Department

Director, Rice Space Institute

Track Description

College undergraduates are invited to present papers on any of the topics of the Symposium technical tracks during this session. Alternatively, students are asked to imagine how it would be on earth during their lifetime with or without a global interstellar ambition.

Track Summary

The College Track is a session designed to give students of all ages an opportunity to present their thoughts, typically to an audience of their peers. Individual students may also present ideas in a relevant to a specific technical track. The College Track is rather unique in that the collection of presentations can be wide ranging, making it difficult to foster common themes or to structure discussions that bring together the ideas. However, the talks are usually of high quality, the ideas refreshing, and the participants enthusiastic. The 2013 college track session consisted of four separate presentations and a group discussion that included the audience and three of the speakers. In addition to discussing the themes of the presentations, we also discussed ideas for a new format for future student engagement in 100YSS. In this brief summary, I describe the presentations and the discussion and the thoughts that arose from them.

The four presentations in this session started with a talk by David Wilson entitled *Food Design: 100 Year Starship space food systems*. In this talk, Mr. Wilson, emphasized that food design went beyond the provision of nutritious and palatable food to include the "experience" of eating, which is of particular importance when choices are limited on where you eat, what you eat and with whom you eat. The physical limitations of being on a ship force technology considerations when it comes to packaging, delivery and on-board production (e.g. hydroponic gardens). Mr. Wilson contended that incorporating food design into the early planning stages of a long-duration human space mission would lead to significant benefits in the psychological and physical health of the crew.

The discussion broadened with the presentation of Kirk Frenger who focused on whether the human race was ready to make an interstellar journey given our current sociological development. Using science fiction as a backdrop to explore what might be required for humans to succeed as interstellar travelers, Mr. Frenger touched on a number of issues relating to human interactions and how this would help or hinder future interactions when we have a significant population based off-Earth. An important point made in this talk, a point that transcends the goals of 100YSS, is that human sociological development lags far behind human technological development. This factors into many different discussions about space exploration and how much emphasis we can afford to place on it. Mr. Frenger was optimistic, stating that "Humans are clever, adaptable, innovative, and flexible as a whole" and that "Our greatest asset is our largely untapped potential for incredible solidarity". This led to some discussion about how current youth view the future: with optimism or pessimism. As one might expect, there was a range of opinions that were necessarily clouded by the current state of the world and the ability of the human race to deal with current problems on the Earth. A broad conclusion was that by embracing an international goal of space exploration, we could perhaps learn how better to work together to accelerate our sociological development.

The third talk of the session was presented by high school student Scott Lambert. *Issues with Interstellar Travel: Subluminal versus Superluminal* provided a broad discussion of the impact of interstellar space travel depending upon whether space travel could attain greater than light speed velocities or not. Mr. Lambert first considered the purposes for which we on Earth might develop interstellar travel: scientific exploration, commercial development of off-earth resources, and colonization. Each purpose raises its own set of difficulties that require very different solutions depending upon the status of the interstellar transportation (sub- or super-luminal). An interesting discussion ensued from this presentation, namely the question of what is the impact on Earth resulting from the development of an interstellar capability. If propulsion means are restricted to sub-luminal velocities then there is very little impact on the Earth because, for $v/c \ll 1$, the transit times will be so long that there will be little to report back and for large but still sub-luminal velocities, $v/c < 1$, time dilation effects become significant meaning that there will be several years before any meaningful contact from the space travelers. For sub-luminal travel, only colonization survives as a viable purpose in support of developing interstellar space travel. The development of super-luminal travel, however unlikely, is then the only means by which the people of Earth can be engaged directly in the human exploration of interstellar space.

The final presentation of the session came from Jonathan Van who focused on how current approaches to innovation can help stimulate a viable transformative mission, like the 100YSS. *Ensuring Interstellar Research Leaves Footprints on Earth* discussed how business model competitions and the entrepreneurship with the right focus can help translate innovative discoveries into a sustainable and viable enterprise. Mr. Van discussed how this might be applied to the development of technical breakthroughs inspired by, and perhaps derived from, the 100YSS vision. The coupling of innovative strategies and modern approaches to engaging new ideas provided a nice backdrop to the subsequent discussion of how best to engage young people in the College Track in future symposia.

The four presentations described above are quite disparate but a common theme that might be applied, with a little imagination, is that of the significant role that sociology plays when humans are included in the mix. What sociological structures get carried forward with future interstellar crews? How do these crews adapt to their increasing separation from Earth? How do the people of Earth maintain a relationship to their traveling kinsfolk? What benefit does the pursuit of the means to achieve this vision have on Earth? And so on. These themes pervade all of the discussions in all of tracks of the symposium but also go beyond them to encompass the simple fact that, to succeed, all of these issues have to be considered as a collective whole: simply developing advanced propulsion systems, for example, is not enough.

The current format of the College Track session does not lend itself well to the purpose of engaging the younger generation in the mission of the 100YSS. The idea of modifying the track to be centered around a series of challenges to be tackled by student teams at the symposium was discussed and generally well received. We would re-title the track to be named simply The Next Generation, with both human and technological implications, and work to identify meaningful challenges that can be advertized well in advance of the symposium. With the proper preparation, this could be a strong attraction for 2014.

Track Chair Biography

David Alexander, PhD

Professor, Rice University, Physics and Astronomy Department
Director, Rice Space Institute

Dr. David Alexander is a professor in Rice University's Physics & Astronomy Department and the Director of the Rice Space Institute. His research interests include solar activity, sunspots, flares and coronal mass ejections. Professor Alexander is a member of the Rice Faculty Senate and author of "The Sun," part of the Greenwood Press "Guide to the Universe" Series. He a recipient of the Presidential Early Career Award for Scientists and Engineers and a Kavli Frontiers Fellow of the National Academy of Sciences.

Issues with Interstellar Travel: Superluminal versus Subluminal

Scott Lambert

Falmouth High School, 74 Woodville Road, Falmouth, ME 04105

slambert2015@falmouthschools.org

Abstract

To address the problems facing the development of interstellar travel (IST), explicit goals are necessary. Several possible goals for IST are discussed and categorized as "any star" or "many stars." Superluminal and subluminal travel are considered; superluminal travel would be more versatile, but subluminal travel has potential applications.

The technological difficulties of achieving subluminal IST can be as great as those facing superluminal IST. For example, developing a warp drive (a superluminal technology) is presently precluded by an inability to generate sufficient negative energy densities; likewise, inability to initiate proton-proton fusion and create a sufficiently large electromagnetic scoop precludes the development of a Bussard ramjet, a high-velocity subluminal technology. Knowledge gaps present challenges for both superluminal and subluminal IST. The belief that practical manned superluminal IST is farther off than practical manned subluminal IST is unfounded, and recent discoveries concerning spacetime manipulation show that investing in superluminal IST could provide greater payoff for the same effort as investing in subluminal IST.

This paper compares the efficacy, in multiple respects, of currently-envisioned superluminal IST to subluminal IST, including each's versatility, cost-effectiveness, economic benefit, popular appeal, potential destinations, and health complications for astronauts due to spending extended periods in space. Several existing and prospective technologies for interstellar propulsion are identified. Technological readiness, capability, potential strengths and weaknesses, applications, and integration with other technologies are overviewed.

Societal circumstances must be considered when defining realistic goals for interstellar travel. Society's effect on IST is weighed, and means of working within current circumstances are evaluated.

Keywords

superluminal, subluminal, technology, propulsion, society

Symbols Used in This Work

Abbreviations
IST: Interstellar travel
IMRA: Interstellar Mission Reference Architecture

TRL: Technological Readiness Level

NPP: Nuclear Pulse Propulsion

<u>Starship velocities</u>

v_f = final spaceship velocity, m/s

I_{sp} = propulsion system specific impluse, s

v_e = propulsion system exhaust velocity, m/s

m_i = spaceship initial (fully fueled) mass, kg

m_f = spaceship mass after propellant burn, kg

g = gravitational acceleration at Earth's surface, 9.81 m/s^2

ΔV = change in velocity, ly/y

<u>Time Dilation</u>

Δt_s = time interval experienced by spaceship, y

Δt_e = time interval experienced by Earth, y

<u>Transit Costs</u>

r_{ls} = consumables rate, \$/day/person

n = number of crew members

t_s = transit duration, ship time, days

r_c = communication rate, \$/day

t_c = time ship spends in communication with Earth, days

d_c = distance at which communications terminate, ly

f = fraction of time in which ship is between 0 and d_c ly from Earth that ship spends in communication with Earth, days/days

v = ship velocity, ly/y (assumed to be constant; note that the unit in this case is ly/y, not m/s)

C = transit cost, \$

C_{ls} = consumables cost for transit, \$

C_c = communications cost for transit, \$

D = distance to destination, ly

c = speed of light in vacuum, exactly 1 ly/y

1. Introduction

If the author has learned anything in the preparation of this work, it is that attempting to write a single paper adequately covering every issue with interstellar travel would be impossible– it would be a large collection of books. The various issues in this paper are only touched upon– each section, or even each subsection, is broad enough to be the focus of at least a paper, and, in many cases, a book. As the author came to this realization, it became clear that the best function of this paper would be to provide readers with a general overview of the problems and relevant matters around interstellar travel. That stated, there is a definite emphasis in this work on the technical problems facing interstellar travel; societal issues are only briefly touched upon. Whether the greatest problems facing interstellar travel are technical or societal could fuel an endless debate, as the influence between society and technology is mutual.

Content begins in Section 2 with an overview of mission objectives and classification schemes for interstellar travel. Section 3 contains an overview of several ideas, ranging from largely theoretical mathematical constructs to mission-proven technologies, that someday may serve to take humans to the stars. Section 4 assumes that both superluminal and subluminal interstellar travel are possible and makes predictions regarding their respective efficacies. Section 5 briefly discusses two societal issues with interstellar travel: garnering funding for an interstellar mission and the popular appeal of interstellar travel. Throughout this work both manned and unmanned missions will be discussed; its primary emphasis, however, is on manned interstellar travel.

This work was written from an American perspective. The author has assumed that American society's influence on the development of American spaceflight technologies will be similar to other societies' influences on their own respective technological developments. Due to cultural and societal differences this may not be true in all circumstances, and interstellar flight will likely not occur as a result of a single nation's work, but as a result of international cooperation. However, the author has assumed that the American paradigm is a reasonable approximation for that of other nations.

The transportation of living humans to another star system will represent an achievement on par with the first human migrations away from Africa. Interstellar travel, and the developments to be achieved en route to this goal, offer great opportunity for the improvement of human life. It is the author's hope that in some small way this work might further the achievement of interstellar travel.

2. Interstellar Mission Objectives and Classification

As with any mission, interstellar travel must have an explicit goal or set of goals. These goals define the performance requirements for the spacecraft, which indicate what technologies are best suited for the mission and, ultimately, whether such a mission is feasible with current technology and circumstances. A wide variety of objectives have been proposed for interstellar missions, ranging from extrasolar science and the search for extraterrestrial life to the provision of an escape from Earth when it becomes uninhabitable.

Most of these goals fit into three categories: science, colonization, and commerce. Interstellar science missions would serve to increase human awareness of the universe by providing a perspective from outside of the solar system. As stated above, one important subcategory of these science missions is the search for extraterrestrial life; another is the search for habitable exoplanets, which could serve as new homes for humanity. Colonization missions would seek out new worlds for human habitation and attempt to populate these worlds. Commercial missions would attempt to make a profit by exploiting the resources available outside of the solar system.

The three-category classification scheme above groups interstellar missions by their objective; the author created a classification scheme for starships based on how many stars a starship could visit in a human working lifetime of 40 years. This scheme is referred to as the "any/many/none" scheme for its three categories. Starships in the "any" or "any star" category are hypothetically capable or nearly capable of completing a one-way transit to the Alpha Centauri system–the nearest to the solar system– within 40 years. Starships in the "many" or "many stars" category are capable of transiting a distance equivalent to a round trip through the Alpha Centauri and Barnard's Star systems, including a return to Earth, in 40 years. Spacecraft in the "none" or "no stars" category are not capable of meeting either of these standards. It is important to note that spacecraft in the "none" category may still be capable of interstellar travel, albeit at velocities slower than the 0.11 c required to travel to the Alpha Centauri system within 40 years.

The categories in the any/many/none scheme have been called "any stars," "many stars," and "no stars" rather than "any stars within a human working lifetime," "many stars within a human working lifetime," and "no stars within a human working lifetime" for the purpose of brevity.

3. Idea Overview
3.1 Introduction

The devices discussed herein, which range from hypothetical to functional, fall into 4 loose categories: internally-fueled rockets (4.3-4.5), light sails (4.6-4.7), externally-fueled rockets (4.8-4.9), and the more speculative spacetime manipulation schemes (4.10-4.11). The first three categories contain mechanisms for subluminal starflight; the last contains proposed means of superluminal starflight.

This section has been named "idea overview" because most of the means of starflight discussed have not progressed beyond an analytical stage– that is, they are ideas, not functioning technologies. Some exceptions exist, most notably ion thrusters and solar sails. However, none of the technologies described herein have been used for a successful mission to another star; for this reason they remain ideas in the context of interstellar travel, though some have been more thoroughly analyzed than others and may be closer to functionality.

Each of the next nine subsections will contain the following information about the (proposed) technology it describes:

1. A brief summary of the proposed technology's function
2. A rough prediction of maximum velocity change for a starship equipped with the proposed technology, and classification of the proposed technology within the any/many/none scheme described in Section 2
3. A brief description of the device's Technological Readiness Level (TRL)

4. The device's potential strengths and weaknesses, and good and poor applications for the device
5. Some scientific and/or technological developments necessary for the device to become feasible
6. Possible modes of integration with other devices

3.2 Methodology

3.2.1 Source overview

The information described above either came directly from or was synthesized from a variety of sources, ranging from scientific and technical papers to reputable popular sites and books. The author's first choice for information was often the NASA Technical Reports Server, which contained quantitative studies and qualitative information on almost all the ideas discussed in this section. Matloff and Mallove's The Starflight Handbook, NASA.gov, the Tau Zero foundation's blog Centauri Dreams, and other (mostly popular) sites provided the author with overviews of the ideas discussed. If a popular site mentioned a scientific paper with information on an idea, the author referred to the paper if more detailed information was necessary; these papers came from institutions including the British Interplanetary Society and IOP Publishing, among others.

3.2.2 Starship velocities

Values for maximum starship velocities either came directly from the sources described above or were calculated using the Tsiolkovsky rocket equation, shown below[79]:

$$v_f = v_e ln \frac{m_i}{m_f} \tag{3.2.1}$$

Where we have assumed that the initial velocity is zero, all velocities for devices that do not carry their own fuel came directly from external sources. The Tsiolkovsky equation was used when maximum velocities were unavailable from the literature, or when the maximum velocities given were obtained using parameters unlikely for an interstellar mission. In either case, use of the equation required assumptions about a starship's structural (non-propellant) mass, its initial propellant mass, and some basic mission parameters, such as the use of staging. These assumptions will be collectively referenced herein by the term "Interstellar Mission Reference Architecture" or IMRA. The author made the following assumptions when calculating final starship velocities by hand:

$$m_i = 105\ 491\ kg \tag{3.2.2}$$

$$m_f = 19\ 323\ kg \tag{3.2.3}$$

Initial mass is the mass of the Zarya module, the first module of the International Space Station, added to the mass of fuel it uses in a decade of operation at the 2011 fuel consumption rate [52]. Using the same initial and final mass values for different propulsion systems inherently results in misleading final velocity values, since in a real mission a spacecraft's fuel mass and structural mass will be optimized to fit the demands of the individual mission and propulsion system. The given initial and final starship masses were chosen because conducting optimizations for each propulsion system would have been prohibitively time consuming, and because the International Space Station represents a reasonable estimate of the current limit of in-space construction capabilities. Assuming that the starship could begin with a fuel mass equal to ten times the ISS's yearly consumption was considered to be on par with the reasonably conservative assumption that the starship would be about the mass of the ISS.

In addition to initial and final masses, the exhaust velocity of a starship's propulsion system is necessary to determine the ship's final velocity. Exhaust velocity varies by propulsion system. Since exhaust velocities were not generally available in the literature, specific impulse, a value more easily found, was used to determine exhaust velocities. Specific impulse is defined as follows:

$$I_{sp} = \frac{v_e}{g} \tag{3.2.4}$$

Where g is the acceleration due to gravity at the Earth's surface (9.8 m/s2), rearranging this definition and combining with (1) yields

$$v_f = I_{sp}g \ln \frac{m_i}{m_f} \qquad (3.2.5)$$

This is the final form of the equation used (in a Google® spreadsheet) to predict maximum starship velocities. The IMRA assumes no staging, so final dry mass was considered constant.

The author has found that final velocity estimates obtained using the IMRA tend to be less than final velocity estimates obtained using more rigorous methods. The purpose of the IMRA is to provide a basis of rough comparison for various rocket-type propulsion concepts. Final ΔV-values generated using the IMRA should not be treated as necessarily accurate, though they do assist in providing a more concrete comparison of propulsion technologies than the measurement of specific impulse alone.

3.2.3 Technological readiness levels

Technological Readiness Levels (TRLs) were determined using NASA's nine-point scale [61]. The specific NASA-authored document containing TRL descriptors has been reproduced below for the reader's convenience.

Definition Of Technology Readiness Levels:

- TRL 1 Basic principles observed and reported: Transition from scientific research to applied research. Essential characteristics and behaviors of systems and architectures. Descriptive tools are mathematical formulations or algorithms.
- TRL 2 Technology concept and/or application formulated: Applied research. Theory and scientific principles are focused on specific application area to define the concept. Characteristics of the application are described. Analytical tools are developed for simulation or analysis of the application.
- TRL 3 Analytical and experimental critical function and/or characteristic proof-of- concept: Proof of concept validation. Active Research and Development (R&D) is initiated with analytical and laboratory studies. Demonstration of technical feasibility using breadboard or brassboard implementations that are exercised with representative data.
- TRL 4 Component/subsystem validation in laboratory environment: Standalone prototyping implementation and test. Integration of technology elements. Experiments with full-scale problems or data sets.
- TRL 5 System/subsystem/component validation in relevant environment: Thorough testing of prototyping in representative environment. Basic technology elements integrated with reasonably realistic supporting elements. Prototyping implementations conform to target environment and interfaces.
- TRL 6 System/subsystem model or prototyping demonstration in a relevant end-to-end environment (ground or space): Prototyping implementations on full-scale realistic problems. Partially integrated with existing systems. Limited documentation available. Engineering feasibility fully demonstrated in actual system application.
- TRL 7 System prototyping demonstration in an operational environment (ground or space): System prototyping demonstration in operational environment. System is at or near scale of the operational system, with most functions available for demonstration and test. Well integrated with collateral and ancillary systems. Limited documentation available.
- TRL 8 Actual system completed and "mission qualified" through test and demonstration in an operational environment (ground or space): End of system development. Fully integrated with operational hardware and software systems. Most user documentation, training documentation, and maintenance documentation completed. All functionality tested in simulated and operational scenarios. Verification and Validation (V&V) completed.
- TRL 9 Actual system "mission proven" through successful mission operations (ground or space): Fully integrated with operational hardware/software systems. Actual system has been thoroughly demonstrated and tested in its operational environment. All documentation completed. Successful operational experience. Sustaining engineering support in place.

3.3 Ion Thruster

Function

An ion thruster uses an electromagnetic field to accelerate ions through a nozzle [41]. Several schemes exist; the conventional scheme consists of two oppositely charged grids placed in a hollow cylinder [41]. Another brand of ion thruster takes advantage of the Hall effect [41]. In recent years new means of accelerating ions have been found; these include using four grids instead of two and electromagnetic containment [9][58].

Maximum velocity change

Thus far, the greatest delta-v effected using an ion thruster is 0.000 029 c, on NASA's Dawn mission. Assuming IMRA masses and a specific impulse of 14 000 seconds, which is possible with current technology, ion thrusters could boost a starship's velocity by 0.000 78 c [22]. Astronauts on such a starship could not expect to reach any star within a human working lifetime of 40 years, putting this technology in the "none" category within the any/ many/none scheme.

Technological readiness level

Ion thrusters have a TRL of 9: they have been used on several successful missions, and are now often employed on communications satellites [41].

Strengths, weaknesses, and applications

Ion thrusters are efficient compared to other currently available technologies, with Isp values of at least 14 000 s to be available in the near foreseeable future; much higher Isp values have also been claimed [9][58]. However, this Isp is still prohibitively low when the goal is interstellar flight, since it necessitates carrying unfeasible amounts of propellant.

At present ion thrusters' specific impulses make them insufficient for practical interstellar travel. However, their high reliability and TRL would make them a first choice for small "subprobes" to be deployed from an interstellar probe once it reached its destination star system, assuming that ion thrusters are not obsolete by the time such a mission launches.

Necessary developments for interstellar flight

Orders of magnitude increases in electrical power density are necessary to make ion thrusters suitable for interstellar flight. Ion thrusters' specific impulses increase with the power of their electrical power systems– the more electrical power, the greater the specific impulse. However, unless the power system's specific power (kilowatts of electrical power per kilogram of mass) is increased, rather than power alone, improvements in specific impulse come at the cost of acceleration, since adding mass to a spaceship increases the force necessary to achieve a certain acceleration (Newton's second law).

Current thruster working lives must be improved before ion thrusters can be considered an interstellar mission. Ion beams erode the grids used in conventional devices, leading to gradual performance reduction and eventual failure[9]. At present, the longest test of an ion thruster (in a laboratory setting) lasted about 5 years [22]. This will need to be extended in order to make interstellar missions possible with ion thrusters.

Integration with other devices

Some propulsion schemes require auxiliary thrusters: for example, the hypothetical Bussard ramjet (subsection 3.9) requires some means of achieving an initial velocity before it can engage its primary propulsion system; ion thrusters could meet this need.

3.4 Nuclear Rocket

Function

Three general means of using nuclear reactions to propel spacecraft have been proposed. The first, the thermonuclear rocket or fission rocket, uses fission reactions in a solid, liquid, or gaseous core reactor to superheat a reaction mass, which is then expelled through a nozzle, creating thrust[45]. The second, the steady-state fusion rocket, uses steady-state fusion reactions to impart large amounts of energy to a reaction mass and expel this mass through a nozzle; this concept can be best envisioned as a "plasma confinement bottle with a leak" [45]. The third concept, nuclear pulse propulsion (NPP), proposes ejecting small pellets of nuclear fuel through the back of a spacecraft and causing the fuel to undergo fission or fusion a short distance away; the repeated force of the exploding fuel pellets would propel the spacecraft forward [45].

Maximum velocity change

The IMRA predicts a maximum ΔV of 0.000 39 c for a gas-core thermonuclear rocket with a specific impulse of 7 000. s. A steady-state fusion reactor with a specific impulse of 200 000. s could effect a ΔV of 0.011 c according to the IMRA, and a fusion pulse system with a specific impulse of 1 000 000. s could achieve a ΔV of 0.056 c.

Between 1973 and 1978, the British Interplanetary Society developed a concept for an interstellar probe known as Daedalus that would use fusion pulse propulsion to obtain a final velocity of 0.12 c [10]. The Daedalus design called for a fuel mass much greater than that used in the IMRA, and employed staging to increase final ΔV. The IMRA assumes a spacecraft that will use no staging.

Approximate travel times to the Alpha Centauri system (the nearest to the solar system at about 4.4 LY away) using the IMRA maximum ΔVs as average velocity values are as follows: for fission rockets, transit would be approximately 11 000 y; for fusion rockets, about 400 y. These values place both in the "none" category within the any/many/none classification.

The Daedalus team approximated a cruise velocity of 0.12 c for their spacecraft, hypothetically allowing transit to the Alpha Centauri system in under 50 years and putting this concept in the "any star" category.

Technological readiness level

NASA conducted extensive testing of thermonuclear rockets in the 1960s, at which they reached a maximum TRL of 6. The NERVA rocket program conducted several full-power tests of fission rockets with burn durations up to 24 minutes, successfully demonstrating their feasibility[38].

Existing literature has little mention of true steady-state fusion propulsion systems. Their TRL is between 2 and 3; the principles of fusion are well known, and fusion laboratories such as the Lawrence Livermore National Laboratory's National Ignition Facility have sustained fusion for short intervals [53]. However, these intervals generally do not last longer than a few minutes even in the most advanced fusion laboratories, and have not been thoroughly explored in the context of propulsion [23].

Nuclear pulse propulsion reached a TRL of about 4 in the 1960s when NASA conducted its Orion program. The program cumulated in the creation of several detailed spacecraft designs; it also produced an experiment that validated the concept of detonating fuel at a short distance from a spacecraft [45]. This work was done in the context of an interplanetary mission. The Daedalus concept described above was among first analytical applications of NPP to an interstellar mission[10]. The Daedalus study produced no physical prototypes[10].

Strengths, weaknesses, and applications

Compared to ion thrusters, and some of the other concept described herein, thermonuclear rockets have a high thrust to mass ratio; they can produce thrusts in the range of hundreds of kiloNewtons, while ion thrusters produce thrusts on the range of deciNewtons to Newtons[41]. This makes them well-suited to traveling short interplanetary distances with large payloads. However, over longer distances, ion thrusters and other fuel-efficient technologies win out due to their reduced propellant needs; the maximum specific impulse of a fission rocket is predicted to lie near 7 000 s, compared to the 14 000 s of an ion thruster [9]. This specific impulse makes the velocity changes necessary for interstellar flight within a human lifetime, or even several lifetimes, impractical with a fission rocket, due to the amount of fuel that would be necessary for such velocity changes.

Barring an enormous improvement in fusion reactor mass to power ratios, a steady-state fusion propulsion system would carry the disadvantage of being impractically massive. The ITER tokamak-type reactor under construction in Europe, for example, is planned to weigh approximately 23 000 metric tons, roughly half the mass of an aircraft carrier [42]. Such a massive propulsion system would need to be constructed in orbit, and, once built, would need to produce enormous thrust for an appreciable acceleration. At present, their enormous masses make steady-state fusion reactors impractical for any spaceflight; however, predictions of steady-state fusion propulsion specific impulse reside near 200 000 s [45]. If reactor masses can be reduced, steady-state fusion is promising for applications ranging from exploration of distant planets to very long duration (at least 300 year) interstellar missions.

Nuclear pulse propulsion boasts both high thrust and high specific impulse. The Orion study predicted specific impulses ranging from 10 000 s for fission NPP to 100 000 s for fusion NPP and thrusts comparable to those of chemical rockets: a highly favorable combination by today's standards [65]. A possible disadvantage of NPP is the manufacturing cost associated with producing large numbers of finely shaped fuel pellets [65].

495

Necessary developments for interstellar flight

Thermonuclear rockets will probably never be suitable primary propulsion for interstellar missions due to their low specific impulse.

Steady-state fusion propulsion would require several key advancements, which could be summed up in the following three requirements: first, the ability to sustain fusion for periods at least on par with modern chemical rocket burn times; second, orders of magnitude reductions in reactor mass; and third, revision of reactor technology for use as a space propulsion system.

Nuclear pulse propulsion came painfully close to application during the Orion program [45]. NPP systems based on fission, as Orion was, had surpassed the analytical stage of development and moved into the early component testing stage [65]. Fission NPP, assuming designs could be based on work already conducted during the Orion program, would require design modernization, further component testing, systems integration, and design finalization, after which a proof-of-concept spacecraft could be constructed and an in-space test performed. However, in the context of interstellar travel, most of the relevance of this work would be in the technical experience it would provide, which could be used in the development of fusion NPP; fission reactions are not energetic enough to produce the high specific impulse required for a practical interstellar mission [65]. Fusion NPP of the kind envisioned for the Daedalus concept could build off of experience gained with developing fission NPP. Fusion NPP would require physical validation of predicted analytical results, followed by construction and testing of components, systems integration, and, finally, construction of a proof-of-concept. However, even for voyages to the nearest stars, fusion pulse spacecraft would be large enough to require significant improvements in orbit-based construction infrastructure, judging by the size and requirements of the Daedalus concept. The Daedalus craft would have been about the mass of an aircraft carrier, and would have required its helium-3 fuel to be taken from Jupiter's atmosphere; the infrastructure required to construct such a large spacecraft, let alone mine fuel from Jupiter's atmosphere, is far beyond what is currently available [10].

Integration with other devices

Even if not used for propulsion, fission and fusion devices could both serve as spacecraft electrical power sources. Fission reactors have been built and flown; fusion reactors would require the first two improvements described in the strengths, weaknesses, and applications sub-subsection of this subsection.

3.5 Antimatter Rocket

Function

Antimatter rockets would use energy produced during matter-antimatter annihilations to produce thrust. One means of doing so would be to channel the charged particles that result from the annihilations with an electromagnetic nozzle; another would be to use the energy produced to heat a reaction mass and expel it through a conventional or magnetic nozzle [18][19].

Maximum velocity change

The IMRA predicts a maximum ΔV of approximately 0.56 c for an antimatter rocket with a specific impulse of 10 000 000 s. This specific impulse is consistent with predictions made in source [31]. Simulations performed at the Jet Propulsion Laboratory in the 1980s placed maximum antimatter rocket ΔVs at about 0.33 c [19]. Using the IMRA value as an average velocity and assuming no stops, a mission to Alpha Centauri and Barnard's Star could be completed in about 19 years crew time, placing antimatter rockets in the "many stars" category.

Technological readiness level

The antimatter rocket concept has a TRL of 2– the concept has been defined and applied research conducted. Several papers exist describing the hypothetical workings of antimatter rockets [19][31] [59]. However, few of the devices described have been tested in the laboratory.

Strengths, weaknesses, and applications

Antimatter rockets have the highest predicted specific impulse of all devices described herein, exceeding that of the Daedalus rocket by a factor of 10 [31]. Such a high specific impulse could result in a ratio of propellant mass to empty ship mass as low as 5.6 : 1, compared to the approximately 19 : 1 ratio of the Daedalus concept [10]. An antimatter rocket's high predicted specific impulse is a result of the completely efficient conversion of matter to energy that occurs during matter-antimatter annihilations [55]. At present, however, antimatter can only be produced in minute quantities at large cost. Particle accelerators at CERN, for example, would take about 2 billion years to create a gram of antimatter at current production rates [13]. A gram of antimatter would release about 180 trillion joules of energy when annihilated; however, according to [18], sending a starship to the Alpha Centauri system would require about 500 000 trillion joules per kilogram of empty ship mass [18]. Sending a ship with the IMRA empty mass would therefore require about 54 metric tons of antimatter, which would take about 10^{17} years to manufacture. This exceeds the age of the universe (about 13 billion years) by a factor of about 10^7 years. If the rocket uses the first scheme described in the Function sub-subsection, its designers would face the challenge of channeling extremely energetic bursts of particles and gamma rays into a jetstream [45].

Antimatter rockets are also inherently dangerous, since confining their fuel takes energy. Antimatter-powered spacecraft would require magnetic confinement systems for their fuel, since any interaction with ordinary matter (the walls of an ordinary fuel tank, for example) would result in a cataclysmic explosion that would destroy the ship [55]. If the a magnetic confinement system failed, the ship would be destroyed, killing any crew onboard, and, if the ship is near Earth, placing people on Earth in danger from exposure to the explosion.

Necessary developments for interstellar flight
Antimatter production costs must be reduced before it can be considered for use as the primary propellant of an interstellar rocket. Shielding for astronauts on board such a rocket is also a necessity, since matter-antimatter annihilations send gamma rays and dangerous high-energy particles shooting away from the annihilation site in all directions. At present, shielding against gamma rays requires placing a thick wall of a dense material such as lead between the gamma ray source and the protected zone [45]. In order to circumvent the difficulties of launching large quantities of lead or similar material into space, shielding improvements are necessary. Solving this problem may lead to a solution to the problem of channelling the particles and photons produced during the annihilations, which is also necessary for the first scheme proposed in the Function sub-subsection.

Integration with other devices
Antimatter has been proposed as a catalyst for nuclear reactions. Source [57] has found that near-future antimatter production capabilities may allow sufficient quantities to be produced for use as a fission or fusion catalyst [57]. Though antimatter would not be the primary propellant in this case, it could improve the efficacy of fission or fusion-based rockets.

3.6 Solar Sail
Function
A solar sail spacecraft use a large, thin, reflective sheet of material (the "sail") to accelerate under photon pressure from solar radiation [45]. Normally this pressure is negligible, but when it acts on a large, highly reflective surface area such as a solar sail it amounts to a useful force [45].

Maximum velocity change
Estimates by Matloff (quoted in source [34]) place travel time to the Alpha Centauri system at about 1000 years with a solar sail, implying an average velocity of about 0.004 4 c and placing solar sails within the "none in a human lifetime" category in the any/many/none scheme [34]. Final velocities for solar sail spacecraft are highly dependent on mission maneuvers; the mission described above used a close solar approach to maximize photon pressure on the spacecraft's sail [34].

Technological readiness level
Solar sail spacecraft have a TRL of 9. In 2010 the Japanese space agency launched IKAROS, a solar sail probe that successfully traveled to Venus, completed its primary objective, and entered an extended operations phase [1] [2][3][48]. NASA successfully launched a proof-of-concept of its own solar sail technology in 2010 as well, and plans to launch another, larger spacecraft in 2014 [69].

Strengths, weaknesses, and applications
Solar sail spacecraft require no onboard propellant since they use the sun's radiation pressure to produce acceleration. In many cases this makes them less expensive than other spacecraft, and highly effective for missions within the solar system and to its boundary [54][66]. Since solar radiation pressure diminishes as distance from the sun increases, solar sails alone are not likely to be a viable means of rapid interstellar flight[66].

Larger sails are more susceptible to damage from debris than smaller sails. Though this is not usually considered a critical issue for sails operating only within the solar system, it becomes important as flights increase to lightyears in length and centuries in duration [45].

Necessary developments for interstellar flight
Since photon pressure on a surface increases with the area of the surface exposed to radiation, larger sails produce larger accelerations. However, increasing a sail's area also increases its mass, limiting acceleration. For these reasons, increases in sail area and decreases in sail density are necessary to make solar sails a viable option for any interstellar mission. Source [66] estimates current solar sail areal densities at about 15 g/cubic meter, and the largest solar sail currently planned for launch will be a square with sides about 35 meters in length [66][69]. Exploration of the interstellar medium with solar sails could begin in earnest when sail areal densities reach 2.5 g/cubic meter and sail diameters reach about 150 meters [66].

Integration with other devices
Solar sails could serve as a deceleration mechanism for another type of starship if employed favorably; upon reaching the destination star system, the starship could deploy a solar sail to supplement other deceleration mechanisms and save propellant.

Solar sailing could also been used to reposition small spacecraft that accidentally deviate from their intended courses or attitudes. During the Mariner mission, for example, mission controllers used this technique to successfully reposition the Mariner spacecraft when its tracking device locked on to space debris instead of its intended target, the star Canopus[66].

3.7 Beamed Sail
Function
Beamed sail spacecraft would operate on the same principles as solar sail spacecraft, but would use a large laser to supply photon pressure rather than solar radiation [45]. A large laser could put more photon pressure on a sail than solar radiation, allowing greater accelerations [45].

Maximum velocity change
A 1990 NASA study found that a beamed sail could effect a maximum ΔV of about 0.10 c [63]. This would place beamed sails in the "any stars" category in the any/many/none scheme.

Technological readiness level
Despite the high TRL of light-pushed sails, the concept of an interstellar beamed sail spacecraft currently has a TRL of 2. The laser required to push such spacecraft would be massive by modern standards. Early predictions of specifications for such a laser included a 1000-km diameter aperture, 65 gigawatt power output, and jitter reductions of at least 9 orders of magnitude from what was possible at the time those predictions were made [40]. Though subsequent studies that proposed modifying sail materials (e.g. [63]) have reduced laser power requirements to a more manageable 65 megawatts, the challenges of constructing and powering the laser, as well as aiming it over multiple lightyears and maintaining it for hundreds of years of operation, remain unsolved[63]. The overall mode of operation of such a laser– where it will operate from, what will power it, and how it will be built–remain unclear.

Strengths, weaknesses, and applications
Beamed sails share a key advantage of solar sails– they require no onboard propellant– but are capable of greater increases in velocity than solar sails [63]. As described above, constructing, aiming, and powering the laser remain challenges. Deceleration upon reaching the destination star system also presents a challenge– doing so would require the use of an auxiliary propulsion system or a multi-sail scheme as proposed in source [45].
Since beamed sails rely on a solar-system-bound laser for propulsion, a stable political climate is necessary for a beamed sail interstellar mission to be viable. Powering a multi-megawatt laser for hundreds of years would require the cooperation and support of governments and the citizens they govern, which fluctuate over much smaller timescales than those of interstellar missions[45].
Beamed sails could allow humans to escape Earth before it becomes uninhabitable due to solar expansion billions of years in the future. Robots could be left behind to manage the pointing and management of the laser or lasers powering one or more interstellar "arks" [45].

Necessary developments for interstellar flight
Capability to manufacture and deploy sails with diameters of 1000 km or more and areal densities near 0.1 g/square meter must be developed in order for beamed sails to be able to achieve velocities near 0.10 c [66]. Lasers in the megawatt to gigawatt power range with apertures close to 1000 km in diameter and supporting power systems must also be developed[63][45]. Before these can be created, the infrastructure necessary to build and maintain them must be developed; this includes an in-space construction and transport system, as the laser or lasers would need to be located above Earth's atmosphere to avoid beam distortion and weakening [34].

Integration with other devices
One scheme of operation for beamed or solar sails described in source [45] uses the galactic magnetic field to turn and reposition a spacecraft when it is beyond the range of solar or beamed power [45]. This method of repositioning could eliminate difficulties caused by the inability to aim a laser over multiple lightyears.

3.8 Quantum Vacuum Plasma Thruster
Function
The quantum vacuum plasma thruster, or q-thruster, is a new technology currently under development at the Johnson Space Center's Eagleworks Laboratories [64]. Q-thrusters use electrically charged virtual particles as reaction mass. These ubiquitous particles, which arise from interactions between real particles, spontaneously come into existence and vanish over extremely short time intervals [64]. To produce thrust, the q-thruster uses an electromagnetic field to impart momentum to virtual particles, and in doing so imparts momentum to itself [64]. Since it uses ubiquitous virtual particles as reaction mass, a spacecraft using q-thrusters would require no onboard propellant [64].

Maximum velocity change
Source [72] presented data indicating that a starship equipped with q-thrusters could reach the Alpha Centauri system in approximately 30 years, implying a ΔV of about 0.15 c[72]. Q-thrusters have therefore been placed in the "any star" category in the any/many/none scheme.

Technological readiness level
Q-thrusters have a TRL of 3. A small model has been fabricated and tested, and the device may be tested on board the International Space Station in the near future [64].

Strengths, weaknesses, and applications
Source [64] predicts q-thruster specific thrusts to reside near 0.1 N/kW. Using this value, a 100 megawatt reactor could produce a thrust of 10 kN. While this does not compare to the thousands of kN available from chemical rockets, a q-thrusters can operate continuously until it fails or its electrical power source is depleted, since it needs no onboard fuel[27]. This is a tremendous advantage over chemical rockets, which provide all their thrust within a short time. Q-thrusters would also be more powerful than ion thrusters, which produce thrusts in the single-Newton range[41].

Necessary developments for interstellar flight
Q-thrusters must undergo further testing and validation before they can be used in space. Larger thrusters must be tested in a laboratory setting; once these test devices reach acceptable thrust levels, they must be outfitted for use onboard spacecraft[64].

The greatest obstacle to q-thruster use in space is the absence of a suitably powerful electrical power source. The Russian Topaz-1 reactor, among the most powerful ever flown in space, produced a maximum of 10 kW electrical power [77]. Performance improvements of at least 2-4 orders of magnitude from this value are necessary before q-thrusters could be used for interstellar flight [64].

Integration with other devices
Like ion thrusters, q-thrusters could serve as a versatile means of attitude adjustment and fine trajectory refinement for spacecraft using other propulsion systems. Unlike ion thrusters, q-thruster integration would require only an electrical power supply, not an additional fuel supply. Q-thrusters' propellant-free operation would simplify their integration among a spacecraft's other systems.

3.9 Bussard Ramjet

Function

A Bussard ramjet (named for Robert Bussard, who proposed it) would use interstellar hydrogen to provide energy for propulsion through nuclear fusion[80]. A Bussard ramjet's propulsion system would contain three primary components: an auxiliary propulsion system, a fusion reactor, and a large electromagnetic scoop. To reach its maximum speed, the ramjet's auxiliary propulsion system would first boost it to a certain critical speed, at which time the ramjet's magnetic scoop could begin collecting interstellar hydrogen to be used as reaction mass and fuel for nuclear fusion. Past this critical velocity, the main propulsion system, consisting of a steady-state fusion rocket (see subsection 3.4) would engage, boosting the ramjet to its maximum speed[80].

Maximum velocity change

Analytical models, which incorporate interstellar hydrogen density and propulsion system efficiency, place a Bussard ramjet's maximum ΔV near 0.75 c [43]. The Bussard ramjet resides in the "many" category in the any/many/none classification scheme.

Technological readiness level

The Bussard ramjet has a TRL of 2. Though the ramjet remains a concept to be used solely in analytical studies, Bussard's original paper has prompted further research attempting to resolve some of the practical problems associated with the original concept, of which several exist [75][80]. For example, Bussard's paper assumed that interstellar hydrogen could be made to undergo fusion[80]. However, protium, the lightest isotope of hydrogen and the most difficult to use for fusion, constitutes almost all interstellar hydrogen[43]. This makes Bussard's original concept impractical; however, a later paper proposed using a catalytic cycle mimicking that which occurs in some main sequence stars to make the reaction more energy-productive [75]. Further difficulty exists in creating a sufficiently large electromagnetic scoop, which in some estimates must exceed 100 km in diameter [75].

Strengths, weaknesses, and applications

Bussard's paper proposed creating a spacecraft that could accelerate continuously at one to earth gravity. Doing so would provide artificial gravity within the spacecraft. This is of particular relevance to manned missions, because many of the harmful effects of long stays in space arise from microgravity [43][51].

Since Bussard's concept would be able to approach a significant fraction of the speed of light, time dilation, which Einstein predicted in his Special Theory of Relativity, would become significant [25]. At 0.75 c, a voyage would only take about ⅔ of the time for astronauts that it did for earthbound observers. This allows missions to more distant destinations than would be possible without time dilation, since time dilation causes astronauts to age less (compared to stationary observers) over the course of a mission than they would otherwise.

An additional advantage of the Bussard ramjet is its use of interstellar hydrogen as propellant. Using a material present in space significantly reduces spacecraft mass, allowing greater acceleration for the same energy than a rocket that carries all of its fuel [43]. Doing so also reduces mission costs, as the only propellant necessary is that of the auxiliary propulsion system.

Since it relies on interstellar hydrogen for fuel, a Bussard ramjet's performance would vary with the density of the surrounding interstellar medium, rendering the ramjet unusable in particularly sparse regions unless it can first be boosted to a suitable velocity [80]. Conversely, Bussard ramjets would perform well in nebular regions with high hydrogen densities.

The ramjet's speed could make it the interstellar-age equivalent of Columbus' wooden ships. Its development would make voyages to nearby stars possible, though they would take years– to reach the Alpha Centauri system, for example, would take 5.9 years as measured on Earth and 3.9 years for astronauts, traveling at an average speed of 0.75 c [79]. Astronauts making several long voyages (approximately 10 lightyears and greater) would find their earthbound friends and relatives aging faster than they.

Necessary developments for interstellar flight

The two greatest challenges in creating a Bussard ramjet are developing proton-proton fusion and developing sufficiently powerful magnetic field generators for the hydrogen scoop. Prototyping, testing, and the remainder of the standard technology development and mission-certification process can begin once these are solved.

Integration with other devices

As stated in the Function sub-subsection, a Bussard ramjet would require an auxiliary propulsion system to provide it with an initial velocity relative to the interstellar medium. This auxiliary system may be as simple as a tank of pre-stored hydrogen fuel, which the main reactor could use until it reached sufficient speed to use the interstellar medium; alternatively, it could consist of an entirely separate system, such as an ion drive or NPP drive.

Studies by Whitmire and Jackson have suggested that beaming power from earth through a laser could assist a Bussard ramjet in achieving critical velocity. Their conclusions state that such a laser powered ramjet would be more efficient than Bussard's baseline design at speeds less than 0.14 c; however, at greater speeds, the baseline design becomes more efficient [74].

3.10 Alcubierre Warp Drive

Function

The Alcubierre warp drive is not so much a technical concept at present as a mathematical one, though some experiments relevant to its function have been developed[64]. In principle, such a drive would allow a starship to make a voyage to a star faster than a light beam.

Unlike the previous devices, the Alcubierre drive (and the Einstein-Rosen bridge, the subject of the next subsection) does not use a transfer of momentum to accelerate; instead, these devices would allow a spacecraft to circumvent the ultimate limit of the speed of light by changing the structure of spacetime[7]. To move to a distant star, a starship equipped with an Alcubierre drive would expand the spacetime behind it (that is, between it and Earth) while contracting the spacetime between it and its destination, effectively moving the spacecraft towards the destination star[7]. An important consequence of this means of operation is that with respect to the "bubble" of spacetime containing the starship, the starship is not accelerating. Only the "bubble" itself accelerates. Since the speed of light only applies to objects moving within space, and not to space itself, the starship could effectively exceed the speed of light [7]. Evidence of the ability of space to expand and contract faster than the speed of light can be seen in cosmological inflation theory[7].

Maximum velocity change

Calculating the maximum effective ΔV of a moving region of spacetime was beyond the mathematical abilities of the author. Obusy et. al. created a mathematical model of a warp drive whose speed was limited by the size of a theoretical extra dimension, and arrived at the rough conclusion that, mathematically speaking, is the ultimate effective speed of a warp drive. They also concluded that reaching this speed would require more mass-energy than is contained in the entire known universe[81].

Though the basic mathematical model of the warp drive is fairly well established, predicting a maximum ΔV will remain difficult until the concept transitions from a mathematical construct into a physical device or set of devices. Currently, little knowledge exists of the practical constraints on warp drive effective velocity, since such knowledge only comes from experience with physical prototypes. Since cosmological inflation theory places the speed of spacetime expansion and contraction at much higher than the speed of light, it is reasonable to assume that, with sufficient technological advances, spacecraft could be built to reach impressive multiples of the speed of light [64]. Doing so would place the warp drive in the "many stars" category in the any/many/none scheme.

Technological readiness level

The warp drive concept has reached a TRL of 2. Researchers at Eagleworks Laboratories in NASA's Johnson Space Center have developed instrumentation to test for warp-like effects[64]. In addition, the author of this study, Harold White has developed a model that reduces one of the warp drive concept's original problems: its enormous energy demand[73]. Alcubierre's original concept required a mass-energy approximately equivalent to that of the planet Jupiter, clearly beyond practicality[7]. However, White was able to reduce the hypothetical mass-energy requirement by modifying the "warp bubble," the region of flat spacetime in which the warp-equipped ship rests when it is "in warp."

An additional problem with the warp drive concept is that the mass-energy it would use to change the shape of spacetime would need to be negative, violating the weak, dominant, and strong energy conditions[7]. Few definitive solutions to this problem have been posed, though one candidate solution is to somehow employ the Casimir force, which can effectively establish a negative energy density[72].

Strengths, weaknesses, and applications

The occupants of a warp-equipped starship would experience no acceleration when the warp drive was "turned on," since the space containing the starship, not the starship itself, would accelerate [7]. This is advantageous in one respect, since the lack of an artificial gravity effect could simplify starship design, and disadvantageous in another, since artificial gravity would mitigate the negative effects of microgravity on astronauts' bodies.

In Alcubierre's concept, the starship begins and ends its journey with zero velocity relative to its destination [7]. In White's revised concept, the starship establishes an initial velocity, uses a warp effect to scale this velocity to the desired superluminal velocity, and returns to its initial velocity when the warp effect is "turned off" [73]. In each of these cases, the likelihood of "overshooting" the destination is reduced in comparison to some of the concepts that establish high subluminal velocities, since, in the case of a malfunction, less energy is required to correct the spacecraft's trajectory.

Assuming it can enable sufficiently rapid interstellar travel, development of a warp drive would mitigate a number of the problems that would plague subluminal missions, and would circumvent the need to develop solutions to these problems. For example, since a sufficiently fast warp-equipped starship could complete a transit to the Alpha Centauri system in weeks or months rather than years, current biomedical technology would be sufficient for such a mission, since modern astronauts routinely spend months in space aboard the International Space Station[4]. Few radical advances, such as hibernation or DNA hardening, would be required, assuming warp travel does not create any unexpected health problems for astronauts.

Though it could, in principle, travel much faster than a subluminal starship, navigation in a warp-equipped spacecraft would be more difficult. In White and Davis' analysis of the warp drive within the Chung-Freeze metric, it was found that engaging a warp field caused radiation traveling towards the spacecraft to dim as the spacecraft moved "off-brane"[70]. As such, navigation by the stars would be impossible, as the stars would be invisible. Making a trip in several short superluminal bursts while taking stellar headings in the intervals between each burst may mitigate this problem.

Characteristics of matter and radiation fields around moving, warped spacetime such as that of a warp drive are largely unknown; the limited knowledge of these characteristics comes almost entirely from mathematical prediction. Some predictions state that ordinarily benign matter and radiation could pose dangers to astronauts within a warp region; others state that matter and radiation could accumulate at the front of the region and be cataclysmically released when the warp effect ceased, destroying the destination planet and perhaps the starship as well[46][82]. Physical experimentation is ultimately necessary to validate or invalidate these claims.

The invention of a warp drive would allow spacecraft to achieve feats only envisioned today in science fiction. Warp-equipped starships could have as many applications as ocean-going ships, from exploration and colonization of new territories in space to commerce and shipping once humans established themselves in these territories.

Necessary developments for interstellar flight

Laboratory experimentation on physics relevant to warp-enabled travel should continue in order to validate established mathematical theories. Ultimately, a suitable source of negative energy density must be found before a warp drive can be constructed[72]. As stated previously, the Casimir effect may provide such an energy source. If this is found to be true, prototyping of small warp-equipped devices may begin. White suggested equipping small, conventionally-propelled space probes with warp drives to validate the mathematical prediction that warp effects can reduce a spacecraft's mass budget, thereby increasing its power/mass ratio and its maximum ΔV [73]. Such an application could presumably use conventional navigation, as the spacecraft would not necessarily have to move at a superluminal velocity. Once such effects have been validated, work can begin on constructing larger spacecraft whose primary propulsion will be warp effects. New navigation schemes will become necessary when these larger spacecraft finally exceed the speed of light (see Strengths, Weaknesses, and Applications sub-subsection).

Integration with other devices

In White's concept, an initial velocity is required before a warp effect can be initiated [73]. A variety of conventional devices could be used for this purpose; quantum vacuum plasma thrusters hold particular promise in this area, since they require no onboard propellant and can therefore accelerate for longer periods of time than thrusters that carry propellant (see subsection 3.8).

3.11 Non-trivial Spacetime Topologies (Spacetime Tubes)

Function

The terms "non-trivial topologies" and "spacetime tubes" have been used to encompass wormholes and Krasnikov tubes[44]. In the context of starflight, these non-trivial topologies can be envisioned as bridges or tubes between two regions of spacetime. These bridges can be made "shorter" than the shortest path between the two regions that passes only through unaltered space. For example, in an arbitrarily short time, a traversable wormhole could transport a starship between two points lightyears apart[17].

Before a wormhole or Krasnikov tube can be used for interstellar travel, it must be created and extended between Earth and the destination star. This concept is insufficiently developed for one to pose a definite mode of operation, but all spacetime tube scenarios require an initial placing of one end of the tube at the destination. This would require transporting the destination end of the tube on board a subluminal spacecraft. Though the starship could not exceed the speed of light on the outbound leg of the trip, astronauts could return to earth through the tube. Since the tube would connect the ship's final location in space and time to its initial location, astronauts returning through the tube would arrive at or near the time they left[16]. The primary difference between Krasnikov tubes and traversable wormholes is that objects can travel both ways through a wormhole, but only one way through a Krasnikov tube[17].

Maximum velocity change

The idea of maximum ΔV does not apply to starflight schemes that employ spacetime tubes. The "setup" or outbound phase of a tube-equipped trip would take place at a subluminal velocity, while the return trip through the tube would be exceedingly brief in comparison and would deposit travelers near the location in space and time from which they left [16][17]. Outward-bound trip time would be contingent on the carrier spacecraft's velocity; to earthbound observers it would take no less time for the ship to transit to the destination than a photon would, but this would be irrelevant overall, because the astronauts or information on board would return to a time shortly after they had left.

If multiple tubes could be constructed, spacetime tubes would constitute a "many stars" system in the any/many/none scheme.

Technological readiness level

Spacetime tubes have a TRL of 1. Several different mathematical models exist, such as those proposed by Einstein and Rosen, Thorne, Schwarzschild, and others; however, physical prototypes for tube-enabled systems require much better knowledge of spacetime metric engineering than is currently available [24][49]. Spacetime tubes have never been empirically observed[39][44].

Strengths, weaknesses, and applications

Spacetime tubes would not suffer from the difficulty of navigation that warp-enabled starships (subsection 4.10) would experience, since the tube would provide a relatively straightforward path between points in spacetime. Establishing these tubes would require initial subluminal trips, as explained in the Function sub-subsection. Wormholes and Krasnikov tubes have been called "interstellar subway systems." If networks of such tubes could be built, they could function as such, requiring construction but serving to transport people and objects between the stars. Such an approach lacks the versatility of the warp drive concept– like passengers on a train, astronauts in a wormhole would not be able to travel away from the "tracks"– the tube system.

Necessary developments for interstellar flight

Creating spacetime tubes would require large technological advances. To create a traversable wormhole, for example, would require the expansion of a naturally-occurring wormhole from the Planck-scale to a macroatomic scale[16]. Constructing a device that could somehow feed energy into such a small space would constitute an enormous leap in technological capabilities.

Like the warp drive, construction of a spacetime tube would require a negative energy density. A suitable source of negative energy density must be discovered before any spacetime tube can be constructed[16].

Integration with other devices

As stated in the Function sub-subsection, construction of an interstellar spacetime tube system would require initial journeys in subluminal spacecraft. Without better understanding of the physical nature of spacetime tubes it is difficult to determine which type of spacecraft would be best suited for tube mouth transport.

4. Hypothetical Comparison—Superluminal versus Subluminal
4.1 Versatility

The least time, as measured on Earth, in which a subluminal spacecraft could traverse a light year will always be approximately 1 year, regardless of the time measured on board the spacecraft. This places several limitations on the uses of subluminal spacecraft. Assuming velocities arbitrarily close to the speed of light, such spacecraft are appropriate for colonization and long-duration science missions to the nearest stars, though Earthbound scientists would need to wait years for new data from interstellar exploration. Superluminal spacecraft would also be appropriate for these applications, in addition to relatively short manned missions, and, potentially, interstellar prospecting and commerce.

4.2 Cost effectiveness
4.2.1 Introduction

The author constructed a simple mathematical model to give an idea of the effects of starship velocities on overall costs of manned missions. Predictably, superluminal travel yielded less expensive missions in most of the scenarios tested, though time dilation made subluminal travel cheaper in some situations.

4.2.2 Methodology (see Symbols section for variable names and units)

The purpose of this model is to compare transit costs for superluminal and subluminal starships. Only transit costs are calculated; overall mission cost is not considered. Actual missions will vary in expense based on the cost of the starships themselves and the resources they will carry, in addition to the variables described below.

The two variables dependent on ship velocity that have the greatest influence on transit cost are the cost of life support related consumables, , and communications costs .

The total transit cost these variables generate is given by

$$C = C_{ls} + C_c \tag{4.2.1}$$

is given by

$$C_{ls} = r_{ls} n t_s \tag{4.2.2}$$

The ship's transit time, as experienced by the crew, depends on its velocity, as follows:

$$t_s = \frac{D}{v}\sqrt{1 - v^2/c^2} \tag{4.2.3}$$

Where is the time dilation predicted by special relativity. For superluminal travel, the time dilation factor is assumed to be 1.

Time dilation does not affect communications costs, since these depend on earth time, not spaceship time. Since Earth is considered to be at rest in this model, the time dilation factor for a time lapse on Earth is 1. For communications costs, we have

$$C_c = \frac{f d_c}{v} \tag{4.2.4}$$

Combining the expressions giving two velocity-dependent cost variables, the final equation for transit costs accrued during transit itself is given by

$$C = r_{ls} n \frac{D}{v} \sqrt{1 - v^2/c^2} + \frac{f d_c}{v}$$ (4.2.5)

This final equation was used in a Google spreadsheet to provide data on several different scenarios, each comparing the cost of a superluminal mission to that of a subluminal mission for various destinations. The values used, and reason for each, are as follows:

r_{ls} = 100 \$/day/person – assumed reasonable

n = 8 crew members – assumed 4 men, 4 women

r_c = 100 000 \$/day – approximated cost of using Deep Space Network[67] d_c = 0.003 ly – estimated communications cutoff distance of Voyager 1 spacecraft [50]

f = 1/84 days/days – 2 hours out of each week

Costs were evaluated for the following values of D:

D ={4.4 ly, 5.7 ly, 10.7 ly, 15.0 ly, 20.3 ly}

These distances correspond to the distances of the Alpha Centauri, Barnard's Star, Epsilon Eridani, Groombridge 1618, and Wolf 630 star systems from Earth, respectively.

For each D value, costs were evaluated for the following values of v:

v = {0.10c, 0.50c, 0.99c, 1.10c, 5.00c, 10.00c}

4.3.3 Results

The following tables and charts give cost estimates for the scenarios described above. Decimal places after the hundredths place in charts should be disregarded.

Figure 4.2.3.1
Subluminal starship velocity = 0.10c; Superluminal starship velocity = 1.10c

	Subluminal Cost ($)	Superluminal Cost ($)	Cost difference ($)
Alpha Centauri, 4.4 LY	12805399.1242495	1268413.63636364	11536985.4878859
Barnard's Star, 5.9 LY	17166429.0610878	1666868.18181818	15499560.8792697
Epsilon Eridani, 10.7 LY	31121724.8589704	2941922.72727273	28179802.1316977
Groombridge 1618, 15.0 LY	43623344.0112403	4084159.09090909	39539184.9203312
Wolf 630, 20.3 LY	59032316.4547357	5492031.81818182	53540284.6365539

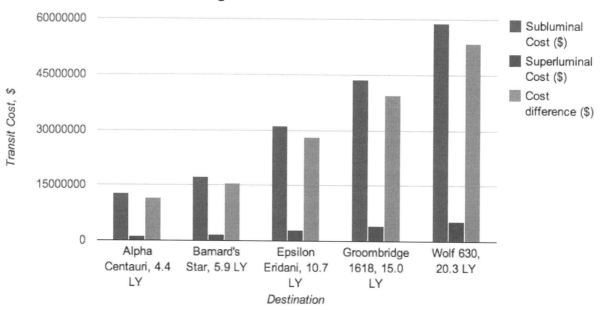

Figure 4.2.3.1 Transit costs.

Figure 4.2.3.2
Subluminal starship velocity = 0.50c; Superluminal starship velocity = 1.10c

	Subluminal Cost ($)	Superluminal Cost ($)	Cost difference ($)
Alpha Centauri, 4.4 LY	2229472.01084658	1268413.63636364	961058.374482947
Barnard's Star, 5.9 LY	2988629.87980402	1666868.18181818	1321761.69798584
Epsilon Eridani, 10.7 LY	5417935.06046782	2941922.72727273	2476012.3331951
Groombridge 1618, 15.0 LY	7594187.61814582	4084159.09090909	3510028.52723673
Wolf 630, 20.3 LY	10276545.4217954	5492031.81818182	4784513.60361362

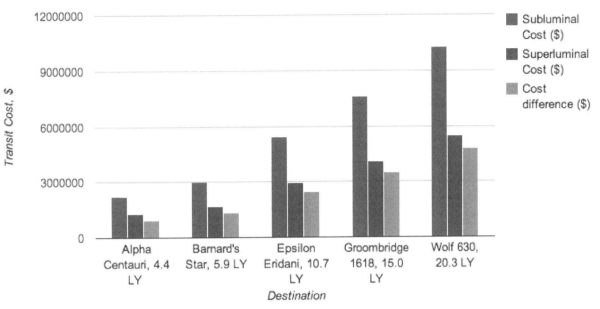

Figure 4.2.3.2 Transit costs.

Figure 4.2.3.3
Subluminal starship velocity = 0.99c; Superluminal starship velocity = 1.10c

	Subluminal Cost ($)	Superluminal Cost ($)	Cost difference ($)
Alpha Centauri, 4.4 LY	184517.118615235	1268413.63636364	-1083896.5177484
Barnard's Star, 5.9 LY	246971.486088847	1666868.18181818	-1419896.69572933
Epsilon Eridani, 10.7 LY	446825.462004404	2941922.72727273	-2495097.26526832
Groombridge 1618, 15.0 LY	625861.315428758	4084159.09090909	-3458297.77548033
Wolf 630, 20.3 LY	846533.41383552	5492031.81818182	-4645498.4043463

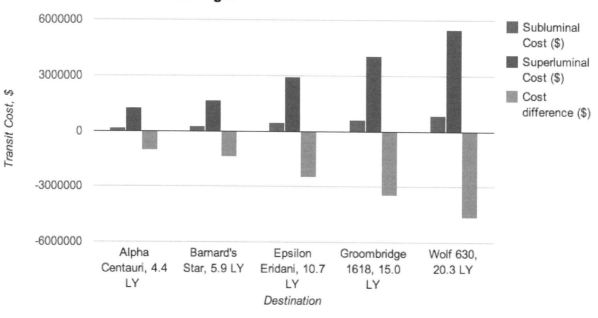

Figure 4.2.3.3 Transit costs.

Figure 4.2.3.4
Subluminal starship velocity = 0.10c; Superluminal starship velocity = 5.00c

	Subluminal Cost ($)	Superluminal Cost ($)	Cost difference ($)
Alpha Centauri, 4.4 LY	12805399.1242495	279051	12526348.1242495
Barnard's Star, 5.9 LY	17166429.0610878	366711	16799718.0610878
Epsilon Eridani, 10.7 LY	31121724.8589704	647223	30474501.8589704
Groombridge 1618, 15.0 LY	43623344.0112403	898515	42724829.0112403
Wolf 630, 20.3 LY	59032316.4547357	1208247	57824069.4547357

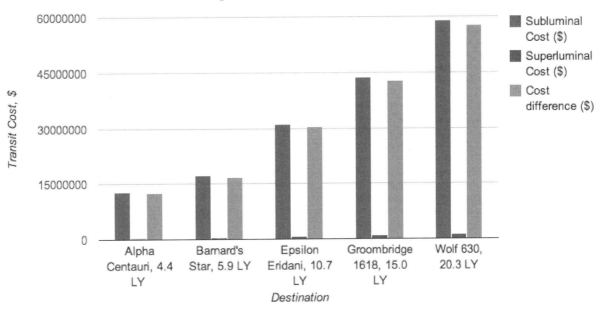

Figure 4.2.3.4 Transit costs.

Figure 4.2.3.5
Subluminal starship velocity = 0.50c; Superluminal starship velocity = 5.00c

	Subluminal Cost ($)	Superluminal Cost ($)	Cost difference ($)
Alpha Centauri, 4.4 LY	2229472.01084658	279051	1950421.01084658
Barnard's Star, 5.9 LY	2988629.87980402	366711	2621918.87980402
Epsilon Eridani, 10.7 LY	5417935.06046782	647223	4770712.06046782
Groombridge 1618, 15.0 LY	7594187.61814582	898515	6695672.61814582
Wolf 630, 20.3 LY	10276545.4217954	1208247	9068298.42179544

509

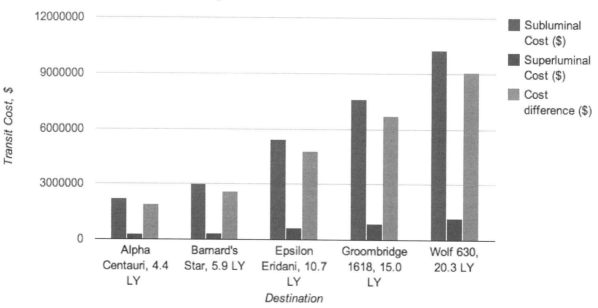

Figure 4.2.3.5 Transit costs.

Figure 4.2.3.6
Subluminal starship velocity = 0.99c; Superluminal starship velocity = 5.00c

	Subluminal Cost ($)	Superluminal Cost ($)	Cost difference ($)
Alpha Centauri, 4.4 LY	184517.118615235	279051	-94533.8813847649
Barnard's Star, 5.9 LY	246971.486088847	366711	-119739.513911153
Epsilon Eridani, 10.7 LY	446825.462004404	647223	-200397.537995596
Groombridge 1618, 15.0 LY	625861.315428758	898515	-272653.684571242
Wolf 630, 20.3 LY	846533.41383552	1208247	-361713.586164481

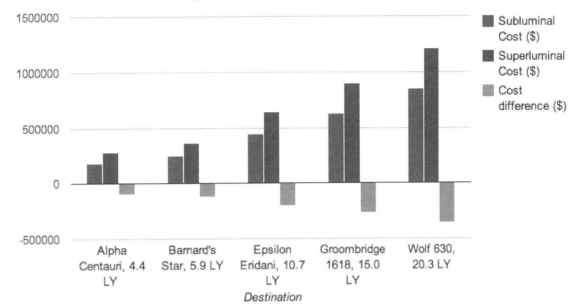

Figure 4.2.3.6 Transit costs.

Figure 4.2.3.7
Subluminal starship velocity = 0.10c; Superluminal starship velocity = 10.00c

	Subluminal Cost ($)	Superluminal Cost ($)	Cost difference ($)
Alpha Centauri, 4.4 LY	12805399.1242495	139525.5	12665873.6242495
Barnard's Star, 5.9 LY	17166429.0610878	183355.5	16983073.5610878
Epsilon Eridani, 10.7 LY	31121724.8589704	323611.5	30798113.3589704
Groombridge 1618, 15.0 LY	43623344.0112403	449257.5	43174086.5112403
Wolf 630, 20.3 LY	59032316.4547357	604123.5	58428192.9547357

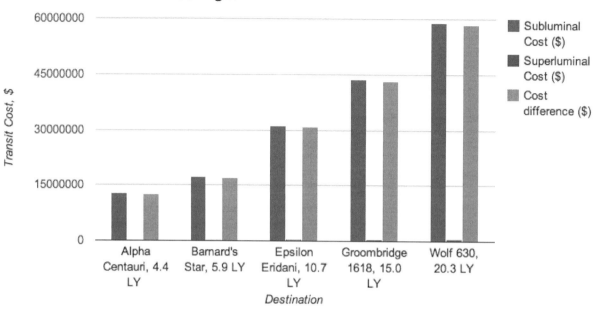

Figure 4.2.3.7 Transit costs.

Figure 4.2.3.8
Subluminal starship velocity = 0.50c; Superluminal starship velocity = 10.00c

	Subluminal Cost ($)	Superluminal Cost ($)	Cost difference ($)
Alpha Centauri, 4.4 LY	2229472.01084658	139525.5	2089946.51084658
Barnard's Star, 5.9 LY	2988629.87980402	183355.5	2805274.37980402
Epsilon Eridani, 10.7 LY	5417935.06046782	323611.5	5094323.56046782
Groombridge 1618, 15.0 LY	7594187.61814582	449257.5	7144930.11814582
Wolf 630, 20.3 LY	10276545.4217954	604123.5	9672421.92179544

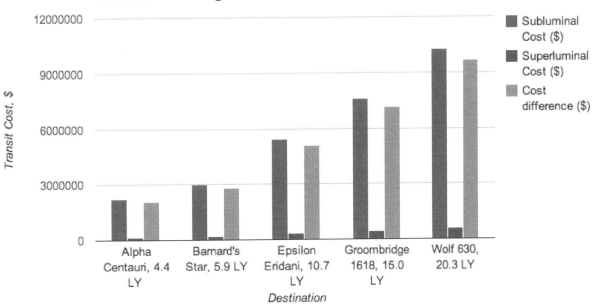

Figure 4.2.3.8 Transit costs.

Figure 4.2.3.9
Subluminal starship velocity = 0.99c; Superluminal starship velocity = 10.00c

	Subluminal Cost ($)	Superluminal Cost ($)	Cost difference ($)
Alpha Centauri, 4.4 LY	184517.118615235	139525.5	44991.6186152351
Barnard's Star, 5.9 LY	246971.486088847	183355.5	63615.9860888469
Epsilon Eridani, 10.7 LY	446825.462004404	323611.5	123213.962004404
Groombridge 1618, 15.0 LY	625861.315428758	449257.5	176603.815428758
Wolf 630, 20.3 LY	846533.41383552	604123.5	242409.913835519

513

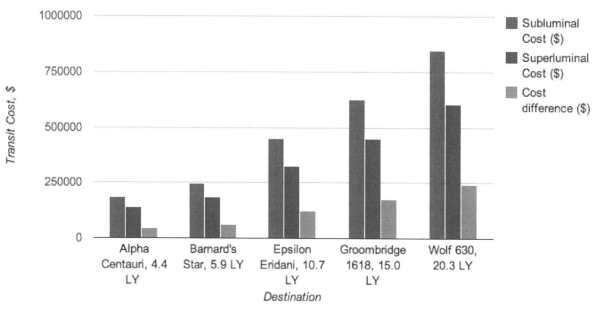

Figure 4.2.3.9 Transit costs.

4.2.4 Conclusions

In terms of transit cost only, superluminal travel is generally less expensive than subluminal travel. However, in two (figures 4.2.3 and 4.2.6) of the nine data sets shown above, subluminal travel is less expensive than superluminal travel, since time dilation lessened the time the crew experienced in transit. Communications costs had only a small effect on overall transit costs, since the duration of the mission spent in communication with Earth was relatively small.

4.3 Economic Benefit
4.3.1 Introduction

Though considered far-fetched at present, the development of interstellar travel may prompt entrepreneurs to attempt to exploit the resources available outside of the solar system– to attempt "interstellar shipping". Entrepreneurs may, for example, wish to harvest some of the diamond theorized to exist in enormous quantities on at least two exoplanets in our galaxy [11][15]. The following model is an attempt to make a rough comparison of the efficacies of superluminal and subluminal starships in this respect. A hypothetical scenario in which starships return diamond to Earth from 55 Cancri E, a so-called "diamond planet" 40 ly away, is presented, and superluminal and subluminal starships are evaluated in terms of income generated over their working lifetimes. For simplicity the price of diamond is assumed constant, though in reality, an influx of diamond as large as would be possible in such a scenario would almost certainly reduce the price of diamond considerably. Predictably, superluminal spacecraft generate more income over their working lifetimes. The purpose of this calculation is to quantify this difference in returns.

4.3.2 Methodology (see Symbols section for variable names and units)

The time the ship takes to make a round trip (out and back) to the destination is given by

$$t = \frac{2D}{v} \tag{4.3.1}$$

514

In years the ship can make round trips, as follows:

$$n = \frac{w}{t} = \frac{vw}{2D} \tag{4.3.2}$$

If the ship earns dollars per round trip, the income the ship earns over its lifetime is given by

$$I = nx = \frac{vwx}{2D} \tag{4.3.3}$$

This final equation was used in a Google spreadsheet to generate the charts and graphs in the following sub-sub-section.

The following values were held constant for both superluminal and subluminal starships:

$$D = 40 \text{ ly}$$

$$w = 100 \text{ y}$$

$$x = \$1 \text{ for simplicity}$$

In reality, the difference in spacecraft cost may be an important factor in the relative profitability of superluminal and subluminal starships; however, spacecraft cost is assumed equal for superluminal and subluminal starships. The following values of v were tested:

$$v = 0.99 \text{ ly/y for subluminal; } v = 2.00 \text{ ly/y and } v = 10.00 \text{ ly/y for superluminal}$$

Since income per round trip is assumed to be $1, the graphs in the following sub-subsection show ratios of incomes, not actual values.

A starship would not leave for another voyage if its working lifetime would expire on that voyage; for this reason, the number of round trips per working lifetime n in equation 4.3.2 was always rounded down to the nearest whole number.

4.3.3 Results

The following graphs and tables show the ratios of subluminal starship's revenues to a superluminal ship's revenues. "Ship A" denotes the subluminal ship, "Ship B" the superluminal ship. As with the previous subsection, decimal places after the hundredths place should be disregarded.

Figure 4.3.3.1
Subluminal starship (Ship A) velocity = 0.99 c; Superluminal starship (Ship B) velocity = 2.00 c

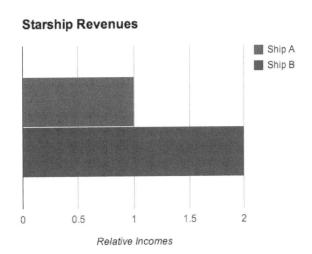

Outputs	Ship A	Ship B
One-way transit time, y	40.4040404040404	20
Round-trip time, y	80.8080808080808	40
Trips in t years	1	2
Income in t years, $	1	2

Figure 4.3.3.1 Starship relative revenues.

Figure 4.3.3.2
Subluminal starship (Ship A) velocity = 0.99 c; Superluminal starship (Ship B) velocity = 10.00 c

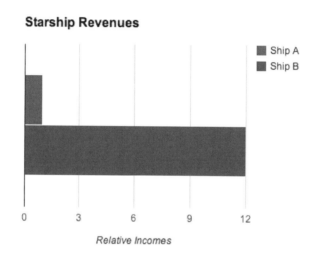

Outputs	Ship A	Ship B
One-way transit time, y	40.4040404040404	4
Round-trip time, y	80.8080808080808	8
Trips in t years	1	12
Income in t years, $	1	12

Figure 4.3.3.2 Starship relative revenues.

4.3.4 Conclusions

If the site from which resources are being extracted is 40 ly away, a superluminal starship traveling at 2.00 c earns twice as much during its working lifetime as a subluminal starship traveling at 0.99c, and a superluminal starship traveling at 10 c earns 12 times as much. The superluminal ship earns 12 times, not 10 times, the revenue of the subluminal starship due to the requirement that the number of round trips be an integer.

If a large starship returned 50 000 kg of high-purity diamond to Earth, this quantity of diamond could be sold for about $275 billion 2013 US dollars[20]. This equates to about 1/50th of the 2012 US gross domestic product for each trip[76]. Any government, corporation, or other entity capable of constructing a starship that meets the parameters outlined herein, superluminal or subluminal, could amass incredible wealth within a lifetime.

4.4 Possible Destinations and Astronaut Health
4.4.1 Possible destinations

Current theory permits superluminal and subluminal starships to travel to any point in the universe within the lives of any astronauts on board if one makes the following assumptions: (1) ample propulsion system energy available to be converted into spacecraft kinetic energy or used for spacetime manipulation and (2) the universe continues to exist indefinitely. Time dilation allows arbitrarily short trip times as experienced by astronauts on board a subluminal starship[25]. Time dilation is quantified in the following equation:

$$\Delta t_s = \Delta t_e \sqrt{1 - v^2} \qquad (4.4.1)$$

To earthbound observers, subluminal starships can never exceed the speed of light, and will thus never be able to make a trip any faster than a light beam. In other words, if a subluminal starship's destination is 3000 ly away, its crew can never make a complete journey in less than 6000 y as measured by earthbound observers. By the time the crew of a subluminal starship returns from such a journey, everyone they had known would have long passed– the crew would likely return to a completely different society than what they had known. Since time will only "slow down" to astronauts on board the starship, condition (2) above may be called into question for extremely long-distance journeys. Poul Anderson's short science fiction story *Tau Zero* offers an illustration of this possibility [83]. Superluminal ships may not experience time dilation. In Alcubierre's warp drive scenario, for example, proper time within the spacecraft is the same as proper time on Earth, meaning that the spacecraft would not experience time dilation[7]. Since superluminal starships could, in theory, travel with arbitrarily high effective velocity, they could in principle transport astronauts anywhere in the known universe within their lifetimes, and these astronauts would be able to return home to the same age from which they left.

4.4.2 Astronaut Health

Two environmental conditions, radiation and microgravity, are the primary known assailants to astronaut health on long-duration missions. Radiation can increase astronaut risk for cancer, cause acute radiation sickness, and lead to central nervous system defects and degenerative diseases [51]. Subluminal starships will be exposed to all known interstellar radiation; radiation risks for superluminal starships are difficult to predict without experience. Some warp drive models predict that photons will become trapped in the warped region of space in front of the starship, gain enormous energy while "in warp," and enter the spacecraft, killing its occupants[46]. Other models have been proposed to mitigate danger from incident radiation[82].

Since subluminal starships carrying astronauts must accelerate and decelerate, astronauts on board will experience at least some artificial gravity, partially mitigating the bone and muscle losses that occur in microgravity[51]. Both of the superluminal starship concepts outlined herein experience minimum prolonged proper acceleration; they provide no artificial gravity by virtue of acceleration, though their shorter transit times would likely make this a minor problem.

5. Societal Issues
5.1 Garnering Funding

Interstellar flight will require advances in scientific knowledge and technological capability, so any discussion on the issues with interstellar flight would be incomplete without mention of funding these advances. This section is intended to provide a general overview of the landscape entrepreneurs must navigate to succeed in funding a large-scale space project such as a starship. Though the details below apply primarily to the American space arena, it will likely serve as a decent model for other nations.

American space projects have historically involved five major groups: government, industry, academia, military, and the public [36]. The relationships between these groups are numerous and complicated, but leverageable for skilled entrepreneurs seeking support. Examples of interrelationships among them include the public influencing the government through voting, the government influencing the military through oversight, and industry and the military funding academic projects with the promise of useful applications.

To receive support, the builders of a starship will need to tailor their approaches to each group[36]. For example, when presenting their goal to members of the general public, starship marketers will need to show how a starship will benefit society at large– this includes "hard" benefits, such as job creation, and "soft" benefits, such as the betterment of the human species through expansion into the cosmos; in contrast, when presenting to the military and industry, marketers must assure their audience that their endeavor will produce a useful product.

Starship marketers must also show each group that they are aware of the relationships between the groups– when attempting to gain financial support from members of academia, for example, marketers must recognize that many members of academia receive funding from industry and the military. As such, academics will tend to support products favorable to these two other groups. Though awareness of all the intricate relationships between the five groups given above would be almost impossible, greater sensitivity towards them allows marketers to create more persuasive requests for funding.

If technological developments make clear that superluminal IST is feasible, members of all five groups will almost certainly favor it over subluminal IST. This applies to military, industry, and academia in particular, since superluminal IST has more potential applications (see subsection 5.1). Successful marketing of superluminal schemes will require proponents of superluminal IST to overcome skepticism among their audiences; this could prove a formidable challenge even if the mechanisms of superluminal IST have been verified among the scientific and engineering communities associated with it.

At present, the general consensus among members of the scientific and technological community surrounding interstellar travel is that manned subluminal interstellar missions are more likely to occur in the next hundred years. This will have a negative effect on attempts to market superluminal IST, and perhaps justifiably so– at present superluminal IST remains science fiction, while subluminal IST, by some definitions, began when Voyager 1 passed through the heliopause[54]. Research such as White's offers tantalizing hints that superluminal IST may not be as difficult as previously imagined [64]. For now, laboratories investigating mechanisms of subluminal IST outnumber those investigating the necessities of superluminal IST. At present, all conceived schemes for superluminal and subluminal IST within a human lifetime remain either too speculative or too expensive to be effectively sold.

5.2 A Note on Popular Appeal

Among the ventures the American space program has pursued, the most popular have been those that pushed the limits of human vision: those that have provided followers with a view of some new part of the universe. These include the Spirit missions to Mars, the Hubble Space Telescope, and the Voyager probes; Fiddelke (2011) wrote, "[none of these missions] were presidentially-mandated … but they were the ones that captured the interest of so many, because of their exploratory nature"[28]. At present any interstellar mission, superluminal or subluminal, would be exploratory in nature, and could become more popular than any other current mission.

6. Conclusion

The issues with interstellar travel can be loosely classified as scientific, technological, or societal. These categories are not necessarily mutually exclusive– for example, many problems are scientific and technological in nature, emerging from both a lack of knowledge of the workings of nature and a lack of engineering experience or a suitable means of bringing a theoretical construct into application.

An explicit goal will preceed an interstellar mission; this goal will define the mission characteristics and technological requirements.

At present, investing in superluminal IST is riskier than investing in subluminal IST, as superluminal IST is still far from technical application, while a subluminal craft has already reached the border of interstellar space. However, superluminal IST promises much greater returns than subluminal IST due to its greater variety of potential applications.

Acknowledgements

John Kraljic of Falmouth High School was instrumental in guiding the author towards sensibility in writing. His advice corrected some of the author's wishful thinking and guided this work towards objectivity.

Gary Glick, of Falmouth High School and the Chandra X-ray Telescope Educational Outreach Program, consented to be interviewed for details on funding large-scale space projects, compensating for the author's lack of experience in this arena.

The author also wishes to thank his parents for their editing assistance, encouragement, and belief in the power of the mind to solve seemingly insurmountable problems.

Works Cited

1. "2010年の締めくくり(12/26)　- Daily Report - Dec 26, 2010". IKAROS Blog (in Japanese). JAXA. 26 December 2010. Retrieved 22 January 2011.

2. "今日の IKAROS(12/10)　- Daily Report - Dec 10, 2010". IKAROS Blog (in Japanese). JAXA. 10 December 2010. Retrieved 22 January 2011

3. "宇宙帆船イカロス、お疲れさま…実験終え「人工惑星」に" (in Japanese). Asahi Shimbun. 10 December 2010. Retrieved 22 January 2011.

4. "Expedition 37." NASA. Ed. Mark Garcia. NASA, 2013. Web. 27 Oct. 2013. <http://www.nasa.gov/mission_pages/station/expeditions/expedition37/index.html>.

5. Ad Astra Rocket Company. "How Fast Could (Should) We Go to Mars?" Ad Astra Rocket Company. Ad Astra Rocket Company, 2013. Web. 30 July 2013.

6. Ad Astra Rocket Company. "VX-200." Ad Astra Rocket Company. Ad Astra Rocket Company, 2013. Web. 30 July 2013.

7. Alcubierre, Miguel. "The warp drive: hyper-fast travel within general relativity." Classical and Quantum Gravity 11.5 (1994): L73.

8. Alexander, David. "Gene - Biography - Roddenberry.com." Gene - Biography - Roddenberry.com. Roddenberry Entertainment, Inc., 2013. Web. 02 Sept. 2013.

9. Bramanti, C., et al. "The Innovative Dual-Stage 4-Grid Ion Thruster Concept–Theory And First Experimental Results." IAC-06-C4. 4.7 presented at 57th International Astronautical Congress, Valencia, Spain, 2006.

10. British Interplanetary Society. "Project Daedalus – Interstellar Mission." Project Daedalus – Interstellar Mission. British Interplanetary Society, 2013. Web. 04 Aug. 2013.

11. Brown, Mark. "Astronomers Find a Planet Made of Diamond in the Milky Way." Wired UK. Condé Nast, 26 Aug. 2011. Web. 31 Aug. 2013.

12. Cartlidge, Edwin. "Magnetic Shield Could Protect Spacecraft." Physicsworld.com Homepage. IOP Science, 6 Nov. 2008. Web. 26 July 2013.

13. CERN. "CERN - European Organization for Nuclear Research - Spotlight On... What's Making the News at CERN." CERN. CERN, Jan. 2008. Web. 31 July 2013.

14. Chaisson, Eric and McMillan, Steve, Astronomy Today, 3rd Ed., Prentice-Hall, (1999).

15. Clark, Liat. "New Exoplanet Is Twice Earth's Size — And Made Largely of Diamond." Wired UK. Condé Nast, 10 Oct. 2012. Web. 31 Aug. 2013.

16. Cramer, John G. "More about Wormholes -To the Stars in No Time." Alternate View Column. Analog Magazine, 13 Oct. 1989. Web. 27 Oct. 2013. <http://www.npl.washington.edu/AV/altvw39.html>.

17. Cramer, John G. "The Krasnikov Tube: A Subway to the Stars." Alternate View Column. Analog Magazine, 12 Apr. 1997. Web. 27 Oct. 2013. <http://www.npl.washington.edu/av/altvw86.html>.

18. Crowl, Adam. "Antimatter Rockets to the Stars." Antimatter Rockets to the Stars. British Interplanetary Society, 2012. Web. 31 July 2013.

19. Crowl, Adam. "Re-Thinking The Antimatter Rocket." Centauri Dreams RSS. Tau Zero Foundation, 2 Apr. 2012. Web. 31 July 2013.

20. D.NEA. "Diamond Prices." Diamond Price. D.NEA, 2013. Web. 01 Sept. 2013.

21. Dunbar, Brian. "Ideas Based on What We Know." Warp Drive, When? NASA, 23 Nov. 2004. Web. 26 July 2013.

22. Dunbar, Brian. "Ion Thruster Sets World Record." NASA. NASA, 28 July 2013. Web. 30 July 2013.

23. EFDA. "How Long Is the Longest Sustained Fusion Reaction Achieved by JET and Elsewhere?" EFDA. European Fusion Development Agreement, 2013. Web. 19 Oct. 2013. <http://www.efda.org/faq/how-long-is-the-longest-sustained-fusion-reaction-achieved-by-jet-and-elsewhere/>.

24. Einstein, Albert and Rosen, Nathan (1935). "The Particle Problem in the General Theory of Relativity". Physical Review 48: 73.

25. Einstein, Albert. Relativity: The special and the general theory. Penguin. com, 1920.

26. Everett, Allen E., and Thomas A. Roman. "Superluminal subway: the Krasnikov tube." Physical Review D 56.4 (1997): 2100.

27. Falcon 9 Heavy. Hawthorne: SpaceX, 2013. Print.

28. Fiddelke, Megan M. "Obama's Giant Leap for Mankind: Exploration through the Private and Public Space Programs." Thesis. Iowa State University, 2011. Print.

29. Fowler, Wallace T. "An Introduction to Space Mission Planning." University of Texas Space Mission Planning Website. University of Texas, 2001. Web. 24 Aug. 2013.

30. Freudenrich, Craig, Ph.D. "How Solar Sail Technology Works." HowStuffWorks. HowStuffWorks, 2013. Web. 24 July 2013.

31. Frisbee, Robert H. "How to Build an Antimatter Rocket for Interstellar Missions - Systems Level Considerations in Designing Advanced Propulsion Technology Vehicles." Technical Reports Server. NASA, 1 June 2003. Web. 20 Oct. 2013.

32. Frisbee, Robert H. "How to Build an Antimatter Rocket for Interstellar Missions." AIAA–2013-4676. Proc. of 39th AIAA/ASME/SAE/ASEE Joint Propulsion Conference and Exhibit, Huntsville. Huntsville: AIAA, 2013. N. pag. Print.

33. Gilster, Paul. "A Laser-Powered Interstellar Ramjet." Centauri Dreams RSS. Tau Zero Foundation, 24 July 2012. Web. 26 July 2013.

34. Gilster, Paul. "Laser Beamed Interstellar Mission: A New Take." Centauri Dreams RSS. Tau Zero Foundation, 2 Oct. 2008. Web. 24 July 2013.

35. Gilster, Paul. "Tuning Up the Interstellar Ramjet." Centauri Dreams RSS. Tau Zero Foundation, 8 June 2009. Web. 26 July 2013.

36. Glick, Gary N., M. Ed. "Interview with Gary Glick." Personal interview. 6 Sept. 2013.

37. Greenleaf, Allan, et al. "Electromagnetic wormholes and virtual magnetic monopoles from metamaterials." Physical review letters 99.18 (2007): 183901.

38. Gunn, Stanley. "Nuclear propulsion—a historical perspective." Space Policy 17.4 (2001): 291-298.

39. Hawking, Stephen. "STEPHEN HAWKING: How to Build a Time Machine." Mail Online. Associated Newspapers, 27 Apr. 2010. Web. 27 Oct. 2013. <http://www.dailymail.co.uk/home/moslive/article-1269288/STEPHEN-HAWKING-How-build-time-machine.html>.

40. Hein, Andreas M. "Laser Sail Propulsion for Interstellar Flight: Novel Concepts." Academia.edu. Academia, 14 July 2011. Web. 25 July 2013.

41. Dunbar, Brian. "Ion Propulsion." NASA. NASA, 21 May 2008. Web. 31 Oct. 2013. <http://www.nasa.gov/centers/glenn/about/fs21grc.html>.

42. ITER. "ITER - the Way to New Energy." ITER - the Way to New Energy. ITER, 2013. Web. 04 Aug. 2013.

43. Kaku, Michio. Physics of the Future: How Science Will Shape Human Destiny and Our Daily Lives by the Year 2100. New York: Doubleday, 2011. Print.

44. Krasnikov, S. V. "Hyperfast travel in general relativity." Physical Review D 57.8 (1998): 4760.

45. Mallove, Eugene F., and Gregory L. Matloff. The Starflight Handbook: A Pioneer's Guide to Interstellar Travel. New York: Wiley, 1989. Print.

46. McMonigal, Brendan, Geraint F. Lewis, and Philip O'Byrne. "Alcubierre warp drive: On the matter of matter." Physical Review D 85.6 (2012): 064024.

47. Mission Planning Website. Mission Planning Website. University of Texas, 2001. Web. 24 Aug. 2013.

48. Mori, Osamu (26 January 2011). "小型ソーラー電力セイル実証機(IKAROS)の定常運用終了報告" (PDF) (in Japanese). JAXA. Retrieved 2 February 2011.

49. Morris, Michael; Thorne, Kip; Yurtsever, Ulvi (1988). "Wormholes, Time Machines, and the Weak Energy Condition". Physical Review Letters 61 (13): 1446–1449.

50. NASA JPL. "Voyager Weekly Reports." Voyager Weekly Reports. California Institute of Technology, 31 May 2013. Web. 26 Aug. 2013.

51. NASA. How Astronauts Are Affected by Space Exploration. 2013. Interactive presentation. Johnson Space Center, Houston.

52. National Aeronautics and Space Administration. "International Space Station." NASA. NASA, 2013. Web. 13 Oct. 2013. <http://www.nasa.gov/mission_pages/station/main/>.

53. National Ignition Facility. "NIF: The "Crown Joule" of Laser Science." NIF. Lawrence Livermore National Laboratory, 2013. Web. 19 Oct. 2013. <https://lasers.llnl.gov/about/nif/about.php>.

54. Nosanov, Jeffery. "Solar System Exploration Architecture for Revolutionary Science." 100 Year Starship 2013 Public Symposium. Hyatt Regency Hotel, Houston. 21 Sept. 2013. Lecture.

55. Particle Data Group. "The Particle Adventure | What Is the World Made Of? | Matter and Antimatter." The Particle Adventure | What Is the World Made Of? | Matter and Antimatter. Lawrence Berkeley National Laboratory, 2013. Web. 20 Oct. 2013. <http://www.particleadventure.org/antipreface.html>.

56. Rayman, Marc, Dr. "NASA Dawn Journal September 27, 2013." SpaceRef. SpaceRef Interactive, 27 Sept. 2013. Web. 13 Oct. 2013. <http://www.spaceref.com/news/viewsr.html?pid=44744>.

57. Schmidt, G. R., H. P. Gerrish, J. J. Martin, G. A. Smith, and K. J. Meyer. "Antimatter Requirements and Energy Costs for Near-Term Propulsion Applications." Nasa Technical Reports Server. NASA, 1 Jan. 1999. Web. 20 Oct. 2013.

58. Shiga, David. "Rocket Company Tests World's Most Powerful Ion Engine." NewScientist–Space. Reed Business Information Ltd., 5 Oct. 2009. Web. 30 July 2013.

59. Smith, Gerald A., Kirby J. Meyer, Kevin J. Kramer, and Dan Coughlin. "Antimatter Space Propulsion at Penn State University (LEPS)." Antimatter Space Propulsion at Penn State University (LEPS). Pennsylvania State University, 27 Feb. 2001. Web. 20 Oct. 2013. <http://www.engr.psu.edu/antimatter/>.

60. The Planetary Society. The Planetary Society Blog. The Planetary Society, 2013. Web. 24 July 2013.

61. USA. NASA. Earth Science Technology Office. For Technologists. By NASA. National Aeronautics and Space Administration, 2013. Web. 01 Sept. 2013.

62. USA. NASA. Glenn Research Center. Nuclear Thermal Propulsion (NTP): A Proven Growth Technology for Human NEO / Mars Exploration Missions. By Stanley K. Borowski, David R. McCurdy, and Thomas W. Packard. Cleveland: NASA, 2012. Print.

63. USA. NASA. Institute for Advanced Concepts. Advanced Solar- and Laser-pushed Lightsail Concepts. By Geoffrey A. Landis. Ohio: Ohio Aerospace Insitute, 1999. Print. 1991 Advanced Aeronautical/Space Concept Studies.

64. USA. NASA. Johnson Space Center. Eagleworks Laboratories: Advanced Propulsion Physics Research. By Harold White, Dr., Paul March, Nehemiah Williams, and William O'Neill. Houston: n.p., 2011. Print.

65. USA. NASA. Marshall Space Flight Center. Nuclear Pulse Propulsion: Orion and Beyond. By George R. Schmidt, J. A. Bonometti, and P. J. Morton. Vol. 20000096503. Huntsville: NASA, 2000. Print.

66. USA. NASA. Marshall Space Flight Center. Solar Sail Propulsion. By Les Johnson. N.p.: n.p., n.d. NTRS. Web. 25 July 2013. <http://ntrs.nasa.gov/archive/nasa/casi.ntrs.nasa.gov/20120016691_2012017340.pdf>.

67. USA. NASA. Mission Planning. NASA's Mission Operations and Communications Services. By NASA. N.p.: n.p., n.d. Print.

68. USA. NASA. The George C. Marshall Space Flight Center and the California Institute of Technology Jet Propulsion Laboratory. Interstellar Exploration: Propulsion Options for Precursors and Beyond. By Les Johnson and Stephanie Leifer. N.p.: NASA, 1999. Print.

69. Wall, Mike. "World's Largest Solar Sail to Launch in November 2014." Space.com. TechMedia, 13 June 2013. Web. 24 July 2013.

70. White, H. G., and E. W. Davis. "The Alcubierre Warp Drive in Higher Dimensional Spacetime." AIP Conference Proceedings. Vol. 813. 2006.

71. White, Harold, Ph. D. "Revolutionary Propulsion and Power for the Next Century of Spaceflight." Proceedings of the 2009 Von Braun Symposium. Von Braun Symposium, League City. N.p.: n.p., 2009. N. pag. Print.

72. White, Harold G., Ph.D. "Warp Field Mechanics." 100 Year Starship 2013 Public Symposium. Hyatt Regency Hotel, Houston. 21 Sept. 2013. Lecture.

73. White, Harold, Ph. D. "Warp Field Mechanics 101." NTRS. NASA, 4 Oct. 2011. Web. 11 Aug. 2013.

74. Whitmire, Daniel P., and Al Jackson; "Laser Powered Interstellar Ramjet," Journal of the British Interplanetary Society Vol. 30, pp. 223-226 (1977).

75. Whitmire, Daniel P.; "Relativistic Spaceflight and the Catalytic Nuclear Ramjet," Acta Astronautica Vol. 2, pp. 497-509 (1975).

76. World Bank. "World DataBank." The World Bank DataBank. World Bank Group, 2013. Web. 01 Sept. 2013.

77. World Nuclear Association. "Nuclear Reactors for Space." Nuclear Reactors for Space. World Nuclear Association, 2013. Web. 07 Aug. 2013.

Food Design: An Introduction to Food Design for Space Food Systems

David Wilson

What is food design? Food design is a new discipline within design. Much of the growing popularity of the idea of food design is owed to Francesca Zampollo of London Metropolitan University, UK and her efforts to promote food design largely through the website: ifooddesign.org. Food design explores the food human relationship and interaction. This dynamic is explored in a number of ways what are today considered sub-categories of food design:

- 'design with food': the food itself may hold a design component,
- 'design for food': a design for food may be something like a package for food,
- 'food product design': a food utensil is one such an example,
- 'design about food': represent food or food related items expressed in representation or abstract through another medium; a piece of furniture made to express food, for example a meatball chair can convey this idea,
- 'interior design/space for food': a dining room or restaurant can express the idea of an interior with the function of dining. A space for food could be something as simple and direct as a table... or even a campfire,
- 'eating design': is a thematic concept where food and eating is involved –from performance art or holiday ritual to personal tradition(s).

What is food design for space; deep space? First what is or can be involved in food design for deep space; in the most basic sense you have people inside of a ship, not unlike the crew of a submarine. So, as far as food goes, you have a captive audience. But there's more to it than that, meaning the above aspects of food design- such as: communal dining space, personal dining space, food types, food presentation, food packaging, food utensils for low gravity... or related solutions to the low gravity environment, and the like.

How are those two ideas similar or different? Fundamentally, the ideas of food on earth or in deep space are the same. However, there may be some different 'rules' both in terms of the environment "physically," meaning the ship itself, or the environment secondarily, meaning the low gravity deep space if or when that may be a factor for the crew, and lastly the policy regarding the food types permitted onboard the star ship.

How does food design apply, or might it apply to/for a 100 YEAR STAR SHIP deep-space mission? Food design will seek to address the design aspect of the issues surrounding food and the related food and feeding systems for deep space. One may view the resultant outcome of designs dealing with fitting food into the mission context. However, food design at this early stage of discussion affords a more proactive involvement thereby producing a more robust and dynamic approach to deep-space food design, and related deep space mission outcomes where humans are involved.

Common misconceptions regarding food design: building an architectural cheeseburger, meaning that food design is about the structure of a physical thing. While the structure of a cheeseburger may contain design elements…food design is a broader vision than whether the cheese might be placed on top or bottom, the type and thickness of the pattie, condiments, sesame seeds or not, peripherals such as lettuce and tomato or pickle perhaps, those are all aspects to the design structure of a cheeseburger, and while tasty sounding…if you like cheeseburgers, food design, as a concept, is a larger idea than that.

What might a vision of food design for a 100YSS look like in 100 years?

Before looking into a really big-picture question, let's consider some smaller… more 'digestible' thoughts:

Who has eaten in a cafeteria? How does that, as an experience, differ from that of dinning at a hotel buffet, or with 'Mickie D's,' or in fine dining restaurants perhaps?

Atmosphere…? Mood…? Music selection…? Decorations…? Are each and all aspects of food design represented as 'eating space design.' But, then again, so is gathering around a campfire and roasting marshmallows a concept of 'eating space design;' in that context there are a list of requisites: camp, 'tee-pee' style fire, roasting sticks; wooden- preferably of a given hardwood tree species, marshmallows and if stowage provisions permits graham crackers, and bars of chocolate. And, for the gourmet, a dab of peanut butter or some fresh-cut slices of ripe banana may be used to add some more to your smores.

As we can see from the previous example, food design happens on a number of levels and in potentially infinite ways. So, what might food design for a long duration deep-space mission look like?…

Today, astronauts dine from a menu of a variety of food preparation, preservation and packaging techniques and choices: fresh foods, freeze-dried, thermostabilized just to name a few. As fresh foods are prone to spoilage and subsequent bacteria may pose a potential threat to sensitive test equipment, it is consumed first. Freeze-dried foods are light in weight which makes sense with current propulsion systems from earth to micro gravity where those foods may be hydrated onboard space craft such as the ISS. And thermostabilized foods are foods, which for some menu items, works quite well in replicating an earth food experience.

Tomorrow deep space travelers may dine in many ways:

A Jetson's style food dispenser where one speaks it and out the food comes is one possibility. Chef Homaro Cantu of Chicago's Moto and Ing restaurants is working with edible papers and inks, both may store well, and 3-D laser-cutting printers could shape such paper to a form including virtually limitless archived representations of foods. Excess scraps of edible paper would be collected, recycled and used in the production of a future meal.

Edible Paper and Ink Homaro Cantu Interview re: 100YSS 3D foods 2013 interview by D. Wilson 2013 (unpublished)

Homaro Cantu worked with NASA on their Institute Advanced Concept's 3-D replication, built from edible 2-D substrate.

Cantu details that there are tech hurdles to the practical application of making a meal of edible paper and ink. "When you want to send a human to another planet there are goals with nutrients; it [the technology] must get to the nano scale to be a reality." There are nano extracts w/flavors however not yet with structures. That's where the technology needs to be. The raw materials don't yet exist. But if those two things come together it could work. In order to create a molecular match with an apple, you need a vast amount of core ingredients in order to produce a match. If 3D food printing were used, a rotation of a menu is a most likely scenario rather than an 'on-demand' printing of foods.

When asked, Chef Cantu said, "'Edible menu'- started with the tasting menu; a clever way to get people to eat right after they get seated." Cantu first started writing on rice paper with edible inks then that idea expanded into other things to create and further refine his edible menu.

A class4 CO_2 laser was used by chef Cantu on the TV show "Iron Chef." Now, Cantu and his team use Z-NA lasers which function to etch names or engrave. He and his team has used laser technology for experimenting with flavor technology- capturing vapors and freezing them to make things like elixirs and extracts but Cantu is quick to note that while fun, "It's expensive to play with."

"Over the years working in restaurants I've always wanted to invent things, and before Moto opened, I invented several things. There is a time and place for classic things, but I don't want to do that at work. Everything else is rapidly evolving, why not food? Food is going to evolve; how do we let it evolve?"

"We're going to find ways to make veggies replicate meats [Cantu cites the 'China Study'] I'm very pro innovation. Cantu designs and beyond eggs worked together to create an egg substitute."

Should the technology catch-up to the idea- Cantu said, "Food printing will revolutionize everything around us."

The lab-grown burger [The Science Behind a Lab-Grown Burger published on Food Manufacturing (food-manufacturing.com)] may be one such possible use for cattle stem cells in deep space. While this represents fairly recent work in the area of stem cell research, the potential for future use is promising. Or Rob Rhinehart's "Soylent" may prove another deep-space dining option; this one is of the liquefied variety. And, while reminiscent of the infamous early sci-fi movie "Soylent Green" is nothing like its predecessor namesake. 'Soylent' is a nutrient-packed beverage generically described as a "Food substitute". The above several ideas suggest a few of the tried and true present-day applications of technology in food. However, that's just the tip of the iceberg; synthetic cells which can be programmed, and that may be an example of yet another food direction. An article on synthetic cell work by Steve Connor Published in Science Editor Friday May 2010 titled: Synthetic Cell is a Giant Leap for Science, and Could Be Bigger Still for Mankind details potentials in such work. Please consider the link in the sources following for further information:

Basically a synthetic cell can be programmed and function in unique ways. In terms of food, this can make food production and tissue growth quite efficient.

The 'above' idea suggests something that is malleable, something which may adjust with the desires of the crew…or chef. And, this adjusting with the ship's crew dynamic suggests an 'organic food system,' if you will. Such an idea of malleability might be extended to food environment(s) aboard a 100 year star ship as well. What does this idea mean? In translating this concept of malleability to a ship, one may ask design aesthetic questions of the environmental construct. …Well, perhaps the physical structure of the facility modulates, or dining arrangements adjust, perhaps delivery modes phase in or out, or all of the above and more. When we think about it, flexibility seems "quite logical" when considering a mission with a duration projected at 50 years. After all, fifty years ago, we were using rotary-dial phones, type writers, and humans were still thinking about how to get to the moon. So, for a mission 'itself' to have a 50-year lifespan, it asks quite a lot for advances onboard the ship to remain static to a crew kinetic.

One final food for thought idea- Brain computer interface (BCI): neural stimulation as an applied food/feeding measure, meaning BCI could possibly be used along with neutrally flavored nutrient-packed substrate and provide sensory fulfillment. Water could be turned quite biodynamically into wine…any wine.

Somewhere between walnuts and doughnuts, a happy medium: while walnuts may provide more nutrients, pack more neatly, and keep longer than a nice fluffy doughnut, but what about the desirability factor? Should factors of desirability be a consideration aboard a 100YSS? And, to what degree should desirability be a factor in food choice(s)? As I write this, I came to this idea with what I thought would be answers to unasked questions. Now, I find there are questions for the questions. The notions shift from postulate to ethics. For instance; here on earth vending machines represent an entrepreneurial presence. Should self-governed feeding be an option aboard a 100YSS? Should a crew-member have the power and rights to eat whenever they choose, whatever they choose? Should a crewmember be able to choose what they want to eat? As you may have noticed, we have moved very quickly from the clear-cut world of food design into ethics which naturally emerge as a result of the exploration of the topic. But, that said, let's get back to the basics of what food design kinda is; understanding that it itself is a new design discipline, and where it may go, and how it might live within a 100YSS initiative.

As this paper is representative of an introduction to food design, as it relates to food design for a generational 'world off world', it is important to realize that the 100YSS is a collaborative effort seeking the best from the minds of humanity, and this effort will extend over the course of many years, I have not attempted to provide absolutes. Who knows; you may be the person with the insight and the work to bring forward the idea of a generational ship into being. As for me, mission accomplished; food and the larger food design is now a discussion for the 100-year star ship in 2013, at the 100YSS public symposium, held in Houston, Texas. There are a number of places for the curious 'space' student to further their education process; NASA, BioServ, as well as the Space Policy Institute exist to name just a few. Best of luck, and direct a path.

Sources

1. Homaro Cantu, Chef/entrepreneur: Cantu Designs, Moto/Ing, 2013

2. NASA- Johnson Space Center, 2012

3. NASA- Space Food Systems Laboratory, Johnson Space Center, Houston Tx, 2012

4. NASA- Advanced Food Systems, Johnson Space Center, Houston Tx, 2012

5. How Food Can Be Art: A Discussion of Taste (Part7 of 8), January 12, 2012 by Art http://abetterwhirlpool.wordpress.com/2012/01/12/food-art-part7/

6. International Food Design Society: http://ifooddesign.org/food_design/index.php

7. International Food Design Society: http://ifooddesign.org/food_design/subcategories.php

8. Cambridge Encyclopedia of Hunters and Gatherers http://books.google.co.uk/books?id=5eE-ASHGLg3MC&pg=PP2&lpg=PP2&dq=%22all+humans+lived+this+way%22+90+12,000&source=bl&ots=E-qs5MKbdn&sig=EmtqQEkdTuHGFX2kSOYfC7MLdXw&hl=en&sa=X&ei=5JG-GUcTIM8qg0wX3pYHACA&ved=0CDcQ6AEwAQ#v=onepage&q=%22all%20humans%20lived%20this%20way%22%2090%2012%2C000&f=false

9. Native American Cultures: history.com

10. Towards a Structural Model of the Tourist Experience: an Illustration from Food Experience in Tourism Quan and Wang 2003, www.sciencedirect.com

11. Food and Anthropology in the Early Works of Matilde Serao by Daria Valentini, https://twpl.library.uto-tonto.ca

12. Anthropology of Food- University of Minnesota Duluth, www.d.umn.edu/cla/faculty/troufs/anthfood/video/meaning_of_food.himl

13. Human Culture: What is Culture? http://anthro.palomar.edu/culture/culture_1.htm

14. Universals of Culture: a list of 10 cultural universals, Jennifer Hanzak, www.learner.org

15. Bloomberg, Myhrvold: Invention is the Mother of Economic Growth, Nathan Myhrvold Dec 19, 2011, http://www.bloomberg.com/news/2011-12-20/invention-is-the-mother-of-economic-growth-nathan-myhrvold.html

16. IGT Vanvitelli/ Istituto technico Per Geometri "L. Vanvitelli" Cava De' Tirreni (SA), Italy: "Food Habits Over the Centuries" 2008/9

17. Project Muse, "Anthropology and the Everyday, from Comfort to Terror, Nancy Ries New Literary History vol 33, Numver 4, Autumn 2002 pp. 725-742, http://muse.jhu.edu

18. University of Buffalo, Delightful, Delicious, Disgusting—the Difficult Pleasure of "Terrible Eating" Patricia Donovan January 9, 2004, http://buffalo.edu/news/releases/2004/01/6533.html

19. Huffington Post, 'A Spoken Dish' Asks Southerners About Their Food Memories (video), Rebecca Orchant, http://www.huffingtonpost.com/2013/06/18/a-spoken-dish-food-memories-video_n_3455136.html

20. Sierra Club, "How Our Mythology of Food Drives Us to Eat the World" John Kurmann, http://missouri.sierraclub.org/sierranOnline/mayjune2000/howourmy.htm

21. History of Furniture and Interior Design part 1: Prehistoric Furniture and Interior design, Inar Yildiz, http://emuonline.emu.edu.tr/inar328/pdf/Part_one_inar_328_furniture_styles_ancient.pdf

22. Around the Dinner table, History of Eating in the United States, Robert Cowley, Della Gibson and Chanda Sewell, 'Family that eats together, stays together', http://historyofeating.umwblogs.org/around-the-dinner-table/

23. Advance Access Publication Dec 21, 2007, Oxford University Press 2007, The Candidate Sour Taste Receptor, PKD2L1, is Expressed by Type III Taste Cells in the Mouse, S. Kataoka et al 2007

24. Open Biology, Evolutionary Origins of Taste Buds: Phylogenetic Analysis of Purinergic Neurotransmission in Epithelial Chemosensors, Open Biol. March 6, 2013, Masato Kirino et al. Rsob.royalsociety.publishing.org

25. Chemoreceptors of taste and Smell- specific material extracted from, 'The Neuron and Neural System: Electrolytic Theory of' by James T. Fulton, http://neuroresearch.net/smell/files/chemoreceptors.htm last update Aug. 14, 2013

26. Food Manufacturing, Mars Food Study Researchers Conclude Experiment, Jennifer Sinco Kelleher, http://www.foodmanufacturing.com

27. Open Access, Nanotechnology, Science and Application 2010:3 1-15, Dove Medical Press Ltd., "Food Nanotechnology- an overview" Bhupinder S. Sekhon

28. Soylent, Rob Rhinehart, http://robrhinehart.com/?=289, http://www.soylent.me/

29. Food Manufacturing, Taste Testers: Lab-Made Burger Lacks Flavor, Maria Cheng Aug 8, 2013, www.foodmanufacturing.com

30. Food Manufacturing, Q&A: The Science Behind a Lab-Grown Burger, Maria Cheng Aug 8, 2013, www.foodmanufacturing.com

31. NASA, "Food For Space Flight," NASA, www.NASA.gov

32. NASA," Space Food," NASA, http://spaceflight.nasa.gov/living/spacefood/index.html

33. NASA, "Cosmic Cuisine," NASA, nasa.gov

34. "From Farm to Fork: How Space Food Standards Impacted the Food Industry and Changed Food Safety Standards", Jennifer Ross-Nazzal, http://history.nasa.gov/sp4801-chapter12.pdf

35. NASA, "Space Food Hall of Fame," http://education.ssc.nasa.gov/fft_halloffame.asp

36. NASA, "The Brain in Space: a Teacher's Guide with Activities for Neuroscience," NASA.gov

37. Space Policy Institute, graduate Education, http://www.gwu.edu/~spi/education.cfm

38. BioServe, http://www.colorado.edu/engineering/BioServe/about.html

39. Synthetic Cell Is a Giant Leap for Science and Could Be Bigger Still For Mankind: http://www.independent.co.uk/news/science/synthetic-cell-is-a-giant-leap-for-science-and-could-be-bigger-still-for-mankind-1978869.html

Technium – Ensuring Interstellar Research Leaves Footprints On Earth

Jonathan Van

Technium, 3315 Mayflower Way, Lehi, Utah, 84043

Jonathan@altaventures.com

technium.com

Abstract

An expansive vision such as in the 100YSS program encompasses broad and advanced technology requirements by definition of the program mission. The 100YSS mission will benefit when novel advanced technology can actually reach the marketplace. Annually, there is roughly $1.5 trillion spent on global R&D. What comes of the technology developed with this huge expenditure of time and money? Due to strong cultural differences between the labs and private industry, a majority of the science stays locked at the lab bench. Technium is pioneering a new path for unlocking these breakthroughs across the energy, security, health, and materials sectors. We have a commitment to solve grand challenges through development of advanced technologies and guiding them to market-ready products by a unique model. This is the path to an abundant future.

Our model includes students competing in the International Business Model Competition that teaches a unique market pull technology commercialization. Our goal is to get advanced technology into the hands of students and entrepreneurs in order to facilitate out-of-the-box business models that can provide revenues and investment capital for commercialization at scale. Cooperative groups with thousands of students working in parallel to optimize business models offer huge momentum to drive novel technologies to the marketplace. Excellent ideas are rewarded through funding and thus, excess innovation capacity will then be adequately met with the proper investment and entrepreneurship capacity.

We have built a common interface via a student accessible to lower the barriers and opening up communication lines between entrepreneurs and the laboratories across the globe.

Keywords

Commercialization, startup, venture capital, interstellar, space, development

Science, from latin scientia, means "knowledge".

The great issues of our time—conservation of the environment, management of global climate, provision of adequate energy, maintenance of human health, insurance of human security, and of course others—will not be solved by geopolitics or by geopolitics alone. We must discover new solutions. Discovery is imperative. New knowledge will transform our world.

However, It is not sufficient to perform a successful experiment and perhaps write a paper about it in a learned journal. Discoveries cannot be left to sit on the laboratory bench. They must be made available to society and they do not move under their own power. This utilization of discovery must become one of our vital goals. —Steven Lazarus

These words remind me of when I was sitting in a class taught by Professor Nichols in the engineering department at UT Austin my freshman year. He was going over a slide deck to encourage us to help with the I2P Competition, which focused mainly on technology commercialization. It was the first time I ever heard these words. Here I learned there is roughly 1.5 trillion spent annually on basic and applied research. Collectively the community has called it R&D, but I choose not to call it development because development implies there's a customer. After learning of our annual expense, I imagined there had to be a way to capitalize on all the research. The modern world around us can be defined by research directly tied to the DoD, DARPA, and NSF.

Now there's a glut of innovation capacity locked inside academic institutions, corporate R&D labs, and national labs. This isn't just of potential products, but services powered by the newest knowledge. There are 11,000,000 graduates students annually working daily on the cutting edge of science. They are doing entrepreneurial work. Someone needs to unlock this potential. Some numbers supporting the latent potential are below.

A study recently performed by the Kauffman Foundation stated: it has been estimated that 8 percent of all university spin-offs had gone public, 114 times the "going public rate" for U.S. enterprises generally (Goldfarb and Henrekson 2003). As impressive as these figures are, they understate the extent of university-based entrepreneurship since they do not include start-up companies represented in business plan competitions, back-door entrepreneurial activities emerging out of faculty consulting, and general spillovers from graduate students creating companies tied to outcomes of university research. Indeed, this is missing some companies like National Instruments, which was founded by a professor's research when he left the university to pursue his business. Additionally, only 3,376 academic spin-off companies were created in the United States from 1980 to 2000, though 68 percent of these companies remained operational in 2001 (Association of University Technology Managers 2002). That's a huge jump in success rate compared to the normal 10% rule.

These data points wake me up on a daily basis. I want to point sophisticated entrepreneurs towards this sort of entrepreneurship. There are grand challenges to be solved and we need people with the courage and the skill to pursue development and deployment into the market.

There's multiple reasons entrepreneurs don't engage in technology commercialization; however, to put it simply—the process gives you brain damage; transaction cost can be insurmountable.

Have you ever used USPTO and/or searched the Tech Transfer Office of a university. Try it here and search for something you're interested in. However, even if you do find something, you'll start a process that will cost you legal fees and a lot of time. Both are things entrepreneurs are short of.

Technium is simplifying the user interface for technology commercialization. Peter Diamandis, the founder of the XPrize and Singularity University, noted that the largest bottlenecks for widespread adoption are cost and an intuitive user interface. Technium makes it as easy to option and license IP at the click of a button. This is possible through our standard license, which allows for the typical 90+ day process to be reduced to a 10-14 day process that reduces headaches on both sides, and distributes the benefits equitably.

Importantly, we are working with the International Business Model Competition and their 1500+ teams to do the market-pull technology commercialization that has been missing for so long. The participants spend 8-12 weeks doing focused market validation, so that when the time comes to build the product according to the commercialization plan, they have paying customers at the end of the process. This shift from technology push to market-pull will both increase the number of technologies that mature and make a difference to society, but also will begin an education cycle where researchers too begin thinking of the commercial possibilities of their research.

We have a growing list of technology partners who come in to have their portfolios go through the market validation process as well as a high potential for more commercialization deals as a result. These range from Department of Energy labs like Sandia, Los Alamos, and Lawrence Livermore to universities including the University of Texas, Chinese University of Hong Kong, Cornell, and the University of Utah.

Technium is growing a community focused on outcomes. That means streamlining the commercialization process and bringing together a synergy of innovation capacity, by collecting and consolidating lab research, entrepreneur capacity, by networking and recruiting entrepreneurial management, and investment capital, by raising capital from the investment community. There are some valuable things in the pipeline coming for Technium that will benefit the 100 Year Starship community.

There are countless promising projects from scientists in the 100YSS consortium and Technium would like to help you through the technology commercialization process. Together we can ensure your interstellar research leaves footprints on Earth.

Jonathan Van

100 YEAR STARSHIP™

Design: Space

Chaired by Karl Aspelund, PhD

Assistant Professor, University of Rhode Island

Track Description

How might we best design the habitats, clothing and equipment for daily use on board a craft on such a journey? This panel will consider how to sustainably fulfill the basic human needs for creature comforts within the constraints presented by long-range, long-term space travel. What innovations and systemic changes may need to be seen first? How would the resulting design solutions benefit the population of Earth? How might they contribute to the establishment of communities on Mars? The panel will address these questions by exploring larger questions of design process and theory as well as focused examinations of concepts for specific design areas.

Track Summary

The "Design: Space" track addressed a number of open questions relating to the habitats and creature comforts of long-term space exploration. Eight talks and the chair's summary addressed, in both formal and informal fashion, issues surrounding the human body itself, communication, life support, food, art and creativity, and sustainability. The last mentioned especially in terms of repairing, recycling, and materials. Among the topics were how to approach the relationship of humans and robots, how to monitor water use and waste production, reparability of components and equipment, new advanced materials, and the need for artistic experiences and creative expression on board the starships and extra-terrestrial bases.

Given that design is a practice of fulfilling needs within a sum of constraints, it was hardly surprising that a common theme emerged in identifying new needs and new constraints of human life and behavior. The conclusions indicated a new kind of dialogue on creativity and innovation may be necessary as the focus on design for space begins to encompass not only the systems and technical solutions, but also the personal and flexible "messiness of human life." In this way the discussion echoed an emerging subtheme of the symposium overall: That long-term space missions and the establishment of permanent off-Earth communities requires a look at the nature of human culture. In doing so we must establish frameworks within which to define what it means to have a human culture in space. Design for Space is therefore about much more than objects and equipment, clothing and habitats. It is also about the structures and systems within which these will all be used, in which they will evolve, and in which our future humanity will be defined.

Track Chair Biography

Karl Aspelund, PhD

Assistant Professor, University of Rhode Island

Karl Aspelund, PhD, is Assistant Professor at the Department of Textiles, Fashion Merchandising and Design at the University of Rhode Island. His research interests lie in examining the role textiles and design play in the creation of identity, the impact of the textile life-cycle on the Earth's environment, and how the design community can contribute to the goal of environmental sustainability. He is now turning toward investigating the design and cultural needs and constraints of apparel in long-term space exploration. After graduating from the Wimbledon School of Art (1986,) with a degree in 3d design, Karl worked as an artist and designer for theater and film for 20 years and has taught design since the early 1990's. Before coming to URI in 1996, he was head of the Department of Industrial Design at the Reykjavik Technical College in Iceland. Karl completed a Ph.D. in 2011 in Anthropology and Material Culture from Boston University's University Professors Program, where his dissertation was awarded the University Professors Edmonds Prize as the best dissertation of the academic year 2010-2011. Karl is the author of two design textbooks, "The Design Process," (2006) and "Fashioning Society,"(2009.) The third, an introduction to designing, is due in early 2014.

Design and Prototyping of Life Support and Agriculture for Extended Space Habitation and Travel

Martin Dudziak, PhD

TetraDyn Ltd.

151 Alger Lane, Broadway, Virginia 22815

martinjd@tetradyn.com

Abstract

An experimental design is presented for a modular, reconfigurable multi-function platform that can be constructed in near-orbit or deep-space, for use in life support and emergency repair/reconstruction tasks within extended long-distance and long-duration space missions. This design is based upon a series of predecessor designs and deployments originating in applications ranging from emergency services to environmental monitoring and testing labs. The novelty in this "PodAtrium" architecture is the emphasis upon multi-functionality for structural components as well as internal apparatus including furnishings that are composed of basic elements that can be disassembled and reassembled as necessary and as demanded by the needs of a crew operating in isolation from any support craft or stationary habitation such as an exoplanetary base. Attention in the present phase of research and development has been upon the use of structural elements within a PodAtrium complex that can serve alternatively for a hydroponics-based greenhouse, a fuel-cell based power plant, and an asteroid mining operation, each of which could conceivably fulfill important roles at different times in the lifespan operations for a long-distance interstellar space vehicle with human crew onboard.

Keywords

agriculture, energy, habitation, life-support, sustainability, reusability

1. Introduction

The challenges of extreme long-distance and long-duration space travel and habitation require consideration of potentially radically different architectures and systems. A total "clean slate" in thinking about systems design including structural engineering is required. This "clean slate" is for more than what is generally the most common topic of discussion in "starship" design circles – propulsion and fuel. "Life support" – including mechanisms for dealing with consequences of structural and systematic breakdowns, or unforeseen changes in requirements for shelter, workspace, residence, food, water, non-propulsion fuels, and other commodities – requires a fresh start in how any type of large-scale, very-long-duration mission can be undertaken.

Almost all suggested "starship" (i.e., interstellar mission) designs to date have tended to be based upon the notion of a singular "spaceship" that has everything onboard and is itself a fixed physical architecture. Such a design leaves many gaps and room for disaster "down the road" when it comes to the critical maintenance of production and variance in production for food, water, air, power and shelter itself for space inhabitants. Operations must provide for not only fault tolerance but truly fail-safe performance, and part of how any species in any circumstances is able to approach such a goal-state is through adaptability and at many different scales of action. In biology we find this simply everywhere. From the molecular level to the performance of many creatures (not only humans, not only primates and not only mammals!) for interchangeable use and re-use of objects to fit the current and critical need of the moment, be it a need driven by necessity for survival or desire for pleasure.

An intensely modular and multi-functional architecture is required for spaceships that will carry life forms (and for that matter, even a population of robots) to distant interstellar and multi-generational destinations. There is a need for an "organic" (organism-like) model of system integration and symbiosis that extends beyond the most common and popular historical models, experiments, and thought-experiments for interplanetary and interstellar travel. The spaceship itself must possess and manifest some of the same characteristics of biological engineering that are found in what we typically regard as "living creatures" and which are the mainstay of survivability and adaptation to new surroundings, environments, situations.

In other words, it would be excellent if certain components of a spaceship or space base could, when needs arise and change, be transformed and re-used in order to replace some physical assemblies (e.g., residence, agricultural use, fabrication workspace), or to increase some functional outputs (e.g., electrical energy, propulsion fuel, food or water production). It would be excellent if different parts of a ship or base could be very rapidly converted, with minimal disassembly and minimal risk-intense labor, into other components as the situation arises. Foreseeable needs change. Supplies and availabilities change. Special circumstances arise. Reconfigurability and reusability are solutions for both minimizing the need for "extra (redundant) baggage" and the risks from losing critical resources due to no possibility of resupply or repair. All the better if the "building block' materials can be manufactured or even, literally, grown during the mission. We are not talking about spaceships having a timber forest, but with materials like PLA (polylactic acid) and explorations in synthetic biology there are interesting possibilities indeed.

2. StarGate Alpha Project

"StarGate Alpha" is a current new-generation experimental platform that has been designed and is presently in the early stages of construction by Team TetraDyn and a growing collaborative consortium. The work is entering into the physical stage and two teams at two sites will be active in this next phase – One is at a facility in western Virginia (USA) and the second is planned for a site in Northern Ireland (UK). "StarGate Alpha" ("SGA") is a "PodAtrium." This is an architecture employing multiple modular units ("nPods"). The main body of this paper discussed these structural design elements and methods of assembly, because this is the first stage of work in building any platform, earth-based for simulation and testing (as with the SGA; construction goal: 2014) and later in near-earth orbit (goal: 2018-2020).

An nPod is a "<u>P</u>urposive <u>O</u>perational <u>D</u>esign Structure" that can be constructed from a variety of materials and in a variety of geometries, and which can be assembled and disassembled easily into larger structures ("PodAtriums"). Moreover, all of the nPods are designed and constructed in such a manner that they may be disassembled into basic structural and functional elements that can be employed as basic construction "blocks". In essence, this is a kind of LEGO or Knex or Erector Set approach to building almost everything that goes into a large-scale complete spaceship system, and indeed, the aforementioned "toys" have directly been an inspiration in the design of nPods and PodAtriums, coupled with the real-life experience of building precursors using many different materials and structures, ranging from tents to shipping containers to trailers. Figures provided below in this paper illustrate a few of the precursor projects leading up to "PodWorld" and also the elementary designs for PodAtrium structures that are intended for the "StarGate Alpha" experimentation laboratory soon to be built in both USA and UK.

This particular platform, "StarGate Alpha" (SGA) incorporates reconfigurable and redirected-function modules for agriculture (including selective livestock cultivation), hybrid energy generation and management with an emphasis upon independence from other vessel or station power systems, and structural and habitation features for short-term life support during periods of necessary reconstruction, sequestration or quarantine due to CBRNE emergencies. Often the thought about "chem-bio-radiation-nuclear-explosive" is relegated to thoughts about earth-based disasters, terrorists, accidents. There are many natural and accidental circumstances where a toxic chemical or biological release, for instance, could demand rapid reconstructive engineering onboard an interstellar craft. The system must be prepared for dealing with such situations. That such a comprehensive roster of functions has been targeted for one experimental platform is deliberately based upon the simple fact that any and all of these factors and possible conditions need to be addressed and accommodated in any realistic starship lifecycle and its design.

An important feature of the SGA design is the emphasis upon multi-functional utility for such a platform to serve in many space-based physical environments as well as on terrestrial-like planets. The experiment has been proceeding through design and simulation and is entering into phase-1 of a physical prototype environment. The goal of the project now is to demonstrate the effectiveness and the critical importance of an agri-energy-life-support "PodAtrium" that will function equally well in space and on a planet such as Earth. In phase-1 of SGA, emphasis is upon multi-modal agriculture using hydroponic, bromeliad and aquatics, combined and supported with a hybrid "permaculture" approach to energy, water, and air maintenance. The physical structures being designed and constructed will employ composite materials such that the actual prototype system could be feasibly demonstrated on a space mission in earth-orbit or deep-space. Phase-1 involves building the self-sufficient, stand-alone PodAtrium and then performing agricultural and energy/fuel production tasks on site with zero or minimal interaction with the outside environment. Phase-2 extends this into a stable high-orbit platform ("HALO" – High Altitude Lift and Launch Operations) or ideally into near-earth orbit.

Figures 1, 2 and 3 below provide three schematic illustrations of how nPods can routinely be assembled and reassembled into different configurations based upon whatever are the overall system requirements. As will be shown further, the dimensionality of an nPod, by definition, is not restricted to a particular geometry (such as a rectangular prism, as shown here). These illustrations (alpha, beta and gamma layouts, as examples taken among many) are shown in the "total abstract" - there can be any number of basic functions which need to be thus aligned – food production, water production, various types of fuel production (e.g., artificial photosynthesis), residence, medical care, "fab-lab" for mechanical workshop tasks, and even laboratories for the study of extraterrestrial objects of interest.

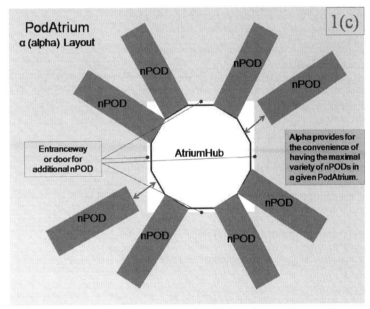

Figure 1: Alpha configuration of PodAtrium layout (abstraction)

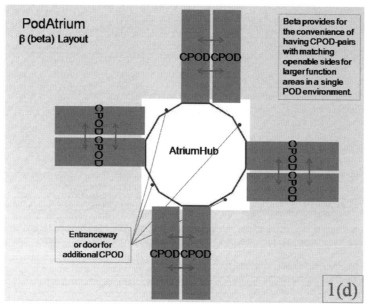

Figure 2: Beta configuration of PodAtrium layout (abstraction)

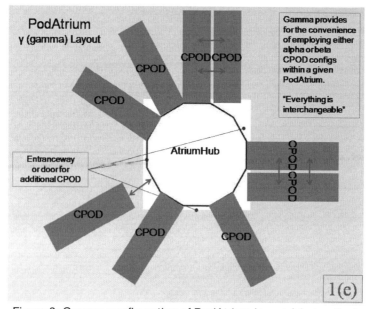

Figure 3: Gamma configuration of PodAtrium layout (abstraction)

3. Precursors and Early Prototypes of nPods ("Inspirational" Phase)

Precursors of nPods include singular and compound structures that were designed and erected for many applications. All precursor work involved "fixed" designs and architectures – thus, none of the "total reconfigurability" of nPods and PodAtriums. These included the use of shipping containers for educational purposes in remote villages of Costa Rica, Central America and the Caribbean [1], emergency and general-use provisions for electrical power generation and battery recharging [2], modular and mobile laboratories for environmental monitoring of air, water and soil samples [3], and rapidly deployable air-inflated structures for provisioning of blast-resistant and toxin-barrier workspaces within hazardous industrial complexes (petrochem field) [4]. Figures 4, 5, 6 and 7 provide collage views of several such prior projects. The nPod design is a consequence of the author and colleagues working for an extended period of more than two decades in such types of application and system design, fabrication, and use.

Figure 4: Intel-sponsored computing-lab pod structures deployed in Central America 2000-2002

Figure 5: Private-funded community power recharging station deployed in India 2005

As radically different as such early pod-like structures may seem from what are now the subject of the SGA Project, these have performed multiple important learning tasks, in addition to the foremost and most valuable task of serving the needs of people in varying circumstances of need and in most cases poverty. Consciously, however, the work with these structures was driven toward the goal of refining how to construct easily, manage easily, transport easily, and transform easily, structures that could provide the maximum of services (e.g., water purification, computing, analytical chemistry, biomedical testing) in the most compact physical spaces and with a realistic opportunity to transform these units from one function (e.g., emergency use or environmental testing) into another, and "at a moment's notice." Setting up and operating these "service pods" in very remote, often harsh and challenging environments, and without many of the conveniences of the modern industrialized world, provided a unique learning-testing experience that is almost the closest one can come – within affordability for contemporary space-focused R&D projects - to modeling what operations could be like in an exoplanetary environment.

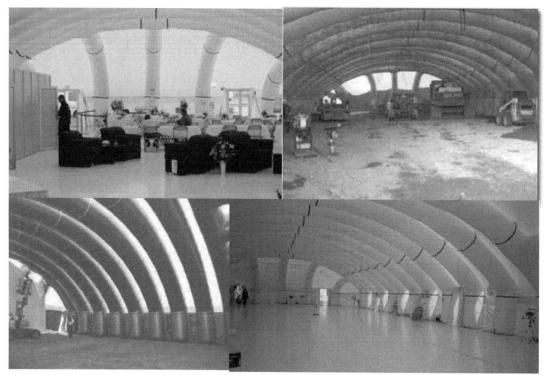

Figure 6: Air-inflated structures used in studies and experiments on rapid mobility and blast-resistance

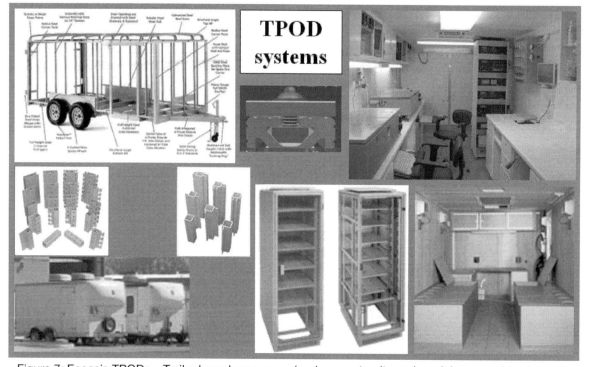

Figure 7: Ecoasis TPODs – Trailer-based emergency/environment units and modular assembly elements

4. nPods and PodAtriums – the Engineering Archetypes

All of the various precursors employed different structures and composition materials. All were proto-experiments leading to the nPod – "n" for n-sided, n-shaped, and "n" being the composition material for its structural elements. Make something that can be made from almost any material and shape at hand, and reshaped according to the needed function, and one has <u>versatility</u>, <u>adapatability</u>, and <u>survivability</u>. without these three attributes, there can be no realiable, sustainable mission to the stars, by robots, humans, or both.

The basic nPod, and any PodAtrium built from nPods, derives from the principle that any one major and common structural element should be usable in as many different configurations and for as many different purposes as possible, and that construction, disassembly and reassembly should be as simple, easy, straightforward as possible – an operation that can be done in minimum time, with minimum number of persons (or robots), with minimum consumption of energy, and at minimum risk to the local operation or to other structures and inhabitants nearby. Thus, in simple words, build and play and mix-and-match and do it all at the least expense, with no accidents to nearby Anything. Remembering, all the time, that this applies for any place and situation on Earth, but also, for any use in Space. Deep Space. Interstellar Space. Space without Home Depot, Exxon or Bob's Small Engine Repair.

The physical nPod evolved out of mathematics and computational algorithms designed for control and optimization in assembly and configuration of nPod-based structures. First came the model and the software, the nPOD Design and Layout Schema (nDLS). The purpose of the nDLS is to simplify planning, assembling, and deployment of any nPod systems. nPODs are described by logical schemas that identify specific coordinate locations for all elements and all equipment that is positioned on nPOD component faces including interior walls, floors and ceilings. By referencing a specific nDLS identification code, one knows where any specific piece of equipment or structural part is or belongs.

The full abstract nDLS for a given nPOD object is:

[nPOD identifier].[nPOD component identifier].[nPOD sequence location].[nPOD component type].
[Face identifier].[Entity-coordinate-location set]. [Position-orientation set].
[Specification-attribute set].[Constraint-discriminator set]

From the nDLS is derived the nDocSim. The nDOCSIM is a web-based, mobile-accessible database and expert system for use in specifying, designing, ordering and organizing parts for, shipping and transporting, and operating an nPOD. This system is used by the TetraDyn team responsible for the given nPOD project before, during, and after fabrication. This system is also used, in a limited fashion, by any customer/client purchaser or lease-holder of an nPOD. nDOCSIM makes extensive use of the nDLS and there is strict code enforcement for nDLS program correctness. This strict control applies to all aspects of nPOD design, specification, fabrication, operation, and includes all aspects of reconfiguration including disassembly, transport, replacement of components, elements and onboard equipment, and reassembly.

The implementation of the nPod specification and assembly control software is in PHP and Java and constitutes the nPOD Programming Language (nPL). The nPL is a formal programming language for the design, assembly and operation of nPod systems. It is a functional language and is currently script-based. In nPL one can express different functions and procedures to be executed by either humans or robots, either computationally or physically, pertaining to nPods and the various devices and equipment that are incorporated with(in) nPods. nPL is designed to allow for easy and efficient expression of algorithms and methods of work, and many of these are not intended for automated processing on a computer but for sequential/parallel physical activity. nPL enables clear and concise expression and the power of rule-checking.

4.1 nDLS, nPL, nDOCSIM – the Computational Foundations of nPods

The heart of nPL is the nDLS and the heart of the nDOCSIM is nPL. Essentially, nPL offers a set of scripts for manipulating different expressions within the nDLS and enabling the nDOCSIM to operate.

The following excerpt from the nDLS as expressed in EBNF (Extended Backus-Naur Form) illustrates some of the high-level features (syntax) of the language created for specification and control of nPod and PodAtrium design that can in principle be handed over to a crew of humans – or robots. Certainly it is the approach to be taken by a crew of humans who are managing a crew of robots – on Earth or in Space.

```
<nPOD_id> ::= <unique_name>      /* original def <nPOD_id> ::= 'nPOD_' <unique_name>   */
<unique_name> ::= <ent_id>      /* de facto, at least three characters, using "a-z", "A-Z", "0-9" */
<nPOD_component_id> ::= <core_component> | <aux_component>
<core_component> ::= 0      /* a unique central core element such as an OctaPod for an octagonal PodAtrium */
<aux_component> ::= 1 | 2 | ... | 255
        /* a unique component or component-location; these begin in an arbitrary "North" direction and are numbered
consecutively in a clockwise direction; 255 is arbitrary cut-off */
```

```
<nPOD-seq-loc> ::= 1 | 2 | ... | n          /* in theory, there is no limit but 3 or 4 would be typical max */
<nPOD_component_type> ::=
     'nGon' '(' <nGon_subtype> ')' |
'xPod' '(' <xPod_subtype> ')' |
<nGon_subtype> ::=                           ||| etc. |||
```

From this logic, there arises the basic nPod frame element (Figure 8) and variants that follow (Figures 9 –10) for all the types of frame element uses that can be needed in any type of PodAtrium. All are derivatives of the basic alpha frame element. The variations are either in orientation or in the addition of struts and cables for providing special strength for a floor base or ceiling panel, or for the incorporation of a passageway (e.g., doorway) or the fitting of some type of equipment.

Given that there is essentially only one fundamental frame element (Alpha type, - see fig. 8) this means that a wide variety of nPods can be built, or taken apart and reused elsewhere, as the need arises. All other elements including Beta, Gamma, Delta and composite types (also see figs. 8-10), are constructed and can be configured in real time in a space-based operational setting, from Alpha elements. With the nDLS and nDOCSIM software, it is possible to maintain complete accounting of all nPod elements, within even a city-sized installation such as a base vessel, and also to perform straightforward optimization calculations in order to plan the most economical and "organic" deployment of any nPod types in order to meet current or expected situations, both emergency and non-emergency in nature.

As is briefly discussed in Section 6 below, the nPod elements are designed to be constructed themselves from virtually any material. Steel, aluminum, polylactic acid (PLA), compositions which are themselves power-generation units (hydrogen production and hydrogen fuel-cell units, or RTG (radioisotope thermoelectric generators), or even, hypothetically, synthetic biological components – living vines and limbs, perhaps, of a synthetic species yet to be designed. The same versatility applies to the surface materials that will cover the exteriors and interiors of the nPods. All emphasis here is upon the structures, the skeletons, providing shape and strength, but of course the nPods are enclosed, covered, sealed. But with what depends, again, upon the need and function of the unit in space. Is it a greenhouse, or a human habitation, or a "fab-lab" or a warehouse or a power generation unit or simply "in reserve" for the future?

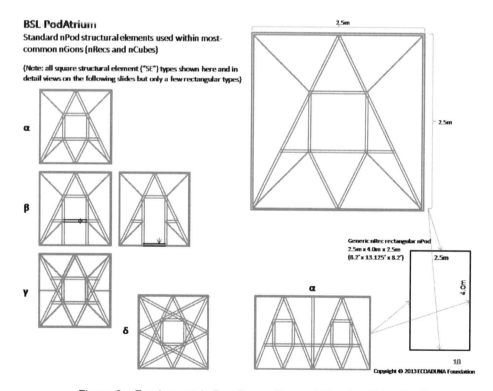

Figure 8 – Fundamental nPod Frame Element Panel – Alpha Config

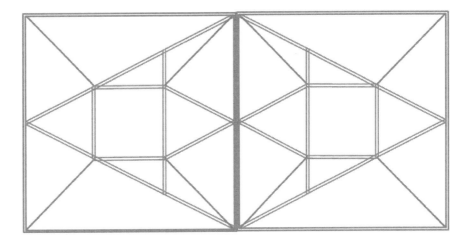

Figure 9 – Two Alpha elements make a cantilever structure for multi-level nPod complexes

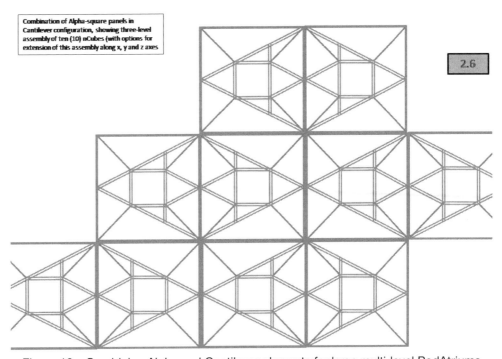

Figure 10 – Combining Alpha and Cantilever elements for large multi-level PodAtriums

5. nPod Types – Getting Down to Applications

The initial objective in the nPod and PodAtrium project, and specifically for StarGate Alpha ("SGA"), has been to design an architecture, and with it the physical components, for building many different components of a space-ship or space station. The focus was and remains upon food, water, power, and other production tasks, as well as for residence and other types of shelter and accommodation for humans and any other living creatures onboard such a vessel or station. The following are four examples of different nPods that can be constructed using the exact same types and the same numbers of nPod elements. Overall, taken together, these constitute the four principle functions that are deemed to be not only critical but the most likely to face needs for increase or decrease in number and changes in location within something like an interstellar spaceship. These are:

- DAQ – Data Acquisition and Collection nPod
- BSL – Biological and Chemistry Laboratory/Workspace nPod
- C4 – Command Control Communications and Computing nPod
- EMP – Electro-Mechanical-Power (Energy) Pod

Are these the only uses for nPods? Hardly. However, these are four major functions needed for any interstellar mission vessel or base, even if entirely roboticized. Furthermore, these are four that can easily be coverted, with a minimum of work, expense of energy, and risk, into one another, and these are among the four functions that will be most likely to change in needs and numbers during a mission's duration. We have targeted these four functions also because they are all part of the "natural" outlay of nPods for the SGA in its phase-1 implementation on Earth and in phase-2, as intended, in near-earth orbit. figures 11 – 14 illustrate the high-level layouts of each of these four types. The materials used for the structures are the Alpha type nPod frame elements, and for phase-1, made from standard 1" steel tubing. The materials for the interior hardware and furnishings are the same "80x20" brand of erector-set type components used in earlier trailer-based and container-based pods as shown in Figures 4-7 above.

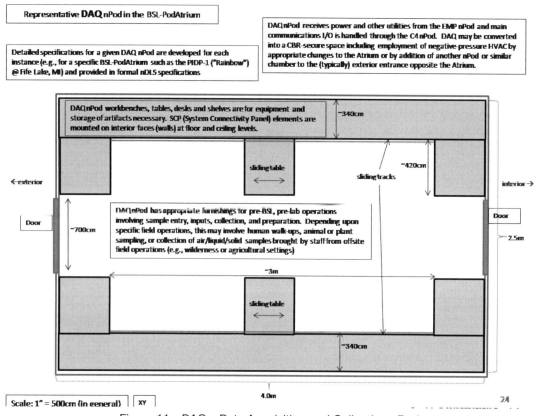

Figure 11 – DAQ – Data Acquisition and Collection nPod

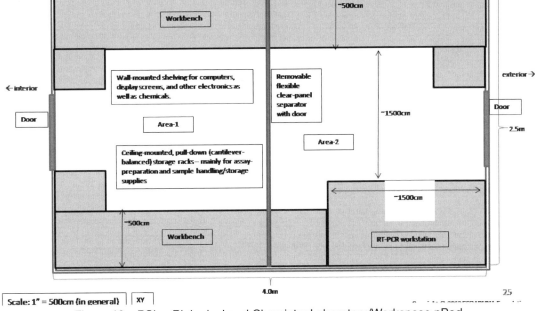

Figure 12 – BSL – Biological and Chemistry Laboratory/Workspace nPod

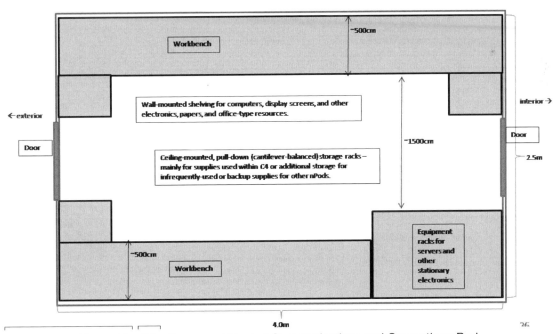

Figure 13 - C4 – Command Control Communications and Computing nPod

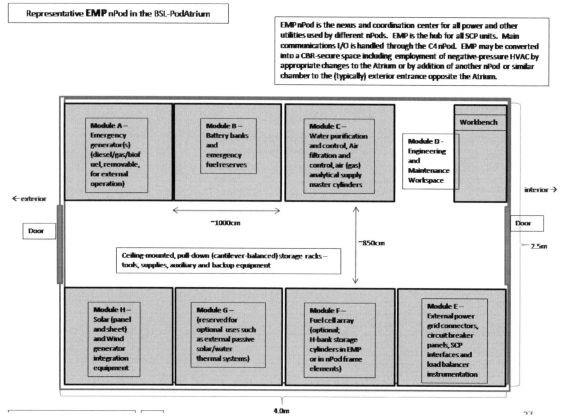

Figure 14 - EMP – Electro-Mechanical-Power (Energy) Pod

6. nPod Frame Element Composition

From what materials and elementary building-block units can nPods be constructed? The illustrations above indicate the use of tubes, rods, shafts, linked together to form principally square frame elements that in turn are linked together to form completed nPods. Here again is where versatility and interchangeability of parts is the rule, the norm, and not the exception.

Thinking radically outside the box is a critical need for designing an interstellar mission of exploration and any spaceship to operate within such a mission. We are accustomed to building craft for our seas and skies out of wood, steel, aluminum, and lately carbon composites. From what should nPods in Space be constructed, for both their critical structural frame elements - the "Alpha", "Beta", "Gamma" and "Delta" elements – and the exterior/ interior shell coverings, the panels, and those structural furnishings inside? Metal is one general material, and for phase-1 the SGA will be built in part from simple steel tubing. No welding required! This is important – simplicity, safety, ease, and above all, simplicity. the same applies to carbon composites and PLA-type plastics – also planned for phase-1 here on Earth, in quiet, peaceful rural Virginia. But may be we consider other materials? There are two types of special interest: (1) systems that generate power, actual equipment, that need not be using up space inside an nPod or any other structure, but which can actually compose the structure itself, and (2) futuristic, conceivable albeit not yet here, synthetic organics, synthetic biological materials, which could emulate and even surpass the capabilities of wood and other fibre-based construction materials. Remember that the МИР (MIR) space station which operated so successfully and so long in Earth orbit actually had significant elements of its construction made from – balsa wood.

Figure 15 illustrates the concept behind the employment of power generation systems within the actual structures of nPods and thus PodAtriums and thus entire sections, even the majority sections, of large spaceships and space bases. This is taken from earlier work by the author and TetraDyn Ltd. in the hybrid automotive and electric vehicle arena (Project "THERA"). Figure 16 illustrates the basic composition of a standard RTG (radio-isotope thermoelectric generator), another power generation device that could be conveniently employed within the actual structural elements of space-based nPods. In both cases of hydrogen fuel cell systems and RTGs, one gains the triple benefit of (1) structural strength and integrity, (2) power generation, and (3) mass-material defense and protection against radiation and penetration by both small and larger external objects.

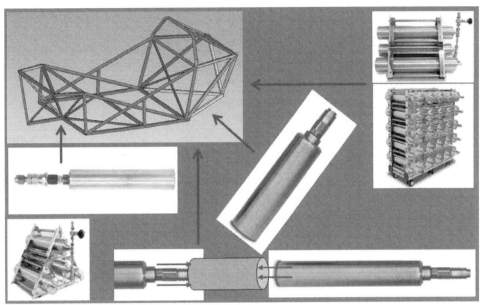

Figure 15 – Hydrogen Fuel Cell Storage and Generator Units - as nPod Structural Elements

GPHS-RTG

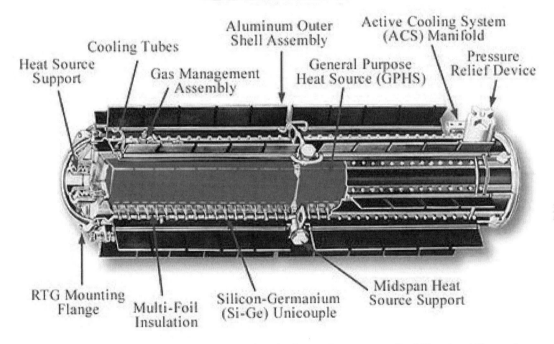

Figure 16 - RTG – Radioisotope Thermoelectric Generator – as an nPod Structural Element

7. Conclusion

The challenges of extreme long-distance and long-duration space travel and habitation require serious "thinking outside the box." That phrase has been used so often that it often now seems trite. However, in the case of an interstellar spaceship, there are going to be many "boxes." They may be in many different shapes and sizes. Rectangles, parallelograms, and prisms of any type are not necessarily what will need to be deployed! However, the fact remains, that the "boxes" need to be very adaptable and easily changed and moved around. Nobody knows what types of situations will arise in an interstellar mission other than that there will be many that are varied and unexpected. nPods and PodAtriums offer a path to some very rock-solid "in the box" architectures that can also allow, at any time during The Mission, for creatively getting "outside the box" with respect to physical structures and functions.

For instance, any of the nPod frame elements that have been designed thus far and are intended for use in StarGate Alpha are also capable of being used in the construction and deployment of what are seemingly very different, even radically different, geometries. Consider the ROC – the rhombicuboctahedron nPod. In Figure 17 are presented a few views of a very different type of nPod and PodAtrium. However, the same nDLS algorithms and software apply, and the same nPod frame elements.

The ROC has its own set of unique advantages for spaceship and space-based station construction. The ROC panels themselves can contain the structural skeleton elements, thus simplifying assembly and disassembly. Also, a ROC structure can be fabricated in a manner that results in a collapsible structure of panels that can be entirely connected to each other during transport, thus enabling simpler accordion-style motion assembly into a full volume, without risk of panel elements and other parts slipping and floating away in zero-g space and causing innumerable problems for the assembly crew. This method of compact transport also can aid in reducing weight and the volume required for such transport operations.

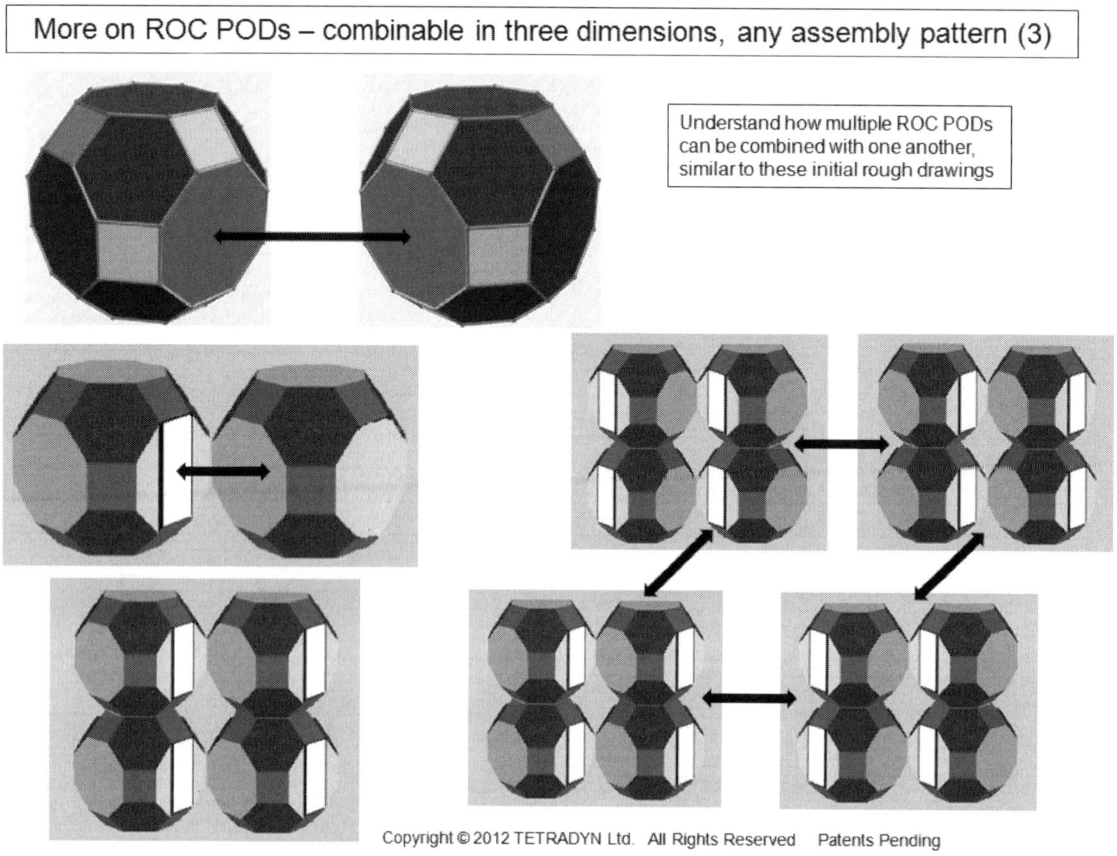

More on ROC PODs – combinable in three dimensions, any assembly pattern (3)

Understand how multiple ROC PODs can be combined with one another, similar to these initial rough drawings

Figure 17 – ROC (rhombicuboctahedron) type of nPod and multi-nPod assemblies

Finally, one simple illustration (figure 18 below) portrays the current status of the SGA experimental platform design and an illustration of the next phase of work. Based upon projected, expected and anticipated resources and support, a physical PodAtrium for experimentation with several of the agricultural and energy tasks described and mentioned briefly here will be constructed and staffed by a crew of technical and volunteer staff. This installation will allow for physical demonstration of the modularity in design and reassembly, and for several longer-term experiments particularly in novel hydroponics agriculture along with simulations of water and fuel production.

Notice that in this Earth-based phase-1 installation, there are facilities for not only agricultural and laboratory work but for education, seminars, workshops, and public communications. It is essential to convey a new level of both understanding and also enthusiasm for the space sciences, and for manned space exploration and inhabitation, into the general public. The relevance of something as bold, great, and long-term as interstellar space exploration is something that is not well understood or accepted by the mainstream population of Earth. We can change this. And we shall change it by demonstrating, right here on planet Earth, right in the "fields of wheat" so to speak. Literally, by building the StarGate Alpha and presenting it to the world, both on site and online. Here, people of Earth, you can not only see the science and technology being done, but you can even participate directly in the process, experience it and understand its importance. This mission is for us all and for our futures.

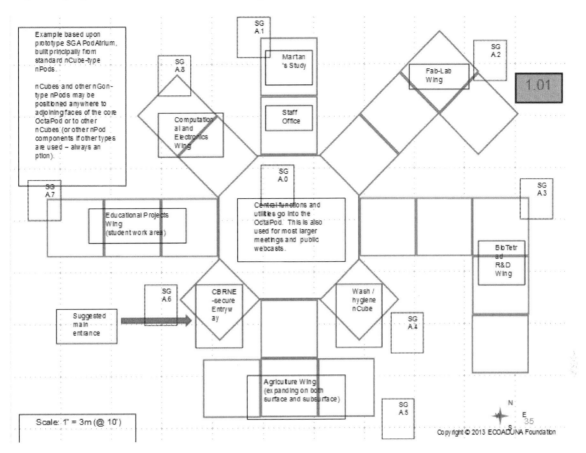

Figure 19: Phase-1 PodAtrium, StarGate Alpha, (planned for construction, 2014, in Virginia)

End Notes

1. Projects included self-sustained, solar-powered internet stations set up in remote villages in Central America and the Caribbean, involving Intel Corporation (author was employed as sicneitst and manager), MIT, Lincos Project, and with financial and in-kind support from Apple, Microsoft, Cisco and Sun.

2. Author was involved as co-designer for several "EcOasis Pod" systems that were single-instance projects built for specific sites in Louisiana, Mexico, India and Afghanistan during 2005 through 2010.

3. Trailer-based environmental monitoring labs designed and built by author and subcontractors for petrochem facilities in the Houston and Galveston areas.

4. Study performed under support from US Army, US Air Force, Dept. of Homeland Security and Canadian government for development and proofing of blast-resistant structures based upon air-inflated building components, for use in both industrial and counter-IED applications.

Planetary Habitat Systems Monitoring On a Mars Analog Mission

Simon Engler, MSc

Electrical and Computer Engineering, 856 Campus Place N.W., University of Calgary, 2500 University Drive NW ,Calgary, AB, Canada, T2N 1N4

stengler@ucalgary.ca

Oleg Abramov, PhD

U.S. Geological Survey, Astrogeology Science Center, 2255 N. Gemini Dr, Flagstaff, AZ 86001

oabramov@usgs.gov

Kim Binsted, PhD

Department of Information and Computer Sciences, University of Hawai'i at Manoa, POST 317, 1680 East-West Road , Honolulu, HI 96822

binsted@hawaii.edu

Jean Hunter, PhD

Department Biological and Environmental Engineering, Cornell University 207 Riley-Robb Hall, Ithaca, NY 14853-5701

Jbh5@cornell.edu

Henry Leung, PhD

Electrical and Computer Engineering, 856 Campus Place N.W., University of Calgary, 2500 University Drive NW ,Calgary, AB, Canada, T2N 1N4

leungh@ucalgary.ca

William Wiecking, PhD

Hawaii Preparatory Academy, 65-1692 Kohala Mtn. Rd., Kamuela, HI 96743

bill@hpa.edu

Abstract

The NASA funded HI-SEAS (Hawaii Space Exploration Analog and Simulation) is a planetary surface exploration analog site at ~8500 feet on the Mauna Loa side of the saddle area on the Big Island of Hawaii. This first mission will involve six astronaut-like (in terms of education, experience, and attitude) crew members living in the habitat for 120 days under Mars-exploration conditions. The habitat itself has been outfitted with a variety of real time sensors for water, heat, and energy consumption. This data shows a variety of traits within habitat living conditions that can be utilized for energy and water conservation. This mission started in February and will conclude on August 13th. Data of this type will give a picture of what resources are required for exploration or colonization on other planetary bodies. Future steps for habitat monitoring will be presenting outlining a data fusion model. This model will incorporate fuzzy logic for a centralized intelligent monitoring system.

Keywords
mars, analog, sensors, telemetry, habitat, planetary

1. Introduction

Telemetry data for planetary simulations or more specifically water and energy consumption are analyzed from the Hawaii Space Exploration and Analog Simulation (HI-SEAS) which was a 120 day analog mission located on the Big Island of Hawaii in the saddle area on the Mona Loa side. The flagship study for this project funded by NASA was to study food and the differences between pre-prepared and the cooking of five year shelf stable ingredients during an analog mission. The six member crew was selected for their astronaut like qualifications, and subjected to living and working conditions expected on a mission to Mars. The resources that are required by the crew for living and working are revealed during the four month experiment through the collection and analysis of resource usage. To collect these resources a variety of real time sensors have been placed in the system.

Figure 1: HI-SEAS habitat on Mauna Loa volcano

Mars Analog missions have been collecting resource usage in past. The Flashline Mars Arctic Research Station (FMARS) regularly collects water consumption and usage data, along with the Mars Desert Research Station (MDRS). This data collection is done along the lines of manual measurements of resource usage leading to rough approximations of data. The amount of diesel fuel burned by the generator can be used to estimate the amount of power used by the crew. However this does not account for the 'idle' time of the generator, nor the amount of time of draw in high power usage. The amount of water used per day in the main tank can be used to measure water consumption. However, this does not have refined enough data to determine the amount of water used in cooking verses showers by crew members.

The HI-SEAS habitat was outfitted with a number of sensors that allowed for detailed examination of water usage and power consumption to a resolution of five minutes or less. This was achieved through a number of sensors placed throughout the habitat that were collected and streamed to off-site data repositories. Upon the completion of this Mars analog mission, data analysis has shown that routines and rhythms in the habitat allow for modeling and prediction of resource usage. The power needs of a crew of this size have been captured accurately for the first time, and utilizing this data missions can use this data as a benchmark for future missions.

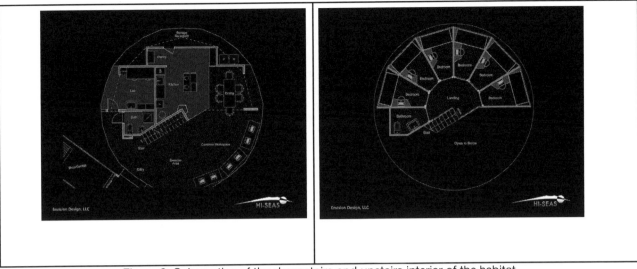

Figure 2: Schematics of the downstairs and upstairs interior of the habitat

2. HI-SEAS habitat

The HI-SEAS habitat is a 36-foot diameter dome that has two levels. The main floor consists of a work area, kitchen, dining room, laboratory, bathroom with shower. It is attached to an 8-foot square airlock that is connected to a 20 foot sea container. There is a portion of the dome blocked off by a back door. This area contains the washer and dryer, and the networking/telemetry room. The area of the first floor is 878-square feet that are usable, however it totals 993-square feet.

The habitat is supplied by a Hybrid Generator from Planetary power, and a Honda Backup generator. It has a 500 gallon main water tank with a 250 gallon backup tank. The septic tank consists of two 250 gallon tanks that are fed by a bifurcation in the outgoing pipe. At the time of writing this document, the septic tank is fed by all habitat systems, except the washing machine. The washing machine water goes into the grey tank. This system setup will change to a more efficient one in the future.

2.1 Main Tank

Figure 3: HI-SEAS crew member taking physical measurement of water tank. The yellow simulation suit is a modified bio-hazard suit. Dr. Sian Proctor

The main water tank is a 500 gallon water tank. It uses a ultrasonic level sensor that can detect the water level down to the nearest millimeter. Unfortunately, then water level sensor was subject to calibration issues due to the physical disruption of the sensor caused by refilling the water tank. However, despite the calibration issue, the level sensor was very accurate in determining the change of water depth in the tank from one point to another. Taking a physical measurement once per day allowed one to keep an accurate picture of the amount of water in the tank, while the depth sensor was able to track the rate of water usage in five minute intervals.

Physical measurement of the tank occurred once per day. The crew engineer would exit the habitat in a simulation suit (often a modified bio-hazard suit) and measure the level of water from the top. Using this information the amount of water in the tank is calculated to an accuracy within five liters.

2.2 Backup tank

The backup tank was a 250 gallon (946 L) tank thank had a ruled gauge on the side of it. If the main tank fell in short supply the crew engineer would have to transfer water from the backup tank by manually placing a water pump in-between the two tanks. Dominantly, this tank was dormant for the majority of the mission.

Figure 4: The 250 gallon (946 L) backup tank with graduated measure on the side of the tank highlighted. Photo Credit: Dr. Sian Proctor

2.3 Septic tank

The septic tank consists two 250 gallon (946 L) tanks. At the current setup of the habitat plumbing, all water minus water from the washing machine flows into the septic tank. The tank did not have a meter and required manual measurements for data collection. The translucent material would show the water level inside the septic tank. By measuring the height of the waterline, the volume of sewage inside the tank could be calculated.

Figure 5 The 500 gallon (1893 L) septic tank being manually measured for its current capacity. Photo Credit: Dr. Sian Proctor

2.4 Gray Water Tank

The 250 gallon (946 L) grey water tank was filled entirely be the habitat washing machine. Since the septic tank was drained every six days, so was the grey water tank. The graph in Figure X shows the level of the septic tank over time. The crew used an average of XX gallons per week. The crew was restricted to one wash per week with the washing schedule spread out by allowing only one wash per day.

Figure 6 The 250 gallon grey water tank. Measurements were manual using graded markings on side of the tank. Photo Credit: Dr. Sian Proctor

The current washing machine has proven to be highly inefficient using up to 60 gallons of water for a full wash. It was determined that the washing machine would use 16 gallons per wash on the 'small load' setting. This required the crew to be a bit strategic with the laundry machine.

2.5 Planetary Power Generator

The HyGen system is a trailer with photovoltaic (PV) solar panels. It utilizes a three cylinder disel enginer that is turbocharged to ensure power output is sufficient for an altitude of up to 9000 feet. [2] The generator will produce 90 Hz power output that is converted to alternating current (AC) and direct current (DC) from 350VAC to 395VDC. The direct current is passed through an inverter and converted to 120/208 VAC. The excess power is stored in Lithium Ion (Li-Ion) batteries with a capacity of 7 kWh. The solar panels seen in Image X can produce up to 3kW that is used to charge the batteries. The HyGen is serviced by refueling the diesel supply and monitoring the oil levels of the diesel engine. [2]

Figure 7: Planetary Power generator seen with the Honda backup generator

Figure 8 Solar panels provided potential voltage power to the hybrid generator. Photo Credit: Simon Engler

2.6 Backup Generator

The backup generator was a Honda EB5000 which output 5000 watts at 120V and 240V. Provides 7,000 watts for 10 secs to start larger equipment. Honda commercial iGX engine and heavy duty frame with Long run time - up to 11.2 hrs and a 120/240V selector switch. When the Planetary Power generator had issues, the Honda generator was used to power the habitat. The generator did well supplying power for a number of days at a time. It would consistently burn 13.5 gallons/day of gasoline. [2]

2.7 Solar Water Heater

Hot water for the habitat was provided by a solar water heater. This solar water heater would heat water contained in a 150 gallon insulated tank. Hot water was available to the crew well after sundown. This was a passive system and required no maintenance from the crew Engineer. The daily cycle of temperature of the solar heater can be seen in the temperature telemetry of hot and cold water tanks.

Figure 9: The 150 gallon solar water heater. Photo Credit: Simon Engler

2.8 Habitat appliances

Appliances in the habitat consisted of off the shelf equipment that you would find in any home. To measure the power consumption of each appliance in the kitchen, a power gauge was used to measure the average power consumption per week. Table 1 lists the measured average of kWh per week for each appliance in the habitat kitchen.

Appliance	kWh/week
Induction plates (3)	594
Microwave	200
Oven	50
Bread maker	25
Kettle	250
Coffee maker	60

Table 1: Measured weekly power consumption from habitat appliances.

3. Habitat Crew Routine

The crew would follow a weekly routine that was dominantly consistent. Often patterns in the usage of power and water can be seen to coincide with the schedule of activities within the habitat. The daily schedule was broken down as follows.

Morning workout	0730 - 0815
Breakfast	0830 - 0915
Morning meeting	0930 - 1045 (Average)
Mid-morning workout	1100 - 1200
Morning research	1200 - 1300
Lunch	1300 - 1400
Afternoon research	1400 - 1830
Dinner	1900 - 2000
Free time	2000 - 2200
Quiet hours	2200 - 0730

Table 2: Crew daily routine in the habitat

From this the day can be broken up into four blocks that are used in analysis to evaluate power and water consumption in certain parts of this document.

Morning block	0730 - 1230
Lunch block	1400 - 1630
Dinner block	1700 - 2200
Evening block	2000 - 0730

Table 3: Time blocks used in data analysis

4. Habitat Sensor Systems

The habitat system was outfitted with a sensor telemetry routing system. A ControlByWeb X-310 web interface was utilized to control and collect sensor information and distribute to a remote location. The X-319 is a Ethernet I/O module with four digital inputs that allows for support of up to four temperature and humidity sensors. It also has the ability to control remote relays which allowed the crew to control in air intake/outtake fan. This sensor was interfaced by the web and could be controlled externally to the environment. It has a built in web-server which allows for direct connection to the module and allows for eternal control in this manner. Using this technology, the habitat was enabled to monitor and log power supply using a customization through a web based control page.

559

Software allowed for graphing of telemetry and also the extraction of the data into CVS files allowed for statistical analysis.

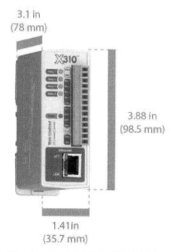

Figure 10: The ControlByWeb X310 Telemetry router

4.1 Sensors and Their Locations

Sensors were located in a variety of spots in the habitat. All power consumption was routed through a X-310 module attached from each circuit breaker. This was broken up into the Laundry room, Downstairs washroom and laboratory, Upstairs rooms and bathrooms, Living Room, Dining Room, and Kitchen. Power used in any of these areas could be monitored separately. A carbon-dioxide sensor was placed in the dining area of the dome. Temperature sensors were then placed in the Dining Room, One of the bedrooms, and the telemetry room. The main water tank had a laser level sensor, and the Planetary Power Generator computer was able to monitor and track power generation and distribution on its own.

4.2 Telemetry

The habitat has two different data links, one for Internet and one for the telemetry. An internet base antenna was placed at the habitat. Another antenna was placed in the Mona Loa Observatory (MLO). A third antenna was placed at the Hawaii Preparatory Academy (HPA). The first link goes from the habitat to MLO to HPA. It is meant to relay telemetry of the habitat and provide backup communication. This link is a A 5.8 GHz 802.11n WAN connection with speeds up to 300 mb/s is transmitted with -50 dB signal strength using a MiMo panel antenna (21 dB) with UBNT Powerbridge units from the Habitat 20 km southeast to the NOAA Mauna Loa Observatory (MLO). [1] From MLO, a pair of 24 dB antennas with UBNT Bullet2HP units then splits the signal into two parallel paths and transmits them with -64 dB signal strength 60 km north to the Hawai'i Preparatory Academy (HPA) on redundant 2.4 GHz 802.11g connections with speeds up to 54 mb/s. [1] The second data link goes from the habitat to Hale Pohaku (HP) on the slope of Mauna Kea. It serves at the primary internet connection and ftp server.

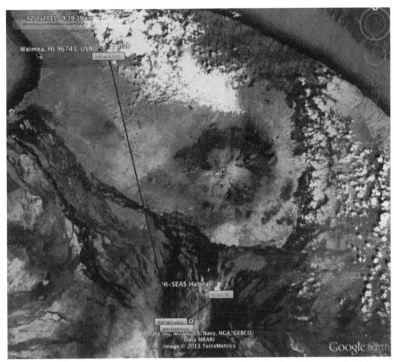

Figure 11: The Hab-MLO-HPA link as shown linking to the HPA over 60 km away [1]

4.3 Sensors and Daily Rhythm

With water, electricity, and CO_2 sensors collecting data every five minutes, it is possible to see the changes that crew members have on the habitat. It was quickly noticed that the habitat had its own rhythm of water usage and crew activity. Water usage followed a repeated cycle over a period of about four days. Figure X shows how the water level is diminished to a nearly empty tank over a period of four days. One of the easiest activities to spot is when the crew wakes or goes to sleep. This is evident simply from the water not being used anymore for long durations.

From the CO_2 sensors, the daily cycle and activities of the crew can be determined. When the crew went to sleep they would shut their bedroom doors. This would trap most of the CO_2 in their rooms, which would be vented to the outside. As a result, the CO_2 levels in the habitat would drop considerably. One can see times that crew members used the restrooms during the evenings by the slight temporary increase in CO_2 levels. Once the crew woke up for the day, some members of the crew would engage in their morning workouts. The crew activity would drive the CO_2 levels in the habitat up to its highest point of the day. Afterwards, the CO_2 levels would drop again once breakfast and the morning meeting had concluded. The crew would then go about their daily business causing fluctuations in the CO_2 levels until they went to bed for the evening.

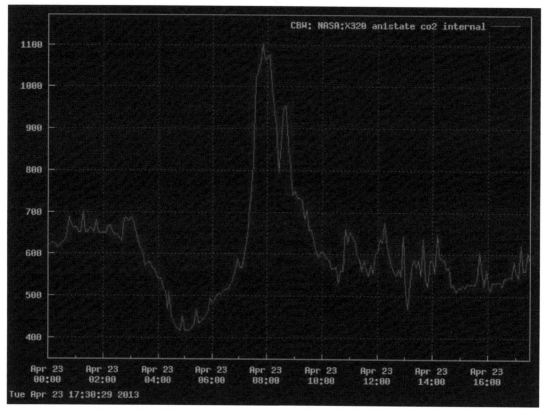

Figure 12: CO2 sensor cycle in the habitat. It is possible to identify crew activities by the changes in the CO2 levels.

These cycles of CO2, water, and electricity usage can be seen in all aspects of the habitat life. Using this information, it should allow for predictions of energy and water usage to a highly accurate degree.

5. Telemetry Data Analysis

The following diagrams display the data collected from the habitat over the entire four month experiment. The analysis of the data shows the overall usage of water and power, and reveals tendencies and patterns of crew usage.

5.1 Planetary Power Generator Performance

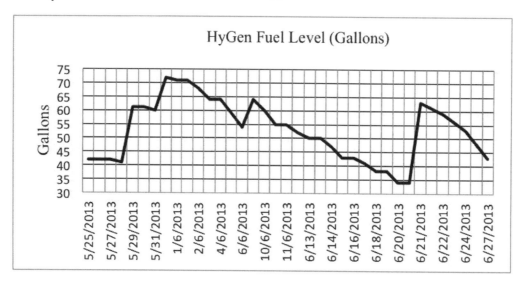

Figure 13: Planetary Power HyGen generator diesel level

Figure 11 displays the performance of the Planetary Power HygGen generator. Performance is directly related to the power usage within the habitat, and the amount of energy collected from the solar panels. Overall, the fuel capacity of the diesel generator was kept high to maintain performance. The average level of diesel fuel was 52.9 gallons with a standard deviation of 9.3 gallons.

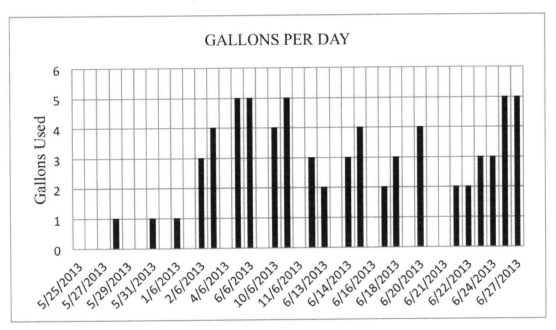

Figure 14: HyGen daily diesel burn rate.

Figure 14 displays the number of gallons burned by the HyGen generator. The average daily burn rate was 3.2 gallons with a standard deviation of 1.12 gallons. The variance in the burn rate was dominantly due to variations in solar energy obtained from the PV panels.

6. Water Consumption

Water consumption data is collected by the water level sensor every five minutes. Figure 16 displays the water data usage over a 24-hour period for the entire four month mission.

Looking at Figure 15, one can easily identify areas of high water usage. Dominantly water usage for breakfast, lunch, and dinner can be identified as the most active times. The average water consumption over a five minute period was 1.16 gallons, with a standard deviation of 1.37 gallons. The total amount of water used in the mission during this time block is 26, 523 gallons. Also, between 12:00 PM – 7:00 PM the water usage of the crew appears to be consistently high over the duration of the mission. Using this data we can examine water usage trends more closely in the morning, breakfast, lunch, dinner, and evening blocks as described in table X.

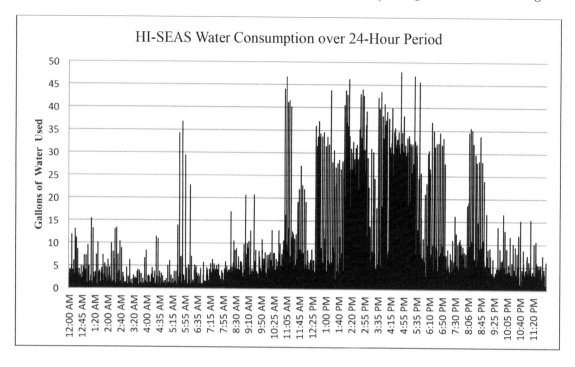

Figure 16: Water consumption in the habitat measuring water usage in five minute intervals, over a 24 hour period. This graph displays data for 120 days.

6.6.1 Morning Block Water Consumption

Water usage in the early morning hours were low in the Habitat . This was to be expected since the crew was dominantly sleeping during this time block. The average water consumption over a five minute period was 0.48 gallons, with a standard deviation of 0.42 gallons. The total amount of water used in the mission during this time block is 2717 gallons.

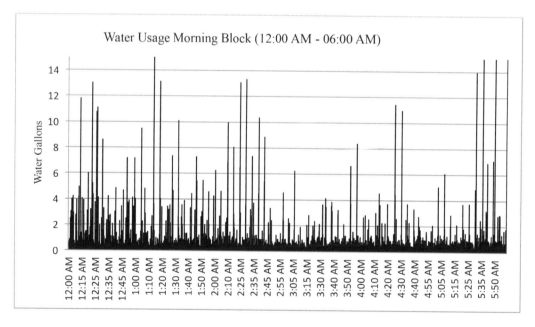

Figure 17: Morning Block water consumption. During the late night hours in the habitat there is consistently little water usage.

6.6.2 Breakfast Block Water Consumption

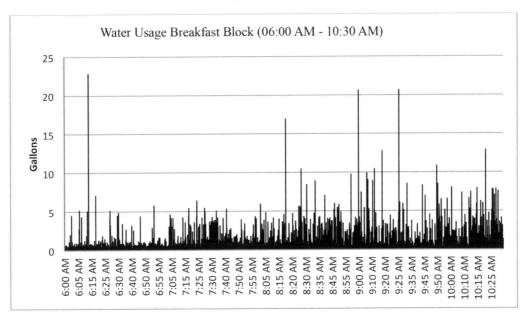

Figure 18: Breakfast block water consumption.

Water consumption during the breakfast block can be characterized by the sudden increase water usage between 7:00 AM – 8:00 AM. This increase coincides with the crew waking from sleep or completing their workouts, and getting ready for breakfast. A second dense usage occurs between 8:20 AM – 9:00 AM, which can dominantly be attributed to water usage for preparing breakfast. Following that, water usage increases again around 10:00 AM and continues for the rest of the block. This could potentially be attributed to crew members starting to prepare lunch early, or to laundry and showering activities. During the four month mission, the crew used 3320 gallons, with a five minute average of 0.76 gallons with a standard deviation of 0.69 gallons.

6.6.3 Lunch block water consumption

Water consumption during the lunch block sees a dense increase of water usage staring between the hours 1:00 PM – 1:45 PM, this coincides with preparing lunch meals. Water usage is then significantly higher between the hours of 1:55 PM -3:25 PM. This time range is consistent with the times crew would be washing dishes from lunch, and would be incorporated to water usage from the laundry machine. Sometimes crew members would start washing dishes at different times during lunch throughout the mission. One can see that the dominant water usage in this block is clearly from washing dishes.

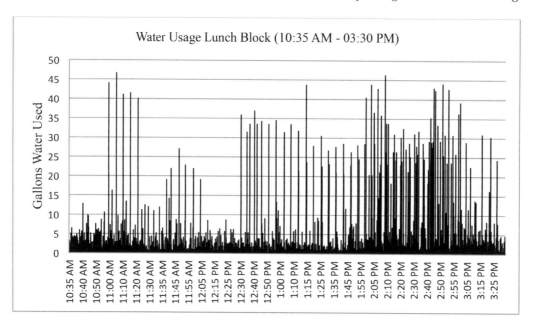

Figure 19: Water consumption over the lunch block.

6.6.4 Dinner Block Water Consumption

Water usage during the dinner block has the highest density between 4:00 PM – 6:00 PM. This is water usage from preparing dinner and doing dishes combined. Dominantly, it is unlikely dishwashing would stay until 5:00 PM at the earliest. From this data, it appears that cooking during the Dinner block uses up more water consumption than any of the other time blocks. During this time block over the entire mission, the crew used a total of 8826 gallons. Over five minute intervals the average water consumption was 1.83 gallons with a standard deviation of 2.3 gallons.

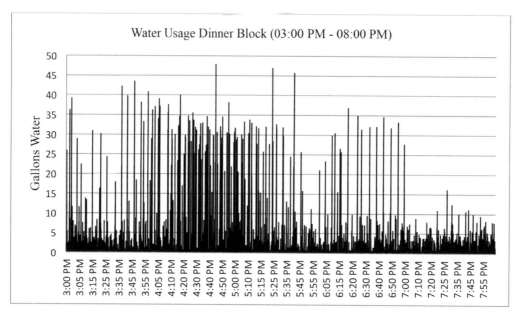

Figure 20: Dinner block water consumption.

6.6.5 Evening Block Water Consumption

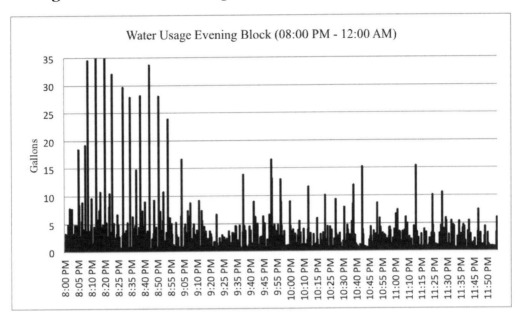

Figure 21: Water usage during the evening block

After dinner time, around 8:00 PM, water usage in the habitat would taper off. Between the hours of 8:00 PM – 8:55 PM there are a number of spikes in the water usage that can be attributed to dish washing. Some of the dish washing evening water usage was significant using up as much as 35 gallons. Over the entire mission, 3334 gallons were used during this time block with a 5 minute consumption average of 0.86 gallons with a standard deviation of 0.95 gallons.

7. Septic Tank Usage

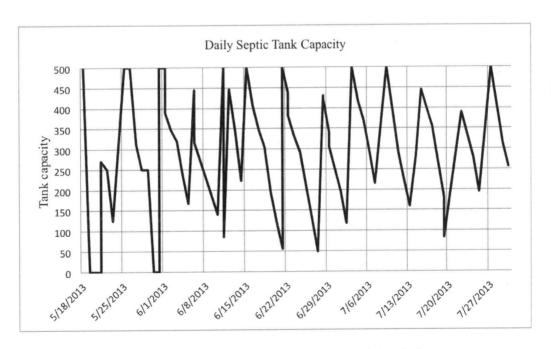

Figure 22: Daily septic tank level over course of the mission

The 500 gallon septic tank would reach its capacity every 6 days. For this reason it was emptied by sea septic removal service. If the septic tank reached its capacity, then the crew would be required to go on water restrictions. This did not occur after the first four weeks of the mission once the crew settled into a regular routine. The septic tank was taking all the water from the habitat, minus water from the washing machine. This was not the ideal setup but was done out of necessity.

8. Power Consumption

This section shows data for the power consumption of the habitat through monitoring of the electricity usage through each of the 2 kW breakers on the habitat power distribution. Each monitored breaker would supply power to the habitat laboratory and main floor bathroom, 2nd Floor rooms and bathrooms, Living Room, Kitchen, Washer/Dryer, and the daily total power usage of the habitat. Telemetry for the power was collected showing total kWh for every five minute period. This data has been collected and split into groups representing each month of the mission. The daily consumption rate for each day, for each month is displayed in section 8.1. Following this, the monthly consumption rates are display, with a final tally of the entire amount of energy consumed in the mission.

8.1 Daily Power Consumption

8.1.1 2nd floor power consumption

The second floor daily power consumption was on average 11.7 kWh with a standard deviation of 3.23 kWh. There was a total usage of 1426 kWh over the course of the four month mission. The second floor contains the crew rooms and washroom. Power consumption was generally low due to high efficiency lighting, and alarm clocks. Some crew members would work on their laptops in their rooms and this causes some additional power consumption. However, overall the power usage on the second floor is low.

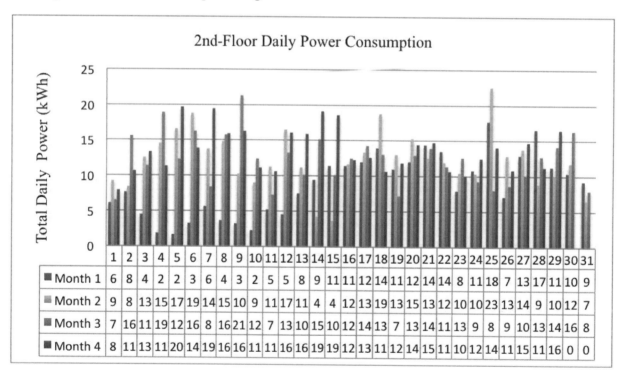

	1	2	3	4	5	6	7	8	9	10	11	12	13	14	15	16	17	18	19	20	21	22	23	24	25	26	27	28	29	30	31
Month 1	6	8	4	2	2	3	6	4	3	2	5	5	8	9	11	11	12	14	11	12	14	14	8	11	18	7	13	17	11	10	9
Month 2	9	8	13	15	17	19	14	15	10	9	11	17	11	4	4	12	13	19	13	15	13	12	10	10	23	13	14	9	10	12	7
Month 3	7	16	11	19	12	16	8	16	21	12	7	13	10	15	10	12	14	13	7	13	14	11	13	9	8	9	10	13	14	16	8
Month 4	8	11	13	11	20	14	19	16	16	11	11	16	16	19	19	12	13	11	12	14	15	11	10	12	14	11	15	11	16	0	0

Figure 23: Second floor daily power consumption in total daily kWh

8.1.2 Laboratory and downstairs bathroom power consumption

The daily power consumption in the laboratory and main floor bathroom totaled 1832 kWh over the course of the mission. The daily average of power consumption was 458 kWh with a standard deviation of 138 kWh. Power usage in the lab and bathroom tended to increase as the mission went on. This was likely due to the increasing activity in the laboratory for using equipment to incubate and freeze samples.

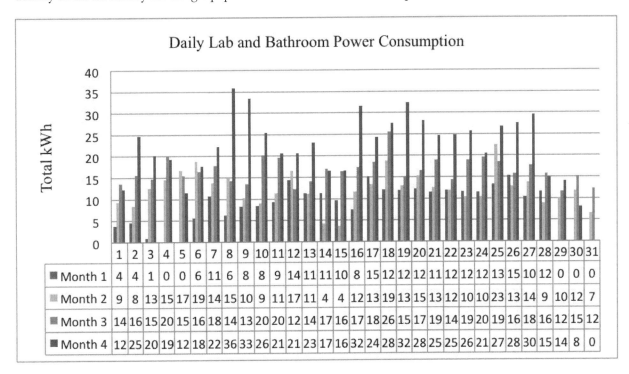

Figure 24: Daily lab and bathroom power consumption

8.1.3 Washing machine power consumption

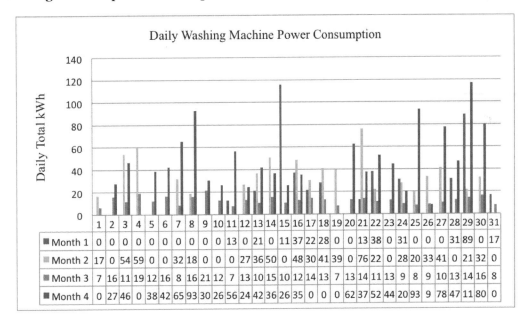

Figure 25: Daily washing machine power consumption over four month mission

The washing machine purchased for this mission turned out to be a highly inefficient machine. On a large load, it would consume a very large 62 gallons per wash. This was a significant issue at the beginning of the mission, as it caused a couple days of water shortages due to the unexpected amount of water used. To combat this extreme water consumption rate, crew was restricted to setting the washing machine on the low setting, which used a more reasonable 16 gallons per load. The crew was also assigned a specific day to do their laundry allowing to spread the crew washes over six days, with an extra day for washing dish clothes and other communal items. There was a higher usage of the washing machine towards the end of the fourth month due to some textile studies, and prepping the habitat for the end of the mission. Overall, the washing machine used a grand total of 2790 kWh, with a monthly average of 697 kWh at standard deviation of 279 kWh.

8.1.4 Living room power consumption

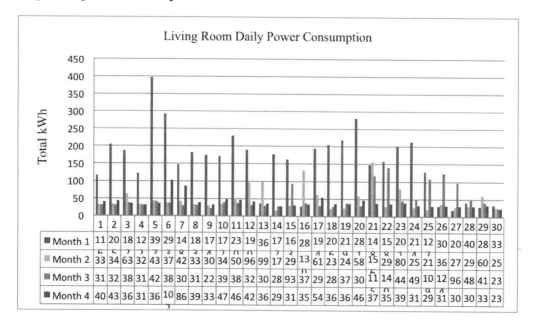

Figure 26: Living room daily power consumption levels

The living room power was significantly higher during the first month of the mission. This was due to the cold temperatures experienced at night time inside the habitat. Heaters would be run nearly continuously in an effort to keep the habitat warm. Each of these heaters rate at 1500 W on full power, leading to a high energy consumption. Towards the end of the first month, the heaters were no longer used causing a significant drop in the power consumption of the living room. The daily average of the living room power consumed is 73 kWh with a standard deviation of 53 kWh

8.1.5 Kitchen power consumption

Kitchen power was the dominant power consumer of the habitat. Every cooking appliance, bread maker, oven, dishwasher, etc. are contained within this power sensor. The daily average power used in the kitchen was 133 kWh with a standard deviation of 50 kWh.

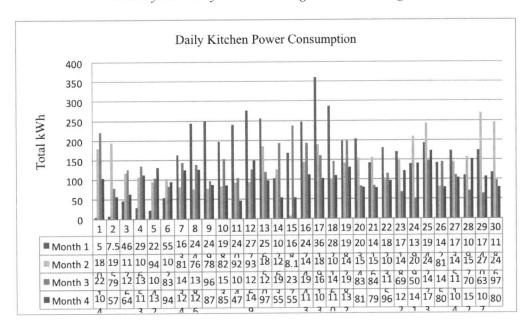

Figure 27: Kitchen power consumption levels

	1	2	3	4	5	6	7	8	9	10	11	12	13	14	15	16	17	18	19	20	21	22	23	24	25	26	27	28	29	30
Month 1	5	7.5	46	29	22	55	16	24	24	19	24	27	25	10	16	24	36	28	19	20	14	18	17	13	19	14	17	10	17	11
Month 2	18	19	11	10	94	10	81	76	78	82	92	93	18	12	8.1	14	18	10	14	15	15	10	14	20	24	81	14	15	27	24
Month 3	22	79	12	13	10	83	14	13	96	15	10	12	12	19	23	19	16	14	19	83	84	11	69	50	14	14	11	70	63	97
Month 4	10	57	64	11	13	94	12	12	87	85	47	14	97	55	55	11	10	11	13	81	79	96	12	14	17	80	10	15	10	80

8.1.6 Total power consumption

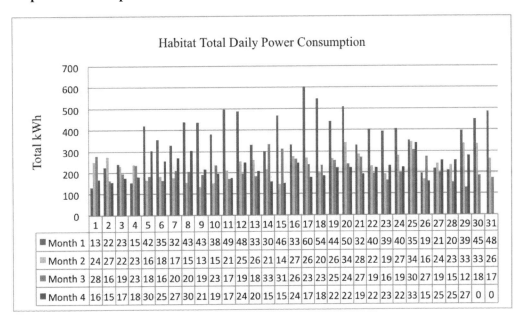

Figure 28: Total daily power consumption for the entire habitat.

	1	2	3	4	5	6	7	8	9	10	11	12	13	14	15	16	17	18	19	20	21	22	23	24	25	26	27	28	29	30	31
Month 1	13	22	23	15	42	35	32	43	43	38	49	48	33	30	46	33	60	54	44	50	32	40	39	40	35	19	21	20	39	45	48
Month 2	24	27	22	23	16	18	17	15	13	15	21	25	26	21	14	27	26	20	26	34	28	22	19	27	34	16	24	23	33	33	26
Month 3	28	16	19	23	18	16	20	20	19	23	17	19	18	33	31	26	23	23	25	24	27	19	16	19	30	27	19	15	12	18	17
Month 4	16	15	17	18	30	25	27	30	21	19	17	24	20	15	15	24	17	18	22	22	19	22	23	22	33	15	25	25	27	0	0

The total daily power consumption in the habitat was an average of 260 kWh with a standard deviation of 75 kWh. Power consumption was significantly higher in the first month. This was dominantly due to the use of heaters to keep the habitat warm in the cool conditions.

8.2 Monthly Power Consumption

This section tallies up the kWh used each day in the habitat and packages it into monthly bar graphs. Using this information, monthly trends in habitat power consumption can be identified and quantified.

8.2.1 2nd floor power consumption

The total power consumption on the second floor over the duration of the mission was 1425 kWh with a monthly average of 356 kWh at a standard deviation of 11 kWh. The usage of power on the second floor was dominantly consistent each month for the duration of the mission. The first month, the crew used less power on the second floor, as the crew was working on the main floor at the start of the mission.

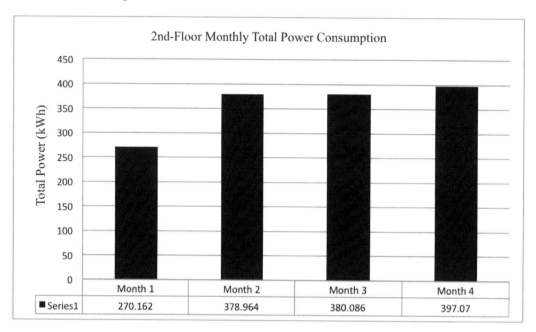

Figure 29: Monthly second floor power consumption in kWh

8.2.2 Laboratory and downstairs bathroom power consumption

The monthly power consumption in the lab and bathroom increased linearly over the mission. The laboratory was used with increasing frequency during the mission, with a larger amount of biological samples to incubate and store. The total amount of power consumed over the four months is 2461 kWh. The average power consumption per month was 458 kWh with a standard deviation 138 kWh.

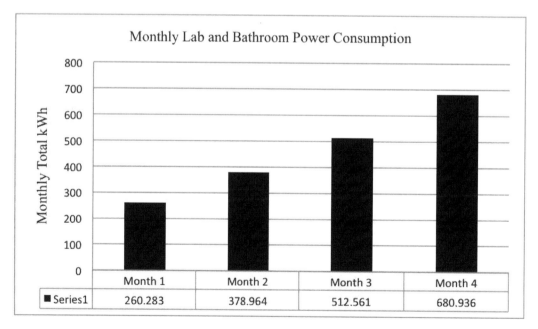

Figure 30: Monthly lab and bathroom total power consumption

8.2.3 Washing machine power consumption

The total monthly power consumption of the washing machine varied throughout the mission. In the fourth month of the mission, the washing machine was used more frequently due to washing necessary for textile studies. For the entire mission, the washing machine consumed 2790 kWh of energy with a monthly average of 697 kWh with a standard deviation of 384 kWh.

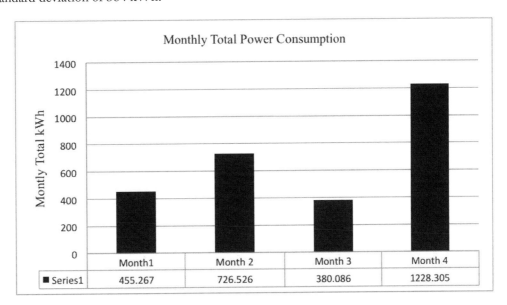

Figure 31: Monthly total power consumption of washing machine

8.2.4 Living room power consumption

The monthly power consumption in the living room is dominated by the first month, which is about four times the amount than the rest of the month. As seen in the daily power consumption levels, this was due to the use of heaters during the first month of the mission.

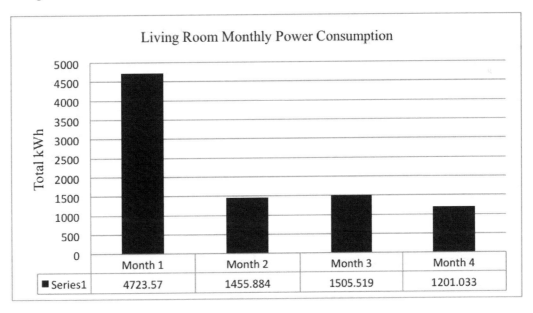

Figure 32: Living room power consumption

573

8.2.5 Kitchen power consumption

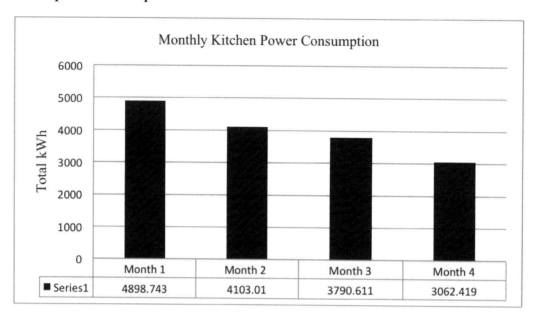

Figure 33: Monthly kitchen power consumption

The monthly kitchen power consumption had a trend downwards each month. This is possibly due to the crew getting more efficient at cooking the various meals. The monthly average was 3963 kWh with a standard deviation of 536 kWh. The total amount of power used in the kitchen over the course of the mission is 15,854 kWh.

8.2.6 Total power consumption

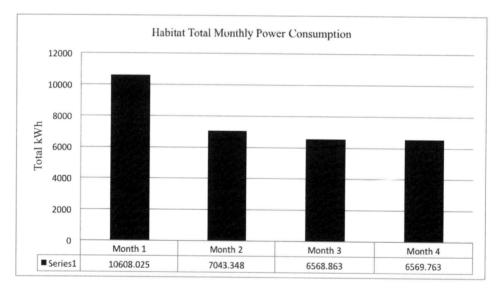

Figure 34:Total habitat Monthly power consumption

The total monthly power consumption of the habitat shows that again the first month is significantly higher due to the use of heats. Subsequent power consumption over the following three months had very little variance in total power usage. The total power consumption over the entire mission was 30,790 kWh with a monthly average of 7697 kWh with a standard deviation of 1455 kWh.

8. Thermal Analysis of Habitat
8.1 Methods
A FLIR T300 thermal imager was used to acquire infrared images of the dome interior and the attached storage container at different time points in the diurnal cycle. Reported temperatures were calibrated by adjusting for thermal emissivities of known materials, particularly the Polyvinyl Chloride (PVC) of the dome, and a thermocouple was used to verify calibration. Thermal emissivities of most objects within the habitat ranged from 0.94 to 0.99, and a mean emissivity value of 0.96 was used to assemble thermal panoramas presented in this paper. In addition, a network of both wired and wireless temperature sensors was used to verify the results of thermal imaging and conduct continuous temperature monitoring within specific locations of interest. Temperatures reported by all of the OMWT-TEMP15 wireless sensors, as well as most of the habitat's built-in temperature sensors, were in close agreement (within 1 °C) to those obtained by FLIR thermography. One exception was the internal temperature sensor in the kitchen, which often reported temperatures ~2 °C higher than either the FLIR or the adjacent OMWT-TEMP15 unit. It is hypothesized that this discrepancy was due to the sensor's relative lack of shielding and proximity to radiative heat sources such as heaters and kitchen appliances. In general, however, there is a high degree of confidence in the temperatures reported here due to the several implemented cross-controls.

The FLIR T300 imager was coupled to a Gigapan Epic 100 unit to perform automated thermal scanning within the habitat. This allowed rapid collection of a large set of thermal images covering a specified area, which was typically defined as 360° × 180°, thus encompassing everything that could be observed from a given location with the exception of a small area directly beneath the scanning platform. The resulting thermal infrared image data was then calibrated and processed using the FLIR ExaminIR software, with results output as standard bitmap images. These images were then stitched into panoramas using Gigapan Stitch software, generating the final products presented here.

8.2 Daytime and Nighttime Thermography
A comparison of daytime and nighttime spherical (360° × 180°) thermal panoramas encompassing the central dome area of the habitat, as well as a visible-light panorama for context, are presented in Figure 35:

Figure 36: A photograph and thermal images of the habitat at day and night.

The daytime panorama was acquired in the afternoon of 7/10. Weather conditions as reported by the habitat's weather stations were clear skies, light and variable winds, and an ambient temperature of 23 °C. Observed temperatures range from a high of ~34 °C along ceiling of the dome to a low of ~18 °C. There is a strong vertical temperature gradient present; temperatures increase with height from ~21 °C underneath crewmembers' work desks to over 34 °C at the dome ceiling. The highest temperatures are concentrated in the southern quadrant of the dome and above crewmembers' staterooms.

The nighttime panorama, acquired on 6/21, provides a thorough overview of the temperature distribution in the hab during the evening. Weather conditions at the time were clear skies, calm winds, and an ambient outdoor temperature of ~10 °C. The mean temperature of the PVC cover is ~15 °C. Heat loss along the side and bottom seams, and especially along the airlock door is clearly visible. A modest temperature gradient of ~2 °C is noted along the walls of the dome, with the ceiling being warmer, likely due to rising air currents. Heat produced by various electrical appliances, particularly the space heater, electric tea kettle, and the dishwasher is clearly visible. Heat appears to be trapped below the floors of the second-floor structure, and appears to be particularly concentrated below room #1 for reasons that are not entirely clear.

9.3 Change Detection and Mapping

Temperature changes over relatively short periods of time are illustrated in Figure 37 by two 250° × 180° spherical thermal panoramas of the central dome area of the habitat, acquired on 7/4 approx. 1.25 hours apart. The mean temperature of the PVC cover is ~22.5 °C in the top image and ~21 °C in the bottom image. A decrease in overall temperatures of ~1.5 °C is noted between the two panoramas. A temperature gradient of ~2 °C is present along the walls of the dome, with the ceiling being warmer due to the rising air currents. Significant vertical temperature gradients of ~2.5 °C are noted along the walls of staterooms in the upper image. Atmospheric conditions were cloudy and foggy with calm winds at the time imaging was performed.

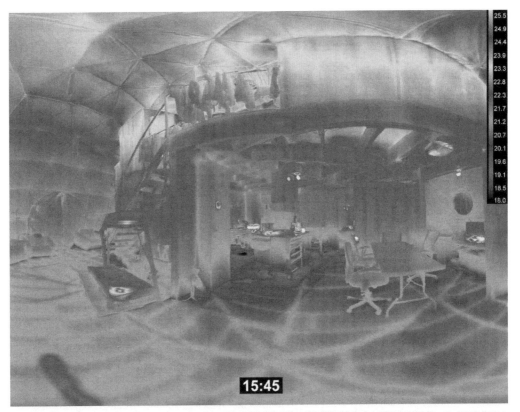

Figure 38: Changes in thermal properties over short periods of time.

9.4 Storage Container Thermal Monitoring

The main food storage area in the HI-SEAS habitat is along the east wall of the steel shipping container that is also used as a workshop and robot garage. Because of concerns of possible food spoilage due to perceived high temperatures within the container, particularly in the afternoons of sunny days, OMWT-TEMP15 wireless temperature sensors and thermal imaging were used to evaluate the diurnal temperature distributions within the container and assess their impact on food storage. The results, including a sample late afternoon spherical (360° × 180°) thermal panorama, a visible-light panorama for context, and data from temperature sensors are presented in Figure 39.

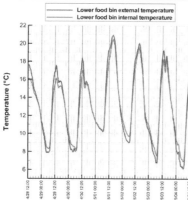

Figure 40: Thermal properties of sea container used for food storage.

The thermal panorama of the storage container shown in Figure 41 was acquired on July 8 at 16:00. Atmospheric conditions at the time of imaging were clear skies and winds averaging 16 mph from the north. Observed temperatures range from a high of 34 °C along the west well to a low of 17 °C in the southeast ceiling quadrant. The high temperatures along the west wall are explained by direct incident sunlight in the late afternoon, and the low temperatures in the southeast part of the ceiling are due to shade provided by the solar panels and the hot water tank installed in that area (Fig. 9). In general, the ceiling area remains fairly cool despite direct sunlight due to a layer of insulation present there. The second-coolest locations are near the container floor and the east wall, which is adjacent to a cinder cone (Fig. 9) and remains mostly shaded throughout the day. Temperatures increase with height, and both horizontal and vertical thermal gradients are present across the food storage boxes. Temperatures of the lowermost food boxes have range from 19 to 22 °C.

In addition, a wireless temperature sensor was placed inside a sterilized plastic food storage bin positioned on the floor of the container, while another temperature sensor was placed on the lid of the same bin to record external temperature. Temperature data from a period of six diurnal cycles is presented in Figure 42, (bottom).

The overall conclusions from this assessment were as follows: (i) Temperatures within the lower bins are acceptable for food storage; they had a mean of ~13 °C during the observation period and briefly reached a maximum of ~20 °C on the hottest day of the week. (ii) Food storage acceptability decreases with increasing height above the container floor. It was recommended that foods with any degree of perishability (processed cheese, cured meats, etc.) are only stored in the lower bin, or, at most, near the wall-facing side of the upper bin. (iii) Only very temperature-stable foods should be stored in the cardboard boxes above the bins. (iv) Insulation and/or a reflective layer added to the west wall of the container would significantly reduce daytime temperature spikes.

9.5 Stateroom Temperatures

Figure 43a presents data collected in May from a wireless temperature sensor in stateroom #4, and, for comparison, one in the kitchen/dining room area. Prior to May 10, it was standard practice to leave one of the portable 1500-watt Lasko heaters running overnight on the ground floor. The results of turning off the heater beginning the night of May 10 – May 11 are clearly visible in Figure 43a. The dining room temperature decreased ~2.5 °C from the baseline mean; however, the effect on bedroom temperatures was significantly less pronounced, with a decrease of ~1-1.5 C from the baseline mean, suggesting that the heating benefits were fairly marginal and did not outweigh the electrical power costs of running the heater overnight.

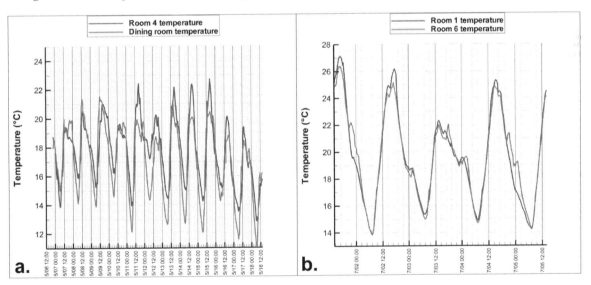

Figure 43: Temperatures in habitat staterooms

The effects of installing single-paned acrylic windows on May 15 are also apparent, with daytime highs in both the dining area and the bedrooms being ~1-2 °C lower. Based on this data, it was recommended that the window in the lab be removed and replaced with the PVC cover that was there previously, and the window in the dining room area be double-paned.

In addition, wireless temperature sensors in staterooms #1 and #6 were used to evaluate the differences in temperature at the opposite ends of the second floor and determine whether there was a significant lateral temperature difference across the second floor. The data collected from OMWT-TEMP15 sensors at these locations for four diurnal cycles in July is presented in Figure 43b. The results indicate that, although stateroom #1 experienced higher daytime temperature peaks, the difference is relatively small, being ~0.5 to ~1 °C.

11. Conclusions

Utilizing the data collected in the analog mission, an understanding of water, and electricity consumption was obtained. In the short term, this data can be used to strengthen future analog missions. Having detailed knowledge of the weekly water and power consumptions will allow for accurate planning. In the long term, daily power and water consumption trends can be used to predict water and power usage for specific activities. It can be surmised that in planning out daily activities, it will be possible to predict with great accuracy water and power usage of a crew over short term activities. What this allows for is a more dynamic model that will be able to accurately predict consumption even when there are major changes in routines. Every statistical model that utilizes statistics from routine behavior seen on the large scale will break down almost immediately when the model is changed even moderately. However, because we are able to see extremely fine resolution of crew activities and consumption, it will be possible to model consumption on a fine resolution of activity. This fine resolution of statistical data provides tremendous flexibility in the models. Creating a fuzzy logic system to predict these consumption rates and compare to the real world is the next step in this research.

With the thermal imaging data, it was found that the integrated and mostly automated use of thermal imaging and temperature sensors presented here allowed for comprehensive monitoring of the thermal state of the HI-SEAS analog habitat. The near-real-time feedback provided by this methodology allowed for rapid identification of heat sources and sinks within the habitat, and resulted in several immediate improvements to temperature control in the habitat. Specific findings included the relative ineffectiveness of centrally-located portable heaters for increasing temperatures in crewmember staterooms, the significant loss of heat due to (originally) single-paned windows, temperature distributions in the storage container and locations acceptable for food storage, and pronounced temperature gradients within the dome (as well as within individual staterooms) during daytime hours.

Acknowledgements

Processing of thermal imaging data by Jennifer Steil (HI-SEAS first-tier support) is gratefully acknowledged.

References

1. Shiro, B.; HI-SEAS mission support, https://sites.google.com/site/hiseasmission/engineering

2. Lenard, R.; Mellberg E., Kohut J., "Hygen Demonstrator Operating Manual", Planetary Power, Inc. Operating Manual HGD-2013-100 v3.0, (2013)

3. ControlByWeb website: http://www.controlbyweb.com/

4. Bamsey, M., Berinstain, A., Auclair, S., Battler, M., Binsted, K., Bywaters, K., Harris, J., Kobrick, R., McKay., C. (2009). Four month Moon and Mars crew water utilization study conducted at the Flashline Mars Arctic Research Station, Devon Island, Nunavut. Advances in Space Research.

Sustainable Design for Extended Space Journeys

Antoine G. Faddoul, MS

Tony Sky Design Group, 538 E 89th Street E1, New York, NY 10128

Tony@Tonysky.net

Abstract

The rise of extended space travel age emphasizes the role of sustainable designs that bear products with longer durability, minimal maintenance, energy self-sufficiency, and capability of accommodating remote improvements.

Designing interstellar mechanical spaceships, habitable spaces, architectural furniture, fashion clothing, practical equipment, or accommodating gadgets is barely different from the daily "earthly" design aspects that involve a product's function, budget, esthetic, and lifecycle. The two factors highlighted, however, are time and distance which become extreme aspects.

One case study scenario might be able to highlight the questions to be reevaluated from traditional design. Ten years after a manned-spaceship starts a journey into space:

- What is the status of the equipment, energy, and gadgets used in the past decade?
- Can we transfer a new processor developed on earth to replace an outdated system used to mitigate space asteroids collision? Do we have the material, technology, and craftsmanship onboard to build it?
- Is there a capability onboard to fix unforeseen design deficiency discovered 2 years ago? Or to fix the sewage leakage from last month?
- How do the inhabitants of the space vessel (mostly non-scientists) evaluate their lives and daily/future functions and needs?

The longest manned trip to space was to the moon and lasted less than two weeks. However, the space design development procedures need to address all stages leading to interstellar travel trips. Such need increases daily with the plans to commercialize space trips, and even with trips within our solar system considering that they will be much longer and farther than a trip to Earth's backyard.

Keywords

Sustainable, design, starship, interstellar, architecture, technology

1. Gliina Heads to Antas

The year is 2072 AD. Starship Gliina is about one light year away from Earth. The simulated time is 5:00 AM, 10 years after leaving the lunar orbit. The destination is planet Antas in Constellation Cygnus.

The remaining distance to reach target is about 7.5 light years. The signal-to-Earth delay is 24:23:12.56

Every day at this time a long check list is run. Discrepancies are reported and directed to the corresponding crews. The list has three main areas: structure, ecosystem, and the status of the inhabitants of the starship.

These items have hundreds of thousands of sub-items. We only have time to demonstrate a few of them and talk about aspects of sustainability, durability and functionality.

Over a hundred items related to these three areas were evaluated, assessing their needs to achieve sustainable spaceship that would function for hundreds of years. They were analyzed according to their status whether current technology, developing technology or future technology. In addition, each item was mapped according to how the science, technology, and design behind it would evolve in tens of years and how we expect the correspondence product to function in the future. The items are mostly associated with structures that are used on Earth, yet need to be reevaluated to be suitable to function in space for long periods of time. Only few items are designed solely for space travel, and much less are those only needed for a starship without earthly corresponding usage.

Fifteen of those items will be presented directly or indirectly through the check list.

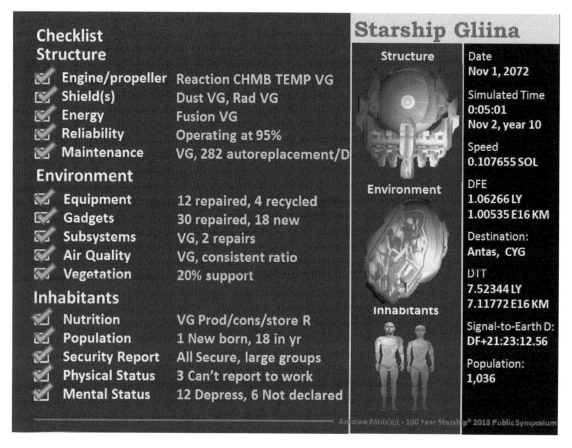

Figure 1.0 The checklist for starship Gliina represents (directly or indirectly) fifteen of the design points

2. Starship Structure

So, ten years after leaving our lunar orbit, how is Starship Gliina doing – a starship that is on a 75 year trip? From Figure 1 we can pull the following points under the starship structure.

2.1 Engine/propeller: Reaction CHMB TEMP VG

The technology for the propelling system that will drive the starship is still in the theoretical phases. It is still too early to determine whether it will be solar sail, fusion, fission, antimatter fusion, or any other type of propelling system. The sub-points checked in the figure are the chamber temperature of the reaction chamber as one of the aspects we can measure to verify the stability and functionality. The temperature and the foil thickness checked are in good conditions.

It will take several years for each of the currently discussed propelling systems to be brought into physical testing, development, and modeling. Such system is the one of the least developed aspects of designing a spaceship.

That is basically because, unlike most of the rest of the hundred items, a starship propelling engine does not have a counterpart on earth built for any other purpose. Even when comparing it to the spaceships and rocket used now in space programs, we cannot use such engines as prototype since they use liquid fuel which is deemed obsolete in interstellar travel. Once one system proves suitable, it will be a matter of time to realize the needed improvements – that is few decades contemplating the current pace in technology advancement.

2.2 Shield(s): Dust VG, Rad VG

The shielding from dust and space particle is a current technology with a need to apply it to larger surfaces. It has been applied to smaller surface areas in trips where there is less amount of space dust and fragments, than our larger surface needs.. Special design aspects were considered for NASA's spacecraft Stardust that was sent in 1999 in a mission to encounter a comet and collect a sample from it. The development required here includes preparing for longer trips, and more waves or anticipated and uncalculated for space particles.

The other type of shielding needed for the starship is the radiation protection which is currently applied to manned space trips. Further developments are needed especially since we don't know much about the cosmic radiations outside our solar system; in fact we don't know much about the radiation levels beyond Mars. The last information we received was through a spacecraft travelling to Mars in 2012. The radiation levels outside our solar systems are more intense especially when beyond the protective effect of the magnetic field of the sun and the solar wind.

2.3 Energy: Fusion VG

The apparatus checked for this item is a fusion (for Gliina but could be any equivalent energy source) reactor for the energy usage onboard the starship. While the points evaluated above (01 and 02) were mostly from space travel, this item is one of the items that can be developed from current technology utilizing the advanced and developing energy generating systems. For example, fusion and fission energy are current technology and can be built upon unless more efficient sources are discovered.

2.4 Reliability: Operating at 95%

The reliability factor and calculations are important for long trips. Just like current space shuttle, airplanes, or even cars travel from the day they are brand new until their life span expire, a starship will function likewise. While a starship reliability will decrease through the years as it travels, it should be able to function with less than the original perfect conditions. Gliina is now operating at 95% and will be expected to continue to operate despite decreased reliability as the the years pass away.

2.5 Maintenance: VG, 282 auto-replacement/D

Auto-repair or auto-replacement for parts is an important aspect of maintenance for the starship. It is a key factor in keeping the required reliability to maintain the desired functionality. The current space crafts have different aspects of auto replacement. The check list shows that 282 auto parts were replaced in past 24 hours, which is normal after ten years and within the reliability factor for extended space trips. The number of repaired parts is expected to increase as the time and distance pass in such journeys. The development in robotics is a promising tool in autoreplacement.

It looks like the structure and mechanism for the starship (once they are available) will function well. When any structure, or even a piece of equipment, is engineered a safety factor is always included. That safety factor ensures functioning at satisfactory levels for a period much longer than the required lifetime.

That is why starship Gliina is most likely to function normally in space taking into consideration the intensive testing it endured. Also, in 2050 we sent a similar starship for colonizing purposes within our solar system. As for testing the "road" many space probes were sent beyond the solar system on a similar path to planet Antas for data collection in the couple decades before Gliina left.

3. Starship Environment

The ecosystem or the interior environment inside the starship will be a mix of a real and simulated systems.

3.1 Equipment: 12 repaired, 3 recycled

Repairing and recycling is a normal procedure on extended trips. The amount of recycled equipment will rise with time. Evaluating the energy needed for recycling vs. rebuilding and how it factors in the life cycle is a major aspect in determining whether to repair, recycle, or build new. Energy calculations are part of every design item for a starship second by the consumption and recycling cycle of the raw materials.

3.2 Gadgets: 30 repaired, 18 new

The new gadgets in space will be fabricated, and the development of 3D printers play a major role. The development of the 3D printers in the past 2 years is by itself a breakthrough that could be built upon to reach more efficient printers in both raw material consumption and final products. Building of new gadgets in space is not limited to reproducing expired devices. It includes, like on Earth, advancing and upgrading with each new version. The research and development will continue in space and not depend completely on Earth's technology advancement as the time elapsing will be a real barrier as the distance will incur inevitable delay in communication with Earth.

3.3 Subsystems: VG, 2 repairs

Electrical, plumbing, HVAC, fire sprinklers and other mechanical systems have longer lifespan on a starship. Util-closed-loop water systems can be advanced to handle the size and complexity of Gliina's vehicle size.

3.4 Air Quality: VG, consistent ratio

Air quality consists of the closed systems which includes oxygen recirculating, vegetation, and other living systems on the starship. With vegetation introduced on a starship, there is a gradual increased contribution of O_2 and CO_2 into the air cycle. The air cycle sill not be an ideal ratio for human breathing, but rather a balanced simulation of Earth's air, with possible inclusion of parasite or bacteria needed to improve the inhabitants health and immune system.

3.5 Vegetation: 20% support

Vegetation on a starship is a helpful element to improve human's onboard life onboard. It is also an ongoing process as it is not a fixed element especially since it increases its impact over time instead of deteriorating. The checked item shows the vegetation reaching 20% of its full capacity. That is on the scheduled growth and will increase with time. Cultivation is also a source for food as well as raw materials. Farming is one of humanity's oldest capabilities and therefore provides a lot of technical knowledge to advance and adapt for a closed system away from the our Sun.

4. Starship inhabitants

Looking at the inhabitants of a manned, one-way, interstellar trip utilizing a small-medium sized starship and population, there are many aspects that affect the daily life of a true communal society in a habitat that is a mix of simulated and natural ecosystems.

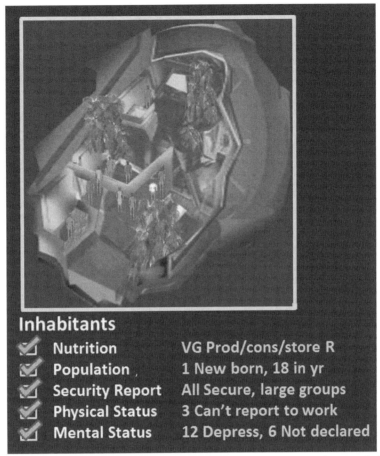

Figure 2.0 The checklist for starship Gliina inhabitants reveals much more than statistics and census

Let's take the nutrition level for example which covers the nutrition for the trip and for many years after arrival to destination. It covers the continuous variety of food dishes provided on the starship as well. Also, the contribution of the food produced onboard to the main food chain. Genetic engineering is one of the factor to account for.

The trip started 10 years ago with 999 people. 700 of them are not scientists, 100 were under 12.

Despite all screening, training, and preparation, that the inhabitants undertook, the 700 non-scientists onboard may have not fully comprehended what a one-way trip in a confined place would entail. The security report says no incidents were reported. It also sheds some light on noticeable gathering of people in groups. What the police report didn't pick up is reported in the mental status. 12 cases of depression were reported to the health team, while the thermal detectors revealed 6 undeclared cases of depression.

That simply shows the two most common ways of dealing with depression; more isolation, or trying to encounter more people, which is a healthier attitude.

The trip started with a variety of fashion choices unlike what we see in sci-fii movies of people wearing the same uniform. Over the past few years, the style of the people onboard shifted towards more unified clothing color and themes. People who tend to live or work in the same place and with the same people for a while lose interest in keeping up with their attire in the places where they are doing routine work – in this case, to many onboard, the whole life experience on SS Gliina became routine.

One newborn in the past 24 hours - Congrats space boy or girl! The starship left with a population of 999 and in the past 10 years 37 newborns were recorded. That is a low rate, again by our earthly standards. In the first five years only 5 babies were born on Starship Gliina. Couples that are not stable tend to have less desire to have kids, and obviously the majority of people on this starship did not feel they are "settled" enough to consider having babies on a 75 year trip until they made peace with all the aspects of their new lives.

The starship inhabitants are not used to babies' cries, and the mothers are not that excited to take their babies in public. Some are not going to work. The checklist also showed that 3 people cannot report to work. Regardless of the reason behind their absence, and even though such absence is accounted for, it is not easy to stop working and stay home in a Communal society.

5. Spaceship Sustainable Aspects

Designing daily "earthly" needs from habitat and equipment is barely different from designing interstellar mechanical spaceships, habitable spaces, architectural furniture, fashion clothing, practical equipment, or accommodating gadgets in the aspects that involve the products' function, budget, esthetic, and lifecycle.

For extended space travel we need sustainable designs that bear products with longer durability, minimal maintenance, energy self-sufficiency, and capability of accommodating remote improvements.

The two factors highlighted however are time and distance. Such factors affect all aspects of design, yet are critical mainly to the lifecycle factor. The basis of design need to be evaluated against extremes such as absence of raw material and the need for complete self-sufficiency.

Sustainable Design Requirements on Earth	Space Sustainable Design Effects
Use less Natural resources Recycle Reuse Selfsufficiency	Extremely needed Varies Extremely needed Extremely needed A Must

Table 1.0 The effects of space sustainable design on the five main elements of sustainable design

What we consider on earth as naturally sustainable are the renewable energy resources such as solar, wind, and geothermal energy, in addition to the naturally renewable raw materials. Such items depend on Earth-bound conditions and its position from the sun. In outer space, the traditional renewable resources become obsolete.

6. Conclusion

Dealing with extended space journeys, design and sustainability move to entire different levels and their aspects and resources reach extreme levels.

Simulating comprehensive futuristic scenarios need to utilize current and future capabilities for all structural, ecosystem, and human aspects to be able to develop the means for a functional and vivid manned interstellar travel.

The first generation to leave Earth will need the most adaptation skills to live in space. After all, it seems that once we reach the levels of development needed to allow interstellar travel, the starship might be in a better shape than its human inhabitants -- at least for the first generation that will journey beyond our star.

Biography

Antoine Faddoul is an architect, designer, and project manager with a multidisciplinary research background in astronomy, science, archeology, history, art, ancient mythology, and linguistics.

Faddoul has a bachelor's degree in architecture and master's degree in project management. In his professional field, Faddoul utilizes green building and innovative aspects of technology in answering modern construction and energy queries. He has worked in development, design, construction, and program management nationwide and internationally.

Faddoul is a regular speaker on astronomy, scientific, cultural, socio-political, mythology, and linguistic topics and he has several publications covering such areas.

Redefining Astronaut Support for Deep Space

Paul Frenger M.D.

A Working Hypothesis Inc, 814 Silvergate Drive, Houston, TX 77079

pfrenger@alumni.rice.edu

Abstract

Manned deep space voyages will be prolonged and hazardous. The author advocates establishing nontraditional astronaut selection criteria for deep space based on the mission's planned distance from the sun. For example, shorter astronauts with a height under one meter can benefit spacecraft design and produce launch vehicles with lower mission risks right up to the edge of the solar system. Beyond the heliopause, cybernetic-augmented crewmembers with an enhanced life span would be able to accomplish the nearest interstellar flights. For intergalactic travel, inorganic, computerized avatar astronauts derived from living humans could survive with their DNA and neural patterns stored for reconstitution into flesh at their final destination. New support techniques, such as stasis pods, will allow unconscious, living crewmembers to cover vast distances while using greatly reduced resources. Robotic crew members will assist humans on deep space missions. The author's gynoid robot GRAN-NIE would work in space with minimal Earth guidance and would monitor crewmembers in stasis. The author's Doppelgänger cognitive mirror A.I. system would replicate each astronaut's knowledge, emotional responses and personality, to prompt their decisions and actions should their mental clarity falter. Sustainability issues of long voyages must be addressed, such as power generation and acquisition of raw materials. A manufacturing capability in space to produce new tools, human prosthetics, robots and spacecraft parts en route is essential. For example, a 3D additive printer for the ISS has been tested. There will be numerous spin-off benefits to Earth-bound residents of this deep space Astronaut support program.

Keywords:
cybernetics, dwarf, genetics, robotics, space, stasis

1. Introduction to Long Extraterrestrial Voyages

The international astronaut corps has performed admirably for over a half-century, from Yuri Gagarin's first manned spaceflight on April 12, 1961, through Neil Armstrong's Apollo 11 Moon landing on July 20, 1969, to those currently crewing the International Space Station in near Earth orbit.

Why risk life and limb to journey to the stars in person instead of just sending robotic craft? After all, the near-fatal Apollo 13 mission demonstrated that space travel is exceedingly dangerous. A manned program will inevitably be more expensive and take longer to get ready for launch. This author believes that the best justification for human interstellar missions is to try to offset a possible future catastrophe which would destroy the Earth's biosphere and wipe out Mankind. This horrific outcome has been graphically described in many popular cinematic productions such as "Knowing" (where Earthlings are annihilated) and "Mission to Mars" (where the original Martians were destroyed).

This paper hopes to provoke the thoughtful imagination of the reader regarding the support systems for deep space missions which astronauts will require, many of which have yet to be invented or even conceived.

2. Effects of Spacecraft Design on Astronauts

Because of the requirements of living Earthlings for air, moisture, food and warmth, spacecraft need to provide a "bubble" containing these attributes for them while they are away from Earth. It is ironic that Astronauts going into the vastness of deep space will find that their craft will inevitably be too small, too cluttered and too confining for comfort and efficiency.

2.1 Spacecraft Limitations Affect Astronaut Activities

Looking at the current Orion space capsule with its six tightly packed astronauts reveals that this vehicle would only be suitable for short duration Earth departures and landings. For longer missions such as investigating asteroids, additional modules would be required to be attached to it: a service module, crew quarters and an asteroid lander, for example. A NASA publication shows that as a mission's duration increases in days, there must be a corresponding increase in spacecraft total pressurized volume in cubic meters per crewmember [1].

This NASA handbook also depicts typical individual accommodations designed for partial gravity and for zero-gravity situations, the latter being only about one-third as spacious as the former. Pressurized volume also must be provided for experiments, computers, exercise equipment, medical bay, dining, entertainment, toilet and hygiene systems, general storage and other uses. Add to that a volume for growing fruits and vegetables for long voyages in zero-G. Multipurpose areas can help reduce overall demands but dedicated zones will always be required.

One way to relax vessel requirement is to provide shielded but unpressurized spacecraft areas for some activities. Crew would have to wear lightweight, supple pressure suits while using such facilities. This was depicted in the computer game "Mass Effect" where the Quarian race, evicted 300 years ago from their home planet, wore similar suits for pressure maintenance and germ protection reasons at all times. This partial solution to the lack of spaciousness would probably not be popular with most astronauts, who would prefer to work in cotton polo shirts, shorts and socks.

2.2. Stasis Pods

Placing astronauts in some kind of suspended animation during the voyage, to save supplies, has been a staple of science fiction movies for decades (viz, "2001, A Space Odyssey", "Alien" and "Prometheus", to name a few). The purpose of such "stasis pods" or sleep cells would be to reduce the consumption of air, water and nutrients while an astronaut's services were not specifically required. The crewmember's metabolic functions would be decreased substantially, for example: heart rate under 30 bpm, respirations twice a minute, glucose metabolism under one-fourth of normal and core body temperature greatly reduced. This kind of response is quite unusual for humans, but common for mammals which routinely hibernate.

Stasis looks like sleep or coma in many ways. It may be induced by medication or electrical current, or be a byproduct of advanced meditation techniques. The author described an experiment in 1977 at a US Air Force hospital where he was one of four test subjects studying conscious control of their EEG waves and autonomic functions [2]. Using biofeedback equipment initially, the four test subjects learned within weeks to consciously control their skin temperature, blood pressure, heart rate, electro-galvanic skin responses, muscle tension and EEG frequency. In addition to changes in metabolic rate, the subjects noted a reduction in stress after each test session. During the deep meditation the subjects remained aware of their surroundings but with eyes closed. Some subjects could induce a "lucid dream" state, in which a sleeper knows he is dreaming and can direct the actions taking place while in the dream [3].

What kind of cortical functions might be possible while in stasis? Serena Gondek discovered in 1998 that the sleeping frontal cortex and auditory cortex still reacted as seen on PET scans to musical tones played into the ears [4]. Learning new things during stasis might be possible so that the awakened dreamer has new capabilities, as suggested in the movies "Demolition Man" and "The Matrix". Lucid dreaming might be technically augmented by sounds and smells to produce a video game-like virtual life experience.

A stasis pod with semi-conscious neural links to a robotic guardian was shown in the movie "Prometheus", where the David android observes the dreams of sleeping crewmember Dr. Elizabeth Shaw. Direct communication by brainwave transmission with the cortical columns of the brain might be possible. The author postulated in 2010 that the electrical outputs of individual columns are summed with millions of surrounding columns additively; also, neurons form electrical diodes which are the central receptive element of the crystal radios of previous generations [5]. An attendee to this presentation noted that this thesis forms the basis of a testable hypothesis to explain telepathic communication. One expects that a simple amplification device would be required to accomplish this data transmission reliably.

Stasis by freezing is currently not an option, since the formation of large ice crystals in the body destroys cellular structures, preventing normal organ function upon thawing. That is unfortunate, since having crewmembers reversibly frozen would constitute a fail-safe lifesaving strategy in the event of a massive starship life support failure or hull breach. The astronauts could float freely in space in unpowered, unpressurized pods with no particular time limits for rescue since all metabolic life functions would be suspended and the bodies preserved. Recent research in this area suggests that freezing water can be made to form harmless small ice crystals that would prevent cellular damage, using disaccharide sugars (maltose, sucrose, trehalose), glycerol, and dimethyl sulfoxide (DMSO) as antifreeze agents [6].

2.3 Nontraditional Astronauts

In his other presentation at the 100 Year Starship™ 2013 Public Symposium [7], the author described how mission duration and purpose would affect astronaut selection. This might be depicted by drawing familiar concentric ringed "bull's-eye target" around the Earth (for missions up to Moon-distance) or the Sun (for missions to any of the planets or beyond). In the first ring, which includes Earth orbit and the Moon, the existing corps performs well.

The second ring begins at the Moon's orbit and extends to the edge of our solar system. Missions within this area would utilize Small Astronauts (abbreviated SAs), those persons up to a meter in height or about one-half the height of current near-Earth crewmembers. This includes achondroplastic and pituitary dwarfs, lower extremity amputees and persons with certain birth defects which reduce their height (such as phocomelia). In his other presentation, the author described augmenting the strength and mobility of SAs by using motorized exoskeletons suggested by devices shown by Berkeley, EKSO and Sagawa Electronics [8-10]. This includes advanced computerized prostheses for limb amputees. This presentation described a detailed justification for using SAs in deep space.

What kind of astronauts will voyage beyond the heliopause into the third ring: interstellar space? The author has laid out various options which may be chosen. If stasis pods described above are available, SAs could be employed here. The next option would be cybernetic crewmembers (part organic, part machine) who would be able to live and work in space under drastically different conditions than other humans. Like the Murphy character in the "Robocop" movies, these astronauts would have their most essential organs secured within a pressurized container, with built-in radiation shielding, power and communications directly with shipboard computer systems. Their machine envelope might appear quite lifelike and natural. Cybernetic crewmembers might survive for over 100 years and travel dozens of light years while their systems continue to function undamaged.

Finally, pure artificial crewmembers could be derived from ordinary humans but who will have no living tissue inside. These astronauts would have their human minds copied and rendered electronically, with a form of consciousness indistinguishable from the original humans. Their DNA and synaptic patterns would be stored for later physical reconstitution upon arrival. These astronauts would be in effect "immortal" in transit, since their minds and bodies could be repeatedly renewed, to live centuries beyond the demise of their human selves on Earth. Such crewmembers should be able to travel outside of the Milky Way for the first intergalactic voyages which might take millennia to accomplish. Efforts to accomplish this outcome are already underway, supported by Russian billionaire Dmitry Itskov and with the assistance of Japanese android roboticist Hiroshi Ishiguro [11]. The mental component of these nontraditional astronauts may spend much of their time in a video game-like virtual reality plane of existence, to work, socially interact, engage in recreation and for relief of boredom.

3. Robot Support Systems

At a previous conference this year at NASA Houston, the author proposed adding one or more robot crewmembers to future voyages to assist the human astronauts [12]. He called this synthetic member "GRANNIE", an acronym for General Robotic Assistant with Neural Network, Intellect and Emotions, the latest instantiation of his 40-year robot-artificial intelligence (A.I.) series. GRANNIE would be utilized to maintain the physical and mental well-being of the human crew. As described in the presentation's abstract,

"With a human-like personality, intellectual and emotional traits, GRANNIE would interact with the people on board, chatting in an informal, cheerful way, in a natural voice, or playing interactive games such as poker-chess-mahjongg, but always making correlations which turn medical data into immediately useful information. In addition, with a compact folding robotic avatar body and artificial vision, complex hands and facial expressivity, GRANNIE could perform a variety of tasks: from menial ones such as serving meals, to important ones such as suturing a laceration, medicating a patient or helping to handle a surgical emergency."

GRANNIE is an extension of the author's ANNIE robot with A.I. which began development in 1973. It is a head-arm-torso robot like Robonaut, AILA and SAR-400 [13-15] mentioned below, embodies a multiprocessor-multicore network, uses a bytecoded plug-and-play OS (IEEE 1275), artificial emotions and personality, a schema-script based A.I., an extensive vocabulary-knowledge base, artificial color vision, OCR reading via neural network, speech synthesis and recognition, complex dexterous hands, facial expressivity and electrophysiologic signals (i.e.: action potentials, EKGs and EEGs). The simian version also has a foot which works like that of a monkey (called "APE" by the author for Autonomous Planetary Explorer), to grasp hand-holds for stability in space. Figure 1 below depicts the author's concept of the meter-tall APE robot in spacesuit ready for EVA or planetary exploration activities.

ANNIE has been used to simulate pediatric growth and development; the effects of hormones (adrenalin, oxytocin and sex hormones); addiction reactions to opioid narcotics and cannabinoids; the fear mechanism, including when elevated carbon dioxide is present; autism, depression and anxiety; fibromyalgia; dementia and sexual stimulation with reproduction. GRANNIE can be made to closely resemble and behave like a specific person, or like some historic or literary character as desired.

GRANNIE extends the functionality of existing anthropomorphic robots, such as Robonaut 2 (already on the ISS), the German AILA robot and Russian SAR-400 (both in ground testing for later ISS deployment). These are only remote-control avatars of ground-based human controllers; this limits their value at a distance from Earth in space. What GRANNIE adds to these devices is autonomous control from her on-board processor network and computational assistance from the ship's main computer when necessary, and available. In the event of some incapacitation of the human crew on shorter voyages, she could abort or complete the mission on her own and return the astronauts safely to base.

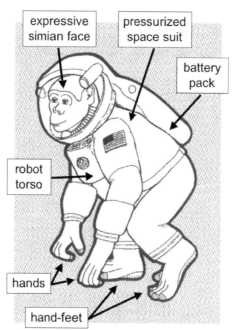

Figure 1: Author's APE simian robot in EVA gear.

As an experimental proof-of-concept the author placed much of his own knowledge, emotional reactions and personality into a blank ANNIE program to create his Doppelgänger cognitive mirror (an A.I. which thinks it is a specific person and which can control a robot). Using this technology, virtual Doppelgängers of each crew member could be created, to observe the actions of "their" human and to prompt them to perform appropriate responses if they suffer mild-to-moderate cognitive dysfunction en route, as with early Alzheimer's disease. The author previously presented both of these uses at NASA meetings in 2011 and 2012, respectively [16, 17]. GRANNIE's A.I. would be ideal to interact with nontraditional astronauts in their game-like virtual reality planes of existence for work or play.

At the 100 Year Starship™ 2013 Public Symposium, the issue of the "uncanny valley" was raised during the author's presentation question period. This term was first used by robotics professor Masahiro Mori in 1970 [18]. The concept is that robots which closely (but not exactly) imitate human beings, can cause an esthetic revulsion or rejection by the observer. The "valley" is the dip in the observer's comfort level graph over time. The author believes that this is not generally a long-term problem (Mori's research showed that most observers soon "climbed out of" the valley and moved on to acceptance of the robots). Recent research with battlefield ordnance disposal robots deployed in combat with human soldiers indicates that the soldiers develop strong emotional attachments to them, considering them to be full team members. Soldiers would give them names, treat them like pets, grieve for destroyed robots and even hold funerals for them [19].

The author suggests that the first GRANNIE should be constructed to appear human; female gender with apparent age over 50 years. A standard astronaut coverall garment, possibly with a medical smock, would improve the effect. The author prefers a speech synthesizer which produces American or British English, for example the Nuance product, which also includes speech recognition [20]. The author has been making life masks and facially-expressive robot heads for over 50 years using flameproof cloth, natural latex, silicone rubber and molded thermoplastic polyvinyl chloride liquid. Cloth, latex or silicone gloves fit onto the mechanical hand armatures. The miniature CCD or CMOS board cameras used for artificial vision fit easily into human-sized orbit gimbals, moved by radio-control servomechanisms. The author's first ANNIE designs were scaled to fit a six foot robot. Later models including the APE were half that size after the author discovered that "smaller was better" for robot construction. This was discussed in more detail in the author's other 100 Year Starship™ 2013 Public Symposium presentation.

4. Sustainability Issues

Deep space missions will cut the comfortable umbilical cord of proximity to Earth. Astronauts will not be able to "pop next door" for a cup of sugar should they run out. Aboard their starship, all necessities must be made available on demand: power, air, water, food, clothing, equipment and additional quarters for new arrivals. Ship's stores will last only so long; replenishment en route will be the order of the day to assure survival. At least, software updates and the latest movie DVDs can be transmitted from Earth's mission control to astronauts right up to the limits of the solar system where Voyager 1 currently resides, even though the transmission time at the speed of light would exceed 17 hours.

4.1 Starship Power

Solar power, used for satellites since 1958, by definition will not be feasible in deep space because the Sun's radiation will be too weak to be usefully harvested. Hydrogen-oxygen fuel cells have been employed by NASA in space since August, 1962. These will be useful for ship power as long as sources of hydrogen and oxygen are available, i.e.: from ship's stores or retrieved from comet debris [21].

First used in space in 1961, nuclear power will be required as a self-sustaining source of energy. Traditionally, Plutonium-238 (^{238}Pu) has been preferred in a radioisotope thermoelectric generator (RTG) as it produces 0.54 kilowatts per kilogram, emits only easily-shielded alpha particles, and has a half-life of about 88 years. This approach would be useful right to the very limits of our solar system [22]. For example, the 36-year old Voyager 1 spacecraft recently exited the heliosphere into interstellar space, about 12 billion miles (19 billion kilometers) from Sol. Its ^{238}Pu power cell has exhausted over half of its expected life and probably will be unusable beyond 2025. RTG's of this design would not be suitable for interstellar missions as they would fail long before approaching any other solar system, and they do not produce very abundant amounts of energy.

Much longer-lived power sources are needed; true nuclear reactors could fulfill this requirement. In 1965 the United States launched the SNAP-10A spacecraft into polar low Earth orbit with a 500 watt Uranium-235 (^{235}U) powered nuclear reactor [23]. The Soviet Union orbited 33 RORSAT ocean reconnaissance satellites in low Earth orbit between 1966-1988. A NASA SAFE-400 ^{235}U reactor producing 100-400 kW of power was built in 1998 [24]. Nuclear reactors should not require refueling oftener than once every 25 years or longer.

Thorium-cycle reactors have a number of advantages over Uranium-fueled types [25]. Thorium is about four times more plentiful than Uranium in the Earth's crust; we may assume this is also true in space, so replenishing supplies would be easier. Thorium exists primarily as a single isotope (atomic weight 232, half life estimated at 14 billion years) which is virtually non-radioactive and requires no enrichment to create reactor fuel; it only needs bombardment by neutrons to convert "fertile" ^{232}Th to "fissile" ^{233}U. One design of Thorium reactor (molten salt reactor or MSR) is inherently safe and cannot "melt down". MSR Thorium reactors can burn a variety of fuels including high level radioactive wastes.

Since Hydrogen is the most abundant element in the universe, light-element fusion reactors would make good sense in space (if only a suitable reactor can be devised). Hydrogen could be collected while moving through space (for example, by fictional Star Trek magnetic "Bussard collectors" or by actual proposed "Bussard ramjets"), or be recovered from water in comets [26]. This technology needs considerable research to become practical, however.

4.2 Manufacturing in Space

NASA will place a space-certified additive 3D printer aboard the ISS in 2014. The Made in Space and NASA team "envisions a future where space missions can be virtually self-sufficient and manufacture most of what they need in space. This includes such things as consumables, common tools, and replacements for lost or broken parts and eventually even such things as small, deployable satellites" [27]. Other US researchers have created a 3D printer to make objects from melted simulated lunar rocks. This would help future missions minimize initial spacecraft mass and volume by carrying fewer finished materials into space, needing only to harvest found matter along the way and using digital files of those objects which need to be manufactured by the 3D printers.

As an interstellar mission ventures beyond the orbit of Neptune, it encounters the Kuiper Belt, a region extending up to approximately 50 AU from the sun, where Pluto is located. This area is much larger and has possibly 200 times more mass than the asteroid belt, containing rocks, metallic bodies and frozen volatiles (water, ammonia, methane and others). Small autonomous robotic satellites as proposed by NASA and the Swiss Space Center would be deployed to capture these valuable small bodies in space and return them to the mission spacecraft for processing into equipment, ship components, fuel and supplies for human astronauts [28]. These robotic satellites would be manufactured aboard the starship itself.

Exiting the Kuiper Belt, the spacecraft would encounter the Oort Cloud, which extends about 50,000 AU (almost 1 light year) from solar center. Its composition is thought to be about the same as that of the Kuiper Belt, and so it could provide additional supplies for an expanded human space-faring population and their now-massive interstellar vehicle(s). From the edge of the Oort Cloud, the nearest star (Proxima Centauri) is only about 3 more light years distant. The binary system Alpha Centauri is nearby, and any suitable planet orbiting there might make an excellent staging location for all other human interstellar missions. About 1 of 5 solar systems studied so far have structures surrounding them which are similar to our Kuiper Belt and which might be used in much the same way for fuel and other supplies en route.

4.3 Final Thoughts

Regarding the vastness of space, recall the words of the Breton fisherman, engraved on a brass plaque presented to President John F. Kennedy by U.S. Navy Admiral Hyman Rickover:

"O, God Thy Sea Is So Great And My Boat Is So Small" [29].

The extent of space is unimaginably large. Note that Voyager 1, the furthest man-made object ever sent from Earth, was launched 36 years ago and has traveled only 0.00198 light years from the sun. At this rate reaching a distance equivalent to Alpha Centauri (the closest star system) would take well over 70,000 years. As a human benchmark, 8000 years ago humans were still in the late Stone Age, with the Bronze Age still 1500 years in their future and the Iron Age coming in about another 5000 years. Agriculture had been invented approximately 2000 years earlier. Jesus Christ would arrive in 6000 years and Mohammad 570 years later. What would Earth society be like 70,000 years from now? This time elapse is just too great to be viable for human deep space flight at that velocity.

During the presentation question period at the 100 Year Starship™ 2013 Public Symposium, an attendee raised this drawback. The author suggested that the relevant issue in space travel was not distance but time. Therefore, we should stop building "space ships" per se, and begin building "time ships" which could circumvent the passage of time while moving through space. The author has a preliminary plan for doing so, which is a subject for next year's 100 Year Starship™ Public Symposium.

Dodson has pointed out that quantum entanglement enables information transfer at least 10,000 times the speed of light, possibly much faster [30]. The author hopes that some as yet undiscovered technology will make space travel much more rapid. Failing that, the above commentary of support for astronauts' deep space voyages would necessarily apply.

5. Conclusion

This paper brings together many of the latest ideas on supporting deep space travel by human astronauts.
Several spin-off benefits of this program to non-astronauts, such as employing persons with reduced stature, establishing a stasis state, providing robot-derived cybernetic prosthetics, exoskeletons and tools for activities of daily living (ADL) to people Earthside, as well as inventing enhanced autonomous robots and the sophisticated A.I. systems needed to control them, were discussed. The time for action to develop deep space travel is now, before an unexpected life-ending event overtakes Earth.

Acknowledgements

The following entertainment resources were referenced in the text of this paper.
- "2001, A Space Odyssey" movie, Metro-Goldwyn-Mayer (1968)
- "Alien" movie, Twentieth Century Fox (1979)
- "Apollo 13" movie, Universal Movies (1995)
- "Demolition Man" movie, Warner Brothers (1993)
- "The Matrix" movie, Warner Brothers (1999)
- "Knowing" movie, Summit Entertainment (2009)
- "Mission to Mars" movie, Touchstone Pictures (2000)
- "Prometheus" movie, Twentieth Century Fox (2012)
- "Robocop" movie, Orion Pictures (1987)
- "Star Trek" TV series, Paramount Pictures (1966)
- "Mass Effect" game, Bioware, Canada (2007)

Bibliography

1. Human Integration Design Handbook (HIDH), NASA/SP-2010-3407, 27 Jan 2010, Figure 8.2-2, pg.562. Available: http://ston.jsc.nasa.gov/collections/trs/_techrep/SP-2010-3407.pdf.

2. Frenger, P., "Emulating i", Biomed Sci Instrum, 46, 2010, pg.26-32.

3. Lucid dream. Wikipedia. Available: http://en.wikipedia.org/wiki/Lucid_dream.

4. Gondek, S., "How Do We Hear While We Sleep?" ScienceDaily Web, 30 Apr 1998, reported 30 Oct. 2013. Available: http://www.sciencedaily.com/releases/1998/04/980430044534.htm.

5. Frenger, P., "Avatar and More: Concepts of Mind and Body", IEEE Galveston Bay Section, 18 Feb 2010, NASA / JSC.

6. Uchida, T., Takeya, S., Nagayama, M., and Gohara, K., "Freezing Properties of Disaccharide Solutions: Inhibition of Hexagonal Ice Crystal Growth and Formation of Cubic Ice," in: Crystallization and Materials Science of Modern Artificial and Natural Crystals, Elena Borisenko (Ed.), InTech, 2012. Available: http://www.intechopen.com/books/crystallization-and-materials-science-of-modern-artificial-and-natural-crystals/freezing-properties-of-disaccharide-solutions-inhibition-of-hexagonal-ice-crystal-growth-and-formation-of-cubic-ice.

7. Frenger, P., "Redefining the Astronaut Corps for Deep Space", 100 Year Starship™ 2013 Public Symposium, 19-22 Sept 2013.

8. Berkeley Lower Extremity Exoskeleton (BLEEX). Available: http://bleex.me.berkeley.edu/research/exoskeleton/bleex.

9. EKSO Bionic Suit. Available: http://www.eksobionics.com/ekso.

10. Powered Jacket Sagawa Electronics MK3 Exoskeleton Suit. Available: http://www.techngadgets.com/tag/exoskeleton.

11. Svennson, P., "Living Forever in a Robot Body", Real Clear Technology, 17 June 2013. Available: http://www.realcleartechnology.com/articles/2013/06/17/living_forever_in_a_robot_body_

12. 529-full.html.

13. Frenger, P., "GRANNIE 4: Helping Astronauts in Deep Space", AIAA Symposium, 17 May 2013, NASA / JSC, pg.29.

14. NASA Robonaut Official Website. Available: http://robonaut.jsc.nasa.gov.

15. AILA Mobile Dual-Arm-Manipulation. DFKI Gmbh Robotics Innovation Center. Available: http://robotik.dfki-bremen.de/en/research/robot-systems/aila-1.html.

16. "SAR-400: Russia begins testing an android for EVA." Technology.org, 4 Oct 2013. Available: http://www.technology.org/tag/sar-400.

17. Frenger, P., "The Doppelgänger Project: The Robot Who Thinks He's Me", Workshop on Automation and Robotics, 2011, NASA / JSC, pg.7.

18. Frenger, P., "The Dementia Coprocessor: Reducing the Tragedy of Alzheimer's Disease", Workshop on Automation and Robotics, 2012, NASA / JSC, pg.6.

19. Uncanny valley. Wikipedia. Available: http://en.wikipedia.org/wiki/Uncanny_valley.

20. Ackerman, E., "Soldiers can get emotionally attached to Robots, and that may not be a good thing", IEEE Spectrum, 19 Sept 2013. Available: http://spectrum.ieee.org/automaton/robotics/military-robots/soldiers-can-get-emotionally-attached-to-robots-and-that-may-not-be-a-good-thing.

21. Nuance Official Website. Available: http://www.nuance.com/index.htm.

22. Spacecraft. Wikipedia. Available: http://en.wikipedia.org/wiki/Spacecraft.

23. Radioisotope thermoelectric generator. Wikipedia. Available: http://en.wikipedia.org/wiki/Radioisotope_thermoelectric_generator.

24. SNAP-10A. Wikipedia. Available: http://en.wikipedia.org/wiki/SNAP-10A.

25. Safe Affordable Fission Engine. Wikipedia. Available: http://en.wikipedia.org/wiki/SAFE-400.

26. Thorium fuel cycle. Wikipedia. Available: http://en.wikipedia.org/wiki/Thorium_cycle.

27. Bussard, R., "Galactic Matter and Interstellar Flight," Astronautica Acta, Vol. 6 (1960), pp. 179–94

28. "Made in Space and NASA to send first 3d printer into space", Made in Space, 31 May 2013. Available: http://www.madeinspace.us.

29. Seidler, C., "Swiss Develop Satellite to Dispose of Space Junk", ABC News, 18 Feb 2012. Available: http://abcnews.go.com/Technology/swiss-develop-satellite-dispose-space-junk/story?id=15721188.

30. Feldman, G., "O, God Thy Sea Is So Great And My Boat Is So Small", NASA Earth Observatory, 26 July 2009.

31. Available: http://earthobservatory.nasa.gov/blogs/fromthefield/2009/07/26/o-god-thy-sea-is-so-great-and-my-boat-is-so-small.

32. Dodson, B., "Quantum 'spooky action at a distance' travels at least 10,000 times faster than light", Gizmag, 10 March 2013. Available: http://www.gizmag.com/quantum-entanglement-speed-10000-faster-light/26587.

Artists in Space?

Charles Lindsay

Artist in Residence, SETI Institute

189 Bernardo Ave, Suite 100, Mountain View, CA 94043

charles@charleslindsay.com

Abstract

Synopsis of live presentation considering the potential roles for artists on interstellar missions.

Keywords

art, future, culture, space, technology, philosophy, anthropology, psychology

First I should say that I have no hypothesis or answers, only questions about a future that will be imagined into being, collectively. Artists ask questions. Mine relate to the art that has yet to be realized.

Humans have always made art, lots of it. These visceral performances and acts of transcendence, whether private or public, protected or forgotten, attempt to communicate what can't be communicated in any other way. Does it's historic existence justify it's future? Long duration space travel offers an enormous opportunity to re-invent ourselves.

I'm interested in pattern recognition, bio mimicry and error recovery. The act of researching and capturing ideas is stimulating. It can also be fun, wonderful in the truest sense. Perhaps as we consider the technical and intellectual challenges of space travel, and of art, we should also keep extreme pleasure in mind. Long duration space travel is going to be slow going. Better to leave the doors open.

Will the art made and exhibited in space be curated, or censored? Who decides? Inexplicable things happen on the fringes, exploration leads to surprises. Is everything that is relevant to us on Earth relevant to us beyond Earth? Can art help to improve the astronaut's psychological well being? What if an artist on a distant mission comes up with the psychological equivalent of *A Clockwork Orange*. Do they get cryo-vacked for a couple centuries?

A vast digital archive of human art and culture will be along for the ride through space as cultural memory for the astronauts to study, enjoy and perhaps one day share. This kind of digital baggage occupies so little space we might as well bring it with us. It's difficult to imagine a commentary on consumerism mattering to astronauts in space, but with that much time on one's hands, who knows. The Land and Light Artists are dying to get out there. The Surrealists apparently went and came back. The Conceptualists just think about it. Even though we've supposedly outgrown art movements, art in space will be in motion, the evolutionary arc will continue.

So what might be the opportunities for artists in interstellar space? Who gets to go? Will our space programs foster situations where discoveries occur through non-linear questioning, spontaneity and chance? Will non-linear and eccentric personalities be invited? Sending artists on these missions would encourage alternate approaches to problem solving through non-empirical investigations. How can we prepare for what we don't know? How do we encourage the future? What will be Art to the astronaut?

The Artist in space asks "What seeds are we spreading?"' Will we accept our flaws, vices, emotional and illogical behaviors? Must these be edited, or engineered away? Can we see ourselves as we really are? Is our species mature enough to go? What of the individual astronaut's impulse to make art in order to communicate abstract or existential thoughts while en route to distant worlds? Or perhaps the augmented humans of the future will be more Spock-like, less idiosyncratic... if so would art even matter? Will we continue to make pictures of ourselves in front of landmarks?

Artists evolve as their possibilities expand. Would a space station even have objects as art or would such things be entirely virtual? Is tactile art making essential to humans or could a virtual experience suffice? Might astronauts who have left Earth for good realize physical sculptures through virtual reality 'hands-on' modeling and a rapid prototyping device? Perhaps the output stage would utilize matter from asteroids, distant moons or planets. Can we have fun, merrily terra forming ridiculous giant teddy bears as we go? Or has the time of inanimate art passed, a waste of energy and valuable resources? Is nuclear art fair game? Or did we already accomplish that here on earth? Should we leave only foot prints on pristine topographies?

One could imagine an efficiency mandate where the sculpture of the future can't just sit there but has to actually do something, it requires audience participation in order to 'activate.' Perhaps it will produce a net gain in energy, and music too. Can there be art that is not anthropocentric?

A multi-use chamber on a space station could function as an immersive installation theater, for surround sound works, Space Butoh, weather-experience simulation or live music. At other times it could host dream-yoga. Would martial arts be practiced? Can we still make beer and play with hand guns? Does religious dogma finally get left behind? Would all nature of evangelists be discouraged, art evangelists, space evangelists, religious evangelists, war mongers? Hopefully comedy would get more than equal billing - we'll require a sense of humor in space. The questions art poses are the questions of who we are and what we want to become. Might we place more value in the ephemeral and experiential and less on the notion of commodity? Art without residue or record...

When a viewer's first question upon encountering a work of art is 'what does it cost' it seems to me there's been a failure of imagination on the part of the viewer, an unwillingness to go deep with the ideas and emotions coded in the work. Perhaps its the same failure of imagination, or fear, that results in a general under funding of both art and space programs. What are people so afraid of? Space Travel requires fearlessness, so does opening oneself to new ideas or committing oneself to develop these things.

Art is one of our species' defining characteristics. It mirrors human progress and often presages it. An optimistic and expansionary philosophy might imagine human's greatest potential lies ahead and that artists will be essential to interpreting the journey. As we seek the radical leaps in technology required for space travel we might look to the arts for premonitions, especially as the borders between disciplines and ideas become increasingly permeable.

In conclusion I believe we should be brave enough to encourage the creation and discovery of things we don't yet and might never understand.

Constraints Facing Future Deep Space Missions

Joanne Stockton

The University of Liverpool

bokemon_56@hotmail.com

Abstract

Deep space missions are a realistic possibility in the future and can only be successful if the constraints faced are fully understood. Physical and psychological stressors constrain space missions. Physical stressors such as microgravity, radiation, confinement and hygiene prevent missions lasting for extended periods of time. Similarly, psychological stressors such as monotony, disorientation and sustained stress need to be researched for successful interstellar missions. Constraints are also seen in the new group dynamics of ever diversifying crews. The shift from military based astronauts to those with academic backgrounds can lead to conflict. Conflicts can arise due to crew diversification in terms of culture, personality and gender. Recent crews have started to include female members. While this has been shown to reduce stress, it does lead to the possibility of sexual relations in space and pregnancy. Zero-gravity conception need to be understood for successful deep space missions as environment severely affects embryonic development. Likewise, evolutionary constraints can affect future deep space missions. Research designed to overcome these constraints will hopefully lead to the resolution of these problems in future deep space travel. Space organisations have carried out research on missions and under extreme circumstances such as in Antarctica. Expansion of this research is required to build on possible solutions to the constraints suggested.

Keywords

constraints, deep space missions.

1. Introduction

The accepted cosmological theory states there are multiple universes or 'domains' in existence which are constantly expanding [1]. This, breakthroughs in astronautics and previous successful missions into space suggest deep-space travel is a realistic possibility in the future. The astronautics; the shuttle, other equipment to survive in deep-space and methods for successful study, are the most prominent constraint needed to be overcome. However, there are also other constraints which could affect the outcome of future deep-space missions.

2. Stressors
2.1 Physical Stressors

Physical stresses of space travel can be observed from previous missions. General flight stresses such as microgravity, radiation, noise, confinement and cabin hygiene are all part of an astronaut's daily life [2]. The microgravity and radiation can impede physiological health and lead to muscle atrophy, cardiovascular, bone and immune system decay [3] and most prominently, space motion sickness; which can affect 50-80% of astronauts on their first zero-G experience [4]. Increased hemispheric lateralisation function has also been found in Antarctica studies and this has been suggested to be due to confinement and reduced muscular activity [5]. Physical constraints may have severe consequences for space travel; where these effects occur over a sustained period of time. Space organisations have developed a strict diet and daily exercises to decrease the physical effects of space travel [6] but these vary little which can lower enjoyment and motivation; factors that are even more important in longer space missions.

2.2 Psychological Stressors

Psychological constraints can be on a personal or group level; which can severely affect the outcome of space missions. On an individual level, monotony [7], spatial and temporal disorientation, sleeplessness, loss of concentration and confinement [8] can lead to territorial behaviour [9]. Separation from loved ones [7], general exhaustion [9] and sustained stress of mission operations and the danger related to this [10] can all detrimentally affect ones wellbeing. These will be harder to control on longer space missions as family conference calls which are used on International Space Stations to relieve psychological constraints will be problematic due to time delays [7]. Therefore other methods of reducing psychological constraints need to be proposed, one possibility is to include someone with psychiatric training in the crew or give intense psychological training to the cosmonauts. Also relaxation techniques and hypnosis have been suggested to alleviate psychological stressors in cosmonauts [11].

2.3 Effects of Stressors and Possible Solutions

Both physical and psychological stressors have been linked with many important factors of space missions; arousal, performance, attention, perception and memory [12]. Studies looking at the effect personal stressors may have on task ability suggest performance on elementary cognitive tasks are fairly unaffected but attentional and perceptual-motor tasks are significantly disturbed [13]. They suggest these stressors result from the physiological constraints, work-rest schedules, sleep disturbances and the extreme living conditions of space travel. However, a study on long-term space flight found that neither cognitive, attentional or perceptual-motor tasks were affected by stressors except in the first two weeks in space and on return to Earth [13]. More research is needed to understand these effects but ways of alleviating stressors have been proposed; appraisal, free time, communication with loved ones and varying environmental conditions have all been suggested to counter stress while isolated in space [12].

3. The Third Quarter Phenomenon

The third quarter phenomenon is the suggestion that a significant decrease in mood and motivation occurs in the third quarter of a mission; evidence has been found in Antarctica outposts [14, 15], submarines [16] and space missions [17]. The impact this may have on space missions could be severe especially on deep space missions when more time is spent in space and conditions are more isolated. Linking to this, as space missions are becoming a fairly frequent occurrence, the novelty and interest in them is decreasing which can intensify the monotony; decreasing motivation [18]. These constraints may be rectified if the importance of morale and motivation, especially in the third quarter of the mission, are considered by space agencies.

4. Mission Crews
4.1 Crew Diversity, Group Dynamics and Their Effects

NASA and other space organisations have carried out many missions of growing crew size and space shuttle complexity [18]. This, the introduction of women into crews and the increased size and time in space has led to group dynamic constraints. With deep-space missions, these phenomena will be intensified so need to be understood and prevented to enable long term space travel.

The diversity of crews now used in space travel has led to challenges within crew dynamics and relationships. The crew has moved from 'right-stuff' military based crews to including diversified cosmonauts, academics and scientists; this may cause tension between the mentality and personality of the two groups [18]. Secondly, there are more and major cultural and personality differences between crew members. These effects may be in coping with other stressors, mental health manifestation, cognitive and decision making and behavioural norms significantly differing across cultures [9] and can arise from confinement [7], gender relations [19] and intragroup tensions [7]. These effects and conflicts may cause severe tension or stress so need to be understood and prevented for successful deep space missions. Group sensitivity training and longer crew training have been suggested to reduce the effects of personal and cultural problems [7, 10].

Strong interpersonal bonds can alleviate stressors in space [20]; these bonds hold the support and comfort needed to relieve psychological strains. This further marks the importance of positive group dynamics in successful deep space mission.

4.2 Crew Diversity and Interrelated Constraints

The group dynamic constraints can be linked to group psychological issues relating to deep space travel. Psychodynamics factors have been suggested in space travel but NASA adheres to a behaviouristic management-style of human behaviours [9]. This has caused little research into the psychological constraints of space travel, although this will hopefully change as NASA starts to recognise the importance of psychological factors. NASA administrator, Dan Goldin states; "If we expect to send people on missions of two or three years, we darn well better deal with the psychological aspects in addition to the physiological ones. This hasn't been our tendency in the past." [21] (p. 75). This will potentially lead to further research into psychological constraints of space travel; displacement, automatization and psychological closing have all been shown in cosmonaut crews [22, 23]. These factors can improve the cohesion of the crew group but could have detrimental costs to mission control; as mission control may struggle to keep control, one of their most prominent fears on longer deep-space missions.

4.3 Control

Control in this respect can also be affected by other factors. For example, group dynamics could lead to extreme consequences such as revolt, disobedience and displacement [23]. Also there is an increased time delay with distance so instructions made by mission control may not be relevant when received. In relation to the time deep-space missions will take, political instabilities on Earth may have an impact on the cosmonauts, as in the past Sergei Krikalev was stranded in space for 4 months when the Soviet Union collapsed [24]. This highlights that space exploration is under the control of politics and space corporations [25] who would lose some of this power on deep space missions. The group on deep space missions may also change culturally from the norm [20]. These factors need to be taken into consideration when discussing deep space travel so as not to lose the integrity and purpose of the mission.

4.4 Hypnosis

Hypnosis offers both a solution and problem in deep space travel. A higher susceptibility in hypnotisability has been shown in studies based in the Antarctica and could have implications for space travel [26]. This can include hallucinations, dissociative states that may affect vigilant performance and could endanger or degrade human performance [27]. On the other hand, hypnosis may be a possible solution to control and in alleviating psychological constraints [11].

5. Females in Space Crews and the Possibility of Sexual Relations

More recent diversified crews have the inclusion of women for the first time. The presence of women has been suggested to reduce stress overall in Antarctic studies [28]. However, it does pose a constraint of sexual relations in space travel. Although space associations' refuse to acknowledge the possibility of sex in space, worries have been highlighted regarding 'singles bar atmospheres' even with married couples [29]. There is also the possibility of conception in space, which could lead to enormous consequences. Pregnancy relies on a number of terrestrial variables including atmosphere, pressure, nutrients and antibody stimulants, all of which a zero-gravity environment lacks [29]. This and the fact that muscular and skeletal structures are not needed within space could significantly alter the foetus [30]. Due to no environmental cues, the resultant baby may be of a different DNA altogether as ionising radiation can cause chromosomal breaks [31]. Even without these mutations, the child would be considered an alien, unable to return or live on earth [29]. It is not understood how a human embryo would react to zero-G environments; it may be that the zygote would not survive in these conditions due to pregnancy traumas of the environment and immune system desecration from no/new pathogens. Whether this is the case or not, the possibility needs to be understood to allow successful deep space mission as banning sex on space missions is not a viable solution and normal contraception methods may be ineffective [29]. Suitable solutions to this constraint can only be formulated when the issues are recognised by the organisation and research is allowed into these areas. Until this occurs understanding and planning personal, intimate relations and stressors cannot be fully comprehended and a fully comfortable living and working environment will not exist on space missions [32].

6. Extra-Terrestrials

The possibility of extra-terrestrial communication has to be anticipated for successful deep space travel. Similar experiences have been covered in many literary and cinematic forms but in real life it is suggested when deep space travel occurs, the universe and other life forms will still be vastly misunderstood [1]. Also the Strong Anthropic Principle states once intelligent information processing life forms comes into existence, they can never die out so possible other life forms may exist. This is a constraint of deep space travel which cannot be prepared for, it is therefore the hope that the strict astronaut training results in wholly remarkable humans. This also further reiterates the time-delay constraint in deep space travel as astronauts would have to act alone.

7. Evolutionary Constraints
7.1 Kardashev Phases of Species Evolution

Evolutionary constraints will also affect deep space travel. According to the Kardashev Phases in the evolution of a species, successful interstellar survival needs a transition from K1 to a K2 civilisation. Ziolo suggests this transition will not take place until other evolutionary and cultural constraints are acknowledged and challenged [33]. This transition would cause high anxiety within the unconscious, so it is suggested to [proactively] instigate the transition to K2 to avoid this and in case the current phase collapses [33]. Long-wave economic cycles have been suggested to aid convergence of K1 and transition to K2 civilisations; which core technological advances initiate [34]. Tylecote suggests an economic and technological cycle is imminent involving genetics, robotics, artificial intelligence and nanotech [34]. This transition and the corresponding technological advances proposed to occur will allow ultimate interstellar exploration and deep space travel to be conducted not by humans but by the products of transhuman speciation.

7.2 Resulting Autonomous Groups

Social change is also catalysed by groups, so may aid the K2 transition. This suggests an autonomous group, whether human or transhuman is essential for deep space travel. Humans are highly adaptive and unspecified organisms, these factors are important in coping strategies for stressors [7], this may result in an autonomous group which will be required in successful deep space missions. Alternatively a crew of metacomplex process ability would be capable of a successful mission into deep space; one of polycentric structure and cyborgian practise [35, 36]. This would be a group capable of dealing with any crises by being flexible [35, 36].

8. Conclusion

To conclude, solutions to the physical, group, psychological and evolutionary constraints discussed in this article will potentially allow deep-space travel in the future. This will allow broader information and knowledge of the universe but fundamentally more research is needed to understand the psychological constraints related to deep space travel as "the failure of NASA to give behavioural sciences an equal footing with biological and natural sciences is an omission that needs to be rectified" [37] (p. 53).

Acknowledgements

I would like to firstly acknowledge Dr. Paul Ziolo, one of my undergraduate lecturers, for presenting the 100YSS opportunity and the wisdom he bestowed in relation to this and other topics throughout my degree. I also thank the 100YSS for giving me the opportunity to broaden my knowledge in this area and inclusion in an insightful symposium. Finally, I acknowledge the support of my family in this endeavour, especially my sister Laura who lent her excellent proof-reading skills to this article.

Bibliography

1. Çirkoviç, M. M., & Bostrom, N., "Cosmological constant and the final anthropic hypothesis". Astrophysics and Space Science 274, 675 (2000).

2. Price, J. F., "Physiological and Psychological Effects of Space Flight: A Bibliography Volume II. Weightlessness and Subgravity (No. RB44)," TRW Space Technology Labs, Los Angeles CA, 1963.

3. Levine, B. D. & Berkowitz, D. E., "Cardiovascular alterations". Retrieved December 10, 2012 from http://www.nsbri.org/SCIENCE-and-TECHNOLOGY/Cardiovascular-Alterations/ (n. d.).

4. Heer, M. & Paloski, W. H., "Space motion sickness: incidence, etiology and countermeasures". Autonomic Neuroscience 129, 77 (2006).

5. Natani, K., "Psychophysiology". In Harrison, A. A., Clearwater Y. A. & McKay, C. P. (Eds.), "From Antarctica to outer space: life in isolation and confinement" (pp. 297-304), Springer-Verlag, New York & London, 1990.

6. Cheston, T. S., "The psychology of orbital human factors". Retrieved November 23, 2012, from http://er.jsc.nasa.gov/seh/psychology.html (n. d.).

7. Kanas, N., Sandal, G., Boyd, J. E., Gushin, V. I., Manzey, D., North, R., Leon, G. R., Suedfeld, P., Bishop, S., Fiedler, E. R., Inoue, N., Johannes, B., Kealeym, D. J., Kraft, N., Matsuzaki, I., Musson, D., Palinkas, L. A., Salnitskiy, V. P., Sipes, W., Stuster, J. & Wang, J., "Psychology and culture during long-duration space missions," Acta Astronautica 64, 659 (2009).

8. Suedfeld, P., "Canadian space psychology: the future may be almost here," Canadian Psychology 44, 85 (2003).

9. Kanas, N., Salnitskiy, V., Gushin, V., Weiss, D. S., Grund, E. M., Flynn, C., Kozerenko, O., Sled, A., Marmar, C. R., "Asthenia—does it exist in space?," Psychosomatic Medicine 63, 874 (2001).

10. "Long Duration Psychology". Retrieved November 10, 2012 from http://history.nasa.gov/SP-4225/long-duration/long.html (n. d.).

11. Levine, A. S., "Psychological effects of long-duration space missions and stress amelioration techniques". In Harrison, A. A., Clearwater Y. A. &McKay, C. P. (Eds.), "From Antarctica to outer space: life in isolation and confinement" (pp. 297-304), Springer-Verlag, New York & London, 1990.

12. Bourne, L. E., & Yaroush, R. A., "Stress and cognition: A cognitive psychological perspective," Unpublished manuscript, NASA grant NAG2-1561, 2003.

13. Manzey, D., Lorenz, B. (1998), "Mental performance during short-term and long-term spaceflight," Brain Research Reviews 28, 215 (1998).

14. Steel, G. D., "Polar moods third-quarter phenomena in the Antarctic," Environment and Behavior 33, 126 (2001).

15. Bechtel, R. B., & Berning, A., "The third-quarter phenomenon: Do people experience discomfort after stress has passed". In Harrison, A. A., Clearwater Y. A. &McKay, C. P. (Eds.), "From Antarctica to outer space: life in isolation and confinement" (pp.261-266), Springer-Verlag, New York & London, 1990.

16. Brasher, K. S., Dew, A. B., Kilminster, S. G., & Bridger, R. S., "Occupational stress in submariners: The impact of isolated and confined work on psychological well-being," Ergonomics 53, 305 (2010).

17. Myasnikov, V. I. & Zamaletdinov, I. S., "Psychological states and group interactions of crew members in flight," Human Performance in Extreme Environment, 3, 44 (1998).

18. Harrison, A. A. & Fiedler, E. R., "Introduction: psychology and the U.S. space program". In D. A. Vakoch (Eds.), "Psychology of space exploration: contemporary research in historical perspective" (pp. 1-16), National Aeronautics and Space Administration, Washington DC, 2011.

19. Scandal, G. M., "Culture and tension during an international space station simulation: Results from SFINCSS'99," Aviation, Space, and Environmental Medicine 75, C44 (2004).

20. Kanas, M. & Manzey, D., "Space Psychology and Psychiatry," Kluwer, New York, 2003.

21. Morphew, M. E., "Psychological and human factors in long duration spaceflight," McGill Journal of Medicine 6, 74 (2001).

22. Kanas, N., Salnitskiy, V., Weiss, D. S., Grund, E. M., Gushin, V., Kozerenko, O., Sled, A., Bostrom, A., Marmar, C. R., "Crewmember and ground personnel interactions over time during Shuttle/Mir space missions," Aviation, Space and Environmental Medicine 72, 453 (2001).

23. Kanas, N. A., Salnitskiy, V. P., Boyd, J. E., Gushin, V. I., Weiss, D. S., Saylor, S. A., Kozerenko, O. P., Marmar, C. R., "Crewmember and mission control interactions during International Space Station missions," Aviation, Space and Environmental Medicine 78, 601 (2007).

24. Gorst, I., "USSR and Russia: Sergei Krikalev". Retrieved December 11, 2012 from http://www.ft.com/cms/s/2/2be6c3d2-5a70-11e0-8367-00144feab49a.html#axzz2El78Scng (2011).

25. Vergano, D., "For NASA, there is no liftoff from politics". Retrieved December 11, 2012 from http://usatoday30.usatoday.com/tech/science/columnist/vergano/story/2012-07-28/nasa-politics/56542592/1 (2012).

26. Barabasz, A., "Effects of isolation on states of consciousness". In Harrison, A. A., Clearwater Y. A. & McKay, C. P. (Eds.), "From Antarctica to outer space: life in isolation and confinement" (pp. 201-208), Springer-Verlag, New York & London, 1990.

27. Barabasz, A. F., "EEG alpha, skin conductance and hypnotizability in Antarctica," International Journal of Clinical and Experimental Hypnosis 28, 63 (1980).

28. Harrison, A. A., & Connors, M. M., "Groups in exotic environments". In L. Berkowitz (Ed.), "Advances in experimental social psychology: vol. 18" (pp. 49-87), New York: Academic Press, Inc, 1984.

29. Sturgeon, J., "Sex in Space". Retrieved December 8, 2012 from http://www.space.edu/LibraryResearch/sex.html (n. d.).

30. Frazer, L., "Sex in space: the science of extraterrestrial reproduction," Ad Astra 3, 42 (1991).

31. Colón, A. R., & Colón, P. A., "The psychosocial adaptation of children in space: a speculation," The Journal of Practical Applications in Space 3, 5 (1992).

32. Clearwater, Y., "A human place in outer space," Psychology Today 19, 34 (1985).

33. Ziolo, P., "Futures". Retrieved November 29, 2012, from www.spacerenaissance.org/papers/PaulZiolo_Futures.pdf (n. d.).

34. Tylecote, A., "The long wave in the world economy: the present crisis in historical perspective," London: Routledge, 1993.

35. Satish, U., "Behavioural complexity: a review," The Journal of Applied Social Psychology 27, 2047 (1997).

36. Streufert, S. & Satish, U., "Complexity theory: predictions based on the confluence of science-wide and behavioural theories," The Journal of Applied Social Psychology 27, 2096 (1997).

37. Taylor, A. J. W., "The research program of the International Biomedical Expedition to the Antarctic (IBEA) and its implications for research in outer space". In Harrison, A. A., Clearwater Y. A. &McKay, C. P. (Eds.), "From Antarctica to outer space: life in isolation and confinement" (pp. 297-304), Springer-Verlag, New York & London, 1991.

A Pathway for Global Communications as an Inclusive Means of Participation

David Orban

Singularity University, Moffett Field, CA, 94035

david@singularityu.org

Abstract

Global communication is evolving rapidly, allowing for effective, fine tuned, interactive messages to reinforce the support that a complex project can receive, beyond the limits of traditional broadcast models. It is unlikely that a starship project could be directly financed via crowd funding, but it is necessary to increase and to sustain the understanding and sharing of its value in the larger public, with carefully designed and wide-ranging, inclusive communications.

This paper concentrates on what can be done now with ubiquitous online video that goes beyond the barriers of language to establish a new global conversation, as well as forecast what new tools can be designed and deployed as new technologies become available. The project of designing, building, and launching a starship is as much an engineering effort as one of public relations, of willpower, which must be sustained, together with the political and financial resources necessary.

Emotional intelligence is an important component in human endeavors, on par with analytical and logical skills: being able to powerfully communicate goals that can be not only understood, but with which people all around the world can identify with. Online video today is the medium of broadest emotional bandwidth, and its use is key for a broad public understanding and participation in the starship project.

Among other developments, it is going to be possible to generate, disseminate, analyze, and aggregate videos not only produced by the project itself, but those that are created by the global conversation around it. These components are going to be an essential part of the project, sustaining its ambitious dream. The adoption of a distributed communication model is the basis for taking advantage of innovative ideation and design components, which can concretely involve groups of passionate followers of the project, complementing the professional team dedicated to it.

Keywords

Communication, support, identity, interaction, crowd

1. Introduction

This paper covers what are, in my opinion, important principles for designing in the next decades, types of social structures that are conducive to desirable futures. Our society is brittle, and the more complex, the more global it gets, the less we can afford this brittleness. I may lead to wider and deeper crises as it has been the case in the past periods because, for the moment, we do not have an alternative. Social collapse or the passing of empires did not mean that the human civilization would be put in peril in the past. If a planet-wide civilization collapses as it could very well today, after globalization, it would put our entire civilization at risk.

2. Assumptions

I want to start with some assumptions that are the basis of this paper.

2.1 Continued exponential trends

The assumption that the exponential trends that we see around us—the most famous example of which is Moore's Law [1], stating that the density of electronic circuits doubles every 18 months and its price halves during that time, but there are many, many others—that these trends will continue. The linear thinking that informs our policies and that is the basis of thinking of our policy makers is something that we cannot afford anymore, because the prevalence and the visibility of the exponential trends is just too strong.

2.2 No new physics

At the same time, as much as one would want otherwise, the assumption for this paper is that within the next few decades we will not have radically new physics, such as a warp drive would represent. That there are no shortcuts. If we want to colonize the galaxy, we will have to do it the hard way. It is going to take a couple of million years to do so, and we have to do it step-by-step. We cannot jump across 100,000 light years.

2.3 Human nature to stay the same

Even if I have been the chairman of Humanity+, the world transhumanist association which defines humanity as an entity that overcomes itself, that sees its limits as the barrier to go through and redefining what it means to be human [2], I will assume that for the next few decades what it means to be human is not going to radically change.

2.4 No self-modifying artificial general intelligence

My final assumption, and I am a card carrying singularitarian, is that what is called the technological singularity—the theoretical moment in time, in the future when self-modifying artificial intelligence is brought to the scene many more active agents, participants, in the global civilization alongside humanity with their own goals, with their own rules, with their own active capacity of acquiring and managing the sources—it is not going to happen.

If any of these assumptions is falsified, every bet is off, and the trajectory of human development will take a very different, and possibly hard to forecast direction.

3. Network Society

What we are seeing and what we are seeing around us, in my opinion, is that hierarchies are breaking down everywhere. They are breaking down at the level of the family, at the level of a city, at a level of the company, at the level of the nation states. What used to be the case that hierarchies defined the role that plays the behavior of individuals and groups of individuals is now turning into what I call the Network Society which is defined by distributed peer-to-peer systems substituting centralized systems. Energy production based on solar; 3D printing for distributed manufacturing; plant labs allowing food production to be available at every home rather than centralizing agribusinesses; massively online open courses making learning and education available to everybody regardless of their economical means or geographical or social provenience; and our financial technologies are also explosively changing through digital currencies becoming platforms of innovation. The nation state is taking notice and is enacting policies that are more and more violently against those new entities that appear to the nation state as invading forces. Its immune system is rebelling against this rate of destabilizing innovation.

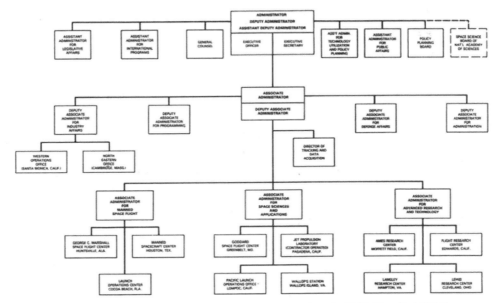

Fig. 1. The organizational chart of NASA, November 1, 1963 (Credit: NASA)

4. Empathic Communications

Individuals, as emotional machines, have immense power, and if somebody asked me what my superpower would be if I could have one, this is what it would be. It would be the arbitrary extension of the circle of empathy in a given moment. Empathy is our strongest power to overcome in people and groups of people. Artificial isolation that is engendered by our superstructures is a threat to that empathic power. We can overcome. We have this power. It is also not only something that is available to us, we have to use this power. If we do not, then the existential risk of global annihilation, the global destruction of planetary civilization is almost guaranteed.

We are in a system of networks. We are in a system of participating, aware, capable, and well-educated people who are empathic to each other who want to give back. And we know how important it is to be able to identify with an objective, to be able to feel that we are able to influence a project, that even if we are not part of the core team, what we say, what we do, has an impact.

A tool that is available today, the most powerful with the broadest, emotional bandwidth in order to overcome our communication barriers, is online media, especially online video [3]. When we see another person in our discussions, in our conversations, there is a subtext of emotional content that written or verbal communication without seeing the other person is not capable of transmitting. That is why we are so excited about seeing video. That is why on YouTube today every minute 72 hours of new content is uploaded because we just love seeing another human person. Seeing is not enough. We have to understand. We have to engage. And it is, today, possible in online video, to eliminate the language barrier.

We are not going to be able to crowd fund the creation of a Starship. We can dream of it, but it is not going to happen. We have to be extremely persuasive, not only among the group of passionate individuals regardless of their connections, regardless of their knowledge and skills. We have to be persuasive among tens and hundreds of millions, hopefully billions, of people who have to share our mission. We have to be almost evangelistic, you know, or desire of and making sure that what we learn, what we know is shared among as many of us as possible. And today this is available in online video. We can start doing it; we actually have started doing it.

One of the members of the 100 Year Starship community just took what were static images from the website, and turned them into a beautiful video. And the organization took that, and is now on the homepage of this symposium. Others can do the same, and the way to do this is in a distributed way rather than in a top-down manner, in a hierarchical decision making process, the way it would have been natural for NASA to make in the 20th century.

We know how important collaborative design and collaborative, participatory design is becoming in several systems. It is not the case of our integrated circuits, but it is definitely, for example, the case of Wikipedia, which everybody said would be a failing project among the experts. The experts are the best in telling you what cannot be done ever. That is why a lot of people should not listen to the experts.

Our interfaces are changing constantly and becoming more and more evolved in systems from punch cards to teletypes to common layer interfaces, initially fairly simple and then more sophisticated graphical user interfaces emulating our desktops to today in touch interfaces, and you will know if you are familiar with the history of computing that these cycles are actually getting shorter and shorter. It is just a few years that touch interfaces have become ubiquitous, and now we cannot imagine living without them. But gesture-based interfaces, dialogue systems, and computer systems that perceive us more and more are becoming available, and already on the horizon we see the next steps towards direct brain computer interfaces that are going to be fabulous and very interesting and intriguing.

Today's most engaging interface, what is available to billions of people, and billions of people, at least hundreds of millions of people, are taking advantage of these interfaces as active participants rather than passive consumers of the content that is being created, is online video. The reason why online video is so important is because it represents in the most simple terms possible with requirements that contrary to some of the previous examples of our evolving human-computer interaction platforms that I showed do not need the design and the deployment of new devices. Online video is available on computers, on mobile phones, in high income or even low income countries. But they are extremely rich in giving you not only information content but also emotional content.

In order to evangelize in a humanistic, naturalistic spirituality the beauty, the ambition of the mission of a starship, we do need to leverage all the emotional impact that we can have. However, we can drastically broaden from a few hundred accolades to hundreds of millions of people who believe in the mission without which we wouldn't be able to participate and to convince the key decision makers that what we want to do deserves their attention, their resources, and their decisions.

The vast amounts of human creativity are digested, prioritized, and presented in terms of relevancy by our computers that in turn base these decisions on our actions, measuring and acting on every viewing or closing of our videos that are being watched. So what we need is to make sure that as many of the people that we can reach become active participants.

YouTube creators rather than YouTube watchers, programmers rather than video game players, video game makers, and we need to design systems that are extremely inclusive, When we are welcoming to this creativity, we engender participation and are reflective of the nature of our peer to peer networks that break down hierarchies.

I understand that some of this is difficult for some of those among us who have been accustomed to NASA-style top-down engineering approaches.

When we are talking about the starship itself, just like when we are talking about a spaceship today, we are not going to be designing it by a committee of millions. It is going to be a different engineering approach. But in the meantime, when we are talking about popularizing the idea, when we are talking about how to reach our goal of making these things happen, we need to make sure that we are leveraging the desires of those who cannot be here with us today. Those that have been complaining about the fact that we are not streaming live, who will be clamoring to see the videos of these sessions being recorded by the volunteer crews of film faculty here in Houston, we need to leverage that passion, and we can leverage that passion by creating infrastructure that goes in that direction. Innovation that we need is, yes, technological.

We need to invent systems that understand how human nature works. Without that, we not going to be able to achieve the impact we desire. If we don't adapt to the world and ignore the rules are embedded in our human nature, we can't learn from our mistakes. We need to embrace our mistakes, so that we can enthusiastically go out and evangelize our mission.

5. Sustainable Bottom Up Organization

We are in the 21st century now and in this century, the risks and the opportunities that we have are huge. Our goal is to minimize the risks, and to maximize the opportunities ahead of us. Our current industrial civilization is unsustainable, but on Starship Earth unsustainability itself is unsustainable. We have to learn that; we have to realize that. Only sustainable systems can sustain themselves. The way we go building the new network society, it will be crucial, to try to minimize the violent reactions of the dying nation states as we achieve this phase change. As we go into the new organization of the network society, we have to face the new questions presented in front of us. Is it right? Is it wrong? What is a natural path? What is some extremely artificial legislation that is being promoted because it is in the interest of a very, very restricted group? These are the questions that we have to ask in order to bridge our knowledge through our ignorance. And we have to be extremely inventive because the only way we can try to succeed in our exponential dreams is by powerful application of our inventiveness.

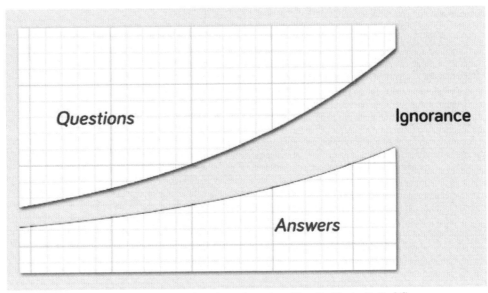

Fig. 2. Building blocks of our learning (Credit: Kevin Kelly [4])

6. Conclusion

There is no guarantee of our continued progress, and Moore's Law, as well as many others, is a total misnomer. It is the common self-fulfilling prophecy of engineers worldwide, who have been inspired for the past 40 years by the little dots that Gordon Moore jotted down in his notebook. When the transistor had been invented, he said, "Yeah, this is how I think it's going to work." They just kept going at it to prove him right, and that is the only way to go. In our quest of going to make the dream of the 100 years Starship true, we have to prove our dreams right, in an inclusive fashion, that leverages the passion and the dedication of people globally. The best tool for doing so is available to us right now, and it is online video.

We have to try, and we will fail a lot of times, but that is it: sometimes we will win, and sometimes we will learn.

Acknowledgements

The author would like to thank Michael Smolens, the Founder of Dotsub [5], for his guidance, and passion in analyzing, presenting, and implementing the values of online video in overcoming the language barrier to global communications.

Notes

1. Intel Corporation uses Moore's Law as a guiding principle in its engineering planning, and, with evolving technologies, strives to prove it right for decades to come. http://www.intel.com/content/www/us/en/silicon-innovations/moores-law-technology.html
2. Humanity+ http://humanityplus.org
3. The Cisco Visual Networking Index projects that online the "sum of all forms of video (TV, video on demand, Internet, and P2P) will be in the range of 80 to 90 percent of global consumer traffic by 2017," http://www.cisco.com/en/US/solutions/collateral/ns341/ns525/ns537/ns705/ns827/white_paper_c11-481360_ns827_Networking_Solutions_White_Paper.html
4. Inspired by Kevin Kelly's post "The Expansion of Ignorance" in The Technium, http://kk.org/thetechnium/archives/2008/10/the_expansion_o.php
5. Dotsub http://dotsub.com. The author is CEO of Dotsub, an online platform for language powered video.

Bibliography

1. Blackmore, Susan. The Meme Machine. Oxford University Press, 2000

2. Kelly, Kevin. What Technology Wants. Penguin Books, 2011

3. Kurzweil, Ray. The Singularity Is Near. Penguin Books, 2005

4. Maxwell , JC. Sometimes You Win--Sometimes You Learn. Hachette Digital, 2013

5. Rifkin, Jeremy. The Empathic Civilization. Tarcher, 2009

Food Design: A Primer with Thoughts on Food Design in Space

David Wilson

1. Why Food Design for a Deep Space Mission is Relevant and Important as an Aspect to Humanity in Space

What is food design? Throughout this paper, concepts on food design will be explored; food design for space is also discussed.

In this paper, I shall attempt to illustrate a dynamic relationship, while building a basic outline to support an argument for an ongoing dialogue, with food at the forefront of an effort to fulfill the completion of a generational deep space star ship and mission where humans are aboard. When humans are present, what/who, when, where, and how shall they eat? The why behind why humans eat seems easy at first glance, but the question is a more complex and dynamic relationship to our existence. We eat for nutrition, to survive, we eat to enjoy, we eat for a number of reasons perhaps as yet theorized or studied; being an organic form, a neurobiochemical-endocrine basis may be involved...at least to some degree in human food selection. But, it would seem that there is great room for research in these areas today.

About this paper: This work is written with a seemingly strong focus on anthropology, however, it is the author's opinion that strong design elements happen as a direct result of deep anthropological appreciation. Also, this paper returns to themes to reinforce as well as to develop other directions.

What is culture; what is culture in deep space; what is culture as it relates to food design?

1.1 Culture

The common understanding of culture, loosely speaking, is the collective mind of humanity in environment. Culture is represented in the ideas of the minds of humans. Therefore, culture functions as a number of intangible concepts represented as a relative inseparable total.

The 'space community,' meaning culture in space, is an interchangeable term which represents the collective idea of those individuals experiencing microgravity, as well as the larger group of people which provide support for the individuals in microgravity.

Culture as it relates to food design, it is the body of people concerned with food design, yet not necessarily limited to the consumer-group of people that use or are directly affected by the food design of food for a space community.

2. Food Culture

What are the feeding traditions of various cultures on earth? Most people eat together; feeding happens as a social act- from time of birth, or of prehistoric humanity, meaning from suckling to present- from hunters /gatherers to drive-through fast-foods, there is a social tether.

What are present-day feeding traditions in space? In a recent visit to Houston's Control Room in the Johnson Space Center (2012), I was privileged to observe that all activity of the astronaut is part of a scheduled event dynamic. That is to say that all time and activity is accounted for. Astronauts have appointed timeframes where feeding is scheduled. These represent points of course in measures of duration critical awareness not directives that the crewmembers must follow.

In the following feeding social section(s), where applicable, ideas will be compared and contrasted to highlight relationship of earth-based social food design related activity to that of space.

3. Feeding Social

Historically, humanity, as far as the human record presently shows, reveals mankind as first being hunter and gatherers, and later developing agriculture. We may be hunters and gatherers again, when we hunt and gather the best specimens to clone. Only the quest for sheer and utter perfection leads potentially to that next logical step, meaning the generation of a perfect specimen; the agricultural phase, the "farming" of the perfect cell.

Mesa, mensa, table, tabele, tabula, and bord are each names throughout humanity to describe the concept of the table. It's quite likely that any flat-topped surface may have served the utility function of table. An altar, for example, may represent a gathering point with a social purpose anchored to it. While eating at the altar is a speculative leap, the idea of gathering around it and the act of sacrifice is a well-known fact [of some cultures].

The dinner table in America: While assembly-oriented food rituals and table rituals are world-over, I have elected to speak on the American dinner table, because this is where I am, this is what I know. America still functions as a cultural hub where diversity springs eternal.

The economic idea of lap trays and personal food management devices has gone through phases in NASA; much of the early food program, meaning food delivery to human(s) was in the form of tubes which resembled toothpaste containers (this was during the Mercury Program of the early 1960's when John Glenn first tried apple sauce from a squeeze tube onboard his Friendship 7 spacecraft in 1962. "Space Food Hall of Fame" http://education.ssc.nasa.gov/fft_halloffame.asp). The significant part of the act of eating in space proved that man could eat in space, and survive, which laid the groundwork to support the idea that manned space missions were a possibility. Although for Astronaut Glen's 5-hour flight, starvation concerns were not immediate, the idea that missions would grow from hours to days to weeks made the realization of food-needs an exciting proposition and progressive aspect to the overall NASA mission(s).At one point in the history of space food, NASA used food cubes; a type of jell-cube as a later advancement; the food was covered in jell.

The 'spoon bowl' and other warming and hydration "gadgets" vastly altered space dining. These alterations; warm food, spoon-like and bowl-like structures, similar home-like textures enhanced food memories carrying concepts of home into the recall of those in space, which in terms of comfort for astronauts; being so far from home, vastly improved the feeling of home-like similarities…even when the foods themselves were comparably, at the time, far from their earth-bound equivalents. Early energy bars made an appearance as the "Space Food Stick" which, conceptually, remains popular today. The space food stick represents NASA seeking professional outside solutions to a challenge; make an energy-packed product that can be highly portable and meet the requirements of a space mission; that is to say that it must not have free-floating crumbs which could damage sensitive equipment.

Automat, refectory, cafeteria, food court, etc.: each of the listed food environments represents potential eating environments. The words mess hall or galley are nautical terms, common for ships, are reflective of the ideas used in feeding on board such a vessel. Skylab had a more robust 'galley' than other space craft before or since. And the Skylab galley encouraged, by fact of existence, an enhanced social aspect of crewmember dining.

At first glance, this seems a rather obvious question, and may even sound a bit comical. However, when we really think about the act of consuming food; especially on earth where desirability and means can constitute the latitude of a culinary experience. Eating can be many things. It can be the act of riutal, refueling, social interaction, action, etc. Throughout history there have been many food habits as approaches to eating throughout the human record. This idea will be explored further at a future point in this paper. We shall now consider eating as it relates to the following ideas on food memories.

4. Food Memories and Psychological Effects of Food:

If a food was flawlessly recreated for flight and an element was in place to purposefully make the dish just slightly less than perfect, would the space diner appreciate the attempt and compare and contrasting with home long for it?

When should the perfect replica be less than perfect and what is the produced effect, if any, by this act?

Should the perfect replica of a dish be strived for in a long duration deep space mission context, and if so why?

Why should food design consideration be brought to the forefront of discussion in a generational starship discussion? Scientists already know the physiological effects of humans in low gravity, therefore, the work is perhaps more about going the distance while observing what can be learned about humans in that processes context: that is to say, what is to be learned of humans on a generational star ship? If that is indeed a subtext larger-question, then ideas on culture rest squarely upon this question. Food remains central to present-day culture here on earth. Will it be similar for deep space? How might it differ? What are the questions that should be asked of food design for a project such as this?

Some questions include- how much space, divisions of space; meaning space used for: growing food, processing food, cooking food, serving food, stowing food and the like will be available? Scientists will explore those types of questions to eventually arrive at a blend of best practice approaches. One thought to add to the mix is that a lot can happen over the course of 50 years as a crewmember aboard a star ship, and perhaps a degree of flexibility may accompany any design. What work, if any, has been done in the area of AI (artificial Intelligence) and food, or AI food and space? Is intuitive food design a model that could be a viable food system for consideration? Intuitive food design, in one sense, may be defined as culturally adaptive; the food system is or may function 'intuitively', while maintaining standards of importance/structure set forward by policy and administration.

A culturally adaptive model flows with the changes in culture, but is it a worthwhile consideration?

Is a culturally adaptive model a worthwhile consideration? Will there be the more basic (though difficult to execute) culturally aware model? This is where the cultural considerations of others may be recognized, included as features or add-ons [American Day for instance, or hotdog Tuesday], and/or maintained in the form of a planned fest or custom. Today the ISS follows a basic American diet of 3-meals per day. What might a 100YSS feeding schedule look like?

When we think of comfort, as it relates to food, we think of "comfort food(s)". Well, what is comfort food? Comfort food is the type of food that we are familiar with, foods which call forth strong personal food memories of "nostalgic" association; mom's meatloaf, Aunt Matilda's pot roast, Uncle Willie's BBQ for instance.

Not all food memories are pleasant ones, or have to be, for that matter- Perhaps Aunt Matilda's pot roast was a Sunday early-supper affair. And, the roast was dry, which would lead to your parents fighting violently on the drive home. Yet, this was an every Sunday event. And Aunt Matilda passed away one year- 15 years ago. No more pot roast, until one day when a college sweetheart cooks you a meal; the first meal of the courtship—you guessed it, pot roast- as dry and wooded as Aunt Matilda's. You laugh warmly under your breath, and when asked what's so funny? The pot roast is just like my Aunt Matilda used to make.

Each person has had unique food memories- everyone has. Food memories, in some cases have become, in a broader social context, food traditions—Thanksgiving, Christmas, Seder meal, Eid al-Fitr, New Year's, the 4th of July, Labor Day, and many, many more. Who knows, a 100YSS may have food traditions, too. There will undoubtedly be certain food traditions of the personal/collective variety, Valentine's Day, Birthday, Anniversary and the like. Food traditions will blend with belief systems and find expression there too. And, how might a 100YSS address the food traditions expressed of various belief systems? Should that be a consideration? And if so, how will those food considerations be met; among other questions around the topic of food ethics? So, food design can shift from the basic and fundamental to the philosophical, and theoretically challenging.

What is comfort, in deep space, as it relates to food design? Comfort can be measured against the degree of effort and challenge; the greater the amount of ease, and greater the relaxation, the more the comfort. Comfort as it relates to space, with regard to food(s) implies; safe [radiation-proof packaging, free of microbes or physical contaminates], nutritious foods, which taste acceptable that are also healthy. While it is no argument that NASA has proven with early missions that foods can be made safe for flight, any foods designed to last and be eaten up to two years later face acceptable gustatory palate challenges.

Comfort as it relates to food design is when an ease and relaxation, on the end user of the food design, is satisfied; that is to say expectations are met or exceeded.

Food design is a relatively new discipline which addresses sensory, and experiential and or other dimensions in food. Food design, as a discipline, is a functional means to describe and then identify what are conscious constructs regarding food and food dynamics.

Food design subcategories as described by the International Food Design Society: Design with food; food product design; design for food; design about food, food space design/interior design for food; and eating design. Design with food is when the food itself is transformed. Food product design is when the food is structured often to be purpose specific, and often geared toward mass-production. Design for food is the support for the food; containers appliances, utensils and the like. Design about food is the peripherals which iconize food-stuff. Food space/interior design for food is the design of food spaces/environments from home dining rooms to grocery stores and beyond. Eating design is focused on eating situations and differs from food-space/environment in that thematic presence is the focus.

5. Anthropology

Native American cultures may function as promising examples of hunter-gatherers in early society when considering early American/Mesoamerican cultures in nomadic context post last glacial period (last ice age). This seeming segue is to remind us that exploration is as much part of the human record as it is part of being human. Deep space exploration reflects another leg in the human journey. One constant is our need for food on a journey 10,000 years ago as it will be for deep space voyages 100 years from now. And, our resilient innovative approaches to food management will be as relevant tomorrow as in prehistoric yester-year.

Early American cultures, as did many cultures around the globe, enjoyed mineral salt. Salt was a food staple amid nomadic life of early Americans/Mesoamericans. And, as with most long-lived cultures have less-apparent layers, subtext to support the choices they make, meaning salt may have provided more than just flavor for ancient cultures.

The role of salt on earth as it may serve to contrast low-gravity space- the human body is often measured in mass composition or atomic composition. The 'mass' body is composed of roughly six elements. Those big six account for 99% of human mass. Basic mass composition elements are oxygen, hydrogen nitrogen, calcium and phosphorus. That leaves roughly 1% trace elements, and about .85% remaining is comprised of magnesium, chlorine, sulfur, potassium and sodium… good ol' salt. However, from an elemental perspective, the human body is composed of .15% sodium. Humans require salt, to a large degree, for replenishments of vital fluids, and to a questionably lesser degree to flavor food. I don't want to get too far off the rails on the theoretical crazy train here; because we have over 10,000 taste receptors in the human mouth, to have them stimulated with one of the few known edible minerals, just may produce psycho-physio-endoneurological effects. In other words, the salt stimulus may the seasoning which gets the wheel spinning on the whole biochemical soup. And yet, in space, the capillary action of humans in low gravity produce what NASA commonly refers to "Bird legs" and "Fat head." This is when the blood pools in the face as fluid is 'wicked through capillary action into the weightless face. That coupled with the dual effect of heart placement in relation to feet, meaning the distance which the heart must pump blood without the aid of gravity the feet and legs and to a degree the arm extremities suffer depletion and 'thin-out.' Salt may complicate the phenomenon as sodium will function to increase fluid retention; in a low gravity environment and this may lead to intracranial pressure or undue ocular stress as eyes bulge wildly in their sockets. The effect of fluid retention may be short-lived in micro gravity, once the nutrition is digested; salt in the body, in micro gravity, is overly expelled in the urine and can contribute to dehydration. So, while salt on food may remain a tasty flavorful notion, its practicality in a low gravity scenario *today* may be limited for health reasons. However, that is not to say that salt wouldn't have a role to play should a gravity-based destination be considered, or a ship with a form of artificial gravity. Sodium for humans, within standard health guidelines, is normal; however, low gravity is the pink elephant in the equation.

Food experience in tourism- in fact, a 100yss journey may not be all that different, in a generic sense, than having food experiences while being a tourist, or those of an early-period nomad. Presently we operate from the knowledge-based assumption that we are *it* as far as intelligent life goes, in space. Although, those of us gathered here today are optimistic, if by nothing more than the objectivized idea of our own presence; here, that life, to some degree and extent, elsewhere 'in space' will ultimately be contacted, supports a thought that there just may be exciting new foods… or at least new food constructs to dine on along the way. And by food constructs, I mean all the good stuff in the cornucopia of tomorrow's food technology.

The very act of this 100-year starship, a bold and ambitious project, becomes, like the entirety of the broader NASA project or human research project. It takes its place among the anthropology of the human record. Today, I am not certain if this will be represented as a branch or a completely separate idea of humanity, but I am certain that this second step for humanity, this deep space step, is as relevant as its first.

Serano explores Italy, the city of Naples, and centers a focus on food's socio-anthropological importance in family and community. This work set the stage for the growing discipline of food anthropology.

The goal of food anthropology is to provide context regarding the rituals and the act(s) of food and eating as it relates to humanity and the human record.

Categorization and labeling helps further reduce the abstract of culture to put a fine point on what is being asked and defining culture. Edward B. Tylor, English anthropologist in his work, 'Primitive Culture 1871efforts to define culture.

"Culture is the full range of learned human behavior patterns." Edward B. Tylor Presently, culture, it is theorized, has layers to it known as subculture. Subculture is often viewed in a number of ways; people within a culture may be an example of direct culture, whereas cultural universals, those things present in any culture/ group of people which helps to define culture. Cultural universals differ from the habits, rituals, customs and traditions of any given culture. That is to say that, cultural universals are present in all of culture that culture is by virtue of cultural universal presence and inclusion.

Tracing the habits of food, in broad brush strokes, is a fairly doable task; in prehistory man ate foods hunted and gathered, and later progressed to agriculture and domestic meats. Later the Silk Road expressed a cross-cultural exposure, meaning diffusion of food ideas. Or that during the dark ages in Europe experienced a shift from Roman influenced cuisine toward Arab influenced cooking, with a larger and more complex strife-driven dynamic [war lead to lack of refinement]. Or prior to Columbus bringing tomatoes back from the new world to the old that Italy had no tomato-based sauces, Ireland no potatoes; these key turning points of diffusion affected cuisine represent a few among many. But, the point is that these influences are, or become easily traceable. It is interesting to note that some newly exchanged influence ingredients held interest in a culture greater than others- take the tomato for instance; resembling an over-grown belladonna may have held significance in some instances and dread in others.

The act of following food habits over time is example of food anthropology; the anthropology of food is a fairly new discipline in anthropology. The idea of space food or food-in-space will continue to take its unique place among the human record.

In the early stages of the space program, NASA astronauts during the Gemini mission ate applesauce from toothpaste-like tubes. That represented a high level of terror on the eating scale; there was fear of health hazard like the astronaut choking on the food in micro gravity, or food particles getting into sensitive equipment. Today, the scale has shifted away from 'eating to survive' and the terrors associated with it as astronauts today aboard the ISS enjoy much more comfort choosing from an extensive menu of familiar foods including foods like cornbread stuffing as well as macaroni and cheese. To what degree of comfort to terror might be experienced aboard a generational starship? How much eating to survive VS eating for comfort will be experienced? Will foods hold a familiar 'tethering to the crewmember life on earth? Should it, or should food be expressed as a radical departure from that of earth?

Carolyn Korsmeyer's work (1999) centers on elevation of consciousness in the life/death relationship between eater and food source. Often we think a hamburger comes from the store, Korsmeyer's work puts a face on that food. Should there be a consideration of cycle awareness of food on a generational starship? That's assuming food will still come from conventional sources. Perhaps a food source on a generational starship includes a derivative of edible paper and ink- How might that as a scenario look?

Edible Paper and Ink Homaro Cantu Interview re: 100YSS 3D foods 2013 interview by D. Wilson 2013 (unpublished)

Homaro Cantu worked with NASA on their Institute Advanced Concept's 3-D replication, built from edible 2-D substrate.

Cantu details that there are tech hurdles to the practical application of making a meal of edible paper and ink. "When you want to send a human to another planet there are goals with nutrients; it [the technology] must get to the nano scale to be a reality." There are nano extracts w/flavors however not yet with structures. That's where the technology needs to be. The raw materials don't yet exist. But if those two things come together it could work. In order to create a molecular match with an apple, you need a vast amount of core ingredients in order to produce a match. If 3D food printing were used, a rotation of a menu is a most likely scenario rather than an 'on-demand' printing of foods.

When asked, Chef Cantu said, "Edible menu'- started with the tasting menu; a clever way to get people to eat right after they get seated." Cantu first started writing on rice paper with edible inks then that idea expanded into other things to create and further refine his edible menu.

A class4 CO2 laser was used by chef Cantu on the TV show "Iron Chef." Now, Cantu and his team use Z-NA lasers which function to etch names or engrave. He and his team has used laser technology for experimenting with flavor technology- capturing vapors and freezing g them to make things like elixirs and extracts but Cantu is quick to note that while fun, "It's expensive to play with."

"Over the years working in restaurants I've always wanted to invent things, and before Moto opened, I invented several things. There is a time and place for classic things, but I don't want to do that at work. Everything else is rapidly evolving, why not food? Food is going to evolve; how do we let it evolve?"

"We're going to find ways to make veggies replicate meats [Cantu cites the 'China Study'] I'm very pro innovation. Cantu designs and beyond eggs worked together to create an egg substitute."

Should the technology catch-up to the idea- Cantu said, "Food printing will revolutionize everything around us."

"It's a single celled protein combined with synthetic aminos, vitamins and minerals. Everything the body needs." Dozer from the movie *The Matrix*

Factors that influence food choice(s):- culture, finance, convenience/time, taste, 'food choice questioner' etc. What factors may influence the crew of a generational deep space starship? The rules of food standards set forth by NASA will likely stay the same; that "foods must be safe, nutritious and appetizing, minimize volume, minimize mass, and minimize waste." But what will influence the crewmember's individual choice? To some extent it will depend on the food system(s), the design of the food system, food substance availability. Eating and food choice aboard a modern-day submarine: it is widely known that, "When a submarine leaves on patrol, food fills every available corner." (http://americanhistory.si.edu/subs/operating/aboard/leisure/).

And because food is bulky, and may be present in degrees of perishability, fresh foods like fruits and vegetables are eaten first, and then preserved foods are consumed. The submarine provides a sound basis for sociological study in consideration for a long-duration deep space mission. Such research may function in contrast analysis of what is learned from crewmembers in micro gravity dining aboard Skylab, which sported a virtual dining room (wardroom) and kitchen VS the space shuttle which offered a slightly less social dining environment through the use of personal dining trays.

That was then and this is now; recently research was conducted in Hawaii on foods and cooking for a mission to Mars, which focused on NASA's idea of "pick and eat veggies" items such as "lettuce, spinach, carrots, tomatoes, green onions, radishes, bell peppers, strawberries, herbs and cabbages" are among consideration. These food items represent choices for application in crops which may theoretically be grown on Mars, the Moon or an Asteroid.

But, what of tomorrow? What will food and eating look like on a 100 year star ship? Eventually the submarine pulls in port to reload, a thing a generational star ship in deep space will perhaps, be hard-pressed to do… perhaps. Perhaps food won't look like edible paper substraites with nano flavorites sprinkled on the stacked layers which are then run through a 3-D printer with recycled scraps all plugged into a world encyclopedia of food. Perhaps food will be built from synthetic programmable cells, thereby still employing a cooking step, or maybe there will be a uniquely different hybrid:

"I know this steak does not exist. I know that when I put it into my mouth the Matrix is telling my brain that it is juicy and delicious." Cypher, the movie, "The Matrix" http://bowling-bash.blogspot.com/2010/01/cinema-matrix-quotes.html

Perhaps food and nutrition may happen through human Brain Computer Interface where neurocepters are stimulated and flavor memories are tickled while the dining crewmember eats a nutrient packed flavorless textured 'canvas' and drinks a flavorless nutrient-packed liquid 'canvas' with sensory data driven through BCI. A virtual encyclopedia of all foods of The Earth could be contained in a digital record. The program for the food could be selected by the person wanting a meal. The BCI and "canvas" generate neural picture with full biochemical and subsequent hormonal response to stimulus.

A spoken dish asks southerners about their food memories: food memories are the collection of related ideas on flavor, foods, textures, temperatures; food memories tell us the difference between a good pizza and a bad one. Food memories take us back to childhood, across time to given events, or rededicate commitments functioning as ritual and tradition. The above is but a taste of what food memories are, where they come from and what makes them, or why we have them. The cause of food memories is much more complex than what was just mentioned; on one level it is a smell or image triggering the recall of a point in time/space once experienced. On another level, it is a biochemical cocktail of an exact formulation; those colors, proximal shapes, olfactoral stimulation and perhaps other sensory stimulations; ambient room temperature, environmental condition, biochemical fluctuations in the individual neurological dynamics all functioning in perfect accord.

Food memories- what was the first thing you remember eating: What are your food memories? How might food memories play a role on a generational star ship? On a submarine, food memories are triggered through customs and familiar foods, like pizza night; this conjures a mood of social ease and encourages comradery while reminding crewmembers of home. The pizza is great, as a source of change, or terrible when contrast to another crewmember's food memories. Stories are exchanged through the dining area where good pizza may be found. Hormonal fluctuations happen and nourishment happens while nutrition occurs. Regardless the food on a generational starship, food memories will happen, if humans are present. The question is: will food traditions and food mythologies of earth accompany the crewmembers on the voyage, or accord the mythologies inherent of the star ship, and should they?

How our mythology of food drives us to eat the world: as the population grows we consume the world; we observe population growth and grow more food assuming to pace population growth rather than consideration that additional food growth may be fueling it. [http://misouri.sierraclub.org/sierranonline/mayjune2000/howourmy.htm] What food mythologies might result from life on board a generational starship? Do food mythologies regarding food in space, or deep space, already exist? What might a food mythology look like for food in deep space?

6. Furniture

This question of furniture is asked because locality proximity and relevance in eating. The jury may still be out on the why of humans are social creatures, but we do like to eat in a social context, generally speaking, we gather around a dining table and nosh. Furniture, according to Inar Yildiz in, History of Furniture/Part 1 "Since ancient times, designing of several furniture objects such as chairs, sofas, cupboards or desks, furniture design and making has been an expression of culture and civilization, of how we view the world and how we think it should be ordered, moving it above and beyond the merely functional aspects."

The table is no new thing; they have been around since time immemorial; of Catalhoyuk, a Neolithic 'tell' in Turkey; the 6300BCE site, "seems to have been a village of mud-brick houses, each built to a fairly standard plan with a kitchen living room and storage area…" [also Inar 328 Yildiz history of Furniture] recalling that food design encompasses food environments as well as food itself.

Gathering to dine is a tradition in many cultures. While ideas on eating, whether communal or solitary, continue to shift, the presence of dining custom persists. On a generational ship there might be the following eating environments:

- Automat, "a fast food restaurant where simple foods and drink are served from vending machines."
- Refectory, "a monastery-style dining hall, refectorum; where one is restored…that through eating one is restored, or that, on a deeper level, that health is restored through eating; that is to say that the saying is perhaps an echoing of the idea that food is medicine."
- Cafeteria, "a space designed for food consumption.
- Food court, "a space for offering foods in stations in a cafeteria-style setting

7. Cosmic Cuisine

"Cosmic Cuisine" is a report from NASA addressing some of the challenges the Advanced Food Systems face in the consideration of a mission to Mars. It also has an eye on long duration missions. Thermostabilized foods have presently gained prominence over freeze dried foods. The report also suggests a diet with lots of hydroponically grown vegetables. The report mentioned findings through studies, not cited, that foods should have a variety of tastes and textures and colors which help foods provide mental as well as physical nutrition.

Space food standards impacted the food industry and changed food safety standards justifiable

Should there be room for connecting with the idea of 'where food comes from' on a generational star ship? Some theorists suggest that a healthy relationship with a respect for food comes from knowing where food comes from. When we ask little urban Johnny or Suzie where does milk come from, you will likely get an answer like the store; a very different answer than farm-savvy Dick and Jane. It is believed that we eat better when we have a relationship with our food, such as when a family has a 'victory garden' the children are more likely to eat vegetables because they have a connection with the food. In a larger and more general sense this translates to healthier food choices. What will a food relationship on-board a generational star ship look like?

As a classically trained visual artist- here's a future thought- perhaps there will be room for art and food together in a generational star ship. And then there's art itself… and what of art on a generational star ship. But that is a question and topic for a different day. What is the answer? A food environment on board a starship could very likely become one that is malleable adaptive and intuitive.

When something is built over time as a fluid organic dynamic, inherent complexity it to be expected. As a chef I know firsthand the difference between when something works, and making it work. Something less abstract is a software program that is launched with the thought that all of the 'bugs' are out. Inevitably there are 'patches' required to 'fix' underappreciated or unobserved issues. A well-thought food system conceived on earth may require real-life feasibility and functionality alteration in real-time in deep space for crew aboard a generational star ship.

About the Author

David Wilson earned his certification in baking and pastry through Le Cordon Bleu College of Culinary Arts of Chicago. David also holds an Associate Degree in Applied Science in Culinary Arts through Le Cordon Bleu College of Culinary Arts in Chicago. While earning his culinary degree, David interned with NASA at the Johnson Space Center in Houston Texas in the Space Food Systems Laboratory.

Sources

1. Homaro Cantu, Chef/entrepreneur: Cantu Designs, Moto/Ing, 2013

2. NASA- Johnson Space Center, 2012

3. NASA- Space Food Systems Laboratory, Johnson Space Center, Houston Tx, 2012

4. NASA- Advanced Food Systems, Johnson Space Center, Houston Tx, 2012

5. How Food Can Be Art: A Discussion of Taste (Part7 of 8), January 12, 2012 by Art http://abetterwhirlpool.wordpress.com/2012/01/12/food-art-part7/

6. International Food Design Society: http://ifooddesign.org/food_design/index.php

7. International Food Design Society: http://ifooddesign.org/food_design/subcategories.php

8. Cambridge Encyclopedia of Hunters and Gatherers http://books.google.co.uk/books?id=5eE-ASHGLg3MC&pg=PP2&lpg-PP2&dq=%22all+humans+lived+this+way%22+90+12,000&source=bl&ots=E-qs5MKbdn&sig=EmtqQEkdTuHGFX2kSOYfC7MLdXw&hl=en&sa=X&ei=5JG-GUcTIM8qg0wX3pYHACA&ved=0CDcQ6AEwAQ#v=onepage&q=%22all%20humans%20lived%20this%20way%22%2090%2012%2C000&f=false

9. Native American Cultures: history.com

10. Towards a Structural Model of the Tourist Experience: an Illustration from Food Experience in Tourism Quan and Wang 2003, www.sciencedirect.com

11. Food and Anthropology in the Early Works of Matilde Serao by Daria Valentini, https://twpl.library.utotonto.ca

12. Anthropology of Food- University of Minnesota Duluth, www.d.umn.edu/cla/faculty/troufs/anthfood/video/meaning_of_food.himl

13. Human Culture: What is Culture? http://anthro.palomar.edu/culture/culture_1.htm

14. Universals of Culture: a list of 10 cultural universals, Jennifer Hanzak, www.learner.org

15. Bloomberg, Myhrvold: Invention is the Mother of Economic Growth, Nathan Myhrvold Dec 19, 2011, http://www.bloomberg.com/news/2011-12-20/invention-is-the-mother-of-economic-growth-nathan-myhrvold.html

16. IGT Vanvitelli/ Istituto technico Per Geometri "L.Vanvitelli" Cava De' Tirreni (SA), Italy: "Food Habits Over the Centuries" 2008/9

17. Project Muse, "Anthropology and the Everyday, from Comfort to Terror, Nancy Ries New Literary History vol 33, Numver 4, Autumn 2002 pp. 725-742, http://muse.jhu.edu

18. University of Buffalo, Delightful, Delicious, Disgusting—the Difficult Pleasure of "Terrible Eating" Patricia Donovan January 9, 2004, http://buffalo.edu/news/releases/2004/01/6533.html

19. Huffington Post, 'A Spoken Dish' Asks Southerners About Their Food Memories (video), Rebecca Orchant, http://www.huffingtonpost.com/2013/06/18/a-spoken-dish-food-memories-video_n_3455136.html

20. Sierra Club, "How Our Mythology of Food Drives Us to Eat the World" John Kurmann, http://missouri.sierraclub.org/sierranOnline/mayjune2000/howourmy.htm

21. History of Furniture and Interior Design part 1: Prehistoric Furniture and Interior design, Inar Yildiz, http://emuonline.emu.edu.tr/inar328/pdf/Part_one_inar_328_furniture_styles_ancient.pdf

22. Around the Dinner table, History of Eating in the United States, Robert Cowley, Della Gibson and Chanda Sewell, 'Family that eats together, stays together', http://historyofeating.umwblogs.org/around-the-dinner-table/

23. Advance Access Publication Dec 21, 2007, Oxford University Press 2007, The Candidate Sour Taste Receptor, PKD2L1, is Expressed by Type III Taste Cells in the Mouse, S. Kataoka et al 2007

24. Open Biology, Evolutionary Origins of Taste Buds: Phylogenetic Analysis of Purinergic Neurotransmission in Epithelial Chemosensors, Open Biol. March 6, 2013, Masato Kirino et al. Rsob.royalsociety.publishing.org

25. Chemoreceptors of taste and Smell- specific material extracted from, 'The Neuron and Neural System: Electrolytic Theory of' by James T. Fulton, http://neuroresearch.net/smell/files/chemoreceptors.htm last update Aug. 14, 2013

26. Food Manufacturing, Mars Food Study Researchers Conclude Experiment, Jennifer Sinco Kelleher, http://www.foodmanufacturing.com

27. Open Access, Nanotechnology, Science and Application 2010:3 1-15, Dove Medical Press Ltd., "Food Nanotechnology- an overview" Bhupinder S. Sekhon

28. Soylent, Rob Rhinehart, http://robrhinehart.com/?=289, http://www.soylent.me/

29. Food Manufacturing, Taste Testers: Lab-Made Burger Lacks Flavor, Maria Cheng Aug 8, 2013, www.foodmanufacturing.com

30. Food Manufacturing, Q&A: The Science Behind a Lab-Grown Burger, Maria Cheng Aug 8, 2013, www.foodmanufacturing.com

31. NASA, "Food For Space Flight," NASA, www.NASA.gov

32. NASA," Space Food," NASA, http://spaceflight.nasa.gov/living/spacefood/index.html

33. NASA, "Cosmic Cuisine," NASA, nasa.gov

34. "From Farm to Fork: How Space Food Standards Impacted the Food Industry and Changed Food Safety Standards", Jennifer Ross-Nazzal, http://history.nasa.gov/sp4801-chapter12.pdf

35. NASA, "Space Food Hall of Fame," http://education.ssc.nasa.gov/fft_halloffame.asp

36. NASA, "The Brain in Space: a Teacher's Guide with Activities for Neuroscience," NASA.gov

37. Space Policy Institute, graduate Education, http://www.gwu.edu/~spi/education.cfm

38. BioServe, http://www.colorado.edu/engineering/BioServe/about.html

39. http://en.wikipedia.org/wiki/Eating

40. http://www.montignac.com/en/the-history-of-man-s-eating-habits/

41. http://www.academia.edu/2375711/Paleodietary_reconstruction_of_a_Neolithic_population_in_Slovenia_A_stable_isotope_approach

Design & Layout

The wide variety of disciplines represented and information contained in the preceding papers provides unique design challenges. As in the previous year, the goal was to create a uniform presentation and easily accessible layout while still maintaining the individual author's needs and desires. The overall design is intended to be conducive to the experience of education and engagement. This year's improvements in design have focused on uniformity between the papers. Formulas, illustrations, and other non-text elements are more consistent (although not absolutely so). The challenge engaged and met is to provide a cross-discipline publication that highlights the variety of thought, research, and effort needed to achieve the audacious dream of interstellar travel.

Primary text is typeset in Adobe Caslon Pro. Headings are set in Helvetica Neue and League Gothic.

Design and layout by Jason D. Batt.

Editorial Board

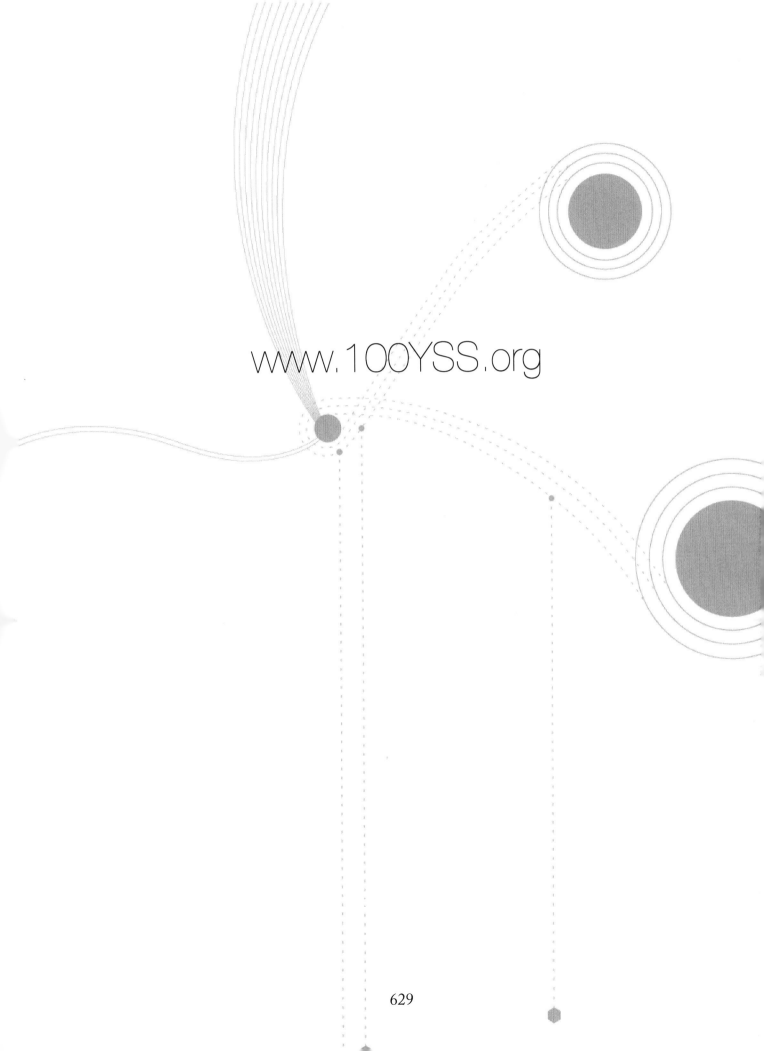

www.100YSS.org

Made in the USA
San Bernardino, CA
31 July 2014